Tables
737

MW00652088

$= (P/A_{8\%,36})(P/F_{8\%,1})$

FOURTEENTH EDITION

Economic Evaluation & Investment Decision Methods

Franklin J. Stermole
Professor Emeritus, Colorado School of Mines

John M. Stermole
Teaching Assoc. Professor, Colorado School of Mines
President, Investment Evaluations Corporation

Investment Evaluations Corporation
3070 S. Newcombe Way, Lakewood, CO 80227
www.stermole.com

Franklin J. Stermole, B.S., M.S., Ph.D., Chemical Engineering, Iowa State University, is Professor Emeritus of Mineral Economics and Chemical and Petroleum Refining at Colorado School of Mines where he has taught since 1963. He has taught economic evaluation techniques for over 50 years to undergraduate and graduate students and has done economic evaluation consulting for numerous mineral and non-mineral companies. Since 1970 when the first short course was presented, Frank has taught more than 700 "Economic Evaluation" short courses to over 16,000 persons from mineral and non-mineral industry companies and government agencies. In addition to the United States these courses have been presented in Armenia, Australia, Canada, Chile, Colombia, Egypt, France, Germany, Great Britain, Guyana, Indonesia, Kazakhstan, Kuwait, Mexico, Norway, Philippines, Saudi Arabia, South Africa, Trinidad and Venezuela. This domestic and foreign industrial consulting and teaching experience has had a direct effect on the applications-oriented content and organization of the text.

John M. Stermole, B.S.B.A., Finance, University of Denver, and M.S., Mineral Economics, Colorado School of Mines, is President of Investment Evaluations Corporation. John is an Associate Teaching Professor at Colorado School of Mines where he has taught since 1988 in the Division of Economics and Business. John has also served as a Fellow to the Institute for Global Resources Policy at Colorado School of Mines, and was co-author in the 1st Edition of the Global Mining Taxation Comparative Study. John has also taught as an Adjunct Professor at The University of Denver, College of Law in the Natural Resources and Environmental Law Program. John has presented more than 550 "Economic Evaluation" short courses for mineral, petroleum and non-mineral companies and government agencies. In addition to the United States, courses have been presented in Australia, Canada, Chile, Colombia, Indonesia, South Africa, Switzerland, United Arab Emirates, Vietnam, South Korea and England. Prior to joining Investment Evaluations Corporation on a full time basis, John gained three years of industry experience with Lowdermilk Construction of Englewood, Colorado, applying economic evaluation techniques to heavy construction projects related to mine site development and highway construction, and in replacement analysis.

3070 South Newcombe Way, Lakewood, CO 80227 USA
Ph: 303-984-9954 Fx: 303-984-9895
Web site: www.stermole.com

ISBN 978-0-9911941-0-0

Printed in the United States of America

TABLE OF CONTENTS

PREFACE

This text is an introduction to the concepts of time value of money and the related decision criteria used to evaluate investments. Application of the criteria in before-tax and after-tax investment situations provide better understanding of the three steps of economic evaluations, which include; 1) defining the problem, 2) analyzing the problem and 3) properly interpreting and presenting the economic meaning of results. In a broad sense, this process involves measuring the economic equivalence of different investment opportunities. A key to properly measuring the economic equivalence of all alternatives is consistency in the three steps just mentioned. Many people have a good understanding of the alternatives, make a proper setup of the problem, and then improperly interpret results. The text examples and problems provide the reader with a comprehensive approach to evaluating the economic equivalence of both income-producing and service-producing alternatives and then properly applying the findings.

Other than the obvious engineering differences, whether you are considering development or expansion of an existing ore body, refinery, coal deposit, oil and gas lease or real estate to name a few, the same economic tools are utilized. Terminology is probably the biggest single difference amongst authors, industries and individuals. For example, when an investor looks at a project's profitability in terms of a compound interest rate, that measure might be described as a rate of return, internal rate of return, discounted cash flow rate of return or yield to maturity. These are not to be confused with measures such as return on capital or return on assets which are financially based around net income and the assets employed to generate it and often look back at what occurred in the last four quarters, rather than what is expected to occur in future years.

Each chapter introduces new concepts and illustrates each with examples. At the end of each chapter are a number of problems designed to provide the reader with an opportunity to explore the calculations on their own. The solutions for each of these problems are available in the Problem Solutions Manual. The Solutions Manual also explores Excel applications and functions available to solve related exercises. The Solutions Manual will also explore the use of financial calculators such as the Hewlett Packard, HP10BII to solve various exercises.

For those interested in learning the basics of time value of money and decision criteria, the Self Teaching Manual is an introduction to the subject matter in a Self Teaching format that is different from the textbook. The Self Teaching Manual may be applicable as refresher material or pre-course reading in different learning situations.

The first six chapters present time value of money and decision criteria on a before-tax basis. This simplifies the evaluation process to understanding the development of criteria and how each are applied to different investment scenarios. Chapter 2 is an introduction to time value of money while Chapter 3 addresses the various decision criteria and related parameters. At the end of Chapter 3 and in Chapters 4, 5 and 6 examples and problems address the application of economic evaluation criteria to different investment situations and the use of these criteria in light of inflation, risk, and uncertainty. Chapters 7 and 8 focus on understanding after-tax cash flow and the related issues and terminology associated with computing Federal and in many cases State income tax liability in the United States. Chapters 9, 10 and 11 get back to analyzing projects with after-tax cash flow. The emphasis in the later chapters is on less tax detail and more economics, to understand the meaning of criteria in an after-tax environment. Chapter 12 addresses personal investment considerations including discussion of stocks, equity options, commodity futures and other investments involving life insurance and retirement.

While the text has a number of examples from the oil and gas and mining industry, it is written with a number of generic scenarios that make it applicable for students in all engineering disciplines as well as those involved in geology, geophysics, business, accounting, finance, management, operations research and anyone interested in economic evaluation issues.

To state the obvious, evaluation work is only as good as the information provided in the analysis. The old saying, "garbage in, garbage out" could not be more appropriate. While today's computing power makes computations much easier, there is a tendency to think that more complex evaluations designed to quantify risk and uncertainty will somehow make up for the vagaries of the input data. Sensitivity and risk models help evaluators quantify uncertainty but they cannot eliminate its very existence.

In most investment decision making situations you will find that proper application of the concepts and techniques presented in this text combined with a little common sense and good management judgment will enable you to do a better job of economic decision making.

Frank Stermole and John Stermole

CHAPTER 1

INVESTMENT DECISION MAKING

1.1 Introduction to Investment Analysis

Economic evaluation of investment alternatives relates to systematically evaluating the relative profit potential of investment alternatives. If systematic, quantitative methods are not used to compare the economic considerations of investment alternatives, it seems evident that in certain investment decision making situations the wrong choices may be made from an economic viewpoint. For example, in the analysis of investment alternatives for a given investment situation, the alternatives under consideration may have differences with respect to costs and profits or savings and the timing of costs and profits or savings. Differences may also exist in project lives, tax considerations, and the effects of escalation and inflation on projected costs and revenues. If a systematic approach is not used to quantify the economic effects of these factors, it is very difficult to correctly assess which alternatives have the best economic potential.

Since the days of the writings of economist Adam Smith it has been recognized that capital accumulation has been the primary investment objective of capitalistic individuals, companies and societies to enable them to improve their standard of living. It is emphasized later in this chapter that factors other than economic considerations enter into most investment decisions, but from an economic viewpoint it is assumed that maximizing capital accumulation (or the value of assets that could be converted to capital) is the objective. The importance of proper economic evaluation techniques in determining the most economically effective way to spend money seems evident whether you analyze it from an individual, corporate, or government viewpoint.

This text presents the development and application of economic evaluation techniques that can be used to enhance your ability to make correct investment decisions from an economic viewpoint. Note that it is not purported that the use of these techniques will enable you to make correct economic decisions all the time. Because of the effects of risk and uncertainty, including escalation and inflation of costs and revenues, it is not possible to develop evaluation techniques that guarantee investment decision making success. However, by using one or more of the economic evaluation techniques presented and recommended in this text, you should be able to do a consistently better job of economic decision making than you can do without using these techniques. Obviously a given analysis is only as good as the input cost and revenue data that go into it. Risk and uncertainty effects make it impossible to know for certain that a given set of data for a proposed investment situation is correct. This, of course, means we cannot be certain of the economic analysis results based on the data. Even when probabilities of success and failure are incorporated into the analyses, as is introduced in Chapter 6, we do not have analysis results that are certain for any given investment situation. However, even under evaluation conditions of great uncertainty, the use of the evaluation techniques presented in this text will give the decision maker a much better feeling for the relative risks and uncertainties between alternatives. This information together with the numerical economic evaluation results usually will put the decision maker in a better position to make a correct decision than he would be in if systematic evaluation procedures were not used.

Evaluation of investment alternatives to select project investments that will maximize profit per dollar invested is a key goal of every successful corporate manager or individual investor. To fully achieve this goal, managers or individuals should be familiar with the principles of economic evaluation and investment decision methods which provide the basis for quantified economic evaluation of alternative engineering projects and general investment opportunities.

Most business decisions are made by choosing what is believed to be the best alternative out of several courses of action. Problems in this area are therefore called *alternative choice problems*. In many business situations, decisions are made intuitively because systematic, quantified decision making methods are not available to weigh the alternatives. This should not be the case for weighing the economic considerations related to most investment decisions. Systematic economic decision methods are available for evaluating individual investment projects and for comparing alternative investment projects. The "whims of management" should not be the basis for reaching decisions concerning economic differences between investment alternatives. In this age of increasingly complex investment situations, to be successful over the long run it is imperative that a primary economic evaluation criterion be selected and applied to compare alternative investment choices. This text presents economic evaluation criteria which are based on the premise that profit maximization is the investment objective; that is, maximization of the future worth of available investment dollars. Methods are developed and illustrated in this text to enable a person to determine the courses of action that will make best economic use of limited resources. In general, this involves answering the question, "Is it better to invest cash in a given investment situation or will the cash earn more if it is invested in an alternative situation?"

1.2 "Engineering Economy" and "Economic Evaluation"

Engineering and science technology in one way or another provide the basis for most of the investment opportunities in this world today. Even the economic desirability of investments in land often relates to engineering technology that may make the land more valuable several years from now for apartments, a park or some industrial plant utilization. In a capitalistic society it is imperative that engineering proposals as well as all other types of investment proposals be evaluated in terms of worth and cost before they are undertaken. Even in public activities, benefits must be greater than costs before expenditures normally are approved. Thus, the term "engineering economy" which is used widely in literature and texts applies in general to the economic evaluation of all types of investment situations. The terms "economic evaluation" and "engineering economy" are considered to have the same meaning in this text. A person does not need to be an engineer to be proficient in the application of engineering economy principles to evaluate investment alternatives. The well known prerequisite of successful engineering ventures is economic feasibility. This prerequisite applies to both engineering and non-engineering investment situations, so the terms "economic evaluation" and "engineering economy" have valid meaning and importance not only to engineers, but also to bankers, accountants, business managers and other personnel in a wide variety of job descriptions where they are concerned with economic evaluation of investment alternatives. This text is written for people with these kinds of backgrounds or interest.

1.3 Making Decisions

Peter Drucker, stated that decision making has five distinct phases:

1. Defining the problem
2. Analyzing the problem
3. Developing alternate solutions
4. Deciding upon the best solution
5. Converting the decision into effective action

These decision making phases apply to economic evaluation decision making as well as general managerial decision making. Defining economic evaluation problems clearly is as important in economic analysis as any other situation that requires a decision. In any situation requiring decision making it is necessary to ask the right questions before one can expect to get the answers that are needed. Analysis of the problem or questions is the next step in the decision making process for economic analysis as well as general managerial decisions. This leads to the third phase of decision making concerning whether alternative approaches or investments might not be better. Analysis of these alternative investments then leaves us in a position to decide upon the best economic choice and to take action to implement the best choice.

This text, and the concept of economic decision making, is primarily concerned with the three middle phases defined by Drucker. Again, this includes presenting and illustrating methods that can be used to analyze correctly various investment situations, develop alternative solutions and the economic analysis of these solutions. Emphasis is directed toward the fact that economic analysis always involves comparison of alternatives, and determining the best way to invest available capital. From an economic viewpoint this means we want to maximize the future profit that can be accumulated from the available investment dollars.

Economic evaluation decision making relates to two basic classifications of projects or investments:

1. Revenue producing investments
2. Service producing investments

Sometimes people think a third investment classification might be "savings producing projects," but it will be illustrated in Chapter 3 that looking at differences between the costs of providing a service by alternative methods gives the savings that incremental investments in the more costly initial investment alternatives will generate. Analysis of these savings and incremental costs is just one of several valid ways of evaluating general service producing projects.

Many analysis techniques are presented and illustrated in this text. However, emphasis is placed on compound interest rate of return analysis and net present value analysis, properly applied on an after tax basis. A large majority of individuals, companies and government organizations that use formal evaluation techniques use rate of return analysis as their primary decision making criterion with net present value the second most used technique. There are other correct techniques for evaluating various investment situations including future and annual value, and several ratios. These techniques are presented in the text. It is necessary in economic evaluation work to be familiar with many different approaches to economic analysis because eventually you will interact with people that have a wide variety of evaluation backgrounds who use or advocate widely varying economic evaluation techniques. Familiarity with different evaluation techniques enhances communication with these people. Also, it will be shown in Chapter 4 that in certain evaluation situations, methods such as net present value have significant advantages over rate of return analysis. To communicate effectively with different evaluation people you must be familiar with the principles and advantages or disadvantages associated with different evaluation techniques. Also, beware that when you discuss rate of return analysis with different people the chances are that the term, "rate of return", may mean something very different to the other person than it does to you. Many different rates of return are defined in the literature, some of which follow: return on initial investment (ROI), which may be defined as being based on initial investment, average investment or some other investment; return on assets (ROA), which is also called accounting rate of return and generally is based on the non-depreciated asset value; return on equity (ROE), which refers to return on individual or stockholder equity capital as the basis of the calculation; return on sales (ROS), which is not an investment rate of return at all; and the compound interest rate of return (ROR), or discounted cash flow rate of return on an after-tax basis (DCFROR) which is analogous to a bank account or mortgage interest rate and is the interest rate that makes project costs and revenues equivalent at a given point in time. Only this latter rate of return, DCFROR, is valid consistently for analyzing alternative investments. The other rates of return may have use in certain analysis or accounting situations but they should not, in general, be used to evaluate the relative economic merits of alternative investments because they do not account for the time value of money properly over the project evaluation life. In general these other rates of return look at project rate of return at a specific point in time, or for some kind of average profit and cost considerations.

It is imperative that the time value of money be handled correctly in all valid economic evaluation methods. Also, since taxes are a cost relevant to most evaluation situations, economic analyses must be done after-tax. To omit a major project cost such as taxes may be more important than omitting operating costs and few people would think we should leave operating costs out of an analysis. In certain government project evaluations where taxes do not apply, it is of course proper to neglect taxes. In general you should think in terms of doing all analyses after tax, omitting tax considerations only when appropriate. In Chapters 2 through 6 of the text, evaluation techniques and illustrations are presented primarily on a before tax basis to avoid confusing the reader with significant tax considerations, at the same time various evaluation techniques and the time value of money are being introduced. Starting in Chapter 7 everything is presented on an after-tax analysis basis and this is the way all evaluations should be done for decision making purposes.

1.4 Definition of Discounted Cash Flow Analysis

In all industries, whether for corporations or individuals, economic analysis of potential investment projects is done to select the investment project or projects that will give maximum value from the investment of available capital. Investors usually use economic analysis techniques based on either rate of return, present value, annual value, future value, or various break-even analyses to reach economic analysis decisions. When the techniques just mentioned are based on handling the time value of money with a compound interest rate, these techniques are all referred to as "Discounted Cash Flow Analysis Techniques". Understanding this concept requires definition of terms "discounted" and "cash flow".

The term "discount" is generally considered to be synonymous with "present worth" in economic evaluation work. In handling the time value of money, investors want to account for the fact that a dollar in hand today has greater value than a dollar at some future time because a dollar in hand today can be put to work now in a bank account or other investments to accrue interest, or return on investment. Compound interest is the generally accepted approach today for calculating accrued interest, or return on investment, in time value of money calculations. The future value that is projected to be accrued from the investment of dollars today at a specified compound interest rate is equal to the sum of the accrued interest and the initial dollars (principal) invested. The concept of present worth is just the opposite of compounding. The present worth of a future value is the sum of money that invested today, at a specified compound interest rate, would grow to the given future value. When you are working with positive interest rates, present values are always less than future values. Since the term "discounting" implies reducing the value of something, the use of the terms "discounting" and "present worth" have equivalent meaning because they both relate to reducing the value of assets or dollars.

The terms "cash flow," "before-tax cash flow," (BTCF) and "after-tax cash flow," (ATCF) are used to refer to the net inflow or outflow of money that occurs during a specified period such as a month, quarter, or year. However, terms like operating profit, earnings before interest, taxes, depreciation and amortization (EBITDA) and others may also be used to measure different levels of profitability before consideration of capital expenditures and interest or income taxes. Economic evaluations generally are based on measures of cash flow reflecting all costs and benefits. The first six chapters of this textbook focus on before-tax measures while the latter chapters address the computation of after-tax cash flow and related economic concepts. Some of these concepts of cash flow and profits are introduced in Equation 1-1 below.

Gross Revenue or Savings
– Operating Expenses
___
Operating Profit or EBITDA
– Capital Expenditures
___
Before-Tax Cash Flow
– Income Tax Expenditures
___
After-Tax Cash Flow — Equation 1-1

Inflows of money from revenues and savings, minus outflows of money for expenditures such as operating costs, income taxes and capital expenditures equals project after-tax cash flow for that period. If inflows of money exceed outflows, then a measure of cash flow will be positive. Sometimes, investors look at projects on a before-tax basis because the company does not pay tax such as a Limited Liability Partnership or Company or a Sub Chapter S Corporation. Generally it is undesirable to evaluate investments on a before-tax basis unless the investor is not subject to income taxation. Another justification of before-tax calculations may be if others in the organization are responsible for the computation of the specific tax considerations that will impact the investment cash flows. The reader can use the various components of Equation 1-1 to help visualize the after-tax cash flow values that are illustrated in more detail in Chapter 7 through 12 examples and problems of this textbook.

The term "discounted cash flow" evolved from the fact that investors most often handle the time value of money using present value calculations so they "present worth" or "discount" positive and negative "cash flow" anticipated from an investment to evaluate the project economic potential.

Discounted cash flow analysis forces an investor to think systematically and quantitatively about all the relevant economic factors that may affect the economic potential of investments. In the past, successful entrepreneurs "intuitively" took into account investment economic analysis factors such as the magnitude and relative timing of investment costs and revenues, the effects that inflation and escalation may have on costs and revenues, the risk of failure involved with the overall investment, the uncertainty associated with projection of specific investment analysis parameters, the tax effects relevant to a proper after-tax evaluation for the financial situation of the investor, and finally, how to assimilate these considerations in a manner that enabled fair, consistent comparison of alternative investments. As investors have become more diversified, it has become more difficult to use entrepreneurial judgments consistently and correctly in analyzing the economic potential of different investments. Discounted cash flow analysis has provided a systematic approach to quantitatively take into account the factors that are relevant in all industries for the proper economic analysis of investments.

Examples of the use of discounted cash flow analysis today are innumerable. Income and service producing project investments of all types are analyzed using discounted cash flow analysis. Investors in minerals, petroleum, timber, real estate, manufacturing, leasing, etc., use discounted cash flow analysis to determine the upper limit that they could be willing to pay for mineral rights, land or assets to generate projected negative and positive cash flows over future years that yield a specified return on invested capital. Major companies use discounted cash flow analysis to evaluate the economic value of other companies. In a simplified form, by evaluating the value of individual properties and businesses that make up a company, the overall company value may be considered to be the cumulative sum of the value of individual properties or businesses that make up the company. The acquisition bids for companies in recent years are situations where discounted cash flow analysis by major investors has indicated the value of companies to be considerably different than the value common stock shareholders had been placing on the companies utilizing net income approaches. Sometimes the discounted cash flow analysis will give a higher indicated value of a project or company than other evaluation approaches might give. Sometimes the discounted cash flow value may be less. The advantage of discounted cash flow analysis is that in all cases the assumptions on which the analysis is based can be explicitly stated and understood by all. If you do not like the input assumptions they can be changed to what you consider more realistic. The non-discounted cash flow, older economic analysis methods have various implicit assumptions built in that may or may not be correct in different analysis situations and, therefore, often lead to incorrect economic evaluations. In particular, the older evaluation techniques do not properly account for the time value of money. This is the single most important consideration that has caused companies and investors in most industries to shift to discounted cash flow analysis since the mid 1960's.

The real utility of discounted cash flow analysis is that it puts all investments on a common evaluation basis of handling the time value of money with compound interest rate of return. In all industries, we are concerned with analyzing inflows of money (such as revenues and savings) and outflows of money (such as operating costs, capital expenditures and income tax costs). Discounted cash flow analysis enables investors to fairly and properly account for the magnitude and timing of these dollar value considerations regardless of the type of investment.

1.5 Example of Discounted Cash Flow

Remembering that investment cash flow in any year represents the net difference between inflows of money from all sources, minus investment outflows of money from all sources, consider the cash flow diagram presented in thousands of dollars:

Year	0	1	2	3	4	5	6
Revenue			170	200	230	260	290
– Operating Cost			–40	–50	–60	–70	–80
– Capital Costs	–200	–100					
– Tax Costs			–30	–40	–50	–60	–70
Project Cash Flow	–200	–100	+100	+110	+120	+130	+140

The negative cash flows incurred during years 0 and 1 will be paid off by the positive cash flows in years 2 through 6, very much like loans of $200 and $100 thousand today and one year from today respectively, would be paid off by mortgage payments in amounts equal to the positive cash flow in years 2 through 6. What after-tax discounted cash flow rate of return (DCFROR) would an investor be receiving if he incurs the negative cash flows in years 0 and 1 to generate the positive cash flow from revenue in years 2 through 6? The compound interest rate that makes the present worth positive cash flow plus the present worth negative cash flow equal to zero is the desired rate of return, compound interest rate, or DCFROR, using those terms interchangeably. This value is 20.8% for this stream of positive and negative cash flows.

Net present value (NPV), is the cumulative present worth of positive and negative investment cash flow using a specified discount rate to handle the time value of money. In general, the discount rate represents the minimum acceptable investment DCFROR. For this example a discount rate of 15% is used. Positive net present value represents the present worth positive cash flow that is above what is needed to cover the present worth negative cash flow for the discount rate used. In other words, positive NPV represents additional costs that could be incurred in the year NPV is calculated, and allow the project to still have a DCFROR equal to the discount rate. Remember that rate of return (or DCFROR) is the discount rate that makes NPV equal to zero. For the 15% discount rate, the NPV for the above values is +$54.75 thousand. This represents the additional negative cash flow that could be incurred in year 0 (in addition to the -$200 thousand cash flow in year zero) and have the project yield a 15% DCFROR.

Sensitivity analyses can be made to see how the acquisition cost of $54.75 thousand is affected by changing the relative timing of when the costs and revenues are to be incurred. First, instead of incurring the cumulative positive investment cash flow of $600 thousand over years 2 through 6, assume the same cumulative positive cash flow will be realized over years 2 and 3 with +$280 thousand in year 2 and +$320 thousand in year 3.

Project Cash Flow	–200	–100	+280	+320
Year	0	1	2	3

For this case the DCFROR will increase to 37.1% and the NPV grows to +$135.2 thousand. Accounting for the time value of money, and realizing positive cash flow much quicker, enhances the economics of a project significantly. Second, if we slow down the receipt of positive cumulative cash flow of $600 thousand so that the cash flow is realized more slowly over years 2 through 9 with +$55, +$60, +$65, +$70, +$75, +$85, +$90, and +$100 thousand per year respectively, what is the effect on the project economics?

Project Cash Flow	–200	–100	+55	+60	+65	+70	+75	+85	+90	+100
	0	1	2	3	4	5	6	7	8	9

Deferring positive cash flow into the future drops the NPV to -$11.7 thousand and the DCFROR to 14%. Both values indicate that the project is unsatisfactory compared to other opportunities thought to exist at a 15% rate of return and, in fact, the NPV indicates that we would have to be paid $11.7 thousand to take this project and receive a 15% return on invested capital.

Summary of Findings

Investment Life	3 Years	6 Years	9 Years
Project DCFROR	37%	21%	14%
Project NPV @ 15%	+$135.2	+$ 54.7	–$ 11.7
Cumulative +CF, Thousands	$600.0	$600.0	$600.0
Cumulative –CF, Thousands	$300.0	$300.0	$300.0

In this example we have looked at three different evaluations of the same cumulative negative cash flow (investment dollars) of $300 thousand and cumulative positive cash flow of $600 thousand. If we neglect the time value of money, we would consistently determine that the project yields $300 thousand in profits. Yet the economic conclusions that account for the time value of money indicate a range of NPV's for these three cases from -$11.7 thousand to +$135.2 thousand. Obviously, project economics properly accounting for the time value of money can be very sensitive to the relative timing of investment capital costs and revenues over the expected project life.

The discount rate selected can also have a very significant effect on economic evaluation results. To illustrate this concept we will analyze the NPV of the six year life analysis for discount rates of 10 and 20 percent, as well as 15 percent. The results are presented below:

Discount Rate	NPV
10%	+$116.1
15%	+$ 54.8
20%	+$ 6.8

NPV results vary by a factor of 17 from +$116.1 to +$6.8 thousand as the discount rate is increased by a factor of two from 10 to 20 percent. DCFROR may also be defined as the compound interest rate that causes project NPV to equal zero. Note that for a larger discount rate of 20%, the 6-year project NPV is approaching zero. In fact, at 20.8% the project NPV is exactly equal to zero which satisfies our definition. The smaller 10% discount rate would suggest that for an investor with other opportunities at that level, the value of this project is greater than his or her other perceived opportunities for investing money. Therefore, value is being added to the investor's portfolio. On the other hand, if an investor has other opportunities at 20%, this project is nearly an economic breakeven with those other investments. In the following section, discussion is related to determining the appropriate discount rate.

1.6 Minimum Rate of Return/Opportunity Cost of Capital/Discount Rate

It is widely accepted *in industry and government practice for private companies, government organizations, and regulated utilities alike that the desired or allowed investment rate of return should equal the "cost of capital"*. Proper application of this concept is based on *defining the "cost of capital" as the accepted rate of return that could be realized on similar alternative investments of equivalent risk.* Many investors refer to this rate more explicitly as the "opportunity cost of capital" since it reflects the rate of return that the investor feels represents other opportunities in which to invest available capital with a similar level of risk. If these other investment opportunities are passed up, then the investor forgoes realizing the potential rate of return and thereby incurs an "opportunity cost of capital" equal to the foregone rate of return. *The terms "minimum rate of return," "hurdle rate," "discount rate," "minimum discount rate," and "opportunity cost of capital" are all interchangeable with the term "cost of capital" as used in this text and in common practice. These interchangeable terms which represent "opportunity cost of capital" must not be confused with the "financial cost of capital" which is the cost of raising money by borrowing or issuing new bond, debenture, common stock or related debt/equity offerings.* Regardless of the source of investment dollars, the objective of discounted cash flow analysis is to evaluate the economic potential of alternative income-producing and service-producing investments to select the optimum investments that will maximize the future value that can be generated from available investment capital. To achieve this objective, "opportunity cost of capital" rather than "financial cost of capital" must be used in discounted cash flow calculations and economic decision-making. Many people are confused by the differences in "opportunity cost of capital" and "financial cost of capital". It is not uncommon for people to mistakenly either physically use or think of a company "hurdle rate" or "minimum discount rate" as a "financial cost of capital" rate rather than an "opportunity cost of capital" rate. It is shown in Chapters 3 and 4 that when the usual situation of capital rationing exists, the "opportunity cost of capital" generally is larger than the "financial cost of capital" and you will not achieve optimum economic investment decisions if you use "financial cost of capital" rather than "opportunity cost of capital" in your analyses. If borrowed money is unlimited so capital is not rationed, then and only then will the "opportunity cost of capital" equal the "financial cost of capital." These "cost of capital" discount rate considerations are extremely important and fundamental to all discounted cash flow analyses calculations and decisions. Therefore, these "cost of capital" concepts and applications are explained and illustrated in greater detail in section 3.7 of Chapter 3 and in several sections and examples in Chapter 4.

1.7 Investment Analysis

Before proceeding to the development of the compound interest formulas in the next chapter, it should be pointed out that this text is concerned primarily with decision methods for "economic analysis" of alternative investment opportunities. An overall investment analysis should, and usually does, involve three analyses:

1. Economic Analysis
2. Financial Analysis
3. Intangible Analysis

Economic analysis involves evaluation of the relative merits of investment situations from a profit and cost (or economic) viewpoint. *Financial analysis* refers to where the investment funds for proposed investments will be obtained. Some alternate methods of financing investments include use of personal or corporate funds, borrowing from a bank, having a corporate funded debt offering of bonds or debentures, or going to the public with a new common stock offering. *Intangible analysis* involves consideration of factors that affect investments but which cannot be quantified easily in economic terms. Typical intangible factors are legal and safety considerations, public opinion or goodwill, political considerations in foreign ventures, ecological and environmental factors, uncertain regulatory or tax law conditions, and many others.

Often times an alternative that looks best economically may be rejected for financial or intangible reasons. Financial analysis may address the ability to finance a project through a variety of lending options, but it might also incorporate how Wall Street will interpret the financial data related to a major acquisition or sale. Depending on the opportunity, a decision may look good financially but in the long run may not be optimal from a cash flow perspective. Contrarily, decisions based on cash flow may not be optimal in the short run due to financial reporting considerations. Intangible factors that may cause rejection of economically sound projects are innumerable, but high on the list of importance are potential public opinion and legal problems from possible air, land, or water pollution. The importance of financial and intangible analysis factors in relation to economic factors must never be underestimated in management investment decision making. They often are as important as economic considerations.

There is a tendency in the literature and practice to interchange the use of the terms "economic analysis" and "financial analysis". This often leads to confusion and improper use of investment decision methods. It is important to recognize that, as used in this text, "economic analysis" relates to evaluation of the profitability of a proposed project and "financial analysis" relates to how the project will be financed, or the impact on financial reporting. This text primarily is concerned with the development and illustration of economic analysis techniques.

CHAPTER 2

COMPOUND INTEREST FORMULAS

2.1 Introduction to Equivalence

Economic evaluation of investment alternatives requires that the alternatives be evaluated on the same basis and that the time value of money be accounted for properly. When alternate sources of loan money are available with different payment schedules that make it difficult or impossible to determine intuitively the source that is least expensive, it is necessary to convert the alternatives to an "equivalent" basis that permits comparison of the alternatives. This necessitates correct accounting for the time value of money. For example, would you rather have \$100 now or \$102 a year from now? A majority of people would take \$100 now because they intuitively know that putting the \$100 in a bank at 4% or 5% interest will give them more than \$102 a year from now. Would you rather have \$100 now or \$150 a year from now? A majority of people would probably take \$150 a year from now because they intuitively know that they probably do not have other places to invest \$100 where it will earn \$50 profit or a 50% rate of return in one year. Now if you are asked whether you would rather have \$100 now or \$150 five years from now, the problem is more difficult to evaluate intuitively. What compound interest rate will cause \$100 now to grow to \$150 in 5 years? Do you have alternative places to invest the \$100 where it will grow to more than \$150 in 5 years? These questions must be answered by using one of several possible "equivalence" methods to compare the relative economic merits of \$100 today with \$150 five years from today. In the following section the compound interest formulas that provide the basis for equivalence calculations are developed and illustrated.

2.2 Compound Interest Formula Derivations and Illustrations

This section presents the derivation of the six basic compound interest formulas commonly needed to apply engineering economy decision methods for proper comparison of investment alternatives. To develop general formulas, the following letter symbols will be used throughout the remainder of this text:

P: Present single sum of money. Normally, "P" refers to a sum of money at time zero, but may represent a sum of money at any point from which we choose to measure time.

F: A future single sum of money at some designated future date.

A: The amount of each payment in a uniform series of equal payments made at each period. When the periods are years, "A" refers to annual payments or value.

n: The number of interest compounding periods in the project evaluation life.

i: The period compound interest rate. Depending on the situation, "i" may refer to either the cost of borrowed money, the rate of return on invested capital, or the minimum rate of return, in which case this value will be designated as "i*."

To assist in understanding these letter symbols and their relationship to investment evaluation problems, refer to the horizontal time line diagram shown in Figure 2-1.

		A	A	A	A	A	
P	0	1	2	3	n-1	n	F

Figure 2-1 A Time Diagram Illustrated

The interest compounding periods are designated 1, 2, 3, . . . n, below the horizontal line. At time zero, "P" designates a present single sum of money; "A" designates a uniform series of equal payments at each compounding period; and "F" designates a future sum of money at the end of period "n". It usually is desirable to put the monetary numbers from economic evaluation problems on this type of time diagram to reduce confusion that creeps into problem statements before attempting to calculate the desired quantities. Once the given monetary values are determined, it is necessary to establish where they occur on the time diagram, what increment of time designates a period, what the interest rate per period is, and what you want to calculate. At this point, the problem is essentially solved. It is then just a matter of putting the information into the appropriate equation that will calculate the desired quantity.

On the following pages the compound interest formula factors are developed to mathematically relate "P", "F", and "A". In developing and discussing the application of these factors, the terms "worth" and "value" are used interchangeably to refer to either cost or income quantities and calculations.

There are six different two variable relationships that can be developed between "P", "F", and "A", as follows:

Calculated Quantity	=	Given Quantity	X	Appropriate Factor
F	=	P	X	$F/P_{i,n}$
F	=	A	X	$F/A_{i,n}$
P	=	F	X	$P/F_{i,n}$
P	=	A	X	$P/A_{i,n}$
A	=	F	X	$A/F_{i,n}$
A	=	P	X	$A/P_{i,n}$

Table 2-1 Variable Relationships Between "P", "F", and "A" and the Appropriate Factors

The factor symbolism given here and used throughout the text is based on the first letter in each factor designating the quantity that the factor calculates, while the second letter designates the quantity that is given. The two subscripts on each factor are the period interest rate, "i", followed by the number of interest compounding periods, "n". Use of this symbolism eliminates the confusion of trying to memorize the name of each factor and when to use each. For the student initially learning time value of money calculations, this is a great help in becoming familiar with the application of compound interest formulas. However, the common names of the different factors should be learned eventually since literature commonly uses name terminology rather than symbolism.

There are only three basic types of time value of money calculations: (1) calculation of future value, "F", from either "P" or "A"; (2) calculation of uniform and equal period values, "A", from either "F" or "P"; (3) calculation of present value, "P", from either "F" or "A". All time value of money calculations involve writing an equation or equations to calculate either "F", "P", or "A" so familiarity with the development and application of the factors needed to make these calculations is very important.

SINGLE PAYMENT COMPOUND-AMOUNT FACTOR. When a future value, "F", "n" periods from now, is to be calculated from a present sum of money, "P", with compounded interest at "i%" per period, the calculations are made as shown on the time diagram in Figure 2-2.

Principal P, Interest Pi $\}$ P(1+i) | P(1+i), P(1+i)i $\}$ $P(1+i)^2$ | $P(1+i)^{n-1}$, $P(1+i)^{n-1}i$ $\}$ $P(1+i)^n$

P ——————————————————————————

0 1 2 . . . . n $F = P(1+i)^n$

Figure 2-2 Time Diagram Illustration of Calculation of the Single Payment Compound-Amount Factor.

Interest is paid each year on the principal in the account at the beginning of the year. For year one, the principal is "P" and interest is "Pi" which gives P(1+i) accumulated at the end of year one. Therefore, in year two, the principal P(1+i) draws interest P(1+i)i which gives a total value of $P(1+i)^2$ accumulated at the end of year two. The final value accrued at the end of year "n" is given in Equation 2-1.

$$F = P(1+i)^n \qquad 2\text{-}1$$

The mathematical expression $(1+i)^n$ is called the "single payment compound-amount factor" and is designated as F/Pi,n because a future single sum of money, "F", is to be calculated from a present single sum of money, "P" at a given interest rate "i" for a given number of compounding periods "n". Example 2-1 illustrates the use of the F/Pi,n factor.

EXAMPLE 2-1 Single Payment Compound-Amount Factor Illustration

Calculate the future worth that $1,000 today will have six years from now if interest is 10% per year compounded annually.

Solution:

P=$1,000 – – – 1.7716

——————————————— $F = \$1{,}000(F/P_{10\%,6}) = \$1{,}771.6$

0 1 2.............6

The $F/P_{i,n}$ factor is found in the tables in Appendix A, or it can be calculated mathematically to be $(1+.10)^6 = 1.7716$.

SINGLE PAYMENT PRESENT-WORTH FACTOR. If the value of a future sum, "F", is given and the present value, "P", is desired, solve for "P" using Equation 2-1 as follows:

$$P = F\,[1/(1+i)^n] \qquad 2\text{-}2$$

The factor $1/(1+i)^n$ *is called the "single payment present-worth factor," and is designated by* $P/F_{i,n}$. *This factor is used to calculate a present single sum, "P", that is equivalent to a future single sum, "F".*

Note that $P/F_{i,n} = 1/(F/P_{i,n})$. Although one factor can be calculated from the other, the tables of compound interest formulas (Appendix A) give both factors for convenience.

EXAMPLE 2-2 Single Payment Present-Worth Factor Illustration

Calculate the present value of a $1,000 payment to be received six years from now if interest is 10% per year compounded annually.

Solution:

0.5645

$P = \$1,000(P/F_{10\%,6}) = \$564.50$

0 ——————————————————— 6   F = $1,000

The $P/F_{10\%,6}$ factor is found in Appendix A. The result shows that $564.50 invested today at 10% interest per year would grow to $1,000.00 in six years.

UNIFORM SERIES COMPOUND-AMOUNT FACTOR. Uniform series of equal investments are encountered frequently in economic evaluation problems, and it often is necessary to calculate the future worth, "F", of these payments. Derivation of the equation to do this follows. Each equal single investment, "A", draws compound interest for a different number of periods as illustrated in Figure 2-3. The investment, "A", at the end of period "n" draws no interest. The investment, "A", at the end of period "n-1" draws interest for one period, and so forth.

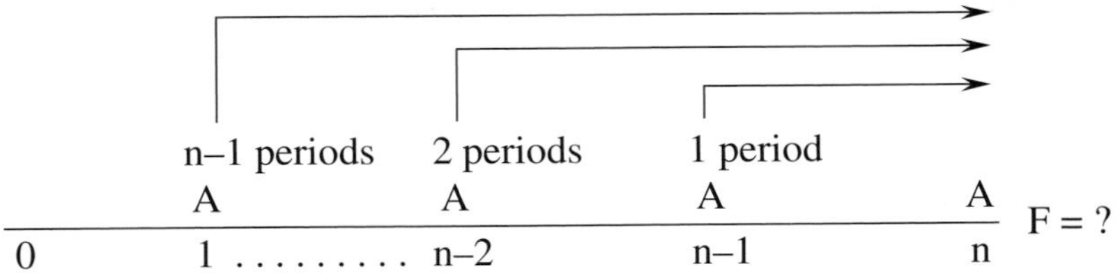

Figure 2-3 Time Diagram Development of Equation 2-3.

Writing the information given in Figure 2-3 into an equation to determine the cumulative future worth of these equal investments for a compound interest rate of "i" per period gives Equation 2-3. Note that each "A" value in this equation corresponds to a present single sum "P" as used in Equation 2-1.

$$F = A(1) + A(1+i) + A(1+i)^2 + \ldots + A(1+i)^{n-1} \qquad 2\text{-}3$$

Multiplying both sides of Equation 2-3 by the quantity (1+i) yields:

$$F(1+i) = A(1+i) + A(1+i)^2 + A(1+i)^3 + \ldots + A(1+i)^n \qquad 2\text{-}4$$

Subtracting 2-3 from 2-4 gives:

$$F(1+i) - F = A(1+i)^n - A$$

or

$$F = A\ [(1+i)^n - 1]/i \qquad 2\text{-}5$$

The factor $[(1+i)^n-1]/i$ is called the "uniform series compound-amount factor" and is designated by $F/A_{i,n}$. This factor is used to calculate a future single sum, "F", that is equivalent to a uniform series of equal end of period payments, "A".

EXAMPLE 2-3 Uniform Series Compound-Amount Factor Illustration

Calculate the future value forty years from now of a uniform series of $2,000 Roth IRA investments made at the end of each year for the next forty years if interest is 12% per year compounded annually.

Solution:

– A=2,000 A=2,000 A=2,000 767.0914

0 1 2 . . . . 40 $F=2{,}000(F/A_{12\%,40})=1{,}534{,}183$

SINKING-FUND DEPOSIT FACTOR. To determine the amount of money, "A", that must be sunk into a fund at the end of each period for "n" periods at "i" interest per period to accumulate "F" dollars, solve Equation 2-5 for "A".

$$A = F\{i/[(1+i)^n - 1]\} \qquad \text{2-6}$$

The factor $i/[(1+i)^n-1]$ is called the "sinking-fund deposit factor" and is designated by $A/F_{i,n}$. The factor is used to calculate a uniform series of equal end-of-period payments, "A", that are equivalent to a future sum, "F".

Note that $A/F_{i,n} = 1/(F/A_{i,n})$

EXAMPLE 2-4 Sinking-Fund Deposit Factor Illustration

Calculate the uniform series of equal investments made at the end of each year for the next forty years that would generate a $2,000,000 value forty years from now. Assume a nominal interest rate of 12% per year compounded annually.

Solution:

— A=? A=? A=? . . . . . . A=?
F = $2,000,000
0 1 2 3 . . . . 40 years

$$A = 2{,}000{,}000\,(\overset{0.00130}{A/F_{12\%,40}}) = 2{,}600$$

CAPITAL-RECOVERY FACTOR. To relate a uniform series of end of period payments, "A", to a present sum, "P", combine Equations 2-6 and 2-1 as follows:

$$A = [P(1+i)^n][i/(1+i)^n-1] = P[i(1+i)^n]/[(1+i)^n-1] \qquad \text{2-7}$$

The factor $i(1+i)^n/[(1+i)^n-1]$ is called the "capital-recovery factor" and is designated by $A/P_{i,n}$. This factor is used to calculate a uniform series of end of period payments, "A", that are equivalent to a present single sum of money, "P".

EXAMPLE 2-5 Capital-Recovery Factor

A retiree has a Roth IRA with a current value of $2,000,000. If the total account value was invested today in a 25-year annuity based on 7.0% annual interest, what annual annuity revenue will be available over the next 25 years?

Solution:

P = 2,000,000 A=? A=? A=? . . . . A=?

0 1 2 3 . . . . 25 years

$$A = 2{,}000{,}000\,(\overset{0.08581}{A/P_{7\%,25}}) = 171{,}620$$

UNIFORM SERIES PRESENT-WORTH FACTOR. To determine the present single sum of money, "P", that is equivalent to a uniform series of equal payments, "A", for "n" periods, at "i" interest per period, solve Equation 2-7 for "P".

$$P = A[(1+i)^n-1]/[i(1+i)^n] \qquad 2\text{-}8$$

The factor $[(1+i)^n-1]/[i(1+i)^n]$ is called the "uniform series present-worth factor" and is designated by $P/A_{i,n}$. This factor is used to calculate the present sum, "P", that is equivalent to a uniform series of equal end of period payments, "A".

Note that $A/P_{i,n} = 1/(P/A_{i,n})$

EXAMPLE 2-6 Uniform Series Present-Worth Factor Illustration

Calculate the present value of a series of $1,000 payments to be made at the end of each year for six years if interest is 10% per year compounded annually.

Solution:

— A=$1,000 A=$1,000

P = ?

0 1 6

$$\text{where at time zero, } P = \$1{,}000(\overset{4.355}{P/A_{10\%,6}}) = \$4{,}355$$

Note that the uniform series present worth factor $P/A_{10\%,6}$ brings the six equal $1,000 values at periods one through six to time zero (which is the beginning of period one), and not to time one, which is assumed to be the end of period one.

SUMMARY OF COMPOUND INTEREST FORMULAS

Name, Formula and Symbol Designation	**Illustration**
Single Payment Compound-Amount Factor $= (1+i)^n = F/P_{i,n}$	P_{given} 0 . . . . n $F=P(F/P_{i,n})$
Single Payment Present-Worth Factor $= 1/(1+i)^n = P/F_{i,n}$	$P=F(P/F_{i,n})$ 0 . . . . n F_{given}
Uniform Series Compound-Amount Factor $= [(1+i)^n-1]/i = F/A_{i,n}$	A_{given} A 0 1. . . . . n $F=A(F/A_{i,n})$
Sinking-Fund Deposit Factor $= i/[(1+i)^n-1] = A/F_{i,n}$	$A=F(A/F_{i,n})$ A 0 1. . . . . n F_{given}
Capital-Recovery Factor $= i(1+i)^n/[(1+i)^n-1] = A/P_{i,n}$	P_{given} $A=P(A/P_{i,n})$ A 0 1. . . . . . . n
Uniform Series Present-Worth Factor $= [(1+i)^n-1]/[i(1+i)^n] = P/A_{i,n}$	$P=A(P/A_{i,n})$ A_{given} A 0 1. . . . n

In applying the formulas as shown in the illustration column, the symbol letters always alternate in each equation. Knowing this may assist the reader in remembering the correct factor to use for various applications of the formulas.

There are several different timing considerations that impact how an investor should place his or her dollars on a time diagram. Up to this point all dollar values have been treated from a time value of money viewpoint as though a check was being received or written at the end of each compounding period. Such values are often referred to as *discrete end of period dollar values.* However, not all dollars are actually realized at the end of a compounding period. In addition to end of period values, investors can also work with *beginning of period values* and *mid-period values*. A fairly common example of beginning of period values might be lease payments. Usually, lease payments are made up front to secure the use of the asset for the following period, whereas mortgage payments are end of period payments made after the accrual of interest during each compounding period. When investors are uncertain as to the exact timing, or, when dollars are truly flowing throughout a time period, it is common evaluation procedure to utilize the mid-period approach. As the name implies this approach literally allocates dollars to the middle of each time period on a diagram. Each of these different timing considerations are illustrated in the Example 2-7.

EXAMPLE 2-7 Time Value of Money Factors and Timing Considerations

A person is to receive five payments in amounts of $300 at the end of year one, $400 at the end of each of years two, three and four, and $500 at the end of year five. If the person considers that places exist to invest money with equivalent risk at 9% annual interest, calculate the time zero lump sum settlement "P", and the end of year five lump sum settlement "F", that would be equivalent to receiving the end of period payments. Next, determine the five equal end of year payments "A", at years one through five that would be equivalent to the stated payments. Finally, recalculate the present value assuming the same annual payments are treated first, as beginning of period values and second, as mid-period values.

Solutions Based on Discrete End of Period Dollar Values:

	—	\$300	\$400	\$400	\$400	\$500	
P = ?	0	1	2	3	4	5	F=?

$$P = 300\overset{0.9174}{(P/F_{9\%,1})} + 400\overset{0.8417}{(P/F_{9\%,2})} + 400\overset{0.7722}{(P/F_{9\%,3})} + 400\overset{0.7084}{(P/F_{9\%,4})}$$

$$+ 500\overset{0.6499}{(P/F_{9\%,5})} = \$1{,}529$$

or,

$$P = 300\overset{0.9174}{(P/F_{9\%,1})} + 400\overset{2.531}{(P/A_{9\%,3})}\overset{0.9174}{(P/F_{9\%,1})} + 500\overset{0.6499}{(P/F_{9\%,5})}$$

$$= \$1{,}529$$

$$F = 300\overset{1.412}{(F/P_{9\%,4})} + 400\overset{1.295}{(F/P_{9\%,3})} + 400\overset{1.188}{(F/P_{9\%,2})}$$

$$+ 400\overset{1.090}{(F/P9\%,1)} + 500 = \$2{,}353$$

or,

$$F = 300\overset{1.412}{(F/P_{9\%,4})} + 400\overset{3.278}{(F/A_{9\%,3})}\overset{1.090}{(F/P_{9\%,1})} + 500 = \$2{,}353$$

or,

$$F = 1{,}529\overset{1.5386}{(F/P_{9\%,5})} = \$2{,}353$$

The equivalent annual payments "A" can be calculated by spreading the present value of \$1,529 forward into five equal payments or by spreading the future value of \$2,353 back into five equal payments as follows:

$$A = 1{,}529\overset{0.2571}{(A/P_{9\%,5})} = \$393 \text{ or, } A = 2{,}353\overset{0.1671}{(A/F_{9\%,5})} = \$393$$

Present Value Based on Discrete Beginning of Period Values:

	\$300	\$400	\$400	\$400	\$500	—
P = ?	0	1	2	3	4	5

$$P = 300 + 400\overset{0.9174}{(P/F_{9\%,1})} + 400\overset{0.8417}{(P/F_{9\%,2})} + 400\overset{0.7722}{(P/F_{9\%,3})}$$

$$+ 500\overset{0.7084}{(P/F_{9\%,4})}$$

$$= \$1{,}667$$

or,

$$P = 300 + 400\overset{2.531}{(P/A_{9\%,3})} + 500\overset{0.7084}{(P/F_{9\%,4})} = \$1{,}667$$

Present Value Based on Discrete Mid-Period Values:

P = ?	\$300	\$400	\$400	\$400	\$500
0	0.5	1.5	2.5	3.5	4.5

Mathematically, $P/F_{i,n} = \dfrac{1}{(1+i)^n}$

$$P = 300(\overset{0.9578}{P/F_{9\%,0.5}}) + 400(\overset{0.8787}{P/F_{9\%,1.5}}) + 400(\overset{0.8062}{P/F_{9\%,2.5}})$$

$$+ 400(\overset{0.7396}{P/F_{9\%,3.5}}) + 500(\overset{0.6785}{P/F_{9\%,4.5}}) = \$1{,}596$$

Note that the mid-period present value is about half way between the beginning of period and end of period results.

2.3 Nominal, Period and Effective Interest Rates Based on Discrete Compounding of Interest

Discrete compounding of interest involves using a finite number of interest compounding periods per year. Interest rates are normally specified by financial agencies on a nominal annual basis with interest compounded a specified number of times per year. For example, if a bank pays 5.0% interest compounded daily, this means that the nominal annual interest rate is 5.0% and the daily period interest rate is 5.0% divided by 365 days which is 0.0137% per day. With daily compounding a depositor would receive interest on the principal and accrued interest in his account at the end of each daily period. Relating this to our compound interest formulas, there would be 365 periods per year with the period interest rate i = 0.0137%. Due to the effect of compounding with more than one interest compounding period per year, the total amount of interest paid per year is greater than the nominal interest rate, "r", times initial principal. The terms "simple interest", "interest" and "nominal interest" are all interchangeable with the, "annual interest rate." The use of the acronym "APR" is now used in lending and related to the annualized interest rate, or the cost of borrowing inclusive of points and other fees related to the loan and paid out of the loan at closing. Be aware that engineering economists often use the term "simple interest" very differently as having interchangeable meaning with "add-on" or "flat" interest described in Section 2.6.

Period interest rate = i = r/m

where m = number of compounding periods per year,
r = nominal interest rate = mi

An effective interest rate is the interest rate that when applied once per year to a principal sum will give the same amount of interest equal to a nominal rate of "r" percent per year compounded "m" times per year. *Annual Percentage Yield* (APY) is the standard term used by the banking industry to identify an effective interest rate. The development of the formula for an effective interest rate "E" follows.

The future worth "F_1" of "P" dollars invested at i% per period for "m" periods is:

P ———————————————— $F_1 = P(F/P_{i,m}) = P(1+i)^m$

0 1 2. . . . . m periods/year

If an effective interest rate, "E", is applied once per year a future worth, "F_2", results from investing "P" dollars.

P ———————————————— $F_2 = P(F/P_{E,1}) = P(1+E)^1$

0 1 period/year

Since the initial principal, "P", is the same in each case, it is necessary to set $F_1 = F_2$ to make the total annual interest the same for both cases. This gives Equation 2-9 for "E".

Effective Annual Interest, $E = (1+i)^m - 1$ 2-9

If an investor knows the effective interest rate but wants to determine the equivalent period i value, compounded m times per year, Equation 2-9 can be rearranged to solve for i as follows:

$$i = (1+E)^{1/m} - 1$$

So, if an investor wanted an annual effective interest rate of 12.0%, but the period interest rate i was to be compounded monthly, the relevant period interest rate $i = 1.12^{(1/12)} - 1 = 0.009489$ or 0.9489% per month.

EXAMPLE 2-8 Discrete Nominal, Period and Effective Interest Rates

An investor is scheduled to receive annual payments of $1,000 at years one, two, and three. For an annual interest rate of 10% compounded semi-annually, calculate the time zero present value and the year three future value of these payments.

Solution: Use semi-annual periods and interest in the first solution.

```
        —     —  $1,000  —  $1,000  —  $1,000
P=? ________________________________________  F=?
    0     1     2     3     4     5     6 semi-annual periods
```

Semi-annual period interest i = 10%/2 = 5%.

$$P = 1{,}000(\overset{0.9070}{P/F_{5\%,2}}) + 1{,}000(\overset{0.8227}{P/F_{5\%,4}}) + 1{,}000(\overset{0.7462}{P/F_{5\%,6}}) = \$2{,}476$$

$$F = 1{,}000(\overset{1.2155}{F/P_{5\%,4}}) + 1{,}000(\overset{1.1025}{F/P_{5\%,2}}) + 1{,}000 = \$3{,}318$$

Checking the answers; $P = 3{,}318(P/F_{5\%,6}) = \$2{,}476$
$F = 2{,}476(F/P_{5\%,6}) = \$3{,}318$

With semi-annual periods, the uniform series factors, $P/A_{i,n}$ and $F/A_{i,n}$ cannot be used, because you do not have a series of equal $1,000 values at the end of each semi-annual period. However, by using annual periods with an annual effective interest rate that is equivalent to 10% annual interest compounded semi-annually, the uniform series factors can be used as follows in the second solution.

```
        —       $1,000     $1,000     $1,000
P=? ______________________________________  F=?
    0           1          2          3 annual periods
```

Effective interest rate per year $= (1+.05)^2 - 1 = 0.1025$ or 10.25%

$$P = 1{,}000\overset{2.476}{(P/A_{10.25,3})} = 1{,}000[(1.1025)^3 - 1]/[(1.1025)^3(0.1025)]$$
$$= \$2{,}476$$

or,

$$P = 1{,}000\overset{0.9070}{(P/F_{10.25\%,1})} + 1{,}000\overset{0.8227}{(P/F_{10.25\%,2})} + 1{,}000\overset{0.7462}{(P/F_{10.25\%,3})}$$
$$= 1{,}000(1/1.1025)^1 + 1{,}000(1/1.1025)^2 + 1{,}000(1/1.1025)^3$$
$$= \$2{,}476$$

$$F = 1{,}000\overset{3.318}{(F/A_{10.25\%,3})} = 1{,}000[(1.1025)^3 - 1]/0.1025 = \$3{,}318$$

or,

$$F = 1{,}000\overset{1.2155}{(F/P_{10.25\%,2})} + 1{,}000\overset{1.1025}{(F/P_{10.25\%,1})} + 1{,}000 = \$3{,}318$$

2.4 Nominal, Period and Effective Interest Rates Based on Continuous Compounding of Interest

If the number of compounding periods, "m", per year become very large the period interest rate, which is the nominal interest rate, "r", divided by "m", becomes very small. In the limit as "m" approaches infinity, period interest "i" approaches zero resulting in a continuous interest situation. With continuous compounding of a nominal interest rate, "r", an infinitesimal amount of period interest, "i", occurs an infinite number of times during the evaluation period. This requires differential calculus derivation of continuous interest time value of money factors equivalent to the discrete compounding of interest factors developed earlier in this chapter. In Appendix B factors are developed and illustrated for continuous interest and discrete dollar values, while Appendix C factors are developed and illustrated for continuous interest and continuously flowing dollar values. Following are the continuous interest compound amount and present worth factors for discrete values from Appendix B.

Continuous Interest Single Discrete Payment Compound Amount Factor ($F/P_{r,n}$)

$$F/P_{r,n} = e^{rn}$$

Continuous Interest Single Discrete Payment Present Worth Factor ($P/F_{r,n}$)

$$P/F_{r,n} = \frac{1}{e^{rn}}$$

Where: r = nominal interest rate compounded continuously
n = number of discrete evaluation periods
e = base of natural log (ln) = 2.7183 . . .

The Equation 2-10 formula for an effective discrete interest rate, "E", that is equivalent to a nominal interest rate, "r", compounded continuously follows for a discrete initial investment of "P" dollars:

Calculate the future worth, "F_1", of "P" discrete dollars invested at a nominal discrete interest rate, "r", compounded continuously for one year.

P ———————————————— $F_1 = P(F/P_{r,1}) = P[e^{r(1)}]$
0 1_{year}

Now calculate the future worth, "F_2", of "P" discrete dollars invested at an effective discrete interest rate, "E", compounded discretely for one year.

P ———————————————— $F_2 = P(F/P_{E,1}) = P(1+E)^1$
0 1_{year}

Setting $F_1 = F_2$ gives $Pe^r = P(1+E)$ or $E = e^r - 1$.

$$E = e^r - 1 \qquad 2\text{-}10$$

If an investor knows the effective discrete interest rate, E, but wants to determine the equivalent continuous interest rate, r, Equation 2-10 can be rearranged to solve for r as follows:

$$r = \ln(1+E)$$

So, if an investor wanted an annual effective discrete compound interest rate of 12.0%, but the nominal interest rate "r" was actually compounded continuously, the equivalent continuous interest rate r = ln(1.12) = 0.1133 or 11.33%. In other words, money earning a continuously compounded interest rate of 11.33% is effectively earning a discrete nominal interest rate of 12.0% compounded annually.

To illustrate, calculating the present worth of \$1 for a year using a discrete interest rate of 12.0%, compounded annually, the present value is \$1(1/(1+.12))1 = \$0.8929. The present value of \$1 using a continuous interest rate of 11.33% is $\$1(1/e^{0.1133}) = \$0.8929$. A similar equality must also exist when comparing future values.

For investors working with continuous interest, results (such as rate of return) may be expressed as a continuously compounded nominal rate, or converted to their effective discrete equivalent annual value. Given that most financial markets deal with discrete interest, some investors working with continuous find it easier to choose the later and compare numbers by converting their continuous results to discrete values using Equation 2-10.

There really is no economic analysis advantage to working with continuous interest rates rather than discrete values for i. In fact, in many ways it simply adds confusion to the analysis procedure. Continuous compounding is legal, just not real common in the financial markets. Therefore, vast majorities of economic evaluations are made using discrete compound interest. Finally, financial calculators and functions built into most spreadsheets today are designed to work with discrete interest rates based on discrete dollar values. This is just another advantage for utilizing the discrete methodology.

The effective interest rate, "E", described in Equation 2-10 is the discrete interest rate that is economically equivalent to a nominal interest rate, "r", compounded continuously.

To illustrate these two different types of interest rates, consider the 1.5% monthly period interest charged on some credit card accounts. This 1.5% monthly period interest rate corresponds to a nominal rate of 18.0% compounded monthly. Using Equation 2-9, the effective annual interest rate that is equivalent to a nominal rate of 18% compounded monthly is $E = (1+.015)^{12} - 1 = 0.1956$ or 19.56% per year on any unpaid balance. If the nominal rate of 18.0% was compounded continuously instead of monthly, Equation 2-10 would be used to get an effective annual interest rate, E = 19.72% from $E = e^{.18} - 1$.

The continuous interest compound amount and present value factors for continuously flowing values from Appendix C are developed as follows:

Continuous Interest, Single Continuous Payment Compound Amount Factor ($F/P^*_{r,n}$)

$$(F/P^*_{r,n}) = [(e^r-1)/r](e^{r(n-1)})$$

$(e^r-1)/r$ is the continuous interest, continuous flow of money, single payment compound amount factor for one period. It converts continuously flowing funds to a discrete end-of-period sum. $(e^{r(n-1)})$ is the continuous interest, discrete dollar value single payment compound amount factor that takes the end-of-period discrete sum forward to the end of period "n."

Continuous Interest, Single Continuous Payment Present Worth Factor ($P/F^*_{r,n}$)

$$(P/F^*_{r,n}) = [(e^r-1)/r]\ [1/\ (e^{rn})]$$

$(e^r-1)/r$ is the continuous interest, continuous flow of money single payment compound amount factor for one period. It converts continuously flowing funds to a discrete end-of-period sum. $1/(e^{rn})$ is the continuous interest discrete dollar value, single payment present worth factor that takes the period "n" discrete sum back to period zero.

Equation 2-10 also results from considering a continuously flowing "P" dollar investment during year one as follows:

Calculate the future value, "F" of "P" dollars invested uniformly during year 1 at a nominal interest rate, "r," compounded continuously for one year.

———— P ————
0 ———————— 1 $F_1 = P[(e^r-1)/r]$

Now calculate the future value, "F_2," of the discrete present value equivalent of "P" dollars invested uniformly during year one at a nominal interest rate "r" compounded continuously for one year. Consider that the discrete present value equivalent of the "P" dollars invested uniformly during year one earns interest at an effective rate, "E," compounded discretely for one year.

$P[(e^r-1)/r][1/e^r]$
0 ———————— 1 $F_2 = P[(e^r-1)/r][1/e^r](1+E)^1$

Equating F_1 and F_2 gives $E = e^r-1$ which is Equation 2-10

EXAMPLE 2-9 Equivalence of Continuous and Discrete Interest Calculations

Calculate the present value of \$100 to be received in the future assuming a continuous compound interest rate of 15% per year for the following timing assumptions:

A) The \$100 is a discrete sum received once at the end of year six.
B) The \$100 is a discrete sum received once at the beginning of year six, which is the end of year five.
C) The \$100 is received uniformly during year six.
D) The \$100 is a discrete sum received at period 5.5 compounded with the equivalent effective interest rate of $E = e^{.15} - 1 = .1618$ or 16.18%.
E) Treat the halves of \$100 flowing during year six as \$50 at year five and \$50 at year six, using the equivalent discrete rate of 16.18% shown in part D to be equivalent to 15% compounded continuously.

Solution:

— — — — F = \$100

A) P = ? ——————————————————————

0 1 . . . . 4 5 6

0.4066

$P = 100(P/F_{15\%,6}) = 100(1/e^{.15(6)}) = \$40.66$

where the 15% annual interest rate is compounded continuously.

(See Appendix B for the continuous interest factor development for discrete values.)

Note from Equation 2-10 an effective annual discrete interest rate of 16.18% is equivalent to 15% compounded continuously since $0.1618 = e^{.15} - 1$. Using the discrete interest rate of 16.18% to calculate present value:

0.4066

$P = 100(P/F_{16.18\%,6}) = 100[1/(1.1618)^6] = \$40.66$

	—	—	—	F = $100	—
B) P = ?	0	1 4		5	6

$$P = 100\overset{0.4724}{(P/F_{15\%,5})} = 100(1/e^{.15(5)}) = \$47.24$$

where the 15% interest rate is compounded continuously.

(See Appendix B for the continuous interest factor development for discrete values.)

For equivalent discrete compounding as presented in part A:

$$P = 100\overset{0.4724}{(P/F_{16.18\%,5})} = 100[1/(1.1618)^5] = \$47.24$$

	—	—	—	—	F = $100	—
C) P = ?	0	1 4		5		6

$$P = 100\overset{0.4386}{(P/F^*_{15\%,6})} = \$43.86$$

(See Appendix C for continuous interest, continuous flow of money, single payment present worth factors.)

	—	—	—	—	F = $100	—
D) P = ?	0	1 4		5	5.5	6

$$P = 100\overset{0.4383}{(P/F_{16.18\%,5.5})} = \$43.83$$

This discrete mid-period value, discrete interest result is very close to the part C continuous interest, continuous flow of money result which shows the approximate equivalence of these analysis methods.

E) P = ?	—	—	—	F=$50	F=$50
	0	1 4		5	6

$$P = 50(\overset{0.4724}{P/F_{16.18\%,5}}) + 50(\overset{0.4066}{P/F_{16.18\%,6}}) = \$43.95$$

This result is also similar to the part C and D results, which demonstrates the equivalence of discrete values and discrete interest to continuous flow of values and continuous interest if proper timing of values are used with equivalent discrete effective interest rates.

It is important to recognize that the time value of money factors introduced in Section 2.4 and developed in Appendices B and C, usually determine a discrete sum at a future point in time rather than a continuously flowing value. The only exception to this rule pertains to the capital recovery factor for continuous interest and continuous flowing funds ($A/P^*_{r,n}$), and the sinking fund deposit factor for continuous interest and continuous flowing funds ($A/F^*_{r,n}$). When making hand calculations with these factors, the resulting calculated values are continuously flowing values, not discrete sums. If further discounting or compounding of the calculated series is required, the appropriate factors developed in Appendix C must be utilized.

Consider a uniform series of continuous flowing funds in years three, four and five that are to be discounted to the present. With methodology utilized in this text, the two most common approaches to discount the values would be: (A) Discount each cash flow back individually with a $P/F^*_{r,n}$ factor, or, (B) Reduce the number of factors by employing a combination of $P/A^*_{r,n}$ and $P/F_{r,n}$ factors for the appropriate periods. Notice the difference in these factors with the (B) approach. The $P/A^*_{r,n}$ factor is taken from Appendix C, which is developed for continuous flowing funds. However, the $P/A^*_{r,n}$ gives us a discrete sum at the beginning of year three, or the end of year two. Again the key word here is a discrete sum, not a year two continuous flowing fund. Therefore, we must discount this sum back to time zero with the appropriate $P/F_{r,n}$ factor utilizing the factor for continuous interest for a discrete sum of money as developed in Appendix B of the text. This process will yield a result within round-off error accuracy provided in the tables.

Throughout this textbook the reader will find constant reminders to carefully consider all relevant timing considerations in laying out a time diagram for any investment. This continuous interest application is another timing related issue to be considered in properly accounting for time value of money.

2.5 Applications of Compound Interest Formulas

EXAMPLE 2-10 $F/P_{i,n}$ Factor Illustration With Interpolation

What is the future worth six years from now of a present sum of $1,000 if:

A) The interest rate is 8% compounded quarterly?
B) The interest rate is 7.5% compounded annually?

Solution:

A) 8% Compounded Quarterly

```
                  —     —     —     —                1.608
P = $1,000    ________________________  F=$1,000(F/P2%,24)=$1,608
                  0     1     2. . . . 24
```

$P = \$1,000$ — time diagram 0, 1, 2. . . . 24 — $F = \$1,000(F/P_{2\%,24}) = \$1,608$, with factor value 1.608

B) 7.5% Compounded Annually

$P = \$1,000$ — time diagram 0, 1, 2 . . . . 6 — $F = \$1,000(F/P_{7.5\%,6}) = \$1,543$, with factor value 1.543

In Part A, the nominal rate of 8% divided by four quarterly compounding periods gives us a period interest rate of 2.0%, (available in Appendix A). In Part B, the 7.5% interest rate is not in the tables. To solve this problem, substitute the values into the $F/P_{7.5\%,6}$ factor mathematical definition and solve that factor for an "i" value of 7.5% (0.075) and six compounding periods. This gives $(1.075)^6 = 1.543$. An alternative approach is to interpolate, as is illustrated below, using the known Appendix A values of 7% and 8%.

Interpolation for $F/P_{7.5\%,6}$:

$F/P_{7.5\%,6} = 1.501 + .5(1.587\text{-}1.501)$
$= 1.544$

In general, $F/P_{7.5\%,6} = 1.501 +$ "a"

and a/b = c/d so, a = b(c/d)
$= (7.5\text{-}7.0)(1.587\text{-}1.501)/(8.0\text{-}7.0)$
$= (.5)(.0860)$
$= 0.0430$

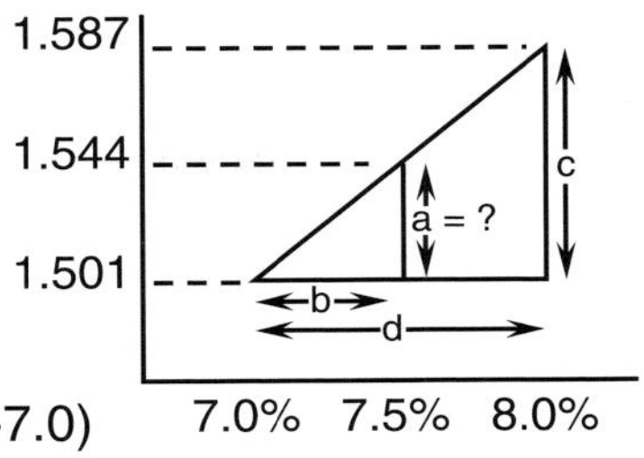

Figure 2-4

Mathematically $F/P_{7.5\%,6} = (1{+}0.075)^6 = 1.543$

The difference in the 1.543 mathematical result and the 1.544 interpolation result is due to interpolation error since the factor varies non-linearly rather than linearly with changes in the interest rate.

EXAMPLE 2-11 $F/P_{i,n}$ Factor Illustrated With Interpolation

How many years will it take for a present sum of $1,000 to grow to $2,000 if interest is 10% compounded annually? (Or, in general, how long does it take to double your money invested at 10% per annum?)

Solution:

$$P = \$1{,}000 \underset{0}{\text{———————}}\underset{n}{} \quad F = \$2{,}000 = \$1{,}000(F/P_{10\%,n})$$

$\$2{,}000/\$1{,}000 = (F/P_{10\%,n}) = 2.0$

Go into the 10% tables in the $F/P_{i,n}$ column of the 10% table for $F/P_{10\%,n} = 2.000$. No factor listed gives exactly 2.000. Choosing the closest values, linear interpolation between $F/P_{10\%,7} = 1.949$ and $F/P_{10\%,8} = 2.144$ gives:

$n = 7 \text{ years} + (1)[(2.000\text{-}1.949)/(2.144\text{-}1.949)] = 7.26 \text{ years}$

The "Rule of 72" is an approximation technique for problems like Example 2-11 where the objective is to determine the period of time "n" required to double your money at a given compound interest rate. This rule is summarized as follows:

$$\frac{\text{Number of Periods}}{\text{to Double Money}} = \frac{72}{\text{Compound Interest Rate per Period x 100}} \qquad 2\text{-}11$$

In Example 2-11 note that 72/10 gives 7.2 years needed to double your money which is very close to the 7.26 year result calculated. To double money at 6% interest per year takes 72/6 = 12 years, while to double money at 12% per year takes only six years. Approximation error becomes very significant when dealing with three or less compounding periods, or interest rates above 30%.

EXAMPLE 2-12 $P/F_{i,n}$ Factor Illustration

What is the present value of two $1,000 payments to be made three and five years from now if interest is 8% compounded semi-annually?

Solution:

	—	—	—	—	—	—	$1,000	—	—	—	$1,000
P = ?	0	1	2	3	4	5	6	7	8	9	10

In this example, "n" is expressed in semi-annual periods. Therefore, the appropriate compound interest rate "i" is 4% per period.

$$P = \$1{,}000(\overset{0.7903}{P/F_{4\%,6}}) + \$1{,}000(\overset{0.6756}{P/F_{4\%,10}}) = \$1{,}465.90$$

EXAMPLE 2-13 $P/A_{i,n}$ Factor Illustration

What is the present value of a series of $100 payments to be made at the end of each month for the next five years if interest is 12% compounded monthly?

Solution:

	—	$100	$100	$100
P = ?	0	1	2	60 months

i = 1% per month

$$P = \$100(\overset{44.95}{P/A_{1\%,60}}) = \$4{,}495$$

EXAMPLE 2-14 Factor Illustration for Multiple Uniform Series

Calculate the present, future and equivalent annual end of period values for the series of incomes presented on the following time line diagram. Assume an interest rate of 15%.

A_1=\$100 A_1=\$100 A_2=\$150 A_2=\$150 A_3=\$200 A_3=\$200

P=? ——————————————————————— F=?

0 1 . . . . . . 5 6 . . . . . . 10 11 15

Solution:

Present Value

$$P = 100\overset{3.352}{(P/A_{15,5})} + 150\overset{3.352}{(P/A_{15,5})}\overset{0.4972}{(P/F_{15,5})} + 200\overset{3.352}{(P/A_{15,5})}\overset{0.2472}{(P/F_{15,10})}$$
$$= \$751$$

$$\text{or} = 100\overset{3.352}{(P/A_{15,5})} + 150(\overset{5.019}{P/A_{15,10}} - \overset{3.352}{P/A_{15,5}}) + 200(\overset{5.847}{P/A_{15,15}} - \overset{5.019}{P/A_{15,10}})$$
$$= \$751$$

Future Value

$$F = 200\overset{6.742}{(F/A_{15,5})} + 150\overset{6.742}{(F/A_{15,5})}\overset{2.011}{(F/P_{15,5})} + 100\overset{6.742}{(F/A_{15,5})}\overset{4.046}{(F/P_{15,10})}$$

$$= \$6,110 \text{ or, } 751\overset{8.137}{(F/P_{15\%,15})} = \$6,110$$

Equivalent Annual Value

$$A = \$751\overset{0.17102}{(A/P_{15\%,15})} = \$128 \text{ or, } \$6,110\overset{0.02102}{(A/F_{15\%,15})} = \$128$$

EXAMPLE 2-15 $A/F_{i,n}$ Factor Illustration

What uniform annual cost for ten years is equivalent to a single \$10,000 cost ten years from now if interest is 8% per year?

Solution:

$$A = \$10,000\overset{0.06903}{(A/F_{8\%,10})} = \$690.30$$

— A = \$690.30 A = \$690.30

——————————————————————— F = \$10,000

0 1 10

EXAMPLE 2-16 Equivalent Annual Payments Illustration

What payments each year are equivalent to $3,000 payments at the end of years three, six and nine from now if interest is 10% compounded annually? Determine the future worth of these payments at the end of year nine.

Solution:

—	—	—	$3,000	—	—	$3,000	—	—	$3,000
0	1	2	3	4	5	6	7	8	9

Equivalent Annual Payments = $\$3{,}000(A/F_{10\%,3}) = \$906.33$ each year for nine years. (factor value 0.30211) Spreading the $3,000 at the end of year three uniformly over years one, two and three gives the same equivalent annual cost as spreading the $3,000 at the end of year six uniformly over years four, five and six. The argument is similar for years seven, eight and nine.

$$\text{Future Worth} = \$906.33\overset{13.579}{(F/A_{10\%,9})} = \$12{,}308$$

$$\text{or} = \$3{,}000\overset{1.331}{(F/P_{10\%,3})} + \$3{,}000\overset{1.772}{(F/P_{10\%,6})} + \$3{,}000 = \$12{,}308$$

$3,000 times a uniform series compound amount factor for the 10% interest rate will not work here because the equal payments do not occur at the end of every annual compounding period. The calculation must be made as shown unless you determine an effective interest rate per three year period and work the problem with three periods of three years each. The effective interest rate approach to this type of problem is based on using Equation 2-9:

$$E = (1.10)^3 - 1 = 0.331 \text{ or } 33.1\%$$

In this case, "E" is the effective interest rate per three year period.

$$\$3{,}000\overset{4.1027}{(F/A_{33.1\%,3})} = \$12{,}308$$

EXAMPLE 2-17 $A/P_{i,n}$ Factor Illustration

What annual end of year mortgage payments are required to pay off a $10,000 mortgage in five years if interest is 10% per year?

Solution:

```
                       —           A = ?              A = ?
P = $10,000  ___________________________________________
             0                     1 . . . . . . . . . . . . . 5
```

$$A = \$10{,}000(\overset{0.2638}{A/P_{10\%,5}}) = \$2{,}638/\text{year}$$

Figure 2-5 shows how these payments amortize, or pay off, the mortgage:

END OF YEAR	PRINCIPAL OWED DURING YEAR	MORTGAGE PAYMENT	INTEREST = .10 (PRINCIPAL)	AMOUNT APPLIED TO REDUCE PRINCIPAL	NEW PRINCIPAL OWED
1	$10,000	$2,638	$1,000	$1,638	$8,362
2	8,362	2,638	836	1,802	6,560
3	6,560	2,638	656	1,982	4,578
4	4,578	2,638	458	2,180	2,398
5	2,398	2,638	240	2,398	0
TOTALS		$13,190	$3,190	$10,000	

Figure 2-5 Mortgage Amortization Schedule

2.6 "Add-On" or "Flat" Interest (Applied to the "Rule of 78")

While compound interest is applied to unpaid investment principal and accrued interest each interest compounding period, *a flat or add-on interest rate is applied to the initial investment principal each interest compounding period.* This means that the cumulative interest paid or received by a borrower or lender on a flat interest loan is proportional to the length of the loan period and not affected by the payment schedule. If "P" = initial investment principal, "i" = flat interest rate per period, and "n" = number of interest paying periods;

$$\text{Cumulative Add-On Interest for "n" Compounding Periods} = (P)(i)(n) \qquad \text{2-12}$$

Be aware that engineering economists often use the term "simple" interest to refer to "flat" or "add-on" interest as defined here. The common banking and financial market use of the term "simple" interest is very different, generally being interchangeable with "nominal" or "annual percentage rate" interest.

Note that the interest paying periods are not necessarily years but may be days, weeks, months, or other periods. When it is necessary to calculate the interest due for a fraction of a year or period, it is common practice to take loan principal, "P," times the flat interest rate, "i", times the fraction of the year or applicable period. For example, \$1,000 principal at flat interest of 9.0% per annum for 100 days gives flat interest equal to:

(0.09)(\$1,000)(100/365) = \$24.66.

It is best to always state explicitly the type of interest and compounding you are using in financial calculations, otherwise, confusion about the meaning of the results can occur. It is generally considered to be completely legitimate and ethical to use either a flat interest or compound interest rate in financial dealings.

EXAMPLE 2-18 Compounding With "Flat" or "Add-on" Interest

What annual end of year mortgage payments are required to pay off a \$10,000 mortgage in five years if the interest rate is 10% per year using "flat" or "add on" compounding of interest? Assume that the loan is paid off with five equal principal plus interest payments in years 1-5.

Solution:

Interest Owed Each Year:	\$10,000(0.10) = \$1,000
Principal Owed Each Year:	\$10,000(0.20) = \$2,000
Total Annual Payment	\$3,000

Note that from Example 2-17, for a 10% compound interest rate, the annual payment is \$2,638; a difference of \$362 per year or \$1,810 over the five year loan life. The flat or add-on interest rate that would be equivalent to a 10% compound interest rate can be calculated by setting the annual cost of each alternative equal to each other and solving for "i":

(Annual Cost = AC)

AC of Compound Interest Rate Payment = AC of Flat Interest Rate Payment

$2,638 = $2,000 principal payment + $10,000(i) flat interest payment
$638 = $10,000(i)
i = $638 / $10,000 = 0.0638 or 6.38% per year

So, a nominal interest rate of 10.0% compounded annually is equivalent to a flat or add-on interest rate of 6.38% for this five year mortgage example.

The "Rule of 78" is a method of allocating the principal and interest components of a loan with flat interest as illustrated in Example 2-18. The interest component of each payment is calculated by multiplying a changing fraction each compounding period by the total amount of flat interest to be paid over the entire loan period (use equation 2-12 to compute the total loan interest). This fraction is determined in the following manner: The numerator is the number of remaining compounding periods in the loan, (therefore changing with each compounding period) while the denominator represents the sum of the numbers that represent the compounding periods over the entire loan life, (this number remains constant.) The number of compounding periods are most easily calculated using Equation 2-13:

Sum of Compounding Periods = [n(n+1)] / 2 2-13

Which is equivalent to = 1 + 2 + 3 + ... + n-1 + n

The principal due each compounding period represents the difference between the total period payment and the accrued interest.

EXAMPLE 2-19 Illustration of the Rule of 78

Using Example 2-18, if the add-on interest rate based payments of $3,000 per year were amortized based on the Rule of 78, what would the principal and interest components of each payment be for the five year loan?

Solution:

Total Flat or Add-on Interest Paid = $10,000(.10)(5 years) = $5,000

Sum of Compounding Periods = [5(5+1)] / 2 = 15 periods

Year	Interest	Principal
1	\$5,000(5/15) = \$1,667	\$3,000 - \$1,667 = \$ 1,333
2	\$5,000(4/15) = \$1,333	\$3,000 - \$1,333 = \$ 1,667
3	\$5,000(3/15) = \$1,000	\$3,000 - \$1,000 = \$ 2,000
4	\$5,000(2/15) = \$ 667	\$3,000 - \$ 667 = \$ 2,333
5	\$5,000(1/15) = \$ 333	\$3,000 - \$ 333 = \$ 2,667
	\$5,000	\$10,000

2.7 Loan Points and Buying Down Interest

Lending organizations such as banks, savings and loans, and insurance companies charge "points" on loans as a way of indirectly increasing the effective interest rate being charged on loans. *Points are a percentage of loan value and vary widely at different times. In a related way, developers who want to sell assets sometimes "buy-down" interest rates on loan money by paying an up front lump-sum fee to lending agencies so that the lending agencies can loan to persons at a lower rate.* However, the developer typically adds the buy-down charge to the price of the property being sold. The buyer needs to understand the economic principles related to "points" and "buying down" interest to make valid investment decisions that involve these considerations. The Truth in Lending Law requires lenders to provide the annual percentage rate (APR) on mortgages which includes the cost associated with points and similar upfront charges. This topic is addressed in more detail in Example 3-5 in conjunction with discussion of the meaning of any compound interest rate of return.

EXAMPLE 2-20 Illustration of Loan Points and Buying Down Interest Rates

If a lender receives six points (a fee of 6% of loan value) to make a \$100,000 loan at a 12% interest rate per year with uniform and equal annual mortgage payments over twenty years, what actual interest rate is the lender receiving?

Solution:

The mortgage payments are based on the \$100,000 loan value at 12% interest per year over twenty years.

$$A = \$100{,}000(\overset{0.13388}{A/P_{12\%,20}}) = \$13{,}388 \text{ per year payments}$$

From the lender viewpoint, the actual net loan amount is:
\$100,000 – \$6,000 point fee = \$94,000.

Net loan = \$94,000 Payments/year = \$13,388 . . . . . \$13,388

0 1 20

Annual Worth Equation: $\$94{,}000(A/P_{i,20}) = \$13{,}388$
where "i" is the actual net loan interest rate for the lender.

$A/P_{i,20} = \$13{,}388/\$94{,}000 = 0.14243$

94,000 = (13,388)[P/A$_{i,20}$]

by interpolation:

$A/P_{15\%,20} = 0.15976$

$A/P_{12\%,20} = 0.13388$

$i = 12\% + 3\%[(0.14243 - 0.13388)/(0.15976 - 0.13388)] = 12.99\%$

12.99% is the interest rate actually being realized on the net loan by the lender. This amount is known as the Annual Percentage Rate or APR and is discussed further in Example 3-5. If the borrower is paying points, the borrower is paying 12.99% interest on the actual net loan amount. If someone else is paying the points, such as the seller of a house to be financed by an FHA loan in the United States, then the borrower is really only paying 12% annual interest.

The concept of buying down interest rates involves similar calculations. Consider a realtor who would like to buy down the interest rate on \$100,000 of twenty year loan money from 12% to 10%. What up-front lump sum payment, similar to points in the previous calculations, will enable the lender to loan \$100,000 at 10% instead of 12% with uniform and equal mortgage payments over twenty years?

Let X = buy-down payment at time of loan

$$(\$100{,}000 - X)(\overset{0.13388}{A/P_{12\%,20}}) = \$100{,}000(\overset{0.11746}{A/P_{10\%,20}})$$

$(\$13{,}388 - \$11{,}746)/0.13388 = X = \$12{,}265$

Equivalently, we could have discounted the actual mortgage payments to be received (based on 10% interest) at the desired yield (which, in this example, is 12%) and subtracted that amount from the loan value to determine the required up-front payment.

$$\text{Actual Payments to be Received} = \$100{,}000\overset{0.11746}{(A/P_{10\%,20})} = \$11{,}746$$

$$\text{Required Buy-Down Payment} = \$100{,}000 - \$11{,}746\overset{7.469}{(P/A_{12\%,20})}$$

$$= \$100{,}000 - \$87{,}731 = \$12{,}269$$

$12,269 is within round-off error accuracy of the previous method of explicitly solving for the payment which was $12,265. The $12,265 up-front payment makes the lender net loan of $100,000 - $12,265 = $87,735 at 12% interest which enables the lender equivalently to loan $100,000 at 10% interest.

2.8 Arithmetic Gradient Series

In many economic evaluation situations, revenues and costs increase or decrease from period to period in an arithmetic gradient series. For example, escalation or de-escalation of projected incomes and operating costs from period to period, including the effects of inflation and supply/demand considerations, often may be approximated by an arithmetic gradient series of values.

Figure 2-6 illustrates a general arithmetic gradient series where the first term in the gradient series is "B" and the constant gradient between period terms is "g".

—	B	B+g	B+2g	....	B+(n–2)g	B+(n-1)g
0	1	2	3	....	n-1	n

Figure 2-6 A General Arithmetic Gradient Series

Computing the present worth or future worth of the series of values shown in Figure 2-6 requires "n" separate calculation terms using the single payment present worth or future worth techniques. To reduce the labor involved in these calculations, it is desirable to be able to convert this arithmetic gradient series of payments to a uniform series of equal payments which can then be converted to present or future worth single sums with $P/A_{i,n}$ or $F/A_{i,n}$ factors.

The uniform series of equal payments which is equivalent to an arithmetic gradient series of payments may be found using Equation 2-14:

$$A = B \pm g(A/G_{i,n}) \qquad 2\text{-}14$$

where $A/G_{i,n} = (1/i)\text{-}\{n/[(1+i)^n\text{-}1]\}$ is a factor tabulated in Appendix A for various interest rates, "i", and project lives, "n". The derivation of this factor is presented in the Appendix E. Example 2-21 illustrates the use of the $A/G_{i,n}$ factor.

Note two things about the gradient series calculations. First, the gradient, "g", is plus or minus depending on whether the gradient series is increasing or decreasing. Second, the arithmetic series factor is calculated for the "n" period project life, not the n-1 periods the gradient is applied. This is due to the way the gradient factor derivation works out as developed in Appendix E, for readers interested in the mathematical development of the factor. In other words, always include the base value period in determining the appropriate value of "n" for the $A/G_{i,n}$ factor. The A/G factor helps when making hand calculations, by reducing the number of factors required in a present worth equation.

EXAMPLE 2-21 Arithmetic Gradient Series

Consider an arithmetically increasing series of royalty payments, where the first payment (the first term in the gradient series) is B = \$1,100. The payments increase by \$100 each year, so g = \$100. The interest rate is 8% per annum and royalty payments are expected to last ten years (n = 10). Calculate the series of equal royalty payments or incomes that is equivalent to the gradient series of values using Equation 2-14.

Solution:

—	\$1,100.00	\$1,200.00 . . . . \$2,000.00
0	1	2 10

$$\text{Uniform Equal Payments, } A = \$1{,}100 + \$100\overset{3.871}{(A/G_{8\%,10})} = \$1{,}487.10$$

This result indicates that if money is valued at 8% per period, the uniform series of ten equal end of period payments of $1,487.10 is exactly equivalent to the original gradient series, as the following diagram illustrates:

—	$1,487.10	$1,487.10 . . . . $1,487.10
0	1	2 10

EXAMPLE 2-22 Arithmetic Gradient Series Factor Illustration

A man expects to invest $1,000 in common stock this year, $1,100 next year and to continue making each year's investment $100 greater than the previous year for twenty years. If he earns a 10% rate of return on his investments, what will the investment value be twenty years from now? Assume end of year investments.

Solution:

—	$1,000	$1,100	$1,200	$1,300	$1,400 — grad. series — $2,900	
0	1	2	3	4	5. 20	F=?

$$F = [\$1{,}000+\$100\overset{6.508}{(A/G_{10\%,20})}]\overset{57.27}{(F/A_{10\%,20})} = \$94{,}500$$

EXAMPLE 2-23 A Uniform Series with an Arithmetic Gradient Series

Find the present worth of the series of payments shown on the diagram if interest is 10% per period.

	—	$500	$500	$500	$600	$700 — grad. series —$1,700
P=?	0	1	2	3	4	5. 15

Solution:

Conversion of the series of gradient terms to a uniform series of equal payments from years three to fifteen yields:

$$\text{Years 3 to 15: } A = \$500+\$100\overset{4.699}{(A/G_{10\%,13})} = \$969.90$$

This gives the following equivalent time diagram:

	—	\$500	\$500	\$969.90	\$969.90	\$969.90
P=?	0	1	2	3	4.	15

Present Worth:

$$P = 500\overset{1.736}{(P/A_{10\%,2})} + 969.90\overset{7.103}{(P/A_{10\%,13})}\overset{.8264}{(P/F_{10\%,2})} = \$6,561$$

$$\text{or} = 500\overset{1.736}{(P/A_{10\%,2})} + 969.90(\overset{7.606}{P/A_{10\%,15}} - \overset{1.736}{P/A_{10\%,2}}) = \$6,561$$

2.9 Alternative Time Line Diagram and the Concept of Cash Flow

An alternative time line diagram that often is used to more graphically illustrate the concept of inflows and outflows of money is presented in Figure 2-7. *The key consideration to any time line diagram is allocating outflows and inflows of money at the point in time closest to when dollar amounts are actually expected to be incurred.* When we speak of inflows and outflows of money, on a before-tax basis, we are referring to revenues and capital or operating costs associated with a particular investment. However, only if your projects are tax-free should you consider making economic evaluations on a before-tax basis. In general, economic evaluations are made on an after-tax basis utilizing cash flow generated from a project for the investor's unique tax position. In Chapters 2 through 6, the dollar value per period generated by adding revenue and capital or operating costs in a time period should really be thought of as representing positive and negative cash flow in that period. As mentioned in Chapter 1, these first six chapters ignore the specifics of tax considerations to reduce confusion while gaining an important understanding of the basic concepts of time value of money. If we had a specified investment "P" at time zero that was expected to generate equal annual revenues "A" over years one through four, the modified time line diagram may appear as follows:

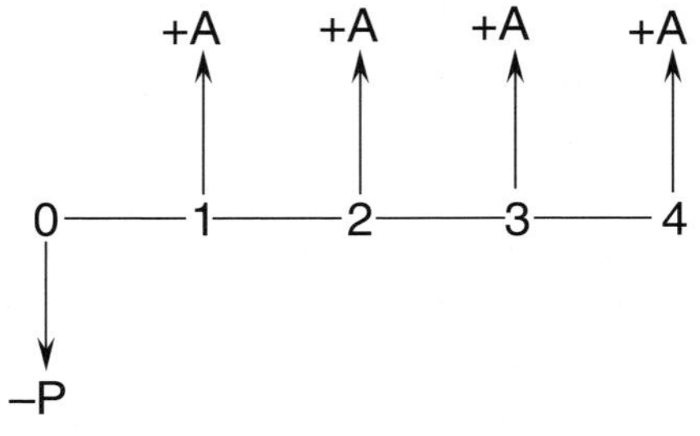

Figure 2-7 Alternative Time Line Diagram Approach

EXAMPLE 2-24 Illustration of the Alternative Time Line Diagram

Investments at time zero of $5,000 and the end of year one of $10,000 are expected to generate revenues of $7,500 each year, for three years, beginning at the end of year 2. Draw the modified time line diagram for this proposed investment and then calculate the present value of future revenues and costs associated with this project for a discount rate of 15%.

Solution:

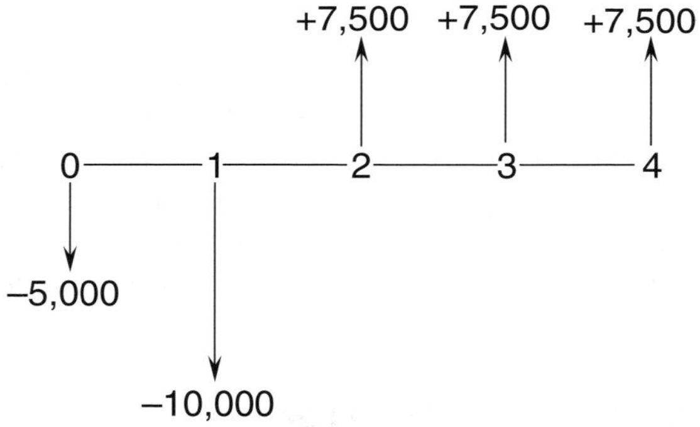

Present Value @ 15% =

$$-5{,}000-10{,}000\overset{0.8696}{(P/F_{15\%,1})}+7{,}500\overset{2.2832}{(P/A_{15\%,3})}\overset{0.8696}{(P/F_{15\%,1})}=+1{,}194$$

The alternative time line approach is not utilized extensively in this textbook because of the author's preference for a straight line time diagram. However, this approach may be preferred by the reader in laying out solutions to problems in the text.

2.10 Introduction of Rate of Return Analysis

In the examples presented to this point, the period interest rate (or rate of return) has been specified and we have calculated equivalent present worth, future worth, or annual quantities for given values of incomes or costs. If we change any of these example problems by specifying both the costs and revenues while leaving the period interest rate, "i", unknown, we generate a rate of return calculation type problem. To illustrate this concept, consider changing Example 2-17 to read, "what borrowed money annual compound interest rate is being paid on a $10,000 mortgage that will be paid off in five years with five equal end of year mortgage payments of $2,638?" The annual mortgage interest rate that the borrower is paying is the annual rate of return that the lender or investor is receiving on the unamortized mortgage investment principal each year. To determine this rate of return we must write an equation comparing costs and revenues at the same point in time or on an equivalent annual or period basis using an unknown rate of return per period, "i". For example, for an unknown "i", we can equate the annual mortgage payments of $2,638 to the equivalent annual investor cost as we did in Example 2-17 to calculate the mortgage payments for a given interest rate.

$\$10{,}000(A/P_{i,5}) = \$2{,}638$

$(A/P_{i,5}) = \$2{,}638/\$10{,}000 = 0.2638$

By trial and error procedures we can check the factor $A/P_{i,5}$ in the tables for different interest rates until we find in the 10% tables that $A/P_{i,5}$ gives the desired value of 0.2638. Therefore, the rate of return, "i", is 10% per year. Usually the "i" value we are looking for occurs between interest rates given in the tables and we must use linear interpolation to calculate the "i" value. The details of this interpolation procedure and general rate of return calculations are illustrated in the next chapter.

EXAMPLE 2-25 Illustration of the Use of All Factors

An investor is to make the following payments for a parcel of land: $5,000 down payment at time zero, a gradient series of payments starting at $2,000 at the end of year one and increasing by a constant gradient of $500 per year in years two through eight plus a lump sum "balloon" payment of $10,000 at the end of year eight. For an interest rate of 12% compounded annually, calculate:

A) The present worth of the payments, i.e. the single time zero payment that would be equivalent to the given series of payments.

B) The future worth of the payments, i.e. the single end of year eight payment that would be equivalent to the given series of payments.

C) The equivalent annual payments, i.e the uniform annual payments at the end of each year that would be equivalent to the given series of payments.

Solution:

			$10,000
$5,000	$2,000	$2,500 — gradient series —	$5,500
0	1	2	8

2.913 4.968 0.4039

A) $P = 5{,}000 + [2{,}000 + 500(A/G_{12,8})](P/A_{12,8}) + 10{,}000(P/F_{12,8}) = \$26{,}211$

2.476 2.913 12.300

B) $F = 5{,}000(F/P_{12,8}) + [2{,}000 + 500(A/G_{12,8})](F/A_{12,8}) + 10{,}000 = \$64{,}895$

0.2013 2.913 0.0813

C) $A = 5{,}000(A/P_{12,8}) + 2{,}000 + 500(A/G_{12,8}) + 10{,}000(A/F_{12,8}) = \$5{,}276$

2.11 Summary

In this chapter, seven different time value of money factors have been introduced that incorporated a number of variables which are summarized below in order of occurrence through the chapter, rather than alphabetically:

P = present single sum of money

F = future single sum of money

A = uniform series of payments, like mortgage payments

i = period compound interest rate

i* = period compound interest minimum rate of return

n = number of compounding periods in an evaluation life

m = number of compounding periods per year

r = nominal (annual) interest rate which in banking terminology is often referred to as the "Annual Percentage Rate" or APR, or just a "simple" interest rate. If an investor has annual compounding, the period interest rate, "i" is equal to the nominal interest rate, "r."

E = effective interest, in banking this is analogous to the term Annual Percentage Yield, or APY. It represents the annual interest that compounded once per year, will yield the same interest as a period rate compounded "m" times per year.

E = $(1+i)^m - 1$, or rearranged to solve for i, $i = (1+E)^{1/m} - 1$ Equation 2-9

E = $e^r - 1$ for continuous interest Equation 2-10

The Rule of 72: 72 / Nominal i(100) = Years Required to Double Your Money

The seven time value of money factors include:

$P/F_{i,n}$ Calculates the present value of a single future sum.
$F/P_{i,n}$ Calculates the future value of a single present sum.
$P/A_{i,n}$ Calculates the present value from a uniform series. On a time diagram, this present value will always be one compounding period to the left of the first value in the uniform series of payments.
$F/A_{i,n}$ Calculates the future value from a uniform series. On a time diagram, this future value is recognized at the end of the last period for which there is a value.
$A/P_{i,n}$ Calculates the series of uniform values at the end of each compounding period that is equivalent to a given present sum. This factor is most commonly used to calculate mortgage payments when "compound interest" is relevant.
$A/F_{i,n}$ Calculates the series of uniform values at the end of each compounding period equivalent to a given future quantity.
$A/G_{i,n}$ Calculates a uniform series of values equivalent to an increasing or decreasing arithmetic series of cash flows.

Page 23 offers a more detailed summary on the six basic time value of money factors.

The factor symbolism is designed so that the first value always designates what is being calculated. For some readers, the forward slash, "/" is often thought of as representing the word "given" and the second letter represents the known quantity. So, using the $P/F_{i,n}$ factor as an example, you calculate P given F at the period compound interest rate for "n" compounding periods. The Summary of Compound Interest Formula's following Example 2-6 offers a more comprehensive summary of the six basic factors including mathematical definitions for each and a time diagram illustration of its application.

Four types of compounding were introduced in Chapter 2 including:

1) Discrete End of Period \$, Discrete Compounding - App A
2) Discrete End of Period \$, Continuous Compounding - App B
3) Continuously Flowing \$, Continuous Compounding - App C
4) Add-on or Flat Compounding

Finally, the timing of cash flows was another relevant issue in this chapter. It was emphasized that while most cash flows are considered to be discrete end-of-period values, dollar values may also be described as beginning of period, mid-period or continuously flowing funds. These timing issues only influence where evaluators should place dollars on their time diagram. The discounting methodology itself remains relatively constant.

PROBLEMS

Excel solutions at Stermole.com

2-1 Your project has an estimated cost for land reclamation to be realized at the end of 20 years from today for $70,000,000. If current long term bond interest rates are 7.0% compounded annually, what would you need to invest in zero coupon (or deep discount) bonds today to cover the estimated cost after 20 years? In other words, calculate the present value "P" at time zero of $70,000,000 20 years from today for an interest rate of 7.0% compounded annually. What uniform series of payments at the end of periods 1 through 20 would also cover the year 20 cost? Use the same annual interest rate of 7.0%.

2-2 Calculate the present value, "P" at time zero and the corresponding future value, "F" at the end of year three for a series of $15,000 payments to be made at the end of each of years one, two and three. Assume that no payment is realized at time zero. Use a nominal interest rate of 15.0% compounded annually.

2-3 An investor has a series of three $15,000 payments expected to be realized at the end of each of evaluation years three, four and five. Calculate the present value, "P" at time zero, and the corresponding future value, "F" at the end of year 7. This analysis assumes that no payments are realized in periods zero, one, two, six or seven. Assume a nominal interest rate of 15.0% compounded annually.

2-4 A loan of $15,000 is incurred today and is to be paid off over the next 4 years. Calculate:

A) The uniform *annual* mortgage payments "A" at the end of each of years 1 through 4 that would pay off the loan for an interest rate of 15% compounded annually.

B) The uniform *monthly* mortgage payments at the end of each of months 1 through 48 that would pay off the loan for a nominal interest rate of 15% compounded monthly.

2-5 Suppose you have a newborn child and want to begin covering the estimated cost of tuition and expenses for four years of college beginning 18 years from now. Your estimated cost is $30,000 per year beginning at the end of year 18 and running through the end of year 21 (4 years). Assume a nominal investment interest rate of 10.0% compounded annually.

A) What is the value of the payments at the beginning of year 18 (end of year 17)?

B) How much would you have to invest today (time zero) to cover the estimated cost of four years of college?

C) What uniform series of deposits at the end of each of years 1 through 17 would be required to cover the tuition costs in years 18 through 21?

2-6 Two alternatives are being considered to finance the acquisition of a new vehicle. The purchase price is assumed to be $20,000 for all scenarios (no discount for a "cash" purchase alternative). The investor's minimum rate of return is a nominal 10.0% compounded monthly.

Alternative A is to accept the dealer finance package which includes a nominal 6.5% interest rate based on "add-on" or "flat" compounding. A down payment equal to 20.0% of the purchase price is required and the loan payments (principal and interest) are spread out uniformly over months 1-36.

Alternative B is to finance the acquisition through a bank at an annual percentage rate of 9.0% compounded monthly (normal compound interest). A down payment of 20.0% is required and the monthly loan payments are uniform over months 1 through 36.

1) Based on the monthly payments, which alternative would you select?

2) Calculate the present worth cost @ $i^*=10\%$ compounded monthly for A and B and compare with the $20,000 cash alternative.

2-7 What future amount of money will be accumulated 10 years from now by investing $1,000 now plus $2,000 5 years from now at 6% interest compounded semi-annually?

2-8 What is the present value of $500 payments to be made at the end of each 6 month period for the next 10 years if interest is 8% compounded semi-annually?

2-9 What equivalent annual end-of-year payments for the next 6 years are equivalent to paying $5,000 now and $10,000 6 years from now if interest is 6% compounded annually?

2-10 What monthly car mortgage payments for the next 36 months are required to amortize a present loan of $30,000 if interest is 6% compounded monthly?

2-11 What amount of money must be deposited in a savings account at the end of each quarter for the next 5 years to accumulate $10,000 in 5 years if interest is 6% compounded quarterly?

2-12 What is the present value of $1,000 payments to be made at the end of each year for the next 10 years if interest is 8% compounded semi-annually?

2-13 A company can lease an asset for the next four years by making lease payments that are equivalent to annual payments of $3,000 at year 0, $6,000 at year 1, $7,000 at year 2, $7,000 at year 3 and $4,000 at year 4. Use a 12% minimum discount rate determining the year 0 present worth lease payments, year 4 future worth lease payments and year 1 through 4 equivalent annual lease payments.

2-14 An investor plans to invest $1,000 at the end of every year for 20 years at 10% interest compounded annually. What is the expected value of this investment 20 years from now? What single sum of money invested now at 10% compounded annually would generate the same expected future worth?

2-15 A payment of $2,000 will be realized today with additional payments of $1,000 at the end of each of the next 5 years. Assume a nominal interest rate of 20% is appropriate and calculate the following:.

A) Determine the future value of all the payments at the end of five years from now.

B) What is the future value 5 years from now of the $2,000 plus $1,000 annual payments if the 20% nominal interest rate is compounded semi-annually?

C) What semi-annual payments are equivalent to the $1,000 payments each year if the 20% interest is compounded semi-annually?

2-16 What effective annual interest rate is equivalent to 20% compounded quarterly?

2-17 What nominal annual interest rate is equivalent to an effective annual interest rate equal to 20% if interest is compounded quarterly?

2-18 What sum of money will be accumulated in 40 years if:

A) $1,000 is invested at the end of each of the next 40 years at a 15% rate of return compounded annually.

B) $1,000 is invested at the end of the first year, $1,100 is invested at the end of the second year and each succeeding year's investment is $100 higher than the previous year's investment for 40 years at 15% compounded annually.

C) What single investment at time zero would generate the part "A" future worth?

2-19 Calculate the present worth cost of service for the following cash flows. The minimum rate of return is a nominal 12.0% compounded monthly.

BTCF	-8,000	-2,000	-3,000	-2,500
Years	0	1	2	3
Months	0	12	24	36

A) Use monthly compounding periods.

B) Use annual compounding periods and the appropriate effective annual interest rate that is equivalent to 12.0% compounded monthly.

2-20 Company A owns a patent with 15 years of remaining life. Company B is paying royalties to Company A for a license to the patent. It is estimated that royalty payments for the next 15 years will be $6,000 per year for the first 5 years, $8,000 per year for the next 4 years and $10,000 per year for the last 6 years. Company B offers to pre-pay the expected royalty payments for $70,000 now. If Company A considers 10% per year to be its minimum acceptable return on investment, should it accept the pre-payment offer for $70,000 now or take the royalty payments year by year?

2-21 What uniform annual payments for the next 15 years are equivalent to the non-uniform series of royalty payments described in Problem 2-20?

2-22 A machine which has a 10 year life will cost $11,000 now with annual operating costs of $500 the first year and increasing $50 per year each of the next 9 years. If the salvage value is estimated to be $2,000 at the end of the 10th year, what is the equivalent annual cost of operating this machine for the next 10 years if other opportunities exist to have the investment dollars invested where they would earn an 8% annual rate of return?

2-23 An investor expects to realize 18 monthly payments of $100 starting at the end of month 31 and running through month 48. For a discrete nominal annual interest rate of 15%, calculate the present worth of these payments for the following cases:

A) Use monthly discrete periods and assume the 15% rate is compounded monthly.

B) Use annual periods and assume the 15% annual discrete rate is compounded annually. Put the payments into the analysis at the closest year to which they are incurred. Compare this result with the result obtained by handling the time value of money using the effective annual interest rate of 16.07% that is equivalent to the annual rate of 15% compounded monthly.

C) Work case "B" for continuous compounding of interest by using the annual continuous interest rate equivalent to 16.07% discrete.

D) Use annual periods assuming continuous flow of payments during year 3 and 4 with continuous interest (as in case "C").

2-24

	$600	$700	$800	$900	$1,000	$1,100	$1,200. . . . $1,200
0	1	2	3	4	5	6	7. 10

For the values shown on the time diagram and a 12% nominal interest rate, find:

A) Present value at time 0.

B) Future value at the end of year 10.

2-25 Determine the sum of money that must be invested today at 9% interest compounded annually to give an investor annuity (annual income) payments of $5,000 per year for 10 years starting 5 years from now.

2-26 Determine the monthly mortgage payments that will pay off a $16,000 car loan with 36 equal end-of-month payments for:

A) 10% per year add-on interest rate.

B) 10% annual interest compounded monthly.

2-27 If you borrow \$15,000 at an APR of 11.5% compounded monthly, calculate the equal end of month mortgage payments that will pay off this loan over four years.

2-28 C = Capital Cost, OC = Operating Cost, L = Salvage Value
All Values are in Thousands.

C=\$1,500	OC=\$400	OC=\$500	OC=\$600	L=\$300
0	1	2	3	

Other opportunities exist to invest money at a nominal 15.0% interest rate compounded annually. Calculate the present, future and equivalent annual cost (end of years 1-3) for providing service with this asset over the 3 year life.

2-29 A person is to receive five revenue payments in amounts of \$300 at year one, \$400 at each of years two, three, and four and \$500 at year five. If the person considers that places exist to invest money with equivalent risk at 9.0% annual interest, calculate the year zero lump sum settlement and the year five lump sum settlement that would be equivalent to receiving the payments. Then determine the five equal yearly payments at years one through five that would be equivalent to the stated payments for the following assumptions, (this is a re-statement of Example 2-7 for which we want to analyze the following continuous interest solution variations):

A) Use 9.0% per year continuous interest and assume that dollar values flow continuously during the year in which they are incurred.

B) Assume the 9.0% is a discrete compound interest rate and the timing of the discrete dollar values in Example 2-7 are correct. Adjust the interest rate and dollar values for valid continuous interest, continuous flow of funds analysis. This requires assuming that half of each annual discrete value flows uniformly through the preceding year, and the other half of each discrete value flows uniformly through the following year.

C) Assuming that the timing of the continuous flow of money values in part (A) is correct, adjust the interest rate to make a valid discrete dollar value, discrete interest rate analysis using mid-period discrete present worth factors.

2-30 An investor expects to realize annual revenues of \$120 uniformly during years 1,2 and 3. Calculate the present value of the revenue assuming a 12% nominal interest rate compounded annually. Assume the revenues to be:

A) Discrete end-of-year values.

B) Discrete beginning-of-year values.

C) Discrete mid-year values.

D) Consider that the annual revenues of \$120 flow uniformly during years 1, 2 and 3. Place the revenues at the closest discrete annual point in time to which they occur by putting the month 1-6 revenue at year 0, month 7-18 revenue at year 1, month 19-30 revenue at year 2, and month 31-36 revenue at year 3. This is the desired approach for putting revenues and costs into analyses based on discrete compounding of interest with discrete annual end of period values, such as most financial calculator and spreadsheet analyses.

2-31 Assume a 10 megawatt power plant is operating at full capacity 6,000 hours per year producing electric power that is sold for \$0.11 per kilowatt-hour (kwh). Calculate the time zero present value of revenues to be generated over years one through ten assuming a 10% nominal interest rate for:

A) Discrete end-of-year revenues with discrete annual compounding of interest.

B) Discrete beginning-of-year revenue with discrete annual compounding of interest.

C) Discrete mid-year revenue with discrete annual compounding of interest.

D) Revenues flowing uniformly during each year are treated as discrete revenues at the closest annual period to which they are incurred. In other words, revenues incurred within plus or minus 6 months of an annual period are treated as discrete sums at that period. With this approach, put month 1-6 revenue at time 0, month 7-18 revenue at year 1, month 19-30 revenue at year 2, and month 31-36 revenue at year 3.

2-32 As a recent new hire in the financial department of your company you have been handed the following schedule of payments and the corresponding variable annual interest rates on an outstanding loan note. The note does not include a stated current loan value. You have been asked to determine the loan value today (time zero), and then to develop a loan amortization schedule for the payments, breaking each payment down into the relevant principal and interest payments each year. Assume the interest is based on discrete annual compounding and payments are made at the end of each year. All dollar values are in (000's)

Year	Loan Payment	Interest Rate
0	0.00	
1	1,100.00	6.5%
2	1,100.00	6.5%
3	1,100.00	7.0%
4	700.00	7.5%
5	700.00	7.5%

CHAPTER 2 AUXILIARY PROBLEMS

A2-1 The following cash flows are all end of period values.

—	200	300	400	400 400
0	1	2	3	4. 10

Use a 10% nominal interest rate compounded annually to determine the economically equivalent present value, "P" of the payments at time 0, the economically equivalent future value, "F" of the payments at the end of year 10, and the equivalent annual series of end of period payments, "A" in years 1-10.

A2-2 Calculate the monthly end of period mortgage payments required to pay off a loan today of $200,000 over the next 30 years. The nominal interest rate is fixed at 6.0% compounded monthly.

A2-3 Your credit card has a current balance of $4,965.20. This balance is accruing interest at a nominal rate of 9.0% compounded monthly.

A) Assuming you didn't spend any more on this card, what uniform end of month payments over the next 36 months would be required to reduce the loan balance to zero at the end of three years from today?

B) Suppose you plan on spending an additional $1,000 at the end of next year (end of month 12) and $1,000 at the end of the following year (end of month 24) on this same card. What uniform end of month payments over the next 36 months would be required to pay off the existing debt along with the additional new purchases?

A2-4 Reclamation of a site is scheduled to begin seven (7) years from today and will require a sustained period of investment amounting to 2.5 million dollars per year for three years at the end of years 7, 8 and 9.

A) What amount would you need to invest today in order to set aside sufficient funds now to meet the future obligations? Assume your money could earn 5.0% per year in low risk securities over the next 9 year period in question.

B) Using the same 5.0% annual compound interest rate, what amount, invested each year for the next 6 years would be sufficient to cover the future costs at the end of years 7 thru 9?

A2-5 If a bank is paying a nominal interest rate of 3.75% on a savings account investment over three years, calculate the following:

A) Effective equivalent annual interest rate if compounding is daily?

B) Annual Percentage Yield (APY) if compounding is monthly?

A2-6 If the Billy Bob Jones Index (BBJI) was at 11,000 and moved up by 10.4% per year for each of the next 8 years, what would be the value of the index at the end of the 8th year of sustained growth?

A2-7 You have been asked to calculate the current balance on a loan that involves 5 equal mortgage payments of $200,000 per year (principal and interest), but the interest rate charged on the loan is variable. In years 1, 2 and 3 the rate is a nominal 6.0% compounded annually and in years 4 and 5 the rate is a nominal 8.0% compounded annually. To verify the accuracy of your current loan balance calculation, develop a loan amortization schedule to demonstrate how the payments are not only sufficient to pay off the accrued interest over time, but also pay off the debt (principal).

A2-8 You just won a Lottery! The annuitized jackpot involves payments to you, with the amounts listed below.

Payment	10,000	15,000	20,000	25,000	30,000	35,000
Year	0	1	2	3	4	5

You currently have savings in a brokerage account that have averaged 10% returns for each of the last 5 years, and you expect that level of annual return to continue over each of the next 5 years. For each of the following questions, support your decision with a proper time value of money calculation.

A) If the Lottery offered you $90,000 today in lieu of the above stated payments, would you take the cash or the six payments over the next 5 years?

B) If you accept the payments and invest the money in your brokerage account; how much cash will have accrued from the lottery payments and accrued interest by the end of year 5?

C) Beginning today (time zero), what five (5) uniform beginning of period payments would be equivalent to the original annual payments?

CHAPTER 3

PRESENT, ANNUAL, AND FUTURE VALUE, RATE OF RETURN AND BREAK-EVEN ANALYSIS

3.1 Introduction

The five economic decision method approaches in the title of this chapter are the basis of virtually all economic analysis decision methods used today. When applied properly, any of these approaches leads to exactly the same economic conclusion. Proper application of these different approaches to analyzing the relative economic merit of alternative projects depends on the type of projects being evaluated and the evaluation situation. As was mentioned in Chapter 1, there are two basic classifications of investments that are analyzed:

1) Revenue-producing investment alternatives
2) Service-producing investment alternatives

The application of present worth, future worth, annual worth and rate of return analysis techniques differs for revenue and service-producing projects. In addition, there are a variety of different break-even analysis approaches that can be applied to analyze both income-producing and service-producing investment alternatives. In this chapter we will concentrate on the application of present worth, annual worth, future worth and rate of return techniques. Variations in the application of present worth analysis techniques using either net present value, present worth cost, present value ratio or benefit cost ratio will be addressed. Break-even analyses of various types are also discussed in this chapter and subsequent chapters of the text. These techniques are presented here on a before-tax analysis basis to avoid confusing the reader with tax considerations at the same time new evaluation techniques are introduced. Starting in Chapter 8, these techniques are applied after-tax, to varying evaluation situations. Valid analyses must be done after-tax unless taxes are not relevant or significant.

3.2 Break-even and Rate of Return (ROR) Calculations Using Present, Annual, and Future Worth Equations

In Chapter 2, several examples and end-of-chapter problems relate to calculating the present worth of a future stream of revenue for a given interest rate or desired rate of return. This calculation gives the initial cost that can be incurred for the future stream of revenue if you want to receive the specified rate of return on your investment dollars. This really is a break-even type of calculation involving calculation of the initial investment cost that will enable you to break-even with a specified rate of return on your invested dollars. Example 3-1 illustrates this type of break-even calculation for different conditions, to emphasize the importance and effect of the time value of money. Break-even calculations can be made for any single project parameter such as initial cost, annual revenue, salvage value, or project life, to name a few. One equation can always be solved for one unknown, either explicitly or by trial and error. The evaluator has a choice of letting the unknown be any desired break-even parameter or evaluation criterion such as rate of return.

EXAMPLE 3-1 Present Worth Revenue Equals Break-even Acquisition Cost

Determine the present worth of the revenue streams, "I", given in alternatives "A" and "B" for minimum rates of return of 10% and 20%. This gives the initial cost that can be incurred to break-even with the 10% or 20% rate of return. Note that the cumulative revenues are the same for the "A" and "B" alternatives but the timing of the revenues is very different.

	P=?	I=$200	I=$300	I=$400	I=$500
A)	0	1	2	3	4

	P=?	I=$500	I=$400	I=$300	I=$200
B)	0	1	2	3	4

Solution:

$$i = 10\%,\ P_A = 200\overset{0.9091}{(P/F_{10\%,1})} + 300\overset{0.8264}{(P/F_{10\%,2})} + 400\overset{0.7513}{(P/F_{10\%,3})}$$

$$+ 500\overset{0.6830}{(P/F_{10\%,4})} = \$1,071.76$$

$$\text{or, } P_A = [200 + 100\overset{1.381}{(A/G_{10\%,4})}]\overset{3.170}{(P/A_{10\%,4})} = \$1,071.78$$

$$i = 20\%,\ P_A = [200 + 100\overset{1.274}{(A/G_{20\%,4})}]\overset{2.589}{(P/A_{20\%,4})} = \$847.64$$

Note that to get a 10% rate of return you can afford to pay \$224 more than the \$847 you would pay to get a 20% rate of return.

$$i = 10\%,\ P_B = 500\overset{0.9091}{(P/F_{10\%,1})} + 400\overset{0.8264}{(P/F_{10\%,2})} + 300\overset{0.7513}{(P/F_{10\%,3})}$$

$$+ 200\overset{0.6830}{(P/F_{10\%,4})} = \$1,147.1$$

Or, using the A/G factor, similar results are obtained within round-off error as follows:

$$i = 10\%,\ P_B = [500 - 100\overset{1.381}{(A/G_{10\%,4})}]\overset{3.170}{(P/A_{10\%,4})} = \$1,147.22$$

$$i = 20\%,\ P_B = [500 - 100\overset{1.274}{(A/G_{20\%,4})}]\overset{2.589}{(P/A_{20\%,4})} = \$964.66$$

Note that in Example 3-1, while you still pay more to get a 10% rate of return than to get a 20% rate of return, the cost that you can incur for the "B" stream of income for a given rate of return is greater than the corresponding cost that you can incur for the "A" income stream. Since the cumulative revenue is identical for "A" and "B", the difference is due to the time value of money. Getting the revenue more quickly in "B" enables us to economically justify paying more for it initially. It is important in evaluation work to account for the time value of money correctly by treating costs and revenues on the time diagram in the amounts and at the points in time most expected. If you think of the incomes in "A" and "B" as being analogous to mortgage payments that will pay off an investor's loan, you will note that the bigger payments in early years for "B" amortize the investor's principal more rapidly than in "A". Compound interest rate of return is directly analogous to the interest rate you receive on money in the bank, or to the interest rate you pay on a loan. *In all cases rate of return refers to the interest rate that the investor will receive on unamortized investment principal each interest compounding period. The term "unamortized investment principal" refers to the investment principal and accrued interest that have not been recovered through profits, salvage, savings, mortgage payments, withdrawals from a bank account, or other revenue forms, depending on the investment situation. It is important that you recognize that the rate of return which banks pay as interest on a savings account is exactly analogous to the interest rate charged on compound interest mortgage loans which in turn is analogous to the rate of return that we will be using to evaluate different types of investments where costs and revenues are known or projected.*

In the next example it is shown that results such as those calculated in Example 3-1 can be obtained using other types of calculations such as annual or future worth equations. When we talk about writing an equation in economic analysis work, this usually means we are going to equate costs and revenue terms on an equivalent basis. However, sometimes we write an equation to equate the costs of alternative service-producing projects. By revenue terms we mean all incomes, profits, savings, salvage or other receipts of revenue. On an after-tax basis, revenues reduced by operating costs and income taxes are represented by positive cash flow. Costs refer to all expenditures or outflows of money and are represented on an after-tax basis by negative cash flow. It also is possible to refer to before-tax positive and negative cash flow if income tax considerations are neglected. Following are the three basic equations used in economic evaluation work:

Present Worth (PW) Equation: Present Worth Costs = Present Worth Revenues
Annual Worth (AW) Equation: Equivalent Annual Costs = Annual Revenues
Future Worth (FW) Equation: Future Worth Costs = Future Worth Revenue

In economic evaluations, whether you are making rate of return analysis, break-even or net value calculations, you can compare costs and revenues at any desired point in time. You are not limited to present worth, annual worth and future worth equations, although they are most commonly used.

Consider the Example 3-2 to illustrate the application and equivalence of present worth, future worth and annual worth equations.

EXAMPLE 3-2 Illustration of Present Worth, Future Worth and Annual Worth Equations

A rental asset is expected to yield $2,000 per year in income after all expenses, for each of the next ten years. It is also expected to have a resale value of $25,000 in ten years. How much can be paid for this asset now if a 12% annual compound interest rate of return before taxes is desired? Note that the wording of this example could be changed to describe a mineral, petroleum, chemical plant, pipeline or other general investment and the solution would be identical.

Solution:

C = Cost, I = Income, L = Salvage Value and i = 12%.

```
C=?          I=$2,000        I=$2,000    I=$2,000
__________________________________________________    L=$25,000
0                1               2. . . . . . . . 10
```

Present Worth (PW) Equation:

Equate costs and income at time zero. The present worth of income and salvage at a ROR of 12% is the break-even cost that can be paid at time zero;

PW Cost = PW Income and PW Salvage
(At the 12.0% minimum rate of return)

$$C = \text{PW Cost} = 2{,}000(\overset{5.6502}{P/A_{12\%,10}}) + 25{,}000(\overset{0.3220}{P/F_{12\%,10}}) = \$19{,}350$$

If $19,350 is paid for the property at time zero, a 12% rate of return per year on the unamortized investment will be realized. It is instructive to note the same result could have been obtained by writing a future worth equation or an annual cost equation.

Future Worth (FW) Equation:

FW Cost = FW Income and FW Salvage
(At the 12% minimum rate of return)

$$C(\overset{3.1058}{F/P_{12\%,10}}) = 2{,}000(\overset{17.5487}{F/A_{12\%,10}}) + 25{,}000$$

$$C = [2{,}000(17.5487) + 25{,}000] / 3.1058 = \$19{,}350$$

Annual Worth (AW) Equation:

AW Cost = AW Income and AW Salvage
(At the 12.0% minimum rate of return)

$$C\overset{0.17698}{(A/P_{12\%,10})} = 2{,}000 + 25{,}000\overset{0.05698}{(A/F_{12\%,10})} \text{ so } C = \$19{,}350$$

It should be noted in Example 3-2 that a present worth quantity, "C", was to be calculated, and it was obtained from a future worth and annual worth equation, as well as a present worth equation. In fact, an equation could be written to equate costs and income at any point in time and the same break-even acquisition cost of $19,350 would be obtained.

Now consider the use of present, future and annual worth equations to determine project rate of return. This requires writing the equations with the unknown rate of return, "i", in evaluation situations where both the costs and revenues are specified but the rate of return, "i", is unknown. A trial and error solution generally is required to calculate "i" as illustrated in the following examples.

EXAMPLE 3-3 Rate of Return (ROR) Illustration

If you pay $20,000 for the asset in Example 3-2, what annual compound interest rate of return on investment dollars will be received?

Solution:

C = Costs, I = Income, L = Salvage Value, i = ?

C=$20,000	I=$2,000	I=$2,000	I=$2,000	
0	1	2	10	L=$25,000

The only unknown in this problem is the rate of return, "i". A present worth, future worth or annual worth equation may be used to obtain "i" by trial and error calculation. In fact, an equation may be written setting costs equal to income at any point in time (the beginning or end of any period), to determine the project rate of return, "i". The result is the same regardless of the point in time chosen to write the cost equals income equation.

Present Worth (PW) Equation at Year 0 to Determine "i"

PW Cost = PW Income + PW Salvage Value

$20{,}000 = 2{,}000(P/A_{i,10}) + 25{,}000(P/F_{i,10})$

Mathematically the equation is:

$20{,}000 = 2{,}000[(1 + i)^{10} - 1]/[i(1 + i)^{10}] + 25{,}000[1/(1 + i)^{10}]$

There is no mathematical way to explicitly solve this equation for "i". A trial and error solution is required and this is more easily done using the equation in factor form, rather than mathematical form. By trial and error we want to find the "i" that makes the right side of the equation equal to the left side, which is $20,000. This is done by picking an "i" value, then looking up the factors from the tables in Appendix A. *To approximate an "i" value in the correct rate of return range, the following approximation is good for project lives of 8 to 10 periods or more.*

$$\text{Approx. } i = \frac{\text{Arithmetic Average Income}}{\text{Cumulative Initial Costs}} = \frac{2{,}000}{20{,}000} = 0.10$$

or 10% for this example.

Salvage value is neglected in this approximation because it is far enough into the future for lives of 8 to 10 periods or more that due to time value of money, it has little effect on analysis results. That is why this approximation is only valid for relatively long lives of 8 to 10 periods or more.

$i = 10\% = 2000(6.1446) + 25{,}000(.3855) = \$21{,}930$
$i = ? \qquad = \$20{,}000$
$i = 12\% = 2000(5.6502) + 25{,}000(.3220) = \$19{,}350$

Because there are no 11% tables in Appendix A, we must interpolate between the 10% and 12% values:

$i = 10\% + 2\%[(21{,}930 - 20{,}000)/(21{,}930 - 19{,}350)] = 11.5\%$

Graphically, the rate of return interpolation for this problem and rate of return analysis in general is presented in Figure 3-1 on the following page.

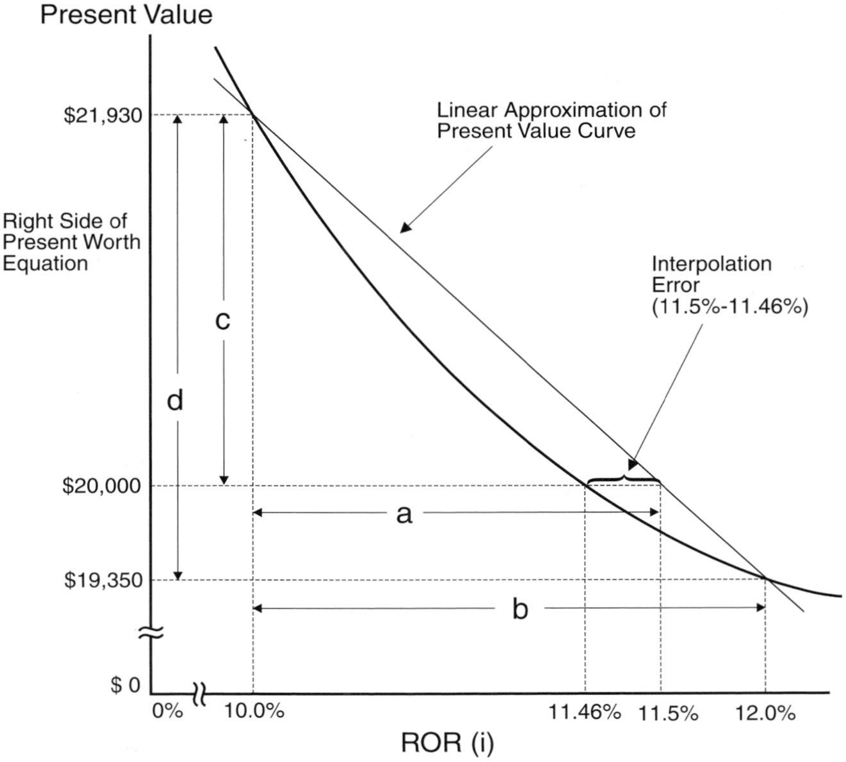

Figure 3-1 Graphic Interpolation for Rate of Return, "i"

Note that although the present worth equation used to calculate the rate of return, "i", has two unknown present worth factors, each factor is a function of only the single variable, "i". There is no limit to the number of unknown factors that can be in an equation used to calculate rate of return as long as all factors are a function of the same variable, "i".

Rate of Return, i = 10% + a

The small triangle with sides "a" and "c" is geometrically similar to the larger triangle with sides "b" and "d" since both triangles have equal angles. Therefore, the sides of the two triangles are proportional.

(a/b) = (c/d), therefore a = b(c/d)

Substituting these values gives:

a = (12%-10%)[(21,930-20,000)/(21,930-19,350)] = 1.5%

Rate of Return, i = 10% + 1.5% = 11.5%

This is the same result shown on the previous page.

Future Worth (FW) Equation to Determine "i"

$20{,}000(F/P_{i,10}) = 2{,}000(F/A_{i,10}) + 25{,}000$

Trial and error solution of this equation gives the same result: i = 11.5%. Only interpolation error will cause the result to be slightly different from the present worth equation result.

Annual Worth (AW) Equation to Determine "i"

$20{,}000(A/P_{i,10}) = 2{,}000 + 25{,}000(A/F_{i,10})$

Trial and error solution of this equation gives the same result: i = 11.5%.

The "i" value of 11.5% in this example is the rate of return per year that the investor would receive on unamortized investment principal. In this text, rate of return often is referred to as "ROR". Other authors sometimes use the term *internal rate of return*, or, "IRR", or, *return on investment*, or "ROI", to refer to the same quantity. Whichever term is adopted, it is helpful and important to note the exact analogy between rate of return on investments in general, and rate of return on mortgage investments or bank account deposits. In each case the ROR to the investor is calculated each year (or period) based on unamortized investment, which is the investment value that remains to be recovered. *Project ROR is not the return received on initial investment each period, it is the return received on unamortized investment each period.* It is very important to look at the unamortized investment values to which rates of return apply in using the rate of return criterion for investment decision-making. A large rate of return that relates to small unamortized investment value can have very different meaning than a smaller rate of return that applies to a larger unamortized investment value. That is why investments with the largest rates of return often are not the best investments from an economic viewpoint as is illustrated in Chapter 4.

The timing as well as the magnitude of costs and revenues that go into discounted cash flow analysis criteria calculations is extremely important as the following example illustrates.

EXAMPLE 3-4 Illustration of ROR and Cumulative Cash Position

For a $10,000 loan, the lender will receive $2,638 in income from mortgage payments at the end of each of the next five years. Calculate the rate of return to the lender on this loan. Note the problem could just as easily have asked you to calculate the annualized cost of borrowing to the borrower, since both compound interest rates are identical.

Solution:

Writing a present worth equation;

Present Worth Cost = Present Worth Revenue

$10{,}000 = 2{,}638(P/A_{i,5})$

Re-arranging this equation isolates the P/A factor as follows:

$10{,}000 / 2{,}638 = (P/A_{i,5}) = 3.7908$

Searching the Appendix A tables for this factor value, the $(P/A_{10\%,5}) = 3.7908$ which indicates the loan rate of return to the lender is 10.0% per year, compounded annually. This is visually summarized by developing the cumulative cash position diagram as defined and presented in Section 3.3 to follow.

Annual Percentage Rates or APR's, represent an annualized expression of the cost of borrowing money. The difference between the loan or note rate (nominal or annual rate the mortgage payment is based on) and the corresponding APR may relate to several transaction costs incurred in acquiring a loan but not necessarily all of your expenditures in acquiring a loan. Examples of costs that might be included in the APR are points, loan origination fees, home inspection fees, and mortgage insurance premiums or other costs directly attributable to the loan itself. Lenders are required to provide APR's under the Federal Truth in Lending Law, Regulation Z. This means the Federal Reserve and Congress could change the definition from time to time and users of this number must be aware of the potential change in meaning and therefore, its proper application. Another way of looking at the calculation of an APR might be to think of it as the rate of return to the lender. Example 3-5 will change the conditions of qualifying for the loan described in Example 3-4 to demonstrate the calculation of a loan APR.

EXAMPLE 3-5 Calculating an Annual Percentage Rate (APR)

For the $10,000 loan in Example 3-4 that had a note rate of 10%, calculate the corresponding APR if the loan required 2 points and a loan origination fee of $150 to qualify. Assume that the fee and the points are paid by reducing the amount of the loan the borrower will receive at closing. One point is equal to 1.0% of the loan value.

Solution:

2 Points = 0.02 * $10,000 = $200

Loan Origination Fee = $150

Total Cost of Qualifying for the Loan = $350

Therefore, at closing the borrower could expect to receive a check for $9,650, but the mortgage payment is based on the original $10,000 loan amount and the note rate of 10% which resulted in the annual payment of $2,638 as previously described in Example 3-4.

Writing a present worth equation to solve for the APR;

Present Worth Cost = Present Worth Revenue

$9{,}650 = 2{,}638(P/A_{i,5})$

Re-arranging this equation to isolate the P/A factor gives:

$9{,}650/2{,}638 = (P/A_{i,5}) = 3.6581$ which occurs between the 10% an 12% tables in Appendix A of the text.

$(P/A_{10\%,5}) = 3.7908$

$(P/A_{12\%,5}) = 3.6048$

Interpolating gives APR,

$$i = 10\% + 2\%(3.7908 - 3.6581) / (3.7908 - 3.6048) = 11.43\%$$

By calculator, the result is 11.41%

Because of the initial costs incurred to acquire the loan, the APR on this loan is 11.41%. APR's are supposed to give the borrower a comparative tool to determine the overall lowest cost in terms of interest and fees paid over the loan life. The problem is that at least two issues come into play. First, not all APR's are calculated the same, borrowers should check with each lender to determine what costs may not be reflected in the calculation. Second, in practice, higher APR's may relate to lower nominal rates that often mean lower monthly payments in the future. The financial implication of lower monthly payments always plays a role in the overall economic and financial decision of what is best for each individual's situation. Finally, with regard to points, it is worth mentioning that smaller loan amounts and shorter loan lives result in larger percentage impacts on APR due to closing costs. This means that for the same closing costs, the differences between loan interest rates and APR's will be far more sensitive on small loans (as illustrated in Example 3-5), relative to a much larger loan.

In Examples 3-6 and 3-7, variations on the same loan concept are introduced. In Example 3-6, a salvage is included that is equal in magnitude to the initial investment. From a loan perspective, this is illustrative of an "interest only" loan with the principal being retired in the final year. Although not described as such, Example 3-7 might be representative of a loan based on negative amortization. In these loans, mortgage payments not made are added to the loan amount, so after five years, one balloon payment is made to pay off the original loan principal and the accrued interest over time. Note how the same investment numbers and calculations can have very different meaning depending upon the investment situation described. The meaning of any rate of return, or "i" value, can be illustrated graphically using the cumulative cash position diagram introduced in Section 3.3.

3.3 Rate of Return and Cumulative Cash Position

The cumulative cash position diagram is a graphical means of explaining the meaning of rate of return and gives results that are analogous to the tabular results presented in Chapter 2 for Example 2-17 to explain the meaning of the 10% interest rate, or rate of return, in that example. The advantage of the cumulative cash position diagram is that a picture is often better than words or tabular figures to clearly explain something. By definition, *cumulative cash position is the investment principal and accrued interest that has not been amortized (or paid off) by revenue such as positive cash flow, profits, salvage value, savings, mortgage payments or other inflows of money. Letting revenue terms have a positive sign gives costs a negative sign, so in investment situations, the cumulative cash position starts in a negative position and works back to zero at the end of a project life when the time value of money is handled at the project rate of return.* Each compounding period the cumulative cash position is adjusted in the negative direction for new investments and accrued interest, and in the positive direction for revenues received. Unamortized investment is another term with a meaning synonymous with cumulative cash position. *With cumulative cash diagrams, it is important to recognize that we are not referring to a plot of individual project cash flows, but rather, are monitoring the overall cash position of an investment opportunity. For a single investment situation, the concept of cumulative cash position is analogous to graphing the balance in a bank savings account over time. Think of an investor making an initial deposit, (the investment of funds into a bank savings account would be analogous to negative cash flow) that deposit accrues interest so the account balance increases with time. In this case, it means the balance becomes more negative. Next, the investor chooses to withdraw a portion of the funds from the account (the investor realizes positive cash flow). The reduced account balance accrues interest during the next compounding period and, eventually the combination of withdrawals from the accrued interest and principal reduce the balance to zero at the end of the project life or savings period.* To demonstrate the meaning of rate of return using this graphical approach, consider the rate of return from Example 3-4. This compound interest rate of 10.0% for the $10,000 cost generating $2,638 in revenue per year for 5 years represents a return on the unpaid portion of the investment over time to a lender. To a borrower, the 10% represents the annual cost of borrowing that is applied to the unpaid portion of the loan. Both scenarios are illustrated in Figure 3-2 as follows:

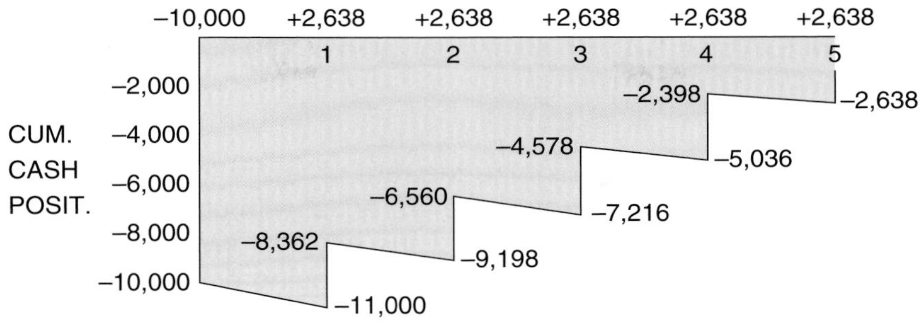

Figure 3-2 Cumulative Cash Position for Example 3-4, ROR = 10%

Plotting the cumulative cash position for the 10% project rate of return in Figure 3-2, we start out in a -$10,000 cash position at time zero. During each year we expect to receive a 10% rate of return on the unamortized investment at the beginning of that year, so the negative cumulative cash position is increased each year by 10% of the unamortized investment at the beginning of the year. For example, if the investor wanted to terminate this investment at the end of year one, he would need to receive a total of $11,000 at year one to realize a 10% ROR on the initial $10,000 investment. If he wanted to terminate it at the end of year two, the cumulative cash position diagram shows that he would need to receive $9,198 at the end of year two in addition to the $2,638 received at the end of year one. The cumulative cash position diagram shows that the investor's rate of return of 10% makes the cumulative cash position zero at the end of the project life. Any other interest rate makes the final cash position either positive for "i" less than 10% or negative for "i" greater than 10%. In other words, for "i" less than 10% the $2,638 annual payments are more than enough to pay i% interest on the unamortized investment each year, with money left over at the end of the fifth year. The opposite, of course, is true for "i" greater than 10%. Note in the cumulative cash position diagram that the rate of return of 10% is applied to the unamortized investment each year, a declining amount of money each year in this problem. It is not applied each year to the initial investment and it is not applied to the income each year. On the contrary, the income each year is used to reduce the amount of principal that the rate of return is applied to in the following year.

EXAMPLE 3-6 Rate of Return When Salvage Equals Initial Cost

Work Example 3-4 with a salvage value of $10,000 instead of zero.

Solution:

Intuitively you can determine the rate of return in your head when initial cost and final salvage value are equal with uniformly equal revenues each period. Regardless of the physical investment, you can always think of this analysis situation as being equivalent to putting the investment dollars in the bank at an interest rate equal to the project rate of return, withdrawing the interest each period, (which is equivalent to the period revenue), and withdrawing the investment principal from your account at the end of the evaluation life (which is equivalent to salvage value). The project interest rate, or rate of return per period, in this situation, where initial investment cost equals salvage, is always equal to the period revenue divided by the initial investment (or salvage value since they are equal). Using the following present worth equation you can verify that the rate of return is 26.38% for this example.

PW Equation: $10{,}000 = 2{,}638(P/A_{i,5}) + 10{,}000(P/F_{i,5})$

$i = 26.38\%$

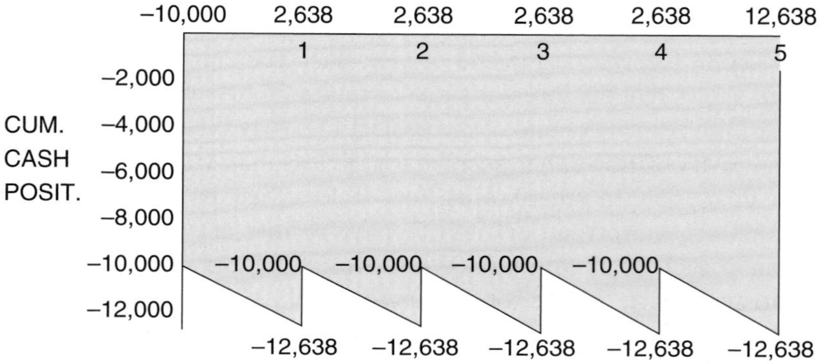

Figure 3-3 Cumulative Cash Position Diagram at ROR = 26.38%

The cumulative cash position diagram in Figure 3-3, illustrates that when salvage value equals the initial investment and annual incomes are uniform, the investor's compound interest rate of return is applied to the initial investment, which is also the unamortized investment value each compounding period ($10,000 per year in this case). When this cash flow situation occurs, the compound interest rate is equivalent to a flat or add-on interest rate. If the initial cost and terminal salvage are the same, and the investment yields a uniform income each compounding period, the ROR may be explicitly calculated by using the approximation technique described in Example 3-3. This technique (average income / cumulative initial investment) computes the flat or add-on interest rate for an investment and uses that value as a starting point for the trial and error solution for regular ROR. Using this approach in Example 3-6, the rate of return is 2,638 / 10,000 = 0.2638 or 26.38%.

EXAMPLE 3-7 Rate of Return for Initial Cost and a Single Revenue

Evaluate the rate of return an investor will receive if $10,000 is invested at time zero and this investment generates a future lump sum income of $16,105 five years later. Develop the cumulative cash position diagram at the project rate of return.

Solution:

C = $10,000 — — — — — I = $16,105

0 1 2 3 4 5

PW Equation:

$10{,}000 = 16{,}105(P/F_{i,5})$, so $P/F_{i,5} = 0.62093$

$i = 10\%$ per year, by trial and error

Notice that the unamortized investment gets larger each year when no annual revenues are received to offset the accrued interest. Also note that Examples 3-5 and 3-7 both involve 10% rate of return projects with a $10,000 initial investment and a five year evaluation life. However, the unamortized investments that the 10% rate of return relates to in Examples 3-5 and 3-7 are very different after the first year for each of these projects. The cumulative cash position diagrams clearly show this.

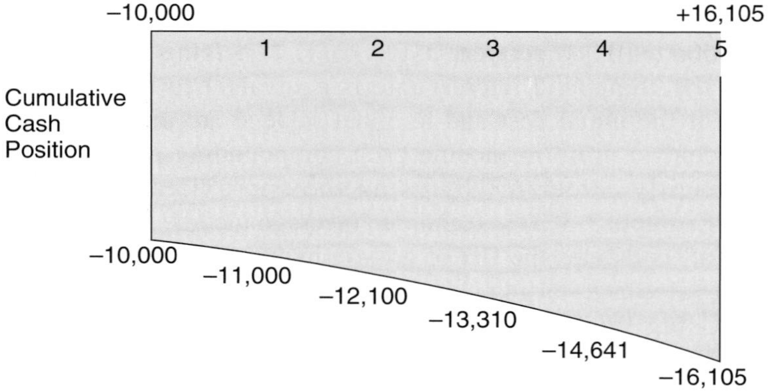

Figure 3-4 Cumulative Cash Position Diagram at ROR = 10%

The next example illustrates a rate of return problem with costs at two points in time.

EXAMPLE 3-8 Rate of Return With More Than One Cost

Consider the investment of $10,000 at time zero and $5,000 at the end of year one to generate incomes of $9,000 at the end of year two and $9,500 at the end of each of years three, four and five. What is the annually compounded project rate of return? Develop the cumulative cash position diagram at the project rate of return.

Solution:

C=$10,000	C=$5,000	I=$9,000	I=$9,500	I=$9,500	I=$9,500
0	1	2	3	4	5

PW Eq:

$$10{,}000 + 5{,}000(P/F_{i,1}) = 9{,}000(P/F_{i,2}) + 9{,}500(P/A_{i,3})(P/F_{i,2})$$

Rearranged Format:

$$0 = -10{,}000 - 5{,}000(P/F_{i,1}) + 9{,}000(P/F_{i,2}) + 9{,}500(P/A_{i,3})(P/F_{i,2})$$

PW Eq: @ i = 30%:

–10,000 – 5,000(.7692) + 9,000(.5917) + 9,500(1.8161)(.5917) = +$1,688

PW Eq: @ i = 40%:

–10,000 – 5,000(.7143) + 9,000(.5102) + 9,500(1.5889)(.5102) = –$1,278

By interpolation:

i = ROR = 30% + (40% – 30%)[(1,688 – 0)/(1,688+1,278)] = 35.69%

Eliminating interpolation error by interpolating over smaller ranges of "i" than 30% to 40% gives 35.254% as the correct ROR result.

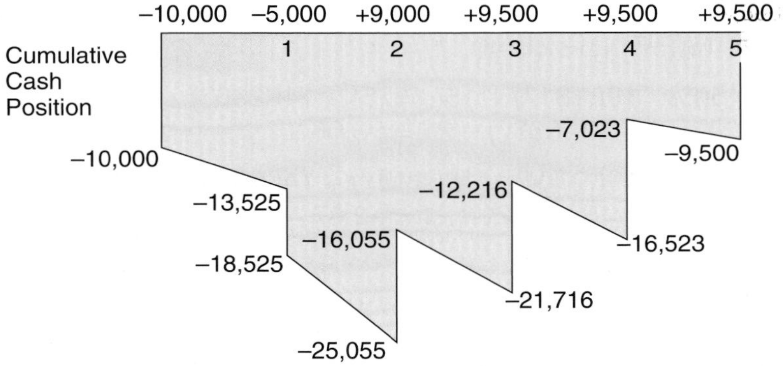

Figure 3-5 Cumulative Cash Position Diagram at ROR = 35.254%

EXAMPLE 3-9 Rate of Return for Discrete or Continuous Interest

For the cash flows presented below calculate rate of return for the following assumptions regarding the type of compounding and flow of funds in a project.

–21	+13	+13	+14	+15	+19
0	1	2	3	4	5

A) Assume discrete end of period dollar values and discrete compounding of interest.

B) Assume a continuous flow of dollar values with continuous compounding of interest.

C) Relate the solutions from (A) & (B) to show that they are equivalent and interchangeable.

Solution:

A) Discrete End of Period Cash Flows, With Discrete Compounding of Interest

PW Eq: $19(P/F_{i,5}) + 15(P/F_{i,4}) + 14(P/F_{i,3}) + 13(P/F_{i,2}) + 13(P/F_{i,1}) - 21 = 0$

PW @ i = 50%: $19(.1317) + 15(.1975) + 14(.2963) + 13(.4444) + 13(.6667) - 21 = +3.06$

PW @ i = 70%: $19(.0704) + 15(.1197) + 14(.2035) + 13(.3468) + 13(.5882) - 21 = -2.87$

By Interpolation:

$i = 50\% + 20\%\{(3.06 - 0)/[3.06 - (-2.87)]\} = 60.3\%$

Eliminating interpolation error by interpolating over much smaller increments of "i", the true ROR is 59.05%.

B) Continuous Cash Flows With Continuous Compounding of Interest

–21	+13	+13	+14	+15	+19

0 1 2 3 4 5 6

Factors are calculated from Appendix C definition of $P/F^*_{r,n}$

PW Eq: $19(P/F^*_{r,6}) + 15(P/F^*_{r,5}) + 14(P/F^*_{r,4}) + 13(P/F^*_{r,3}) + 13(P/F^*_{r,2}) - 21(P/F^*_{r,1}) = 0$

PW Eq @ r = 40%: 19(.1115) + 15(.1664) + 14(.2482) + 13(.3703) + 13(.5525) – 21(.8242) = +2.78

PW Eq @ r = 50%: 19(.0646) + 15(.1065) + 14(.1756) + 13(.2895) + 13(.4773) – 21(.7869) = –1.27

By Interpolation:

i = 40% + 10%{(2.78 – 0)/[2.78 – (–1.27)]} = 46.9%

Eliminating interpolation error by interpolating over much smaller increments of "i", the true ROR is 46.4%.

C) Equivalence of Discrete and Continuous Compounding Results

Given $E = e^r - 1$, From Eq. 2-10.

"E" is the effective discrete compound interest per year, which is the Part (A) result. Nominal period interest compounded continuously is given by "r", the Part (B) result. Natural log base *e* is given by "e".

$E = e^{0.464} - 1 = .5904$ or 59.04%

The equivalence of the discrete and continuous interest rate of return results is demonstrated. Once you have either result (discrete or continuous), you can calculate the other using Eq. 2-10.

3.4 Alternative Methods to Obtain Annual Value From Initial Cost, C, and Salvage Value, L

Determination of the rate of return for problems such as Example 3-6 where initial cost equals salvage, and income is uniform each period can be simplified by introduction of another method to obtain annual value. Until now the normal way to obtain annual value for given initial cost, "C", and salvage value, "L", has been to use Equation 3-1:

$$C(A/P_{i,n}) - L(A/F_{i,n}) = \text{Equivalent Annual Cost} \qquad 3\text{-}1$$

for investment, "C", and salvage, "L", shown on the following time diagram:

C = Investment L = Salvage Value

0 n

An alternate method to convert an initial investment, "C", and a salvage value, "L", into equivalent annual value is to use Equation 3-2:

$$(C - L)(A/P_{i,n}) + Li = \text{Equivalent Annual Cost} \qquad 3\text{-}2$$

It may not be immediately evident that Equations 3-1 and 3-2 are equivalent so the proof follows. Working only with Equation 3-2:

$$(C - L)(A/P_{i,n}) + Li$$

$$= C(A/P_{i,n}) + L(i - A/P_{i,n})$$

$$= C(A/P_{i,n}) + L\{i - [i(1 + i)^n/(1 + i)^n - 1]\}$$

$$= C(A/P_{i,n}) + L\{[(i(1 + i)^n - i) - (i(1 + i)^n]/(1 + i)^n - 1\}$$

$$= C(A/P_{i,n}) - L(A/F_{i,n})$$

This completes the proof showing that Equation 3-1 is equal to Equation 3-2. Either equation may be used to reduce a first cost, "C", and salvage, "L", to an equivalent annual value. One situation where the use of Equation 3-2 is very useful occurs when salvage value equals the initial investment. Writing the annual value equation for Example 3-6 in the form of Equation 3-2 yields the annual worth equation shown:

From Ex 3-6: C = \$10,000   I = \$2,638   I = \$2,638

0   1. 5   L=\$10,000

AW Eq: $(10{,}000 - 10{,}000)(A/P_{i,5}) + 10{,}000i = \$2{,}638$

Therefore, i = .2638 or 26.38% explicitly, without trial and error. This rate of return result is the ratio of average annual income (\$2,638) divided by initial investment cost (\$10,000). That is the approximate ROR calculation introduced in Example 3-3. When initial cost and salvage value are equal and income is uniform and equal, the ROR obtained from the Example 3-3 ROR approximation given earlier is always the exact project ROR. Writing an annual worth equation using Equation 3-2 instead of a present worth equation makes this intuitively evident. An example illustrating that Equation 3-1 and 3-2 give the same equivalent annual cost follows.

EXAMPLE 3-10 Illustration of Two Equivalent Annual Cost Calculation Methods

Determine the equivalent annual cost for equipment with an estimated ten year life having initial cost of \$30,000, estimated salvage value in ten years of \$10,000 for a minimum ROR of 15% per year. Use both Equation 3-1 and Equation 3-2 to show that they give the same result.

Solution:

Using Equation 3-1:

$$A = 30{,}000\overset{0.19925}{(A/P_{15\%,10})} - 10{,}000\overset{0.04925}{(A/F_{15\%,10})} = \$5{,}485$$

Using Equation 3-2:

$$A = (30{,}000 - 10{,}000)\overset{0.19925}{(A/P_{15\%,10})} + 10{,}000(.15) = \$5{,}485$$

3.5 Bond Investments

Bonds are a popular way for corporations and governments to raise debt capital. Often referred to as fixed income securities, bonds pay a fixed amount of interest income each year that generally does not change over the bond life. These securities are the focus of this section but investors should be aware that some bonds are adjusted for the effects of inflation and or market interest rates over time while others, known as accrual, discount, deep discount or strip bonds pay all accrued interest at the maturity date. Some bonds are convertible to common stock or other securities after a period of time. Implicitly, the analysis of bond investments is an important consideration for all investors.

Bonds generally are backed by selected assets of the issuing organization as collateral. However, U.S. Government securities known as Notes and Bonds offer no such asset, yet they are thought to provide the least amount of risk due to the goodwill of the United States Government to pay off its debt obligations in a timely manner. These bonds are said to be "backed by the full faith and credit of the U.S. Government." Debentures are similar to bonds in terms of conditions and timing of interest to be paid, but these securities might be backed by real estate associated with various mortgages or in some cases, only the goodwill of the issuing corporation or government agency. The term "Junk Bond" is often used today to describe a bond that offers no real tangible assets to financially back the purchaser as collateral should the issuer of the debt go bankrupt. Correspondingly, these higher risk bonds and some debentures pay a higher annual interest rate (or nominal rate of return) for the corresponding increased level of risk. In the bond industry, it is common for brokers and investors to measure economic performance in terms of both a compound interest rate of return referred to as, "yield to maturity" which is identified by the acronym "YTM," and an add-on or flat interest rate known as the "current yield." Both measures of economic performance are identified in the examples following this discussion.

It is important to recognize that most bonds, debentures, and notes pay interest on a semi-annual basis, but the related interest rates are described nominally. This means that the evaluation of a bond must be made on a semi-annual basis and then expressed as a nominal value. Three other important factors to remember in a bond evaluation include:

1) At the maturity date of a bond, the holder will receive its face value much like a salvage or terminal value in other project evaluations.

2) The current market value of a bond will vary from its initial offering date until its maturity date, as interest rates fluctuate up and down with the broader money markets.

3) Call privileges are written into most corporate or municipal bond offerings to give issuers the right to pay off a bond issue early (before the maturity date).

Early repayment of bonds is desirable for the bond issuer if market interest rates drop so the old bonds can be refinanced with new debt at lower market rates. Such provisions are similar to that associated with many home mortgages allowing the homeowner to refinance when rates are low enough to justify any costs associated with the transaction. Call privileges can affect the value (and therefore rate of return) of existing bonds significantly so it is important for potential purchasers to account for these considerations before investing.

Today the U.S. Government offers a number of different securities for different economic and financial obligations including Bills, Notes, TIPS, I-Bonds and EE-Bonds and simply Bonds.

Treasury Bills are short term securities usually sold in 13, 26 or 52 week denominations and sold at a discount to face value. Along with all of the above mentioned securities, these issues may be purchased electronically, direct from the government using the TreasuryDirect program or through banks and brokers. Shorter 4-week bills cannot be purchased electronically, but can be transferred into your electronic account after being purchased from a bank or broker.

Treasury Notes are issued for periods of 2, 3, 5 and 10 years. Interest is paid on a semi-annual basis and the principal (or face value) is paid upon maturity of the note. Often times, investors will refer to the 10-year note as a 10-year Treasury Bond.

Treasury Bonds also pay a fixed rate of interest every six months until they mature. Bonds are a long-term investment with maturities as long as 30 years. The 30-year bond is a benchmark of the yield curve providing a measure of risk free return in that investment time frame. The 30-year bond does extend a small portion of the government's debt repayment schedule. It is probably safe to say that maturities on all government securities may come and go with market conditions and the financial needs of the government.

I-Bonds are a savings product that can be purchased through Treasury Direct or in banks and various financial institutions. Like Treasury Inflation Protected Securities (TIPS are discussed below) these bonds are adjusted semi-annually for the impact of U.S. inflation. I-Bonds represent an accrual bond in that the interest accrues to the bond's face value and is payable when the security is sold. I-Bonds have lives ranging from 1 to 30 years and are sold in denominations of $50 to a maximum $5,000 in paper form, and $25 to $5,000 if purchased electronically. I-Bonds may be purchased in amounts up to $5,000 per year per social security number. Redemption penalties exist if the bond is sold in the first 5 years.

EE-Bonds issued after May of 2005 earn a fixed rate of interest while prior issues realized a market based interest rate. EE bonds are also an accrual type of bond and sold at half the face value and in denominations of $50 to $10,000. Early redemption penalties do exist in the first 5 years.

Treasury Inflation Protected Securities, (TIPS), offer investors protection from the effects of inflation as measured by the Consumer Price Index. The face value of the bond is increased for periods of inflation on a semi-annual basis and the fixed semi-annual interest rate is applied to the indexed amount. The bond value calculation may result in a decreased valuation in periods of deflation. Tax implications are another important aspect of these securities. The IRS views both the imputed increase in value of the bond due to inflation and the interest paid as ordinary income subject to tax.

EXAMPLE 3-11 New Bond Rate of Return Analysis

Calculate the new bond rate of return for a new issue of $1,000 bonds with a maturity date twenty years after the issuing date, if the new bond pays interest of $40 every six month period.

Solution:

C = Cost, I = Interest Income (Semi-Annual), L = Maturity Value

C = $1,000	I=$40	I=$40	I=$40 L=$1,000
0	1	2.	40 semi-annual

PW Eq: $0 = -1{,}000 + 40(P/A_{i,40}) + 1{,}000(P/F_{i,40})$

The "i" value may be determined by trial and error. However, since the initial cost is equal to the salvage (or maturity) value and period income is uniform and equal; use the approximation technique from Example 3-3 to explicitly solve for the rate of return.

ROR, i = 40/1,000 = 0.04, or 4.0% per semi-annual period

The nominal rate of return is equal to the 4.0% x 2, or 8.0% per year compounded semi-annually. In bond broker terminology the term "yield to maturity," is used to describe this nominal rate of return and may be listed by the acronym "YTM."

EXAMPLE 3-12 Old Bond Rate of Return Analysis

If the bond described in Example 3-11 was initially offered six years ago and now sells for $800, what rate of return would an investor who holds the bond to maturity receive? Note that only the cost and evaluation life are different from the Example 3-11 new bond evaluation. Fourteen years (28 semi-annual periods) of life remain from the original 20 year life.

Solution:

C = Cost, I = Interest Income (Semi-Annual), L = Maturity Value

```
C=$800        I=$40        I=$40        I=$40
_____________________________________________ L=$1,000
  0             1            2. . . . . . . . . . 28 semi-annual
```

When initial cost does not equal salvage value there is no advantage in writing an annual worth equation over a present worth equation to calculate rate of return.

Present Worth Eq: $800 = 40(P/A_{i,28}) + 1{,}000(P/F_{i,28})$

In selecting the initial trial and error "i" value, remember that "i" is a semi-annual period rate of return. If we paid $1,000 for the bond we know i = 4%, so try a higher value:

$i = 6\% = 40(13.406) + 1000(.1956) = \$731.84$
$i = 5\% = 40(14.898) + 1000(.2551) = \$851.02$

By interpolation i = 5.43% per semi-annual period. The nominal or annual rate of return is 10.86% per year compounded semi-annually, which is the *yield to maturity*. Another broker term, *current yield, is defined as annual interest divided by bond cost.* For this example old bond current yield is 80/800 equaling 0.10 or 10%, which compares to the previously calculated yield to maturity of 10.86% compounded semi-annually.

EXAMPLE 3-13 Old Bond Rate of Return With and Without Call Privileges

Consider that the bond described in Example 3-11 was initially offered 6 years ago and now sells for $1,200 (interest rates have dropped so the bond price has increased). The bond is callable 10 years after the initial offering date (which is 4 years from now) at par value (the original $1,000 value). Calculate the rate of return that an investor paying $1,200 for this bond would receive if, (1) the bond is not called early and is held until normal maturity 14 years from now and (2) the bond is called 4 years from now.

Solution:

(1) No early call privileges, so use a 14 year (28 semi-annual periods) life.

C = Cost, I = Interest Income (Semi-annual), L = Maturity Value

C = $1,200	I=$40	I=$40	I=$40	
0	1	2.	28	L=$1,000

Present Worth Eq: $1{,}200 = 40(P/A_{i,28}) + 1{,}000(P/F_{i,28})$

The semi-annual period rate of return is 2.98%, and the annual rate of return (yield to maturity) is 5.96% compounded semi-annually.

(2) If call privileges exist and can be expected to be exercised, (since interest rates have dropped), use a four year (eight semi-annual periods) life to the call date.

C = Cost, I = Interest Income (Semi-annual), L = Maturity Value

C = $1,200	I=$40	I=$40	I=$40	
0	1	2	8	L=$1,000

Present Worth Eq: $1{,}200 = 40(P/A_{i,8}) + 1{,}000(P/F_{i,8})$

The semi-annual period rate of return is 1.35%, and the annual rate of return (yield to call date maturity) is 2.70% compounded semi-annually. If you pay $1,200 for this bond and it is called four years later, your rate of return is considerably less than the 5.96% annual rate of return to maturity at year 14.

If an investor wants to receive a 6% rate of return compounded semi-annually to the call date, the present worth of interest and maturity "call" value for 8 semi-annual periods at 6.0%/2, or 3.0% interest per semi-annual period gives the bond value:

$$\text{Value of Callable Bond} = 40(\overset{7.020}{P/A_{3\%,8}}) + 1{,}000(\overset{0.7894}{P/F_{3\%,8}}) = \$1{,}070$$

This calculation assumes a flat yield curve exists between 4 and 14 year maturities.

3.6 Rate of Return Related to T-Bill Discount Rates

Treasury Bills, or T-Bills, are short-term securities that you purchase either directly from Treasury or through a bank or broker. "Treasury Bills are sold in denominations of $1,000 and multiples of $1,000." You can hold a T-Bill until maturity or sell prior to maturity at the current market rate. Treasury bills are usually issued for a period of 13, 26 or 52 weeks. Two other bills, 4-week bills and cash management bills, can't be bought through the electronic TreasuryDirect program, but can be purchased through your bank or broker. T-Bills are issued via competitive or non-competitive bids in a Treasury Auction and are sold at a discount as illustrated in Example 3-14. T-Bill discount rates should be converted to equivalent nominal annual compound interest rates for comparison with other similar investments.

Buying Treasury Bills at a discount effectively pays the interest up-front instead of at the maturity date of a Treasury Bill. This makes the T-bill investment compound interest rate of return greater than the T-bill discount rate, as the following example illustrates.

EXAMPLE 3-14 T-Bill Discount Rates and Rate of Return

A $10,000, six month (26 week) T-bill with a 10% discount rate can be purchased. What is the equivalent compound interest rate of return on this investment?

Solution:

T-bill discount rates are always given on an annual basis, so 10% / 2 = 5.0% per 6 months. The 5% discount is realized when the T-bill is purchased by 5% reduction in cost. The face value of the T-Bill is paid as maturity value at the six month maturity date.

Discounted Cost = $9,500	Maturity Value =$10,000
0	6 months

PW Eq: $9{,}500 = 10{,}000(P/F_{i,1})$

Trial and Error, i = 5.263% per six months

Doubling this six month period rate gives an annual rate of return of 10.526% compounded semi-annually as being equivalent to a 10%, six month T-Bill discount rate.

3.7 Financial Cost of Capital vs Opportunity Cost of Capital

This section differentiates the two common approaches used by investors to determine their minimum rate of return, or discount rate. In this textbook, a minimum rate of return, or discount rate, is distinguished from a project compound interest rate of return by placing an asterisk immediately after i, hence, i*. So, how is an investor's minimum rate of return, i* established?

Going back to chapter one, discussion was presented to introduce the reader to two schools of thought concerning this subject. Most managerial finance authors suggest that the appropriate methodology is to determine the investor's financial cost of capital which, for a privately held company may be the average cost of financing projects under consideration or currently being financed. For a publicly traded company it's a little more complex as the return that stockholders are demanding in order to buy the company's stock must now be considered in addition to the after-tax cost of debt. Even though we are focused on before-tax applications at this point, these calculations will in reality, always account for the deductibility of applicable interest.

The theory behind the use of the financial cost of capital is based on the economic concept of operating any business such that the marginal returns received are just sufficient to cover the marginal cost of undertaking that project. After all, if an investor can borrow money at 7.0% and earn a project ROR of 7.5%, that investor is realizing a positive return from the borrowed dollars. Borrowed money is a focus of Chapter 11 in the textbook, but a basic axiom of that material can be stated as follows: if an investor can borrow money at an interest rate that is less than the cash equivalent (100% Equity) return on the same project, borrowed money will always enhance project rate of return. Therefore, the minimum return for any investor is reflected by the incremental cost of financing the next project. When investors or companies reach a point where the next project ROR is less than the cost of borrowing, they stop taking on new projects. Since a company can raise cash from selling stock, issuing bonds or incurring other forms of debt, the weighted average of these various sources is calculated to determine the minimum rate of return available to the firm. Graphically, this is reflected in Figure 3-6a.

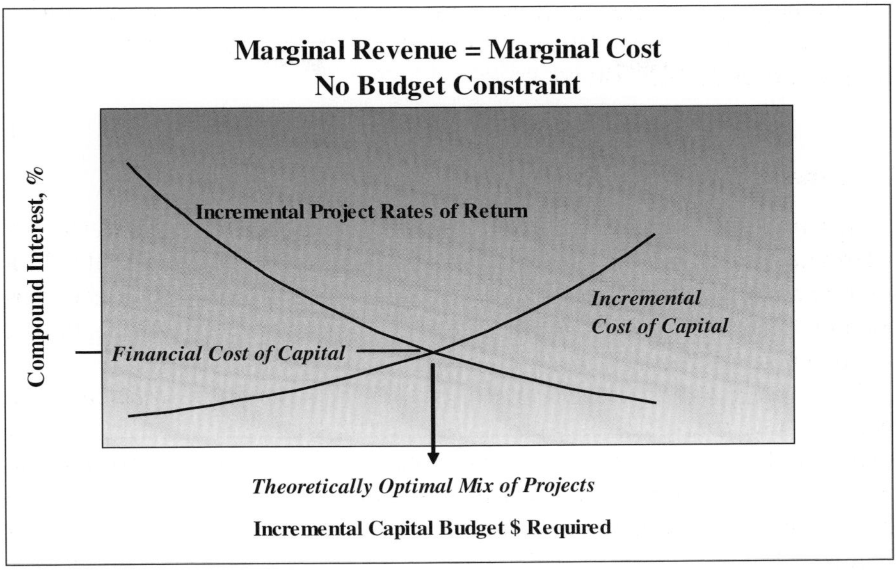

Figure 3-6a Theory of Utilizing Financial Cost of Capital as Discount Rate

The theory illustrated in Figure 3-6a holds true if an investor has sufficient financial resources allowing it to undertake all of the projects represented on the horizontal "X" axis. This line reflects the cumulative budget dollars required for all projects with rates of return greater than the weighted average financial cost of capital. However, in practice, most investors are financially constrained and not capable of taking on all of the projects represented by this theoretically optimal intersection point.

Jan L.A. van de Snepscheut was credited on the internet with the following saying:

"In theory, there is no difference between theory and practice, but, in practice, there is."

The imposition of a budget constraint causes a shift that is upward and to the left in the weighted average cost of capital. The new intersection point is the basis upon which opportunity cost of capital is derived and is reflected in Figure 3-6b.

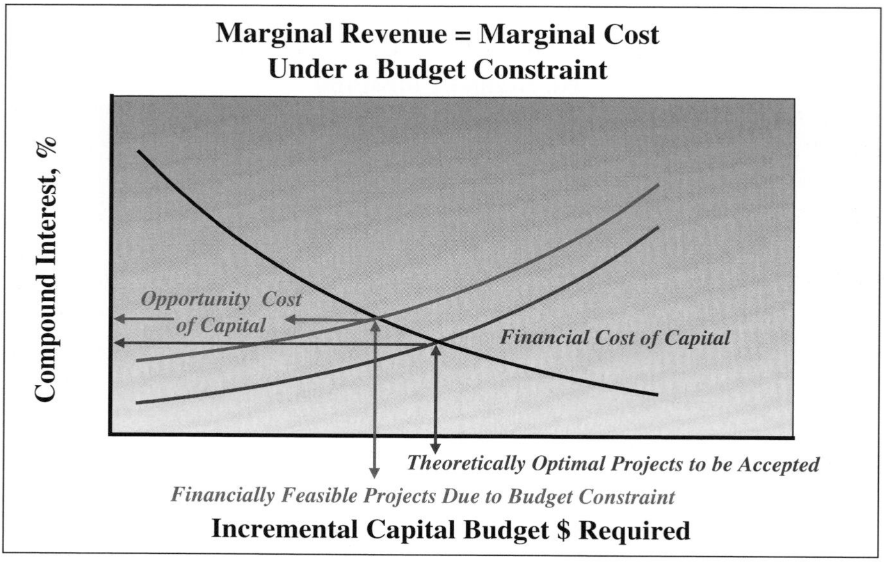

Figure 3-6b Effects of a Budget Constraint

The effects of a capital budget constraint lead to a requirement to adjust the financial cost of capital to properly determine an investor's minimum acceptable rate of return, which some authors refer to by the acronym "MARR." This step leads investors to the concept of economic "hurdle rates" that serve a proxy role for the true opportunity cost of capital reflecting the rate of return to be given up, if another project is accepted. This economic concept is the focus at the project level of Example 3-15. The discussion following Example 3-15 illustrates the basic weighted average cost of capital calculations including the development of the capital asset pricing model, (CAPM). This represents an introduction to determining the rate of return shareholders are seeking when investing in a specific common stock relative to an index such as the S&P 500 representative of a larger basket of equities (stocks).

EXAMPLE 3-15 Financial Cost of Capital Versus Opportunity Cost of Capital

A firm has the opportunity to invest $100,000 in a project that is expected to generate a revenue minus operating cost before-tax cash flow of $15,000 per year, at years one through ten with a $100,000 sale value projected for year ten. The firm's weighted average financial cost of capital (from a combination of borrowed money debt and equity capital) is 10%. Capital budget dollars are limited and other opportunities for investing capital are thought to exist that would give a 20% rate of return. Use rate of return analysis to determine whether or not the firm should invest in the $100,000 project.

Solution:

			L=$100,000
C = $100,000	I=$15,000	I=$15,000	I=$15,000
0	1	2.	10

PW Eq: $0 = -100{,}000 + 15{,}000(P/A_{i,10}) + 100{,}000(P/F_{i,10})$

By trial and error, i = ROR = 15%

Although the project ROR of 15% is satisfactory compared to the 10% financial cost of capital, it is unsatisfactory compared to the rate of return of 20% representing other opportunities for investing capital (opportunity cost of capital). If investors are attempting to maximize profit from limited investment dollars the decision would be to reject the 15% ROR project and invest elsewhere at 20% to optimize the use of investment capital from an economic viewpoint. Obviously if borrowed money were unlimited, investors would want to consider all projects with rates of return exceeding the cost associated with raising funds to finance investments (the financial cost of capital).

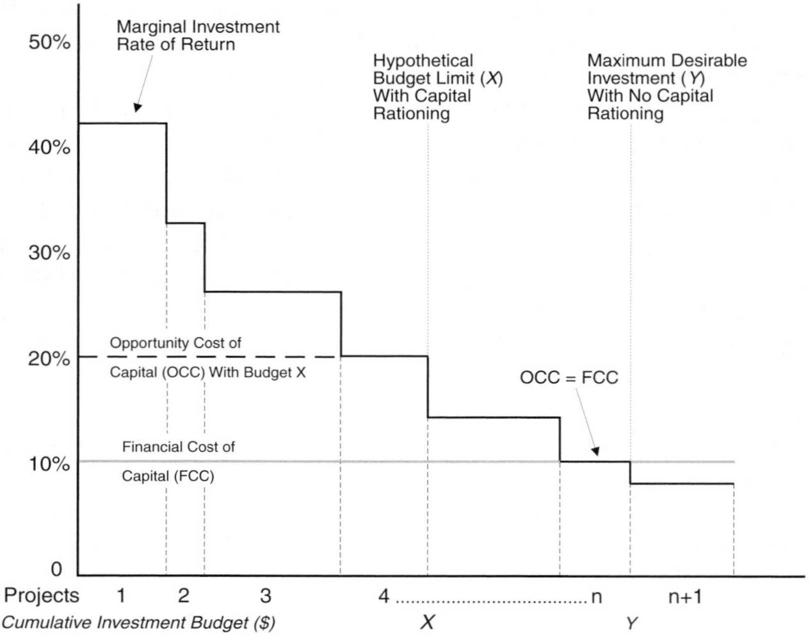

Figure 3-7 Financial Cost of Capital vs Opportunity Cost of Capital

The Figure 3-7 curves for marginal investment rate of return and financial cost of capital versus cumulative investment budget show graphically why the conclusion of Example 3-15 to reject the 15.0% ROR is correct. This graph is a plot of investment rate of return versus cumulative budget dollars with investments one through "n+1" graphed from left to right in the order of decreasing project rate of return. For a given budget this shows the marginal (incremental) rate of return that the marginal investment in the last project will give. For example, under capital rationing with a budget of $*X*, investments with rates of return of 20.0% would have to be rejected to accept and finance the 15.0% ROR project described. This clearly would make sub-optimal use of investor capital by not maximizing the future value that can be generated from available budget dollars. An investor would make money by undertaking the Example 3-15 project, but the investor has the potential of making more money by rejecting the Example 3-15 project and investing budget dollars elsewhere at a 20.0% rate of return. Under capital rationing if the opportunity cost of capital is larger than the financial cost of capital as shown in Figure 3-7, then opportunity cost of capital is the correct minimum discount rate to use in discounted cash flow calculations and investment decision-making. However, it must be recognized that the *opportunity cost of capital represents other opportunities for investing capital now and in the future over the life of projects being analyzed. When using a listing of project rates of return today to determine opportunity cost of capital, it is assumed that today's projects are representative of future and current investment opportunities.* If future investment opportunities are projected to be different from today's investment opportunities, then it is necessary to change opportunity cost of capital with time and use analysis techniques other than rate of return, as illustrated in Section 4.4 of Chapter 4.

If capital is not rationed it is desirable to fund all projects up to the budget limit where marginal investment rate of return equals financial cost of capital. As long as additional investments earn a rate of return greater than the financial cost of capital, additional investments are economically desirable. When an additional investment will give a rate of return less than the financial cost of capital, it is not desirable. Opportunity cost of capital (the rate of return on additional investment opportunities thought to exist) and financial cost of capital are equal at the investment level where the last additional investment earns a rate of return just equal to the financial cost of capital. As described in the last paragraph concerning opportunity cost of capital, *when financial cost of capital is assumed to equal opportunity cost of capital, because capital is not rationed, it is assumed that financial cost of capital will be the same in the future as it is today.* This is the basis upon which many finance textbooks are written. It is assumed there that all projects with rate of return potential greater than the cost of raising money (financial cost of capital) will be done. Financing often is not as easy to obtain as it seems in textbooks. In industry practice capital usually is rationed, making the opportunity cost of capital a bigger rate than financial cost of capital. To determine the opportunity cost of capital requires evaluation of potential future investment opportunities as well as today's investment opportunities.

As shown in Figure 3-7 for the $\$Y$ maximum desirable investment level, opportunity cost of capital and financial cost of capital are equal. For a budget in excess of $\$Y$ the financial cost of capital would exceed the rate of return on the marginal investments so it would not be economically desirable to fund projects beyond the $\$Y$ budget amount. It is very important to note that although Figure 3-7 presents projects in the order of decreasing rate of return, the reader must not imply that rate of return is a valid project ranking technique. This is emphasized and illustrated by example in Chapter 4. Project one is not necessarily better economically then project two, just because the rate of return for project one is bigger than the rate of return for project two. All we can conclude from Figure 3-7 is that the cumulative investment of "$*X*" in projects one through four is better than replacing any of these projects with projects five through "n." In other words, rate of return is an "accept or reject" criterion for each project, relative to investing elsewhere, and not a valid method of ranking projects. Also, *when we say investing in projects one through four is preferable to investing in any other projects, we are assuming projects one through four are indicative of future investment opportunities (in addition to today's opportunities).* Most investors make this assumption, but sometimes changing projected future investment rate of return from what it is today may make more sense. Just because an investor has many high rate of return investment opportunities today often does not mean that similar opportunities will exist in the future. This requires changing the opportunity cost of capital with time by reducing future opportunity cost of capital from what it is today, as illustrated by Example 4-6 in Chapter 4.

Although it is opportunity cost of capital rather than financial cost of capital that is of primary importance in discounted cash flow analysis calculations and decision-making, investors must always verify that their financial cost of capital does not exceed their opportunity cost of capital. Therefore, following is an explanation of a typical before-tax approach that many major companies use to arrive at their "*financial cost of capital*" which generally *is treated as the weighted average cost of equity and debt financing on a prospective basis.* Therefore, we must project the cost of equity capital and debt capital and prorate them using the company debt/equity ratio.

Cost of equity capital represents the economic return that company shareholders expect to receive in the form of dividend payments and/or stock appreciation. This expected equity return equals that which the shareholder investors perceive could be realized on alternative investments of comparable risk. Since company costs and revenues are yet to be incurred in the future, this analysis is on a prospective basis, using the past as a guide when and if it is considered relevant.

The cost of equity capital financing generally exceeds the rate of return on long term U.S. Treasury bonds because of the greater risk that equity shareholders assume. If an investor can invest in U.S. Treasury bonds which are considered to be as safe as any investment in the world today by most people, why would the investor invest in corporate common stock with greater risk, for the same return? To account for a relatively risk-free U.S. Treasury bond rate adjusted for risk, a "Capital Asset Pricing Model," (CAPM) approach to estimating the cost of equity capital is used by many companies today. This simplistically involves three steps: (1) estimating the current yield on long-term U.S. Treasury bonds, considered to be the "risk-free" interest rate (assumed to be 8.0% per year for this illustration), (2) estimating an equity risk premium related to the spread between common stock returns and U.S. Treasury bond yields (assumed to be 6.0% for this analysis), and (3) estimating the companies "Beta" factor which measures stock price volatility for the company relative to the overall market (assume an average risk company, so Beta is 1.0). This gives a cost of equity capital of 14.0% which equals the 8.0% risk-free rate + (6.0% risk rate * 1.0 Beta)

The cost of debt is the interest rate a company would pay for new long-term financing by borrowing directly from banks or through new bond or debenture type offerings. Assume a 9.0% debt rate for our illustration.

For a company with an assumed 40.0% debt, 60.0% equity financial structure, the weighted average financial cost of capital would be 12.0%, based on the assumed rates as follows:

Cost of Equity:	14.0% x 0.60 =	8.40%
Cost of Debt:	9.0% x 0.40 =	3.60%
Financial Cost of Capital	=	12.00%

Many variations occur in the financial cost of capital calculations done by different companies and investors. For example, income tax generally must be taken into account for valid analysis so you need to work with after-tax debt rates, risk-free investment rates and risk adjustment rates. Also, the risk adjustment rate can be attained with varying magnitude using financial data for different historical periods. The risk free rate can be based on short-term U.S. Treasury Bills or intermediate term U.S. Treasury Notes instead of bonds. Debt-to-equity ratios can be based on current market value of common stock and debt rather than historical book value of outstanding debt and equity securities. All of these variations generally cause change in the financial cost of capital results making it obvious that it is an estimate rather than a precise number. Finally, many people have begun to question the validity of beta to measure the relative risk of returns available. In fact, in a June 1, 1992, edition of Fortune Magazine, Eugene Fama, and Kenneth R. French of The University of Chicago declared, "beta is bogus," and therefore, not capable of telling investors much about investment return potential. Beta was designed to measure a correlation in risk return in the stock of one company, relative to an industry or the market. It was never designed to account for the risk often associated with project evaluations such as political, environmental, engineering, marketing or geological risk, which is the focus of this text.

As previously mentioned, for many companies the financial cost of capital is the basis for determining the company's minimum rate of return, i*. However, it is equally important to recognize that in many of these companies; even though they may utilize a discount rate of say, 12.0%, projects earning a 12.0% return are rarely accepted. Instead the company imposes a "hurdle rate" (a higher measure of performance, say 18.0%) for all projects. Hurdle rates indirectly recognize that the company is not willing to accept projects that are just earning the weighted average financial cost of capital. Instead the company demands a higher return for the budget dollars rationed to them for a given period of time (a hurdle rate). Unfortunately, hurdle rates are a short cut to recognition of the true opportunity cost for an investor. Hurdle rates may not properly account for all relevant time value of money considerations. This can only be consistently achieved by using a discount rate that reflects the investor's perceived long-term opportunity cost of capital.

The reader can get more detail on the many variations in financial cost of capital calculations from any good managerial finance textbook.

3.8 Rate of Return and the Revenue Reinvestment Question

Is reinvestment of project revenue or positive cash flow related to the physical meaning of project compound interest rate of return? This is a question that has confused many knowledgeable investment analysts for many years. *Reinvestment of revenues is not implicitly or explicitly tied to the physical meaning of ordinary rate of return.* If reinvestment of investment revenues was tied to the meaning of ordinary compound interest rate of return then the meaning of conventional bond ROR and zero coupon bond ROR would be the same, and they are not the same, as the following example shows.

EXAMPLE 3-16 Rate of Return With and Without Revenue Reinvestment Meaning

Consider either investing $1,000 in a new 30 year zero coupon bond yielding a rate of return of 8% compounded annually or investing $1,000 in a new 30 year conventional bond yielding annual dividends that give the investor a rate of return of 8% compounded annually. What assumptions are explicitly or implicitly involved in determining the bond investment that would generate the greatest future value at year 30? Assume annual conventional bond dividends (rather than semi-annual) of $80 per year.

Calculate the bond values if market interest rates drop to 6.0% or rise to 10.0% or 15.0% within weeks of having purchased the 8.0% interest rate bonds.

Solution

Zero Coupon Bond

C = $1,000 — — —

0 1 2. . . . 30

$F = \$1,000(F/P_{8\%,30})$, with $(F/P_{8\%,30}) = 10.063$, $= \$10,063$

ROR = 8% compounded annually

Conventional Bond

C = $1,000 I = $80 I = $80 I = $80

0 1 2. . . . . . . 30 L=$1,000

ROR = 8% compounded annually

Both bonds have identical 8% compound interest rates of return. However, only the zero coupon bond has reinvestment of accrued interest (equivalent to dividends) at the 8% compound rate of return tied to its meaning because the zero coupon bond ROR has growth ROR meaning as introduced in the next Section 3.9. Whenever one or more investments generate a single future revenue, the meaning of the investment ROR is growth ROR and reinvestment of all accrued interest (return on investment) is tied into the growth ROR meaning. When several revenues are generated by an investment as with the conventional bond, reinvestment of revenues is not tied into the ROR meaning. If reinvestment of conventional bond dividends at a rate of return of 8% per year was explicitly or implicitly tied to the meaning of the conventional bond 8% ROR, then investing in the conventional bond would give the identical future value as investing in the zero coupon bond. While reinvestment of dividend revenues is guaranteed with the zero coupon bond investment so the year 30 future value is known explicitly at the time the zero coupon bond is purchased, assumptions must be made by the investor concerning the conventional bond dividend reinvestment rate that can be realized from year to year. There is no explicit or implicit reinvestment of the conventional bond dividends at any rate tied to the meaning of the 8% conventional bond rate of return.

If an investor assumes that the conventional bond dividends can be reinvested at 10% interest per year, then the conventional bond future value is:

$$F = \$80(\overset{164.494}{F/A_{10\%,30}}) + \$1{,}000 = \$14{,}159$$

If reinvestment of conventional bond dividends at 6% per year is assumed, then:

$$F = \$80(\overset{79.058}{F/A_{6\%,30}}) + \$1{,}000 = \$7{,}324$$

These dividend reinvestment assumptions enable an investor to project whether the zero coupon bond investment or the conventional bond investment combined with reinvestment of dividends will generate the maximum year 30 future value. The reader can see that the revenue reinvestment rate assumption has a very significant effect on potential future value to be accrued, giving a factor of two difference in the future values for revenue reinvestment rates of 10.0% versus 6.0%. However, *reinvestment of bond dividends or project revenues is in no way physically related to the meaning of the conventional bond or general investment ordinary rate of return.*

The sensitivity of 8.0% interest rate bond values to changes in market interest rates is made assuming the 8.0% interest bond was purchased several weeks ago, so years of life are unchanged.

Zero Coupon Bond Sensitivity from $1,000 Value:

6.0% Interest: Year 0 Value = $10{,}063\overset{0.1741}{(P/F_{6\%,30})} = \$1{,}752$
This is a 75.2% increase in value.

10.0% Interest: Year 0 Value = $10{,}063\overset{0.0573}{(P/F_{10\%,30})} = \$567$
This is a 43.3% reduction in value.

15.0% Interest: Year 0 Value = $10{,}063\overset{0.0151}{(P/F_{15\%,30})} = \$152$
This is a 84.8% reduction in value.

Conventional 8.0% Interest Rate Coupon Bond, Sensitivity from $1,000 Value:

6.0% Interest: Year 0 Value = $1{,}000\overset{0.1741}{(P/F_{6\%,30})} + 80\overset{13.765}{(P/A_{6\%,30})}$
$= \$1{,}275$
This is a 27.5% increase in value.

10.0% Interest: Year 0 Value = $1{,}000\overset{0.0573}{(P/F_{10\%,30})} + 80\overset{9.427}{(P/A_{10\%,30})}$
$= \$811$
This is a 18.9% reduction in value.

15.0% Interest: Year 0 Value = $1{,}000\overset{0.0151}{(P/F_{15\%,30})} + 80\overset{6.566}{(P/A_{15\%,30})}$
$= \$540$
This is a 46.0% reduction in value.

Notice that both conventional and zero coupon bond market values are very sensitive to interest rate changes, but zero coupon market values are much more sensitive than conventional bonds. Due to interest rate changes, investors in bonds and debentures can make or lose money just as fast due to market interest rate changes as investors can make or lose money in common stock or real estate investments. This is another way of emphasizing that there is risk of losing capital investment value with all types of investments as well as the possibility of increasing investment value.

An evaluation situation that involves partial reinvestment of revenue meaning associated with rate of return is in analyses involving effective interest rates. Calculation of effective interest rates for either discrete or continuous compounding of interest explicitly assumes accrued interest (revenue) will be reinvested at the period interest rate during the effective interest rate period. However, this reinvestment assumption only applies during the effective interest rate period which is usually one year and does not apply between periods. If you make a 10 year life project analysis using annual periods with costs and revenues each yearly period and calculate the project ROR to be 20.0% compounded annually, this 20.0% ROR is an effective annual interest rate. Reinvestment of annual revenues from year to year is not implicitly or explicitly tied into the 20.0% ROR meaning, but during any year money is considered to grow (be reinvested internally) at the minimum rate of return.

EXAMPLE 3-17a Rate of Return Without Revenue Reinvestment Meaning

Consider the investment of $100,000 at time zero to generate five uniform and equal revenues of $37,185 at each of years one through five with zero salvage at year five. Calculate the project rate of return and discuss the meaning of the result.

Solution:

Cost = $100,000	Rev = $37,185	Rev = $37,185
0	1	5

PW Eq: $0 = -100{,}000 + 37{,}185(P/A_{i,5})$

Trial and Error, i = ROR = 25.0%

The rate of return on this investment is 25%. *Is reinvestment of year one through five revenues at 25% tied into the meaning of the 25% rate of return? That is the classical rate of return revenue reinvestment question. Many analysts have said yes, but the answer is no. Reinvestment of revenues is not tied to the meaning of any ordinary compound interest rate of return and that answer can and will be explained in several different ways.* First, an intuitive approach is used. Consider the $100,000 investment in Example 3-17a to be a loan that would be paid off by five equal mortgage payments of $37,185 at years one through five, the compound mortgage interest rate received by the lender and paid by the borrower would be 25%. Intuitively it is known that the meaning of the 25% compound interest rate, from the viewpoint of either the borrower or lender, is unaffected by what the lender does with the mortgage payments as they are received. The economic welfare of the lender will certainly be affected by what the lender does with the mortgage payments as they are received, but the physical meaning of the 25% rate of return is not affected by what is done with the revenue each year. A second intuitive explanation can be made of why reinvestment of revenues is not related to the meaning of ordinary rate of return by thinking of project investments as being analogous to deposits in a bank account. Then consider that the bank interest rate equals the project ROR with project revenues being equivalent to withdrawals from the bank account each year with the last withdrawal reducing the account balance to zero. Any reasonable person knows that what an investor does with money taken from a bank account each year has no effect on the physical meaning of the bank account compound interest rate of return. Similar rationale applies to compound interest project rates of return in general.

Looking at the cumulative cash position diagram illustration of project ROR, this is a more explicit way of showing that compound interest rates of return in general, relate to remaining unamortized investment each period and have nothing to do with reinvestment of revenue at any rate of return. For this example the cumulative cash position diagram is shown in Figure 3-8.

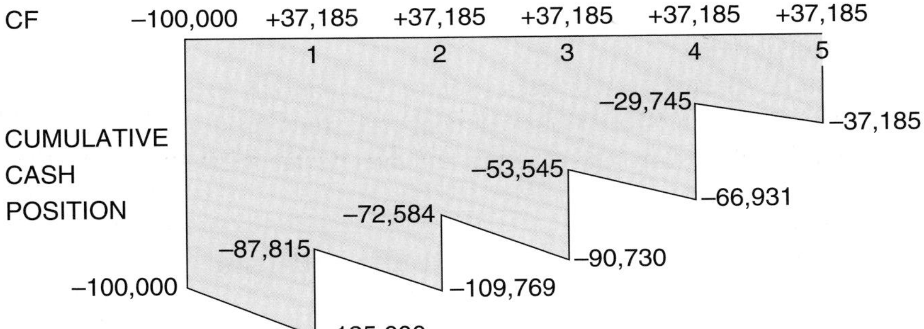

Figure 3-8 Cumulative Cash Position Diagram for 25% ROR Project

It can be seen by analyzing Figure 3-8 that the 25% ROR applies to remaining investment value to be paid off (amortized) each year and that interest from reinvestment of revenues at any rate of return is not related to the diagram in any way. Only if an investor is interested in calculating the rate of growth of investment dollars does reinvestment of revenues affect the calculations and meaning of rate of return results. This relates to the concept of growth rate of return that is introduced and illustrated in the next section.

3.9 Growth Rate of Return

Growth rate of return is the compound interest rate at which investment dollars grow. All compound interest rates of return, however, are not growth rates of return. To determine the compound interest rate at which investment dollars will grow requires making an assumption concerning the rate of return that will be received from the reinvestment of project revenues (or positive cash flow) as they are received. *The minimum rate of return (denoted as "i*") reflects other opportunities that exist for the investment of capital now and in the future, so the minimum rate of return is the reinvestment rate that should be used in growth rate of return calculations.* Note that you do not assume that you will be able to reinvest initial project revenues at a rate of return equal to initial project ROR. You assume that your reinvestment rate represents other opportunities for the investment of capital thought to exist now and in the future over the project life. That is exactly what the minimum rate of return represents as it relates to all discounted cash flow analysis calculations and the proper application of discounted cash flow analysis results for economic decision purposes. With some analysis techniques such as NPV, the meaning of minimum rate of return just described is implicitly built into the calculations, but with growth rate of return the minimum rate of return revenue reinvestment meaning is explicitly built into the analysis calculations.

To illustrate specific growth rate of return calculations, Example 3-17b considers an extension of $100,000 investment case study used in Example 3-17a as the basis for discussing rate of return and the revenue reinvestment question.

EXAMPLE 3-17b Growth Rate of Return Analysis

Consider the investment of $100,000 at time zero to generate five uniform and equal revenues of $37,185 at each of years one through five, with zero salvage value at year five. The rate of return on this investment was shown in the previous Example 3-17a to be 25% and discussion was given in several different ways to emphasize that the reinvestment of the \$37,185 revenue each year has nothing to do with the meaning of the 25% ROR. However, the 25% ROR does not represent the rate of growth of investment dollars (Growth ROR). To calculate Growth ROR, reinvestment of revenues as they are received must be tied into the analysis calculations. Assume that the investor minimum ROR is 12% over the five year project life which means other opportunities for investing capital at a 12% ROR are thought to exist both now and in the future over the next five years. Calculate the investment Growth ROR and develop the cumulative cash position diagram showing its meaning.

Solution:

C = Cost, R = Revenue, F = Future Terminal Value

Initial Project with ROR = 25%	C = \$100,000	R = \$37,185 . . . R = \$37,185	
	0	1 5	
Revenue Reinvest at i* = 12%	—	C = \$37,185 . . C = \$37,185	F=\$236,236
	0	1 5	

6.353

where Future Terminal Value, $F = \$37{,}185(F/A_{12\%,5})$

Total Initial+Reinvest	C = \$100,000	—	—	F=\$236,236
	0	1 5		

PW Eq: $-100{,}000 + 236{,}236(P/F_{i,5}) = 0$

Trial and Error, i = Growth ROR = 18.76%

The Growth ROR of 18.76% is the compound interest ROR on the combination of the initial and revenue reinvestment project. However, it is a special rate of return that has rate of growth on investment dollar meaning since a single future revenue at year five is generated by the initial investment. Whenever a single future revenue is generated by earlier cost or costs, the meaning of project ROR is Growth ROR.

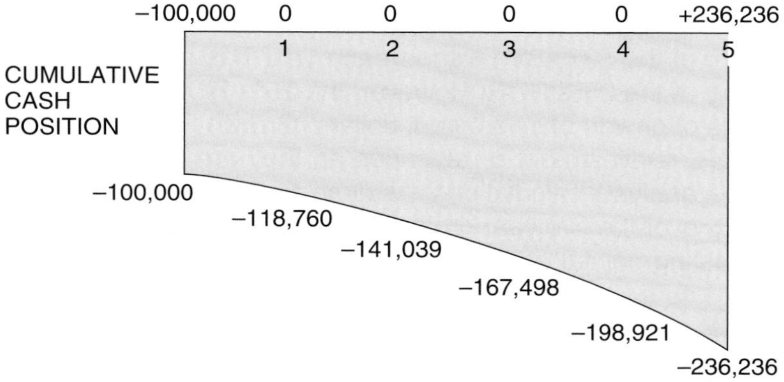

Figure 3-9 Cumulative Cash Position for 18.76% Growth ROR

The Growth ROR of 18.76% relates to larger and larger unamortized investment values each year whereas the initial project ROR of 25% relates to smaller and smaller unamortized investment values each year as was illustrated in Figure 3-8 in Example 3-17a. The initial project ROR of 25% and the Growth ROR of 18.76% not only differ in magnitude but they relate to completely different investment values each year after the first year. A question that often occurs to people at this time is, "why isn't the Growth ROR bigger than the initial project ROR since future value from reinvestment of revenues is being added to the initial project?" The answer relates to the fact that reinvestment costs as well as the revenue reinvestment future value are added to the initial project to get Growth ROR, and the reinvestment costs and future value correspond to a 12% project ROR. Adding the revenue reinvestment 12% project to the initial project which has a 25% ROR, the combination of the two projects will have a weighted average rate of return between 12% and 25%. In this case the weighted average ROR is 18.76%, the project Growth ROR.

A majority of investors do not utilize Growth ROR for evaluating the economic potential of investment projects. However, it will be shown in Chapter 4 that there are two evaluation situations where if you want to make rate of return analysis of projects, using Growth ROR is either necessary or a desirable alternative to ordinary ROR analysis. Remember, however, that there are no evaluation situations where it is necessary to use rate of return analysis. You always have the alternative choice of using present, annual or future value, or break-even analysis to analyze the economic potential of either income or service-producing alternatives.

A second Growth ROR example will now be presented to re-emphasize Growth ROR concepts and additional related considerations.

EXAMPLE 3-18 Growth Rate of Return With Multiple Costs

Consider the time zero initial investment of \$55,000 and a year one investment of \$45,000 in project "A" generate incomes of \$30,000 per year for years two through ten with zero salvage. Determine project ROR. Then assume that each year incomes are reinvested in other investment opportunities yielding a 12% ROR. Refer to revenue reinvestment at a 12% ROR as project "B". Determine the overall growth rate on the time zero and year one investments by combining the initial and revenue reinvestment projects "A" and "B".

Solution: All Values Are In Dollars

	C = 55,000	C = 45,000	I = 30,000	I = 30,000
A)	0	1	2	10

PW Eq: $0 = -55{,}000 - 45{,}000(P/F_{i,1}) + 30{,}000(P/A_{i,9})(P/F_{i,1})$

$i = 25\%{:}\ -55{,}000 - 45{,}000(.8000) + 30{,}000(3.463)(.8000) = -7{,}800$

$i = 20\%{:}\ -55{,}000 - 45{,}000(.8333) + 30{,}000(4.031)(.8333) = +8{,}272$

$i = 0.20 + 0.05[(8{,}272 - 0)/(8{,}272 + 7{,}800)] = 0.226 \text{ or } 22.6\%$

Without interpolation error, the ROR is 22.37% No reinvestment assumption or requirement is associated with the meaning of the initial project rate of return. Reinvestment of revenues only relates to growth rate of return calculations. Reinvestment of revenues at 12% is project "B".

	—	—	C = 30,000	C = 30,000	
B)	0	1	2	10	F = 443,280

$$\text{where Future Reinvestment Value, } F = 30{,}000\overset{14.776}{(F/A_{12\%,9})} = 443{,}280$$

The overall growth rate over ten years on the initial project "A" time zero and year one investments of \$55,000 and \$45,000 respectively can be found by combining the cost and revenue numbers on the project "A" and "B" time diagrams by adding them together. Combining project "A" with a 22.37% ROR and project "B" with a 12% ROR must give an ROR between 12% and 22.37% on the combination of the projects.

	C = 55,000	C = 45,000	—	—	
A+B)	0	1	2	10	F = 443,280

PW Equation: $0 = -55{,}000 - 45{,}000(P/F_{i,1}) + 443{,}280(P/F_{i,10})$

By trial and error:

$i = 15\% = -55{,}000 - 45{,}000(.8696) + 443{,}280(.2472) = +15{,}447$

$i = 20\% = -55{,}000 - 45{,}000(.8333) + 443{,}280(.1615) = -20{,}909$

therefore, $i = 15\% + 5\%[(15{,}447 - 0)/(15{,}447 + 20{,}909)] = 17.1\%$

The rate of return on the combined projects "A" and "B" is 17.1%. This 17.1% ROR is a compound interest rate of return, but it is a special compound interest ROR that represents rate of growth of investment dollars. Whenever a single revenue (such as \$443,288 at year 10) is generated by costs at an earlier point in time, the project ROR is Growth ROR.

A variation of Growth ROR is to bring any net costs or negative cash flows incurred in future periods back to time zero at the minimum ROR, instead of at the unknown project ROR, "i". This gives Growth ROR on the period zero equivalent present worth investment cost instead of Growth ROR on the costs from the points in time where they are actually incurred. This modified present worth cost Growth ROR calculation for Example 3-18 follows:

Modified PW Eq: $0 = -55{,}000 - 45{,}000\overset{0.8929}{(P/F_{i^*=12\%,1})} + 443{,}280(P/F_{i,10})$

or $0 = -95{,}180 + 443{,}280(P/F_{i,10})$

By trial and error, i = Growth ROR = 16.7%

This Growth ROR is slightly different (lower) in magnitude from the 17.1% result because it is based on different (bigger) initial investment value due to the modification in the handling of the year one cost. This result is equivalent to the non-modified 17.1% result and therefore is equally valid. Although both types of results are useful, in some analysis situations, it will be introduced later in Chapter 4 that in using Growth ROR to rank independent income-producing alternatives, it is necessary to use Growth ROR results based on the maximum capital exposure in a project. This is not always the present worth of all negative cash flows but is described in more detail beginning in Example 3-21 and Section 3.11 of this chapter.

Finally, this modification of Growth ROR is similar to the procedures employed in some spreadsheet models. The Excel function known as Modified Internal Rate of Return (MIRR) is always determined from a single investment at time zero growing to a single future value at the end of a project.

3.10 Net Present Value, Net Annual Value and Net Future Value Methods of Analysis

It will have occurred to many readers before now that to determine if a given project is satisfactory by using rate of return analysis, it is not necessary to go through the trial and error calculations required to obtain the project ROR. Depending on the type of equation you have written, comparison of present, annual or future revenues and costs calculated at the minimum rate of return, "i^*", tells you if there is more or less than enough revenue to cover costs at the minimum rate of return.

Net Present Value (NPV)

= Present Worth Revenues or Savings @ i^*

– Present Worth Costs @ i^*

or = Net Present Worth Positive and Negative Cash Flow @ i^*

or = Present Worth of All Cash Flows @ i^*

Net Annual Value (NAV)

= Equivalent Annual Revenues or Savings @ i^*

– Equivalent Annual Costs @ i^*

or = Net Equivalent Annual Positive and Negative Cash Flow @ i^*

Net Future Value (NFV)

$$= \text{Future Worth Revenues or Savings @ } i^* - \text{Future Worth Costs @ } i^*$$

$$\text{or} = \text{Net Future Worth Positive and Negative Cash Flow @ } i^*$$

A positive net value indicates a satisfactory investment relative to investing elsewhere at the minimum ROR, i^*. To illustrate the application of NPV, NAV and NFV to evaluate projects consider the following example.

EXAMPLE 3-19 Net Present, Annual and Future Value Analysis

The time zero initial investment of \$55,000 and a year one investment of \$45,000 in project "A" generate incomes of \$30,000 per year for years two through ten with zero salvage. For a 12.0% minimum discount rate, determine investment net value on a present, annual and future basis. Then analyze the effect on net value from including reinvestment of revenues at the 12.0% minimum discount rate in the net value analyses. Refer to revenue reinvestment at 12.0% as project "B."

Solution: All Values in Dollars

	C = 55,000	C = 45,000	I = 30,000 . . . I = 30,000
A)	0	1	2 10

$$NPV_A = -55{,}000 - 45{,}000\overset{0.8929}{(P/F_{12,1})} + 30{,}000\overset{5.328}{(P/A_{12,9})}\overset{0.8929}{(P/F_{12,1})} = +\$47{,}541 > 0, \text{ ok}$$

$$NAV_A = NPV_A\overset{0.17698}{(A/P_{12,10})} = 47{,}541\overset{0.17698}{(A/P_{12,10})} = +\$8{,}414 > 0, \text{ ok}$$

$$NFV_A = NPV_A\overset{3.106}{(F/P_{12,10})} = 47{,}541\overset{3.106}{(F/P_{12,10})} = +\$147{,}662 > 0, \text{ ok}$$

$$\text{or} = -55{,}000\overset{3.106}{(F/P_{12,10})} - 45{,}000\overset{2.773}{(F/P_{12,9})} + 30{,}000\overset{14.776}{(F/A_{12,9})} = +\$147{,}665$$

B) Net Value based on Reinvestment of Revenues at 12.0%

—	—	C = 30,000 ..... C=30,000	
0	1	2 10	F=443,280

$$\text{where } F = 30{,}000(\overset{14.776}{F/A_{12,9}}) = 443{,}280$$

$$NPV_B = 443{,}280(\overset{0.32197}{P/F_{12,10}}) - 30{,}000(\overset{5.3283}{P/A_{12,9}})(\overset{0.89286}{P/F_{12,1}}) = \$0$$

This indicates a break-even with investing elsewhere at $i^* = 12.0\%$

$$NAV_B = NPV_B(\overset{0.17698}{A/P_{12,10}}) = (0)(A/P_{12,10}) = \$0$$

This indicates a break-even with investing elsewhere at $i^* = 12.0\%$.

$$NFV_B = 443{,}280 - 30{,}000(\overset{14.776}{F/A_{12,9}}) = \$0$$

This indicates a break-even with investing elsewhere at $i^* = 12.0\%$.

A+B)

C = 55,000	C = 45,000	—	—	
0	1	2.....	10	F = 443,280

$$NPV_{A+B} = NPV_A + NPV_B = +47{,}541 + 0 = +\$47{,}541$$

$$\text{or } = 443{,}280(\overset{0.32197}{P/F_{12,10}}) - 45{,}000(\overset{0.89286}{P/F12,1}) - 55{,}000$$
$$= +\$47{,}544 > 0$$

The $3 difference in this NPV result and the initial project NPV is due to factor round-off error.

$$NAV_{A+B} = NAV_A + NAV_B = +8{,}414 + 0 = +\$8{,}414$$

$$\text{or } = NPV_{A+B}(\overset{0.17698}{A/P_{12,10}}) = +47{,}544(\overset{0.17698}{A/P_{12,10}}) = +\$8{,}414$$

$$NFV_{A+B} = NFV_A + NFV_B = +147{,}665 + 0 = +\$147{,}665$$

$$\text{or } = 443{,}280 - 45{,}000(F/P_{12,9}) - 55{,}000(F/P_{12,10})$$
$$= +\$147{,}665$$

Reinvestment of project revenues at the minimum discount rate is implicitly built into net value analysis of projects, but since it has no effect on the final net value results (because investments earning at the minimum discount rate have zero net value), there is no need to explicitly go through the revenue reinvestment calculations as you must do for Growth ROR analysis.

The absence of the need to make trial and error calculations, as is required for rate of return analysis, is a major advantage of net value analysis. The time value of money is accounted for properly and analogously by both rate of return and net value analysis. The meaning of the minimum ROR, "i^*", is identical for both rate of return and net value analysis as well as all other valid discounted cash flow methods of analysis. Net value analysis provides a quick, easy and therefore very useful way of screening mutually exclusive alternatives to determine which is best as discussed in detail in Chapter 4. Finally, remember that a project earning a rate of return equal to the minimum ROR, "i^*", has a zero net value, so projects with a positive net value are better than investing money elsewhere at "i^*".

An important consideration to be aware of when applying NAV or NFV to analyze unequal life income-producing alternatives is that a common evaluation life must be used for all alternatives. Normally the life of the longest life alternative is selected but any common life may be used. If unequal lives are used for different alternatives, the time value of money considerations are different in annual value and future value calculations and the wrong alternative may appear as being best. This means that NFV must be calculated at the same future point in time for all alternatives, or NAV must be calculated by spreading costs and revenues over the same number of years for all alternatives. Analysis related to comparison of unequal life income-producing alternatives is presented in Chapter 4.

EXAMPLE 3-20 NPV Applied to Project Valuation

Determine the maximum cost that an investor can incur to acquire land for an industrial development (or mineral rights for petroleum or mining development) and realize a 12.0% rate of return on invested dollars. If the land is acquired, development is expected to occur two years later for a cost of $1,700,000. Development is projected to generate net revenues after operating costs (before-tax positive cash flow) of $200,000 at year three, $225,000 at year four, $250,000 at year five, with a $2,000,000 sale value also expected to be realized at year five.

Solution, All Values in Thousands of Dollars:

Acq Cost = ?	—	C = 1,700	I = 200	I = 225	I = 2,250
0	1	2	3	4	5

On a before-tax analysis basis, positive NPV represents additional cost that can be incurred at the point in time where NPV has been calculated and give the investor the minimum rate of return on investment capital. It will be illustrated later in the text that on an after-tax basis, NPV represents additional after-tax cost (which is negative cash flow) that can be incurred and give the investor the after-tax minimum rate of return on invested capital. Generally, the tax savings from the tax deductions related to additional costs causes the break-even acquisition cost to be bigger than after-tax NPV.

NPV at the 12.0% minimum rate of return equals:

$$-1{,}700(\overset{0.7972}{P/F_{12\%,2}}) + 200(\overset{0.7118}{P/F_{12\%,3}}) + 225(\overset{0.6355}{P/F_{12\%,4}}) + 2{,}250(\overset{0.5674}{P/F_{12\%,5}})$$
$$= +\$206.758$$

$206,758 is the break-even time zero acquisition cost that could be incurred and still have the project generate a 12.0% rate of return, that is, to have NPV @ 12.0% equal to zero as follows:

$$-206.7 - 1{,}700(\overset{0.7972}{P/F_{12\%,2}}) + 200(\overset{0.7118}{P/F_{12\%,3}}) + 225(\overset{0.6355}{P/F_{12\%,4}})$$
$$+2{,}250(\overset{0.5674}{P/F_{12\%,5}}) = \$0$$

Net Present Value (NPV) may also be expressed in graphical form by plotting the sum of the project's discounted cash flow for each compounding period, (usually years). In this diagram, the vertical Y axis represents the project cumulative NPV over time, the horizontal X axis representing project life. The final data point in this diagram is the overall project NPV. Generally referred to as *Cumulative NPV*, this graphical illustration can be used to illustrate not only NPV, but other evaluation criteria including discounted payback and maximum capital exposure which is useful in ratios.

Discounted payback or *payout is defined as the point in time where the cumulative discounted cash flows for the project equal zero, or the point on the cumulative NPV diagram where NPV equals zero.* The shorter the payback, the less capital exposure to the investor in terms of the time that is required to recover his or her investment. However, discounted payback is not always an accurate tool for assessing the economic profitability of investments, as is discussed in Chapter 9.

The final consideration relevant to the cumulative NPV diagram involves the development of *ratios*. Much confusion exists in practice in determination of the appropriate denominator to use in ratios. This subject is addressed in detail in the next section but is easily illustrated using the lowest point on the cumulative NPV diagram. This lowest point is sometimes defined as project m*aximum capital exposure* or *maximum capital at risk.* Using the Cumulative NPV diagram makes it easier to determine the cash flows that need to be included in the denominator in order to develop ratios that will yield economically consistent results.

The following example uses the Cumulative NPV diagram to make a comparison of ROR and NPV. Note that both criteria are developed from the same present worth equation but offer different approaches to assessing the profitability of an investment.

EXAMPLE 3-21 ROR, NPV and Their Graphical Meaning

A five-year project requires investments of $120,000 at time zero and $70,000 at the end of year one to generate revenues of $100,000 at the end of each of years two through five. The investor's minimum rate of return is 15.0%. Calculate the project ROR and develop the Cumulative Cash Position Diagram to illustrate the meaning of the ROR result. Also, calculate the NPV and develop a Cumulative NPV diagram to show the net present value of the project over time. Using the Cumulative NPV diagram indicate the project discounted payback and maximum capital exposure. Finally, draw an NPV Profile to show how the value of the project is impacted by the selected discount rate.

Solution:

–\$120,000	–\$70,000	\$100,000	\$100,000	\$100,000	\$100,000
0	1	2	3	4	5

Rate of Return (ROR)

PW Eq: $0 = -120{,}000 - 70{,}000(P/F_{i,1}) + 100{,}000(P/A_{i,4})(P/F_{i,1})$

@ 25% = 12,928
@ 30% = –7,212 $i = 25\% + 5\%(12{,}928/20{,}140) = 28.2\%$

By calculator or spreadsheet, i = 28.1%. The rate of return exceeds the minimum of 15.0% and suggests that the project is economically satisfactory. The "Cumulative Cash Position Diagram" illustrates the meaning of the project rate of return. The slope associated with each compounding period is a function of the project rate of return at 28.1%.

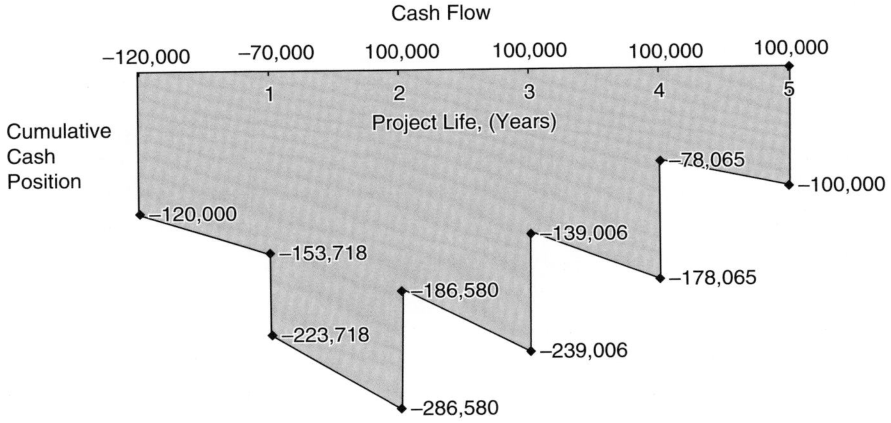

Figure 3-10 Cumulative Cash Position Diagram; ROR, i = 28.1%

Net Present Value (NPV) @ i* = 15%

$$-120{,}000 - 70{,}000\overset{0.8696}{(P/F_{15\%,1})} + 100{,}000\overset{2.8550}{(P/A_{15\%,4})}\overset{0.8696}{(P/F_{15\%,1})}$$

$= \$67{,}389$

To generate the necessary data points for the Cumulative NPV Diagram, an alternative approach is presented that yields the same NPV.

NPV After Time 0	$0 - 120{,}000(P/F_{15\%,0})$	$= -120{,}000$
NPV After Year 1	$-120{,}000 - 70{,}000(P/F_{15\%,1})$	$= -180{,}870$
NPV After Year 2	$-180{,}870 + 100{,}000(P/F_{15\%,2})$	$= -105{,}255$
NPV After Year 3	$-105{,}255 + 100{,}000(P/F_{15\%,3})$	$= -39{,}504$
NPV After Year 4	$-39{,}504 + 100{,}000(P/F_{15\%,4})$	$= 17{,}672$
NPV After Year 5	$17{,}672 + 100{,}000(P/F_{15\%,5})$	$= 67{,}389$

This calculation demonstrates the impact on NPV of one additional year of project cash flow. Note that $67,389 is the time zero project NPV at 15.0% which is greater than $0, indicating acceptable economics compared to investing elsewhere. The yearly measure of NPV represents the data points for the Cumulative NPV diagram as shown.

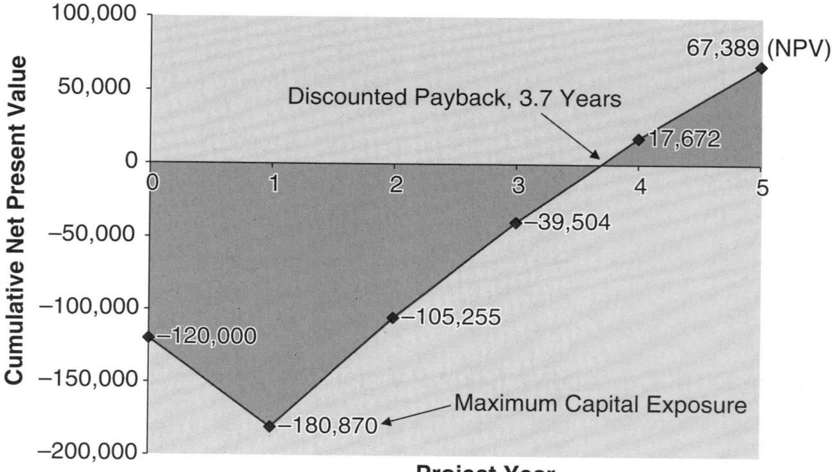

Figure 3-11 Cumulative NPV diagram

Using the Cumulative NPV Diagram, *Discounted Payback* occurs when the cumulative discounted cash flows sum to zero. Visually, this can be seen as occurring during year four. Specifically, the point may be identified as follows:

$$3 \text{ Years of Cash Flow} + (39{,}504/100{,}000\overset{0.5718}{(P/F_{15\%,4})}) = 3.7 \text{ Years}$$

If the cash flows were considered discrete end-of-period values, the period would be rounded up and described as a 4.0-year payback. *Discounted Payback is a measure of financial risk commonly computed with other economic measures such as rate of return and net present value. In this case, it measures the time required for the discounted cash flows to sum to zero.* See Section 9.2 in Chapter 9 for more details on payback and the different ways it might be determined. *Unfortunately payback is an inconsistent measure of "economic profitability" because it tells us nothing about a project's benefits or costs (cash flow) once the payback is achieved.*

Maximum Capital Exposure is the present worth measure of capital an investor has "exposed" in the project. It is the capital an investor would need to have in the bank today, available to invest directly in the project, or in other opportunities at i* to be able to cover immediate and downstream negative cash flows in a project not offset by positive cash flow in earlier years. Maximum capital exposure is always the lowest point, or most negative value on the Cumulative NPV Diagram. This is always the appropriate monetary measure when considering the denominator for any ratio, discussed in the next section.

Finally, by calculating NPV for a range of discount rates the relationship between NPV and ROR may be graphically illustrated as follows. Substituting values of i from 0% to 40% into the present worth equation, the NPV is computed in 5% increments and graphed as shown. Neglecting time value of money (i*=0%), the value of this project is $210,000, but as investors associate more time value with their money, the project value is diminished. Note that this relationship is not linear as is assumed when interpolating for the rate of return. The compound interest rate, i, that makes the project NPV equal zero is the project rate of return. Developing an NPV Profile is a common graphical sensitivity to address uncertainty concerning the true magnitude of the opportunity cost of capital and the impact it may have in an investor's economic decisions.

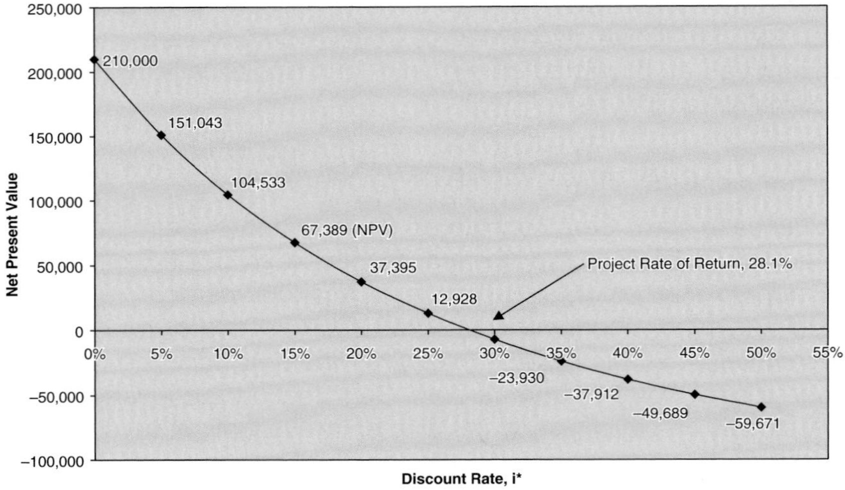

Figure 3-12 NPV Profile

3.11 Benefit Cost Ratio and Present Value Ratio

Instead of examining the difference in present worth positive and negative cash flow to analyze projects with criteria such as net present value or rate of return, certain investors prefer to measure the value of an investment per dollar invested. Two ratios are defined in this section; properly calculated the economic results from these ratios will remain consistent with NPV, ROR, or other economic measures. Further, when properly calculated using Maximum Capital Exposure in the denominator, the two ratios will always differ by unity as developed in the following definitions, discussion, and examples.

Benefit Cost Ratio (B/C Ratio) is defined as the present worth of net positive cash flows discounted at i* divided by the present worth of net negative cash flows not offset by positive cash flows in earlier years, also discounted at i*. To simplify things, the denominator might be restated to reflect "the absolute value of the project Maximum Capital Exposure (MCE)." As defined in the discussion of Example 3-21, MCE is the lowest point occurring in the Cumulative NPV Diagram when developed at the minimum rate of return, i*. In this textbook, *the use of the term Maximum Capital Exposure will always refer to the absolute value of the present worth at i* of negative cash flows, not offset, or paid for economically by positive cash flow* *incurred in earlier years of the project life. MCE is the absolute value of the lowest point in any cumulative NPV diagram.* The present worth of net positive cash flow represents the summation of those cash flows not utilized to pay for negative cash flows that may occur in future years.

$$\textit{Benefit Cost Ratio} = \frac{\textit{PV of Net Positive Cash Flow @ } i^*}{\textit{Maximum Capital Exposure}}$$

Many companies refer to Benefit Cost Ratio as Profitability Index (PI) or Discounted Profitability Index (DPI), but these terms may also describe the second ratio known as Present Value Ratio, which will be introduced shortly. To identify the ratio that your company might be utilizing, consider the economic meaning of the ratio result. Benefit Cost Ratio is a measure of present value created (in terms of net positive cash flow) per present value of the dollars invested (in terms of net negative cash flow). If the present value of net positive cash flow, or economic benefit, is equal to the present worth of net negative cash flow, or cost, this ratio will equal one, therefore when:

B/C Ratio > 1.0, projects are economically satisfactory
B/C Ratio = 1.0, the project is an economic breakeven with other opportunities
B/C Ratio < 1.0, projects are economically not satisfactory

Per the earlier discussion on the development of discount rates, many companies discount future cash flows using financial cost of capital for NPV and ratio calculations. These companies then attempt to account for opportunity cost of capital by imposing economic hurdles that increase the minimum acceptable ratio measure from 1.0 to 1.2, 1.4 or higher depending on economic and or financial budgetary conditions at a given point in time. Such economic hurdles are easily imposed and changed from time to time, but can be arbitrary and may not optimize value for a firm if capital budget dollars are rationed over time.

The denominator is the key to developing ratios that will serve to consistently maximize cumulative profitability from available investment dollars. It is "financially" valid for management to measure value created based on the present worth of the capital budget dollars allocated to a project. In many in-house printouts this measure is known as the "PW Investment," or "Discounted Investment." While it may be appropriate to measure benefits to financial capital budget outlays for financial purposes, such calculations may prove inconsistent in assessing economic value and maximizing cumulative wealth from the available capital budget. For a given compounding period, "negative cash flow" suggests that dollars are leaving the bank account faster than they are coming into the same account. Economically there is no distinction to be made between before-tax checks written from a capital budget and before-tax checks written from an operating budget as both represent an outflow of funds. However, financially and perhaps for internal accounting purposes such numbers may be important and therefore, the corresponding ratios may be appropriate for financial reasons. Once again, a focus on cash flow is the key to a proper economic evaluation with all economic evaluation criteria and the optimization of value from rationed capital budget dollars.

A variation of B/C Ratio is known as Present Value Ratio or PVR, which is defined as:

$$\textit{Present Value Ratio} = \frac{\textit{Net Present Value @ } i^*}{\textit{Maximum Capital Exposure}}$$

Since any amount of positive NPV indicates a satisfactory investment:

PVR > 0 indicates a satisfactory investment
PVR = 0 indicates a breakeven investment relative to other opportunities
PVR < 0 indicates an unsatisfactory investment

Some companies refer to PVR as Investment Efficiency, which accurately reflects the meaning of this ratio result; dollars of NPV generated per out-of-pocket present worth investment dollar expressed in terms of maximum capital exposure. Other companies refer to this ratio as Profitability Index or PI, which may be a B/C Ratio to other companies. Again, PVR is a measure of the NPV generated per present worth net negative cash flow allocated to the project.

It is worth noting that the denominator for both ratios is identical. This leads us to recognition that when properly calculated these two ratios should always differ by unity or 1.0. This mathematical relationship is developed below where PW represents present worth, CF represents Cash Flow, MCE represents the absolute value of the project Maximum Capital Exposure and the term "net negative or positive cash flow" is the result of combining present worth negative cash flow with positive cash flow in earlier years. To identify the mathematical relationship between these two ratios more clearly, PVR is defined as follows:

$$PVR = \frac{NPV\ @\ i^*}{MCE\ @\ i^*}$$

Substituting a previous definition of NPV, PVR is defined as:

$$PVR = \frac{PW\ of\ Net\ Positive\ CF\ @\ i^* - |PW\ of\ Net\ Negative\ CF\ @\ i^*|}{MCE\ @\ i^*}$$

Where |PW of Net Negative CF @ i*| is the absolute value of the negative cash flows that are not offset by positive cash flows in earlier years, or MCE. Applying the denominator to the two terms in the numerator gives:

$$PVR = \frac{PW\ of\ Net\ Positive\ CF\ @\ i^*}{MCE\ @\ i^*} - \frac{|PW\ of\ Net\ Negative\ CF\ @\ i^*|}{MCE\ @\ i^*}$$

Since the |PW of Net Negative CF @ i*| equals MCE @ i*, the definition may also be defined as follows:

$$PVR = \frac{PW\ of\ Net\ Positive\ CF\ @\ i^*}{MCE\ @\ i^*} - 1$$

Since the first term in this equation represents Benefit Cost Ratio, this suggests that:

PVR = B/C Ratio - 1 or, PVR + 1 = B/C Ratio

Since most investors calculate NPV for projects, PVR is obtained by dividing NPV by the project Maximum Capital Exposure. Benefit Cost ratio is then derived by simply adding 1.0 to any PVR result. Visually, PVR parameters are identified on the Cumulative NPV diagram. The numerator is always the last plotted value divided by the absolute value of the diagrams lowest point.

As a final comment, the economic utility of ratios is a subject of Chapter 4; however, the principal application of ratios is in assisting investors with the ranking of alternatives when the capital budget is limited and insufficient to fund all projects with otherwise acceptable economics. This financial aspect of allocating capital budget dollars often is the basis for defining a ratio denominator based on the present worth of capital budget dollars. The objective of economic analysis is to select the investments, for a given budget, that will maximize cumulative wealth to the investor. To consistently achieve this objective using ratios, cash flows must be discounted with opportunity cost of capital rather than financial cost of capital, and ratio denominators must be based on maximum capital exposure.

EXAMPLE 3-22 Calculation of Correct PVR and B/C Ratios

To illustrate proper denominator calculations for both PVR and B/C Ratio, consider the following four scenarios. Calculate the proper denominator, PVR and B/C Ratio for each case for a minimum rate of return of 15.0%.

Case 1

C = 100	Rev = 50	Rev = 50	Rev = 50	Rev = 50
0	1	2	3	10

Correct Ratio Denominator = 100

$$\text{B/C Ratio} = 50(\overset{5.019}{P/A_{15\%,10}})/100 = 2.5045 > 1, \text{ so satisfactory}$$

$$\text{PVR} = [50(\overset{5.019}{P/A_{15\%,10}}) - 100]/100 = 1.5045 > 0, \text{ so satisfactory}$$

Note, PVR + 1 = B/C Ratio for all the cases.

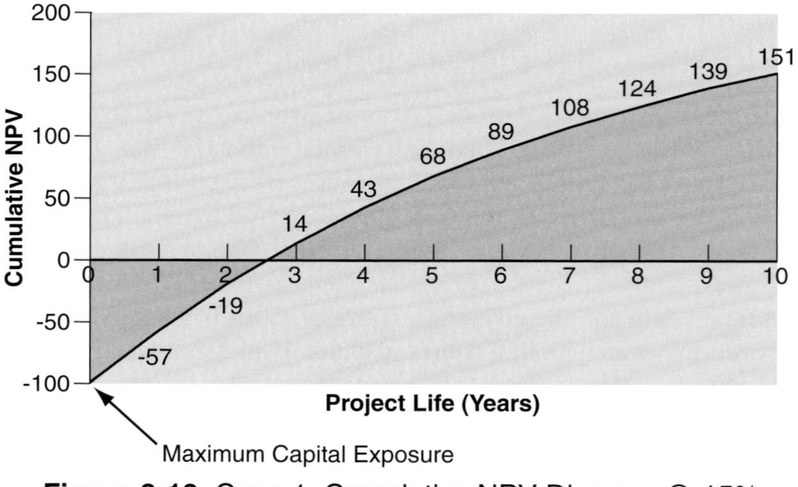

Figure 3-13 Case 1, Cumulative NPV Diagram @ 15%

Figure 3-13 shows that the maximum capital exposure is realized at time zero with the initial investment in this project.

		C = 90			
Case 2	C = 100	Rev = 50	Rev = 50	Rev = 50	Rev = 50
	0	1	2	3	10

Correct Ratio Denominator = $100 + (90\text{-}50)(P/F_{15\%,1})$

$$\text{B/C Ratio} = 50\overset{4.772}{(P/A_{15\%,9})}\overset{.8696}{(P/F_{15\%,1})}/[100 + 40\overset{.8696}{(P/F_{15\%,1})}]$$

$$= 1.5394 > 1, \text{ so satisfactory}$$

$$\text{PVR} = [50\overset{4.772}{(P/A_{15\%,9})}\overset{.8696}{(P/F_{15\%,1})} - 40\overset{.8696}{(P/F_{15\%,1})}$$

$$- 100]/[100 + 40\overset{.8696}{(P/F_{15\%,1})}]$$

$$= 0.5394 > 0, \text{ so satisfactory}$$

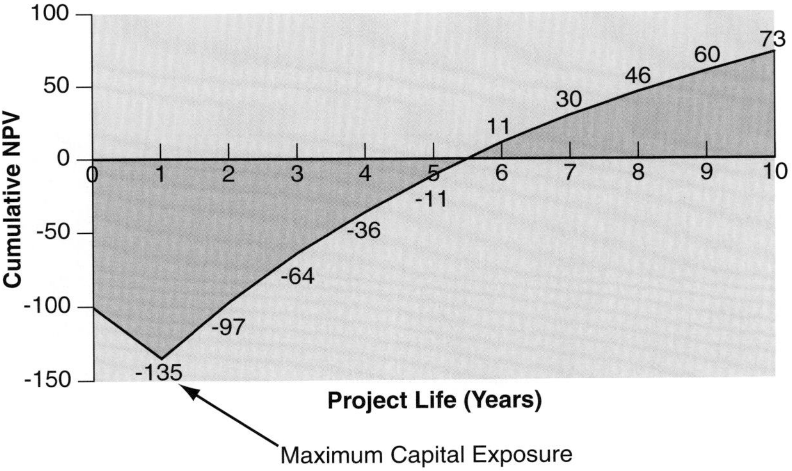

Figure 3-14 Case 2, Cumulative NPV Diagram @ 15%

Note that the denominator is: $\left|-100 - 40\overset{0.8696}{(P/F_{15\%,1})}\right| = 135$

It doesn't make any difference whether the year one net negative cash flow (–40) is derived from a cost (–90) and income (50), or if it's just an investment of (–40). The same cumulative NPV position of –135 is realized either way.

			C = 190		
Case 3	C = 100	Rev = 50	Rev = 50	Rev = 50	Rev = 50
	0	1	2	3	10

Correct Ratio Denominator = $100 + [(190\text{-}50)(P/F_{15\%,1}) - 50](P/F_{15\%,1})$

B/C Ratio:

$$\overset{4.487}{} \quad \overset{.7561}{} \quad \overset{.8696}{} \quad \overset{.8696}{}$$
$$= 50(P/A_{15\%,8})(P/F_{15\%,2})/\{100 + [140(P/F_{15\%,1}) - 50](P/F_{15\%,1})\}$$

= 1.044 > 1, so marginally satisfactory

PVR:

$$\overset{5.019}{} \quad \overset{.7561}{} \quad \overset{.8696}{} \quad \overset{.8696}{}$$
$$= [50(P/A_{15,10}) - 190(P/F_{15,2}) - 100]/\{100 + [140(P/F_{15,1}) - 50](P/F_{15,1})\}$$

= 0.044 > 0, so marginally satisfactory

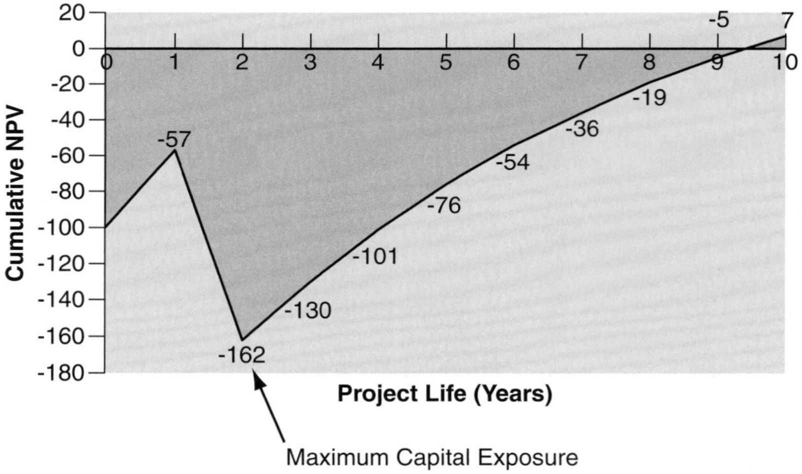

Figure 3-15 Case 3, Cumulative NPV Diagram at 15%

Note that the denominator is:

$$\overset{0.8696}{} \qquad \overset{0.8696}{}$$
$$\left| -100 + [-140(P/F_{15\%,1}) + 50](P/F_{15\%,1}) \right| = 162$$

			C = 90		
Case 4	C = 100	Rev = 50	Rev = 50	Rev = 50	Rev = 50
	0	1	2	3	10

Correct Ratio Denominator = 100

$$\text{B/C Ratio} = \frac{50\overset{4.487}{(P/A_{15,8})}\overset{.7561}{(P/F_{15,2})} - 40\overset{.7561}{(P/F_{15,2})} + 50\overset{.8696}{(P/F_{15,1})}}{100}$$

$= 1.829 > 1$, so satisfactory

$$\text{PVR} = \frac{50\overset{4.487}{(P/A_{15,8})}\overset{.7561}{(P/F_{15,2})} - 40\overset{.7561}{(P/F_{15,2})} + 50\overset{.8696}{(P/F_{15,1})} - 100}{100}$$

$= 0.829 > 0$, so satisfactory

Since the year 2 cost of $90 is entirely offset by the year 1 and 2 revenues of $50 per year, only the initial year 0 cost of $100 is included in the PVR or B/C Ratio denominator. The initial $100 cost is the only cost "not covered by project revenue in the year the cost is incurred or earlier years."

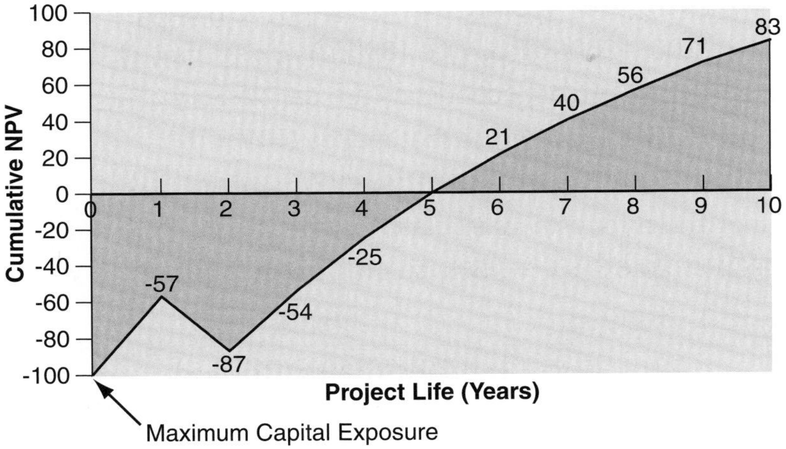

Figure 3-16 Case 4, Cumulative NPV Diagram at 15%

Note that the year two net cost of $40 is offset by positive cash flow in year one and does not cause more capital to be at risk to the investor.

EXAMPLE 3-23 Cash Flow, Rate of Return, NPV and Ratios

An investment project will involve spending $200,000 at time zero and $350,000 at the end of year one. These investments will generate gross revenues of $333,000 at the end of year one and $556,000 at the end of each of years two through eight. A royalty cost of $33,000 in year one and $56,000 in years two through eight will be incurred along with operating costs of $200,000 in year one and $320,000 at the end of each of years two through eight. Calculate the project before-tax cash flow and then, for a minimum rate of return of 15.0%, calculate the rate of return, net present value, present value ratio and benefit cost ratio to determine if the project is economically satisfactory.

Solution: All Dollar Values in Thousands

Year	0	1	2–8
Gross Revenue		333	556
– Royalty Costs		– 33	– 56
– Operating Costs		–200	–320
– Capital Costs	–200	–350	
Before-Tax Cash Flow	–200	–250	180

$$NPV = -200 - 250\overset{0.8696}{(P/F_{15,1})} + 180\overset{4.160}{(P/A_{15,7})}\overset{0.8696}{(P/F_{15,1})} = +\$233.8$$

$233.8 > 0, so project economics are satisfactory.

Project ROR is the "i" value that makes NPV = 0

$$0 = -200 - 250(P/F_{i,1}) + 180(P/A_{i,7})(P/F_{i,1})$$

By trial and error with interpolation:

$i = ROR = 29.6\% > i^* = 15\%$, so the project is satisfactory

$$PVR = \frac{NPV\ @\ i^*}{|PW\ -CF\ @\ i^*|} = \frac{233.8}{200 + 250(P/F_{15\%,1})} = 0.56$$

0.56 > 0, so satisfactory

$$B/C\ Ratio = \frac{PW\ +CF\ @\ i^*}{|PW\ -CF\ @\ i^*|} = \frac{180(P/A_{15\%,7})(P/F_{15\%,1})}{200 + 250(P/F_{15\%,1})} = 1.56$$

1.56 > 1.0, so satisfactory

Note that PVR + 1 = B/C Ratio. Also note that all four evaluation criteria give the same economic conclusion of very satisfactory economics compared with investing elsewhere at a 15% rate of return.

PVR results always give correct economic conclusions if proper "net cost not offset by project revenue" is used in the denominator of each ratio instead of the present worth of costs without any consideration of revenue or savings available to offset part or all of costs. This applies to reclamation or abandonment costs at the end of projects as well as to intermediate project period costs. The following variation of Example 3-23 illustrates the correct handling of downstream costs in ratio denominator calculations.

EXAMPLE 3-23a Downstream Cost Variation of Example 3-23

Suppose the operating cost in year eight of Example 3-23 could be delayed one year till the end year nine without effecting the revenue generated in year eight. For the revised cash flow diagram shown below, calculate the project, net present value, present value ratio, and benefit cost ratio. The minimum rate of return is still 15.0%.

Solution: All Dollar Values in Thousands

Year	0	1	2–7	8	9
Before-Tax Cash Flow	–200	–250	180	500	–320

The cumulative cash flow is the same as for Example 3-23 except the final $320 negative net cash flow is delayed one year to year nine.

$$NPV = -200 - 250\overset{0.8696}{(P/F_{15,1})} + 180\overset{3.784}{(P/A_{15,6})}\overset{0.8696}{(P/F_{15,1})} + 500\overset{0.3269}{(P/F_{15,8})}$$

$$- 320\overset{0.2843}{(P/F_{15,9})} = +247.4$$

This NPV result is larger than the Example 3-23 result of $233.8 as expected intuitively, since delaying the year 8 cost one year, with other values held the same, must give improved economics.

In the denominator of PVR and B/C Ratio, we only use the absolute value of the present worth of negative cash flow not offset by positive cash flow in earlier years. Since the year nine negative cash flow obviously is offset by year eight revenue, only the year zero and year one negative cash flow are relevant for the PVR and B/C Ratio denominators.

$$\text{Correct PVR} = \frac{247.4}{[200 + 250(P/F_{15,1})]} = +0.59$$

This PVR result is greater than the 0.56 PVR for Example 3-23 as we know it should be. The B/C Ratio result is also bigger as follows:

Correct B/C Ratio equals PVR + 1 = 1.59 or:

$$= \frac{180(P/A_{15,6})(P/F_{15,1}) + [500 - 320(P/F_{15,1})](P/F_{15,8})}{[200 + 250(P/F_{15,1})]} = +1.59$$

Note that the numerator of B/C Ratio contains the present worth of revenues not offset by costs in the year revenues are incurred or later years and the denominator is the same as for PVR. *The mistake often made in ratio calculations done in industry practice is to include in ratio denominators the present value of downstream negative cash flows that are offset by positive cash flow in earlier years.* For this example that means including the present value of the year nine negative cash flow in the ratio denominator. This gives the following PVR:

$$\text{Incorrect PVR} = \frac{247.4}{[200 + 250(P/F_{15,1}) + 320(P/F_{15,9}]} = +0.49$$

This is a lower PVR than the 0.56 result for Example 3-23. This indicates that delaying the year eight cost gives less desirable economics than incurring the cost at year eight. You can intuitively see that something is wrong with this PVR calculation, since delaying the cost must and does give better economics as verified by the NPV analysis.

$$\text{Incorrect B/C Ratio} = \frac{180(P/A_{15,6})(P/F_{15,1}) + 500(P/F_{15,8})}{200 + 250(P/F_{15,1}) + 320(P/F_{15,9})} = +1.49$$

This B/C Ratio result is less than the 1.56 result for Example 3-23. The same comments mentioned for incorrect PVR are applicable.

3.12 Effect of Income-Producing Project Life on Project Economics

Because of the time value of money, costs and revenues that occur more than ten years from now are not nearly as important to project economics as the costs and revenues that will occur within the first ten years of project life. However, it is important to recognize that the investment evaluation situation significantly affects the sensitivity that project life has on evaluation results such as rate of return. In general, the rate of return for a project with relatively good profitability will be helped much less by lengthening project life beyond 10 years compared to a project with marginal profitability. The effects of investment profitability and project life on project rate of return are illustrated in the following example.

EXAMPLE 3-24 Sensitivity of Project ROR and NPV to Changes in Investment Size and Project Life

Consider rate of return and NPV analysis of a project that may have an initial cost of either \$20 million or \$36 million depending on final engineering considerations. The project is expected to generate profits of \$6 million per year for either 5, 10 or 20 years with zero salvage value. Use a 10% minimum discount rate.

Solution, All Values Are in Millions of Dollars:

5 Year Evaluation Life

C = 20	I = 6	I = 6
0	1	5

PW Eq: $0 = -20 + 6(P/A_{i,5})$ so, i = ROR = 15.2%

$$NPV = -20 + 6\underset{3.791}{(P/A_{10\%,5})} = +\$2.75$$

C = 36	I = 6	I = 6
0	1	5

PW Eq: $0 = -36 + 6(P/A_{i,5})$ so, i = ROR = –5.8%

$$NPV = -36 + 6\underset{3.791}{(P/A_{10\%,5})} = -\$13.25$$

10 Year Evaluation Life

C = \$20	I = \$6	I = \$6
0	1.	10

PW Eq: $0 = -20 + 6(P/A_{i,10})$ so, i = ROR = 27.3%

$$NPV = -20 + 6\overset{6.144}{(P/A_{10\%,10})} = +\$16.86$$

C = 36	I = 6	I = 6
0	1.	10

PW Eq: $0 = -36 + 6(P/A_{i,10})$ so, i = ROR = 10.6%

$$NPV = -36 + 6\overset{6.144}{(P/A_{10\%,10})} = +\$0.84$$

The effect on ROR and NPV results from doubling the evaluation life from 5 to 10 years has been very significant for both cases. When the evaluation life is less than 10 years, changing the life used has a very significant effect on evaluation results for both economically good and marginal projects. Now double the evaluation life from 10 to 20 years:

20 Year Evaluation Life

C = 20	I = 6	I=6
0	1	20

PW Eq: $0 = -20 + 6(P/A_{i,20})$, so, i = ROR = 29.5%

$$NPV = -20 + 6\overset{8.514}{(P/A_{10\%,20})} = +\$31.08$$

C = 36	I = 6	I = 6
0	1	20

PW Eq: $0 = -36 + 6(P/A_{i,20})$, so, i = ROR = 15.9%

$$NPV = -36 + 6\overset{8.514}{(P/A_{10\%,20})} = +\$15.08$$

Percentage change in ROR and NPV for 10 year to 20 year life change:

<u>$20 Million Cost Project</u>

$$\text{ROR Percent Change} = \frac{(29.5 - 27.3) \times 100}{27.3} = +8\%$$

$$\text{NPV Percent Change} = \frac{(31.08 - 16.86) \times 100}{16.86} = +84\%$$

<u>$36 Million Cost Project</u>

$$\text{ROR Percent Change} = \frac{(15.9 - 10.6) \times 100}{10.6} = +50\%$$

$$\text{NPV Percent Change} = \frac{(15.08 - 0.86) \times 100}{0.86} = +1{,}653\%$$

The purpose of showing these percent change calculation results is to emphasize how much more sensitive positive NPV (and PVR) results are to increases in evaluation life beyond ten years in comparison to ROR results. This greater sensitivity of NPV is due to the fact that the 10% discount rate used in the NPV calculations is much smaller than ROR rates of 29.5% and 27.3% in the $20 million cost analysis or 15.9% and 10.6% in the $36 million cost analysis. The present worth of future values beyond year 10 is relatively insignificant for the larger ROR discount rates, but the present worth of future values beyond year 10 is much more significant for the 10% discount rate used in the NPV calculations.

3.13 Mining and Petroleum Project Analysis

Mining and petroleum projects are evaluated in the same manner using the same evaluation techniques applicable for evaluating non-mining/ petroleum projects. Only income tax considerations differentiate the analysis of mining, petroleum, real estate, chemical plant or other non-mining/ petroleum type of projects. On a before-tax analysis basis, in all industries, all types of costs are outflows of money and revenues for all sources are inflows of money. In laying out a time diagram with costs, revenues and salvage value at different times, except for tax considerations, economic analysis of a project is not affected by the industry source of the costs and revenues. Analyses should be done after-tax in all situations where income tax considerations are relevant, but the details of proper after-tax analysis of mining, petroleum, and general investment projects are presented in Chapters 7 through 11.

Although evaluation considerations are the same for analyzing projects in all industries on a before-tax basis, there are significant differences in common terminology used to refer to costs, revenues and ownership interests in different industries. The petroleum industry especially tends to use unique terminology. Mineral and petroleum rights acquisition costs are analogous to land and patent acquisition costs in general industry analyses. Research costs in all industries are equivalent to exploration costs incurred in searching for petroleum and minerals. Project development costs in all non-mining/ petroleum industries are equivalent to development costs in petroleum and mining projects.

An obvious difference between most mining and petroleum projects is the capital intensive nature of the mining industry. Startup costs and timing effects are often much greater in mining compared to onshore petroleum production projects, but the time and investment in core drilling, metallurgical testing and mine design often reduce extraction and processing risks relative to oil and gas investments. Offshore petroleum project development is more analogous to mining in terms of capital intensiveness and delayed production timing. Mining revenues often are slow coming up to rated capacity of a mine as the bugs are worked out of the mining, milling, and transportation systems. This is different from oil and gas where production often is greatest up front.

Mining can be segmented into several different categories including hard rock, coal, and aggregates. For each of these categories, mine designs can be based on open pit, underground, or a combination of both depending on the ore body, site location, environmental, and other intangible issues. Hard rock mining includes gold, silver, lead, zinc, copper, molybdenum, bauxite and a variety of other precious, strategic and non-strategic minerals. Due to the vertical nature of these industries, mine economics may go substantially beyond the mine itself to include milling and smelting considerations as well as transportation issues that impact the ability of a mine to turn a profit. In addition to those parameters that affect all project economics such as product price, other key parameters in hard rock economic evaluations include ore grades, metallurgical recovery rates, etc. In most hard rock mining evaluations, the product is purchased and sold on a variety of markets but two of the primary markets include the New York Mercantile Exchange (NYMEX) and the London Metals Exchange (LME).

Coal mining is vastly different in that in some situations, the product extracted from the pit may be ready for sale. However, coal often requires treatment to improve the quality of the product by reducing water content, removing non-coal materials, etc. Coal may be sold directly to a consumer such as a utility, by terms of a long-term contract, spot pricing or by futures contract. This provides opportunities for management to hedge or speculate on future pricing of coal but the commodity future based on Appalachian Coal may not reflect the same qualities of a Powder River Basin or other coal.

There are many other investment analysis terms unique to mineral project evaluations but the terms described give the reader sufficient background to understand many mineral project evaluation statements and solutions, as presented in this text.

EXAMPLE 3-25 A Mining Project Analysis

An investor has requested that you evaluate the economic potential of purchasing a gold property now (at time zero) for a $5,000,000 mineral rights acquisition cost. Mine development will be contracted with costs estimated to be $15,000,000 at time zero with an additional $5,000,000 charged at year 1 for pre-production stripping. Mining equipment costs will total $25,000,000 and should also be charged at time zero. $2,500,000 will also be spent at time zero for working capital which is spare parts, the difference in accounts payables and receivables, and product inventory. Production is projected to start in year one with the mining of 350,000 tons of ore. Production in years 2, 3 and 4 is projected to be uniform at 450,000 tons per year. It is assumed that reserves will be depleted by the end of year 4. Average grade is 0.1 ounces of gold per ton of ore with metallurgical recovery estimated to be 93%. The price of gold is estimated to be $850.00 per ounce in year 1 with that amount escalating 15% in year 2 and held constant thereafter for evaluation purposes. Royalties are estimated at 10% of gross revenue. Operating costs include all state and local severance and property taxes and are estimated to be $270 per ounce produced and sold in year 1 with this amount escalating by 8.0% per year over the mine life. Reclamation costs are estimated at $15,000,000 and are expected to be incurred at the end of year 4. Salvage or residual value of mining equipment and inventory or spare parts (working capital) is placed at $12,000,000 and would also be realized at the end of year 4. Calculate the project operating profit and before-tax cash flow (BTCF). For a before-tax minimum rate of return of 15% per year, determine the project rate of return, net present value and present value ratio.

Solution:
Before-Tax Cash Flow, Tons and Recovered Ounces in Thousands.

Year	0	1	2	3	4
Production, Tons of Ore		350	450	450	450
Grade Ounces/Ton		0.1	0.1	0.1	0.1
Metallurgical Recovery		0.93	0.93	0.93	0.93
Recovered Ounces of Au		32.55	41.85	41.85	41.85
Au Price, $/Ounce		$850.00	$977.50	$977.50	$977.50
Operating Cost, $/Ounce		$270.00	$291.60	$314.93	$340.12
Gross Revenue*		27,668	40,908	40,908	40,908
Royalty (10%)**		- 2,767	- 4,091	- 4,091	- 4,091
Net Revenue***		24,901	36,817	36,817	36,817
Salvage Value					12,000
Operating Expenses****		- 8,789	- 12,203	- 13,180	- 14,234
Reclamation					- 15,000
Operating Profit (EBITDA)		16,112	24,614	23,637	19,583
Mine Acquisition	- 5,000				
Mine Development	-15,000	- 5,000			
Inventories & Spare Parts	-2,500				
Mine Equipment	-25,000				
BTCF	-47,500	11,112	24,614	23,637	19,583

Recovered Ounces = Tons x Grade x Metallurgical Recovery
*Gross Revenue = Recovered Ounces x Au Price, $ Per Ounce
**Royalty based on Percentage of Gross Revenue
***Salvage of Equipment Not Subject to Royalty, Accounted for Separately
****Operating Costs = Recovered Ounces x Cash Cost in $ Per Ounce

$$\text{PW Eq: } 0 = -47{,}500 + 11{,}112(P/F_{i,1}) + 24{,}614(P/F_{i,2}) + 23{,}637(P/F_{i,3}) + 19{,}583(P/F_{i,4})$$

ROR = 22.0% > 15.0%, acceptable

ROR is the "i" value causing the PW Equation (or NPV) to equal 0. The above result may be obtained by trial and error or by calculator. The above ROR is a calculator solution.

NPV @ 15% = –47,500 + 11,112(0.8696) + 24,614(0.7561) + 23,637(0.6575) + 19,583(0.5718)

NPV @ 15% = 7,513 > 0, acceptable

Positive NPV is a measure of value added to a portfolio by investing in the proposed project rather than investing in other opportunities where 15% is deemed achievable (NPV @ 15% in these projects is zero). It is worth noting that "value added" is reflective of other economic opportunities being properly measured by the 15% minimum rate of return, not necessarily the financial cost of capital.

PVR = 7,513 / 47,500 = 0.16 > 0, acceptable

PVR is measure of value added (or NPV created) per present worth investment dollar. The denominator is based on the economic concept of maximum capital exposure which in this problem is reflected in the absolute value of the time zero negative cash flow.

NPV and PVR greater than zero and ROR greater than $i^* = 15\%$ consistently indicate economic acceptability of this project compared to investing elsewhere at a 15% rate of return.

In the petroleum industry, exploration or development well costs are often broken into two components and referred to as intangible drilling costs (the cost of drilling oil and gas wells to the point of completion) and tangible well costs (the costs for tubing, producing equipment, tank batteries, separators and gathering pipelines necessary to "complete" bringing a well into production. The acronym "IDC" often is used to refer to "intangible drilling costs" in petroleum drilling projects. Tax deduction considerations are the primary differences in tangible and intangible well costs as discussed in detail for different types of investors in Chapters 7 and 8.

When considering oil and gas investment opportunities, most fall into one of four general categories. First, you can evaluate the project from the viewpoint of the party holding all rights to the property, which might be considered as "development economics," or drilling a property "heads up." Both terms imply that the intent is to look at all revenue and costs as pertinent to the investor's economics. Second, you, the investor might consider passing the rights to develop on to a second party who would put up all or part of the drilling costs and well completion costs. Typically the developer gets all or most of the revenues until the costs are recovered and then you back-in at that future point in time for a working interest in the property. This is sometimes referred to as "farming out" a property. Third, you could also look at the opposite viewpoint of a "farm-out" and consider developing a property that someone else owns for an interest in the property. This often is referred to as "farming in" a property. The "farm-in" party is on the opposite side of a petroleum development agreement as the "farm-out" party. Finally, you could consider selling a property and keeping a royalty, with no liability towards development of the property. This sometimes is referred to as retaining a "carried interest" or an "overriding royalty" in a property.

The following discussion offers some of the basic terminology that is fairly common to many oil and gas deals. From an economic evaluation viewpoint, these terms help to establish royalties to be paid and the portion of capital and operating expenditures paid by the investor involved in various "farm-out" or "farm-in" evaluations. These agreements can be very dynamic over a property life, allowing for interests in costs and revenues to change at various points in the project life as introduced in the definition of some of the following terms:

In most states, it is possible to sever the interest between the land (surface rights) and the mineral interest itself (mineral rights). Rights to the mineral interest itself are transferred by a mineral deed or fee simple title. Before a property is developed, mineral rights to a lease may be retained by paying rentals (lease bonus payments) or drilling the property, at which time a royalty related to production may be paid. In oil and gas, royalties often are calculated as 1/8th (12.5%) of gross revenue, or the wellhead value of the oil and or gas. Royalties are usually the first expense to be deducted from the gross value of production to determine the net revenues available to the producer to cover costs. Revenue after royalties often is referred to as the "net revenue interest" in a property.

A "working interest" is the investor's percentage of responsibility for costs related to an oil and gas lease. When there is just one investor, that person or firm is responsible for all costs associated with developing a lease and they are said to retain a 100% working interest in the lease. A 100% working interest investor incurs 100% of the applicable project costs. However, the revenues available to the investor are a function of the terms of the lease including royalties, overriding royalties or carried interests, reversionary interests, etc. As mentioned earlier, those net revenues that are available often are referred to as a "net revenue interest." Generally, working interests stand independent of the revenue interest in a lease. Again, a net revenue interest can be defined as revenue less royalties, overriding royalties, carried interests, etc. This is a fractional interest based on the gross revenue potential from a lease. Net revenue represents the dollars available to the investor to recover dollars invested to cover the working interest costs to extract the lease resources (drilling costs, lease costs, operating costs, etc.).

On the other side of development economics is the royalty owner. A royalty interest is a mineral or land owner's share of production free and clear of all operating expenses and capital costs. Royalty owners usually are responsible for their share of applicable severance and excise taxes. These taxes usually are paid directly by the operator. The operator then recovers the appropriate prorated portion of these taxes by reducing royalties paid by the prorated tax amount.

Overriding royalties or interests are predominately based on the net revenue interest but could be based on anything from the gross value of the oil and gas to the net revenue adjusted for operating expenses. This interest is free and clear of all production and capital expenditures. It is a royalty in addition to the landowner's royalty. Overriding royalties may also be described as being carved out of the working interest, so in a standard 1/8 of 8/8 royalty situation, a 1/8 overriding royalty may come out of the 7/8 net revenue interest. A carried interest is similar to an overriding royalty; this is a fractional interest in a lease that gives the holder no obligation for operating or development capital costs. It is a royalty and may be calculated on gross revenue or gross revenue adjusted for various out of pocket expenditures incurred by the investor.

In many deals, the interest in the property may change as the property is developed. This relates to reversion(ary) interests which represent the portion of the working interest that reverts or is allocated to another party after a specified occurrence, such as payout of investments by specified criteria.

In reversion calculations, a reversion point is that point where working and or revenue interests in a property are transferred or revised, based on a previous agreement in the lease. This is usually determined by some type of payout calculation. In many cases, payout is based on the before-tax capital expenditures (intangible and tangible) and may involve revenues that reflect anything from gross revenues to gross revenues adjusted for all out of pocket expenditures. After-tax cash flow (discussed beginning in Chapter 7) is rarely used in these calculations due to the complexity and variation of tax positions for each investor in the property.

The following example illustrates a basic drilling evaluation neglecting complex issues of multiple participation, reversionary interests, etc. Note the similarity of these calculations to the other examples throughout the textbook.

Example 3-26 Petroleum Project

Analyze the economics of the following petroleum project in which an investor has a 100% working interest. All costs except operating costs are in thousands of dollars while production is in thousands of barrels of oil equivalent. The selling price and operating costs are in dollars per barrel of oil equivalent (BOE).

Year	0	1	2	3	4	5
Annual Production, BOE		80	45	20	10	5
Price, $/BOE		75.00	75.00	75.00	75.00	75.00
Operating Cost, $/BOE		13.00	13.00	13.00	13.00	13.00
Intangible Drilling Cost	1,900					
Tangible Completion Cost	1,600					
Lease Bonus	1,800					

Royalties associated with the lease are 16% of gross revenue. Net salvage value and abandonment costs at the end of year five are estimated to be zero. Determine the investment Rate of Return (ROR), Net Present Value (NPV) and Present Value Ratio (PVR) for i* = 12%.

Solution, Values in 000's:

Year	0	1	2	3	4	5
Gross Revenue		6,000	3,375	1,500	750	375
-Royalties, 16%		-960	-540	-240	-120	-60
Net Revenue		5,040	2,835	1,260	630	315
-Operating Costs		-1,040	-585	-260	-130	-65
-Intangible Drilling Cost	1,900					
-Tangible Completion Cost	1,600					
-Lease Bonus	1,800					
Before-Tax Cash Flow	-5,300	4,000	2,250	1,000	500	250

Net Present Value (NPV) is the present value of all cash flows discounted at i*.

NPV @ 12% = $-5{,}300 + 4{,}000(P/F_{12\%,1}) + 2{,}250(P/F_{12\%,2})$
$+ 1{,}000(P/F_{12\%,3}) + 500(P/F_{12\%,4}) + 250(P/F_{12\%,5})$

NPV @ 12% = $1,237 > 0, Acceptable

Rate of Return (ROR) is the "i" value making NPV = 0

By calculator, ROR = 27% > 12%, Acceptable

Present Value Ratio (PVR) is the project NPV / Maximum Capital Exposure

PVR = 1,237/5,300 = 0.23 > 0, Acceptable

NPV and PVR are greater than zero and the ROR is greater than the minimum rate of return of 12%. All criteria consistently indicate the economics of this investment opportunity are satisfactory compared to investing elsewhere at 12%.

3.14 ROR, NPV and PVR Analysis of Service-Producing InvestmentsWith Equal Lives

In comparing alternative ways of providing a service, it is common to have only costs and maybe some salvage value given for each alternative being considered. This means that rate of return for individual alterative ways of providing a service is usually negative, and often minus infinity if no net revenue is involved in the analysis. Therefore, rate of return analysis of the individual investments to provide a service does not give useful information for economic decision making. Similar considerations relate to NPV and ratio analysis of service alternatives. In providing a service, the most common situation is that you know the service is needed and from an economic viewpoint you want to provide it as cheaply as possible. *For rate of return, net value or ratio analysis of alternatives that provide a service, investors must make an incremental analysis between the alternatives. Incremental implies the difference in two alternatives. Incremental analyses are made to determine if the additional up front investment(s) in the more capital-intensive alternative generates sufficient reductions in downstream operating costs (incremental savings) to justify the investment.* If the rate of return on the incremental (or additional) investment is greater than the minimum rate of return, or if incremental net value is greater than zero, or if incremental PVR is greater than zero, then the incremental investment is satisfactory from an economic viewpoint and selecting the larger investment alternative is economically justified. The following example illustrates ROR, NPV and Ratio analysis of this type of service-producing alternative evaluation problem for equal life alternatives. The analysis of unequal life service-producing alternatives is addressed in Section 3.16 and Examples 3-29 and 3-30.

EXAMPLE 3-27 ROR, NPV and PVR Analysis of Service-Producing Alternatives with Equal Lives

A company is considering the installation of automated equipment in a processing operation to reduce labor operating costs from \$300,000 to \$220,000 in year one, from \$330,000 to \$240,000 in year two, from \$360,000 to \$260,000 in year three and from \$400,000 to \$290,000 in year four. The automated equipment will cost \$200,000 now with an expected salvage value of \$50,000 in four years. The minimum rate of return, "i*", is 20%. Use ROR, NPV and PVR analysis to determine if the equipment should be installed from an economic viewpoint. Then consider an increase in the minimum ROR to 40% from 20% and re-evaluate the alternatives.

Solution, All Values in Thousands of Dollars:

In setting up a solution for service alternatives, investors have a choice in sign convention. One approach is to label all dollars as capital and operating costs or salvage income. With this approach, costs are treated as positive values and salvage (miscellaneous income) will eventually take on a minus sign so negative incremental operating costs become savings when the present worth equation is modified. This approach is illustrated in the first solution. The second approach is to address the costs in the context of cash flow where costs are an outflow and treated as negative values. This approach is utilized in the second solution. Both approaches are used in various examples and problems throughout the textbook as they are in industry.

Incremental Setup Approach #1 - Label Dollar Values C=Capital Cost, OC=Operating Cost, L=Salvage

A)

C=200	OC=220	OC=240	OC=260	OC=290	
0	1	2	3	4	L=50

B)

C = 0	OC = 300	OC = 330	OC = 360	OC = 400	
0	1	2	3	4	L=0

A-B)

C = 200	OC = −80	OC = −90	OC = −100	OC = −110	
0	1	2	3	4	L=50

Incremental Present Worth Equation:

$$200 - 80(P/F_{i,1}) - 90(P/F_{i,2}) - 100(P/F_{i,3}) - 110(P/F_{i,4}) = 50(P/F_{i,4})$$

In this first equation the present worth of all incremental capital and negative incremental operating costs appear on the left-hand side of the equation. These values are set equal to the present worth of revenues (salvage) on the right side. However, since the operating costs are negative, they represent the operating cost savings that will pay for the investment. To illustrate how negative incremental operating costs are identical to savings, rearrange the equation by adding the present worth of the operating costs and subtracting the capital investment to each side of the equality, this results in the following:

$$0 = -200 + 80(P/Fi,1) + 90(P/Fi,2) + 100(P/Fi,3) + 160(P/Fi,4)$$

Incremental Setup Approach #2 – Cash Flow Sign Convention

The alternative method that yields an identical present worth equation involves using cash flow sign convention where costs are negative values, and revenues (such as salvage) are positive values as follows:

A)	–200	–220	–240	–260	–290	50
	0	1	2	3	4	

B)	0	–300	–330	–360	–400
	0	1	2	3	4

A-B)	–200	80	90	100	110	50
	0	1	2	3	4	

This approach indicates immediately the savings to be derived on the time diagram and leads to the development of the same present worth equation:

$$0 = -200 + 80(P/F_{i,1}) + 90(P/F_{i,2}) + 100(P/F_{i,3}) + 160(P/F_{i,4})$$

Using either approach, solving for the incremental rate of return using trial and error provides the following:

@ 30% = 16
@ 40% = −19

Interpolating: i = 30% + 10%(16/(16+19)) = 34.6%

An incremental rate of return of 34.6% is greater than the 20.0% minimum rate of return and therefore, is satisfactory; so accept the investment in the automated equipment.

Incremental Net Present Value @ 20%

$$-200 + 80\overset{0.8333}{(P/F_{20,1})} + 90\overset{0.6944}{(P/F_{20,2})} + 100\overset{0.5787}{(P/F_{20,3})} + 160\overset{0.4823}{(P/F_{20,4})}$$

= +64.2 > 0, so accept automated equipment.

Incremental Present Value Ratio

64.2/200 = 0.32 > 0, so accept automated equipment.

ROR, NPV and Ratio analyses always give the same economic conclusions if the techniques are used properly. Chapter four will emphasize proper use of these techniques in different analysis situations.

Changing the minimum rate of return, i*

Changing the minimum ROR to 40% from 20% changes the economic conclusion to rejection of the automated equipment with all evaluation criteria.

Comparing the incremental ROR of 34.6% to other opportunities at 40% indicates reject the automated equipment. Investors do not want to purchase equipment that provides an inferior return compared to other opportunities thought to exist for the investment of your capital. This is one illustration of why it is important to know what your true returns from other opportunities really are because the discount rate can and will influence your decision in many investment situations.

Incremental NPV @ 40%

$$-200 + 80\overset{0.7143}{(P/F_{40,1})} + 90\overset{0.5102}{(P/F_{40,2})} + 100\overset{0.3644}{(P/F_{40,3})} + 160\overset{0.2603}{(P/F_{40,4})}$$

= −18.8 < 0, reject the investment in the automated equipment.

Incremental PVR

−18.8/200 = −0.094 < 0, so reject automated equipment.

Consistently with all analysis techniques, the economic choice has shifted to rejecting the automated equipment investment. For an increase in the discount rate to 40%, all methods indicated an economic preference for the labor-intensive approach. Bigger discount rates will always make it more economically difficult to justify capital intensive alternatives versus less capital intensive alternatives.

3.15 Cost Analysis of Service Producing Alternatives That Provide the Same Service Over the Same Period of Time.

Instead of making an incremental analysis of service producing alternatives using rate of return, net value or ratios, *it is equally valid to analyze the present, annual or future cost of providing a service for a common evaluation life*. With any of these methods, economic selection is based on the alternative that provides the service for the minimum cost. Consistent with discussion in Section 3.14, these evaluations can be handled with different sign conventions. *The minimum cost analysis is based on using the cost and revenue sign convention where costs are positive and revenues are negative. Note this is the opposite of the cash flow sign convention where revenues are positive and costs negative. Consistency in application and proper interpretation of results is really the key issue. As mentioned, both approaches are equally valid. Example 3-28 will focus on the cash flow sign convention approach.*

EXAMPLE 3-28 Present, Annual and Future Cost Analysis of Service Producing Alternative With Equal Lives

Evaluate alternatives “A” and “B” from Example 3-27 shown on the following time diagrams using present worth cost analysis. Support those conclusions with an annual and future cost comparison to illustrate the economic equivalence of the results. The minimum rate of return is 20.0%. Finally, re-evaluate the alternatives using present worth cost only for a 40.0% minimum rate of return.

Cash Flow Sign Convention Time Diagrams

A)	–200	–220	–240	–260	–290	50
	0	1	2	3	4	
B)	0	–300	–330	–360	–400	
	0	1	2	3	4	

Solution: All Values in Thousands

Present Worth Cost (PWC_A) @ 20%

$$= -200 - 220\overset{0.8333}{(P/F_{20,1})} - 240\overset{0.6944}{(P/F_{20,2})} - 260\overset{0.5787}{(P/F_{20,3})} - 240\overset{0.4823}{(P/F_{20,4})}$$

–\$816.2, least negative value is "A" (provides minimum cost)

Present Worth Cost (PWC_B) @ 20%

$$= -300\overset{0.8333}{(P/F_{20,1})} - 330\overset{0.6944}{(P/F_{20,2})} - 360\overset{0.5787}{(P/F_{20,3})} - 400\overset{0.4823}{(P/F_{20,4})}$$

= –\$880.4

The incremental analysis presented in Example 3-27 was based on looking at the difference in the A-B costs or cash flows. If you consider the difference in the $PWC_A - PWC_B$ or,

–816.2 – –880.4 = +64.2 This was the incremental NPV for A-B.

Because the calculations are very similar, *(both involve discounting at i*)* some investors fail to recognize the difference in an incremental NPV analysis and an individual cost analysis of the available alternatives. With a cost analysis the investor always wants to minimize cost, whereas in NPV analyses, the objective is to maximize value generated from savings or income from initial investments.

Annual and future cost calculations are alternative methods that will always arrive at the same economic conclusions from a present worth cost analysis as follows:

Annual Cost (AC_A) @ 20%

$$-816.2\overset{0.38629}{(A/P_{20\%,4})} = -\$315.3$$, Least cost alternative is "A"

Annual Cost (AC_B) @ 20%

0.38629

$-880.4(A/P_{20\%,4}) = -\$340.1$

Future Cost (FC_A) @ 20%

2.0736

$-816.2(F/P_{20\%,4}) = -\$1,692.5$, Least cost alternative is "A"

Future Cost (FC_B) @ 20%

2.0736

$-880.4(F/P_{20\%,4}) = -\$1,825.6$

Changing the minimum ROR to 40% from 20% changes the economic choice to rejecting the automated equipment with all cost analysis criteria, just as it changed the economic choice with ROR, NPV and PVR analysis in the previous example. Present worth cost analysis is presented here.

Present Worth Cost (PWC_A) @ 40%

0.7143 0.5102 0.3644 0.2603

$= -200 - 220(P/F_{40,1}) - 240(P/F_{40,2}) - 260(P/F_{40,3}) - 240(P/F_{40,4})$

$= -\$636.8$

Present Worth Cost (PWC_B) @ 40%

0.7143 0.5102 0.3644 0.2603

$= -300(P/F_{40,1}) - 330(P/F_{40,2}) - 360(P/F_{40,3}) - 400(P/F_{40,4})$

$= -\$618.0$, least negative value is "B"

When other opportunities exist to invest your money and earn a 40.0% rate of return, the economics favor the more labor intensive alternative "B." The decision is to take the cash and get the better return potential from other opportunities. The incremental NPV is presented to support this cost analysis and illustrate the equivalence of the result.

Again, if you consider the difference in the $PWC_A - PWC_B$, the incremental NPV at i*=40% is;

$-636.8 - -618.0 = -18.8 < 0$, reject A, select B.

This example and the previous example illustrate that the minimum rate of return is a significant evaluation parameter that has a definite effect on economic conclusions with all evaluation criteria. It must be selected carefully to represent the attainable rate of return thought to exist from investing in other alternatives. The minimum rate of return must not be an arbitrarily determined "hoped for" number.

3.16 Comparison of Unequal Life Alternatives that Provide the Same Service

In this section methods that may be used to compare unequal life alternatives that provide the same service are introduced and illustrated. In general, the methods presented here are not valid for comparing unequal life income-producing alternatives, or for comparing service-producing projects that do not result in the same service. Assumptions for the evaluation of unequal life income-producing projects are presented and illustrated in Chapter 4, while analysis of service alternatives that provide different service is addressed in Section 3.17.

To get a meaningful comparison of unequal life alternatives that provide the same service, assumptions or estimates must be made to permit comparison of the alternatives on an equal life or equal study period basis. You are comparing different total service if you compare project costs for unequal time periods. Three methods will be presented that cover the possible ways of comparing unequal life projects. Combinations of these methods may also be used. The methods are not listed in their order of importance or validity. It is impossible to say that one method is best for all situations. Project circumstances usually dictate the method that is best for given evaluation conditions. However, method 1 is seldom a desirable or valid approach to use. You should be familiar with it because many textbook and literature authors have advocated its use. *Methods 2 and 3 are the approaches that in general should be used to obtain a common study period for unequal life projects that provide the same service.* The three methods for obtaining a common study period for unequal life service-producing alternatives are described and illustrated using the following two unequal life alternatives "A" and "B".

C = Cost, OC = Operating Cost, L = Salvage Value

$$\text{A)}\quad \underset{0}{C_A} \;\text{———}\; \underset{1}{OC_{A1}} \;\text{———}\; \underset{2}{OC_{A2}} \quad L_A$$

B)	C_B	OC_{B1}	OC_{B2}	OC_{B3}	L_B
	0	1	2	3	

Once a common study period is established using one of the following methods, then the resulting equal life alternatives can be compared using the five basic approaches presented earlier in this chapter which are present, annual, and future worth, ROR or break-even analysis. However, for the results from any of these calculation procedures to be valid for economic decision-making, an investor must be looking at the costs for each alternative to provide the same service per day, week or yearly period as well as for a common evaluation life. This means the service alternatives must be compared on the assumed basis of generating identical revenue streams.

Method 1: Replacement In-Kind

This method of getting a common study period for unequal life alternatives is based on the assumption that projects "A" and "B" can be replaced in-kind for the same initial costs, operating costs and salvage values until a common study period equal to the lowest common denominator between the project lives is attained. For alternatives "A" and "B" replacement in-kind gives a six year study period as follows:

A)	C_A	OC_{A1}	OC_{A2} L_A	C_A	OC_{A1}	OC_{A2} L_A	C_A	OC_{A1}	OC_{A2} L_A
	0	1	2	2	3	4	4	5	6

B)	C_B	OC_{B1}	OC_{B2}	OC_{B3} L_B	C_B	OC_{B1}	OC_{B2}	OC_{B3} L_B
	0	1	2	3	3	4	5	6

The obvious shortcoming of this method is that escalation of values is neglected from year to year. Experience of recent decades emphasizes the fact that costs can, and generally do escalate as time goes by. To assume replacement in-kind involves closing our eyes to the true situation that costs change. Economic analysis is only valid when you use actual expected costs and revenues and actual timing of costs and revenues. A method such as replacement in-kind that does not project actual expected costs should not be used. As mentioned earlier in this section, replacement in-kind is presented here to familiarize the reader with the disadvantages of the methods since it is mentioned and advocated widely in other texts and journal literature.

Another approach recommended by some authors is to consider each alternative based solely on their equivalent annual cost. With this method no adjustments are made to compensate for differences in service lives, each asset is measured based on its own useful life and associated costs. This method implicitly assumes the replacement in kind-philosophy. By evaluating unequal life service alternatives with equivalent annual cost, you are really assuming that assets can be replaced now and in the future for the same capital and operating cost structure stated for the initial use period.

Method 2: Neglect Extra Life of Longer Life Alternatives

This method of getting a common study period for unequal life alternatives is based on neglecting the extra life of longer life alternatives over shorter life alternatives and letting salvage values at the end of the shorter life reflect remaining estimated value of the assets from sale or use of the assets elsewhere. This often is a valid assumption if the service provided is only expected to be needed for the short alternative life. Applying this methods to alternatives "A" and "B" gives a two year study period as follows:

$$\text{A)}\quad \underset{0}{C_A}\quad \underset{1}{OC_{A1}}\quad \underset{2}{OC_{A2}}\; L_A$$

$$\text{B)}\quad \underset{0}{C_B}\quad \underset{1}{OC_{B1}}\quad \underset{2}{OC_{B2}}\; L'_B$$

Note that the salvage value of "B" is designated L'_B at the end of year two to designate it differently from L_B. Normally we would expect L'_B to be greater that L_B since the asset will have been used for a shorter time at year two compared to year three.

Method 2 is a valid method of obtaining a common study period in many physical evaluation situations.

Method 3: Estimate Actual Costs to Extend Shorter Life Alternatives to a Longer Life Common Study Period

This method of getting a common study period for unequal life alternatives is based on extending the life of the shorter life alternatives by estimating actual replacement or major repair and operating costs needed to extend the service life of an alternative. This method may result in a study period equal to the longest life alternative or it may result in a study period unrelated to the alternative lives. If we apply this method to alternatives "A" and "B" for a common study period of three years we get the following:

$$\text{A)}\quad \frac{C_A \qquad OC_{A1} \qquad OC_{A2}}{0 \qquad\quad 1 \qquad\quad 2} \; L_A \; \frac{C'_A \qquad OC_{A3}}{2 \qquad\quad 3} \; L'_A$$

$$\text{B)}\quad \frac{C_B \qquad OC_{B1} \qquad OC_{B2} \qquad\quad OC_{B3}}{0 \qquad\quad 1 \qquad\quad 2 \qquad\qquad 3} \; L_B$$

Note that at the end of year two the replacement cost C'_A is not assumed to be the same as the initial cost, C_A. C'_A may be greater or less than C_A depending on whether it is new or used equipment. At the end of year three note that the operating cost, OC_3, and the salvage value, L'_A, are designated differently than earlier values to emphasize that they probably will not be the same as the corresponding values for earlier years.

Engineering and business judgement is required on the part of the investment analyst to use correct assumptions in different analysis situations. In many cases the correct assumptions to use are not clear cut and it may be best to look at a problem from several analysis assumption points of view. It is very important to get into the habit of clearly stating all assumptions used in making an analysis so that the person with the responsibility of evaluating analysis calculations, assumptions and economic conclusions has the necessary information to make his or her evaluation properly. Economic analyses involve intangible considerations (such as the best assumptions to use to convert unequal life projects to equal life projects) and the decision-making manager must know the basis on which an analysis has been made before analysis results can be utilized to reach valid economic decisions.

Once again, before illustrating these three methods, it is important to re-emphasize that these methods or combinations of these methods are valid only for alternatives that provide the same service and not for income-producing projects. Methods 1, 2 and 3 are almost never valid for the comparison of income or service-producing projects that provide different services or benefits.

EXAMPLE 3-29 Comparison of Unequal Life Service Alternatives

A) C=6,000 OC_1=1,500 OC_2=2,000   L=1,000
     0 — 1 — 2

B) C=10,000 OC_1=1,000 OC_2=1,400 OC_3=1,800 OC_4=2,200   L=2,000
     0 — 1 — 2 — 3 — 4

C) C=14,000 OC_1=500 OC_2=600 OC_3=700 OC_4=800 OC_5=900   L=5,000
     0 — 1 — 2 — 3 — 4 — 5

Three alternative methods “A”, “B” and “C” with costs, salvage values and lives given on the time diagrams are being considered to carry out a processing operation for the next three years. It is expected that the process will not be needed after three years. A major repair costing \$3,000 at the end of year two would extend the life of alternative “A” through year three with a third year operating cost of \$2,500 and the salvage value equal to \$1,000 at the end of year three instead of year two. The salvage value of alternative “B” is estimated to be \$3,000 at the end of year three and the salvage value of alternative “C” is estimated to be \$7,000 at the end of year three. For a minimum rate of return of 15%, which alternative is economically best? Use equivalent annual cost analysis for a three year study period.

Solution, The three year study period time diagrams follow with all values in dollars:

A) C=6,000   OC=1,500   C=3,000, OC=2,000   OC=2,500   L=1,000
     0 — 1 — 2 — 3

B) C=10,000   OC=1,000   OC=1,400   OC=1,800   L=3,000
     0 — 1 — 2 — 3

C) C=14,000   OC=500   OC=600   OC=700   L=7,000
     0 — 1 — 2 — 3

The annual cost calculations follow:

$$AC_A = 6000\overset{0.43798}{(A/P_{15\%,3})} + 1500 + 500\overset{0.907}{(A/G_{15\%,3})} - 1000\overset{0.28798}{(A/F_{15\%,3})}$$

$$+ 3000\overset{0.7561}{(P/F_{15\%,2})}\overset{0.43798}{(A/P_{15\%,3})} = \$5{,}287$$

$$AC_B = 10{,}000\overset{0.43798}{(A/P_{15\%,3})} + 1000 + 400\overset{0.907}{(A/G_{15\%,3})} - 3000\overset{0.28798}{(A/F_{15\%,3})}$$

$$= \$4{,}897$$

$$AC_C = 14{,}000\overset{0.43798}{(A/P_{15\%,3})} + 500 + 100\overset{0.907}{(A/G_{15\%,3})} - 7000\overset{0.28798}{(A/F_{15\%,3})}$$

$$= \$4{,}706$$

Select alternative “C” with the smallest equivalent annual cost. This problem is presented again on an after-tax evaluation basis in Chapter 10 and we then find alternative “A” is worst, “B” best and “C” the next best choice which emphasizes the importance of tax considerations and that analyses must be done after-tax to be valid. Once again, taxes are being omitted in the early chapters of this text to avoid confusing the reader with tax considerations at the same time evaluation concepts are being developed.

3.17 Comparison of Service-Producing Alternatives that Provide Different Service

If different service-producing alternatives are projected to give different service per operating period, and if the extra service produced by the more productive alternative can be utilized, then it is necessary to get the alternatives on a common service-producing basis per operating period as well as for a common evaluation life. This simply means that if two old assets are required to do the job of one new asset and service provided by two old assets is needed, then you must either compare the cost of service for two old assets to one new asset, or one old asset to one-half of a new asset, or some other 2 to 1 ratio of old to new assets. Differences in annual operating hours of service as well as volume of work differences per year between alternatives must be taken into account to get all alternatives on a common service basis before making economic comparisons.

EXAMPLE 3-30 Comparison of Alternatives that Provide Different Service

Three used machines can be purchased for $45,000 each to provide a needed service for the next three years. It is estimated that the salvage value of these machines will be zero in three years and that they will need to be replaced at year three with two new machines that each give 150% of the productivity per machine being realized with each old machine. The new machines would cost $145,000 each at year three. The service of the old and new machines is needed for the next five years, so use a five year evaluation life assuming the salvage value of the new machines will be $50,000 per machine at year five. Operating costs per machine for the old machines are estimated to be $30,000 in year one, $35,000 in year two, and $40,000 in year three. Operating costs per new machine are estimated to be $33,000 in year four and $36,000 in year five. Another alternative is to buy the two new machines now for a cost of $125,000 per machine to provide the needed service for the next five years with annual operating costs per machine of $25,000 in year one, $30,000 in year two, $35,000 in year three, $40,000 in year four, and $45,000 in year five. Salvage value at year five would be $15,000 per machine. For a minimum ROR of 15%, use present worth cost analysis to determine the most economical alternative way of providing the needed service. Then determine the uniform and equal revenues for each alternative that would be required at each of years one through five to cover the cost of service at the 15% before-tax minimum ROR.

Solution, All Values in Thousands of Dollars:

Compare the economics of three used machines with two new machines for a five year life to get the alternatives on a common service basis for a five year common study period.

				C=290			
A) "3 Used"	C=135	OC=90	OC=105	OC=120	OC=66	OC=72	L=100
	0	1	2	3	4	5	

B) "2 New"	C=250	OC=50	OC=60	OC=70	OC=80	OC=90	L=30
	0	1	2	3	4	5	

$$\textbf{PW Cost}_A = 135 + 90\overset{0.8696}{(P/F_{15\%,1})} + 105\overset{0.7561}{(P/F_{15\%,2})} + 410\overset{0.6575}{(P/F_{15\%,3})}$$

$$+ 66\overset{0.5718}{(P/F_{15\%,4})} + (72 - 100)\overset{0.4972}{(P/F_{15\%,5})} = \$586$$

$$\textbf{PW Cost}_B = 250 + 50\overset{0.8696}{(P/F_{15\%,1})} + 60\overset{0.7561}{(P/F_{15\%,2})} + 70\overset{0.6575}{(P/F_{15\%,3})}$$

$$+ 80\overset{0.5718}{(P/F_{15\%,4})} + (90\text{-}30)\overset{0.4972}{(P/F_{15\%,5})} = \$460, \text{ select min. cost}$$

Alternative “B” with the minimum present worth cost is the economic choice.

On a before-tax analysis basis, equivalent annual cost represents the equivalent annual revenues required to cover cost of service at a specified minimum ROR as the following calculations illustrate.

$$\text{Annual Revenues} = \text{Annual Cost} = (\text{PW Cost})(A/P_{i^*,n})$$

$$\text{Annual Revenues}_A = AC_A = 586\overset{0.29832}{(A/P_{15\%,5})} = 174.8$$

$$\text{Annual Revenues}_B = AC_B = 460\overset{0.29832}{(A/P_{15\%,5})} = 137.2, \text{ select minimum}$$

The alternative with the minimum revenue requirement is the economic choice. This is alternative “B” which in this case and in general, always agrees with the cost analysis results.

A class of service investments requiring additional economic evaluation consideration is the decision as to which type of environmental remediation is best for a given site, with remediation work having no impact on income generation. In many situations there are several alternatives that might be considered, all of which provide the same service of cleaning the site, but the time required may vary by ten years or more. For example, in cleaning contaminated ground water the alternatives may include the use of activated carbon absorption versus ultra violet radiation, or maybe bio-remediation. In these situations the alternatives may be treated as all providing the same service over different time periods with no impact on income generation. If income is affected in any way by the service provided, income must be included in the analysis of each alternative for valid economic evaluation of the alternatives. If income is not affected by the remediation or service work, then service alternatives can be fairly compared using different service lives for providing the remediation or general service in alternative ways. The following example illustrates service analysis for different service life alternatives that have no impact on income generation.

EXAMPLE 3-31 Environmental Remediation Alternatives

Two soil vapor extraction alternatives are being considered in the cleanup of a former plant site. For a minimum rate of return of 10.0% per year, which option would you consider to be economically best? Use present worth cost and net present value analyses in supporting your decision assuming the same remediation service is realized using either alternative 1 or 2 with no impact on revenue generation.

Alternative 1 would involve drilling a total of twelve wells on a 50 foot radius. The well costs are incurred at time zero and are estimated to be $10,000 per well. End of year operating and maintenance costs are estimated to total $1,000 per well per year. The total life of this operation is estimated to be five years.

Alternative 2 would involve drilling a total of six wells on a 100 foot radius. The well costs are incurred at time zero at a cost of $10,000 per well. End of year operating and maintenance costs are estimated to total $1,000 per well per year. The total life of this operation is estimated to be fifteen years.

Solution:

Alt 1	−120,000	−12,000.	−12,000
	0	1	5

$$\text{PW Cost: } -120{,}000 - 12{,}000\overset{3.7908}{(P/A_{10\%,5})} = -\$165{,}490$$

Alt 2	−60,000	−6,000.	−6,000
	0	1.	15

$$\text{PW Cost: } -60{,}000 - 6{,}000\overset{7.6061}{(P/A_{10\%,15})} = -\$105{,}637\text{, Select A2.}$$

Alt 1–2	–60,000	–6,000. . . . . –6,000	6,000. 6,000
	0	1 5	6. 15

$$NPV = -60{,}000 - 6{,}000(P/A_{10\%,5}) + 6{,}000(P/A_{10\%,10})(P/F_{10\%,5})$$

(factor values printed above: $P/A_{10\%,5} = 3.7908$, $P/A_{10\%,10} = 6.1446$, $P/F_{10\%,5} = 0.6209$)

$$= -\$59{,}853$$

The NPV is less than zero, so reject the incremental investments in A1, select A2.

3.18 Summary

Several decision criteria were introduced in this chapter to help investors evaluate a variety of different investments. Those methodologies and related issues are summarized here along with the related acronyms.

1. Rate of Return, i (ROR or IRR in Many Calculators and Spreadsheets)

Rate of return, "i" is the compound interest rate received on the unpaid portion of the dollars invested over the project life. It is also defined as the compound interest rate that makes NPV equal zero. Solving for ROR involves a trial and error process and interpolation between the two interest rates that bracket a present worth equation equal to zero. To illustrate the meaning of "i" the Cumulative Cash Position Diagram was developed to show how this measure of profitability is identical to the compound interest rate received in a savings account. The ROR is compared with other returns from other perceived opportunities to determine if a project is economically acceptable.

2. Financial Cost of Capital (FCC)

Two schools of thought exist in terms of what should be considered in establishing an investor's minimum rate of return. The theory in utilizing the financial cost of capital is based on the assumption that financing is unlimited and that as a minimum, a company can always use excess cash to pay off existing loans or buy back existing stock. Therefore, a weighted average cost of capital is determined based on the investor's average cost of debt (normally after-tax recognizing the deductibility of most interest) and the cost of equity (stockholders desired return determined using the Capital Asset Pricing Model, CAPM). The company's debt/equity ratio is then applied in proportion to each. This approach should not rely on the current cost of capital but rather, the expected cost of capital over the period of time for which cash flows will be discounted. Although not advocated, FCC is a common basis for determining a company minimum rate of return, i*.

3. Opportunity Cost of Capital (OCC, i*)

The opportunity cost of capital is the preferred approach to establishing an investor's minimum rate of return. The OCC is based on the expected returns to be generated in future years (maybe the next 1-15 years) from investment in new projects. Although this approach does not adhere to any specific doctrine, in general it is the average return measured in terms of compound interest, investors are looking for and believe to be sustainable over the long run. Opportunity cost of capital may also be referred to as a discount rate and is identified in the text by "i*."

4. Hurdle Rates

Hurdle rate is a common term interchangeable with opportunity cost used by investors who discount at their perceived financial cost of capital, FCC. Investor's realize the FCC does not represent the return they are willing to accept from the investment of their funds. In this situation, investors force projects to equal or exceed an imposed "economic hurdle," such as a larger discount rate (rate of return) or a set dollar value for NPV, or a PVR of say 0.5 instead of zero. The hurdle is a way of recognizing that projects earning the financial cost of capital minimum rate of return do not add value to a portfolio but are a breakeven economically with those other perceived opportunities. This approach is very common, but may lead to inconsistent economic conclusions if compared to proper use of a discount rate based on opportunity cost of capital.

5. Reinvestment Meaning Related to ROR

Many analysts and authors have been confused on the subject of the implied reinvestment meaning associated with ROR. There simply is no implied reinvestment meaning associated with individual project compound interest rates of return. However, if an investor or company wants an investment portfolio to grow over time at a given rate, then all projects now and in the future must achieve that level of return to sustain the overall "rate of growth."

6. Growth Rate of Return (GROR or MIRR in Excel)

Growth Rate of Return does consider the reinvestment of funds but not necessarily at the project rate of return. Instead, project positive cash flow is assumed to be reinvested at the project minimum rate of return, i*, which should reflect other perceived investment opportunities both now and in the future.

7. Net Present Value (NPV)

NPV is defined as the sum of all cash flows discounted to a specific point in time at the investor's minimum rate of return, or discount rate, i*. NPV is the measure of value created by investing in a project and not investing money elsewhere at the minimum rate of return. NPV greater than zero is acceptable compared to investing elsewhere at i*. An NPV equal to zero is a breakeven with investing elsewhere while a negative NPV is unacceptable. The Cumulative NPV Diagram illustrated graphically the value of one additional year of cash flow and its impact on the overall project NPV. This diagram also introduced the concept of discounted payback and maximum capital exposure, which identified graphically the correct measure for denominators in ratios such as Present Value Ratio and Benefit Cost Ratio summarized next.

Related "value" approaches include Net Annual Value (sometimes referred to as a Net Uniform Series) and Net Future Value. Like NPV, these measures look a revenue minus costs but as described, on either an equivalent uniform series basis, or at some future point in time.

8. Present Value Ratio (PVR, Also known as Investment Efficiency, or IE)

PVR is defined as;

NPV / |Maximum Capital Exposure|

It is a measure of present worth profit being generated per present worth dollar invested. This profit is measured in terms of dollars above what is required to earn the desired minimum rate of return. PVR greater than zero indicates a satisfactory project, while a PVR equal to zero is a breakeven with investing elsewhere. From the viewpoint of an economic assessment of individual projects, PVR is somewhat redundant in that you already know the project is acceptable by the magnitude of its numerator, NPV. The utility of ratios is described in Chapter 4.

9. Benefit Cost Ratio (B/C Ratio, also known as Profitability Index, PI, or Discounted Profitability Index, DPI)

B/C Ratio is defined as;

PW Net Positive Cash Flow/|Maximum Capital Exposure|

B/C Ratio is a measure of present worth revenue being generated per present worth dollar invested. B/C Ratio results that are greater than one indicate satisfactory projects while a B/C Ratio equal to one is a breakeven with investing elsewhere, (present worth revenues are equal to the present worth costs). If the B/C ratio is less than zero the result is unsatisfactory.

10. Evaluating Service Alternatives Using Incremental Analysis

In evaluating replacement alternatives that involve costs, incremental analysis is required to utilize the various income criteria introduced in this chapter. Incremental means difference. So incremental calculations involve subtracting a less capital-intensive alternative from an alternative requiring a greater initial investment, or simply, bigger initial investment minus smaller. This difference should leave an incremental diagram with an initial cost that generates operating cost savings in future years to provide the desired return on the up-front investment. To properly interpret your analysis the incremental cash flow stream must begin with a cost. For instance, if dollars are not invested up front, there is no way you can talk about rate of return meaning in your results. This topic will be amplified in Chapter 4.

11. Evaluating Service Alternatives with Cost Analysis

Replacement alternatives may also be evaluated individually by looking at the present, future or equivalent annual cost of operating an asset over a specified service period. Present worth cost is by far the most common of the three methods described, but each is consistent when properly applied. Proper interpretation of sign convention is the key consideration along with recognition that the evaluation is a cost analysis, not an income evaluation, so minimizing cost is the key.

Finally, with all service evaluations; alternatives must be compared based on obtaining the same service over the same period of time. If an investment alternative offers additional productivity that can be utilized, then adjustments must be made to account for the additional use in comparison with a less productive approach.

PROBLEMS

Excel solutions at Stermole.com

3-1 A foreman in a processing plant wants to evaluate whether to rebuild and repair five existing assets or replace them with four new assets that are more productive and capable of providing the same service as the current five machines. Four new assets can be acquired at time zero for a total cost of $240,000. The total maintenance, insurance and operating costs for the new equipment is $20,000 at time zero, $40,000 at year one, $50,000 at year 2 and $30,000 at year 3. The anticipated salvage for these assets after three years is $100,000. The alternative is to repair the existing machines for total cost of $50,000 at time zero. However this approach will realize much higher operating costs over the next three years. In addition to the repair cost, the total operating costs for the repaired assets is estimated at $20,000 at time zero but that escalates to $140,000 in each of years one and two and $70,000 in year three. The salvage for the existing assets after three years of service is anticipated to be zero. The used machines have no salvage value today in the marketplace due to their current condition. The desired minimum rate of return on invested capital is a nominal 15.0%. Use present worth cost analysis and support the cost findings with an incremental analysis using rate of return and net present value to determine which alternative is economically preferred.

3-2 The owner of a patent is negotiating a contract with a corporation that will give the corporation the right to use the patent. The corporation will pay the patent owner $3,000 a year at the end of each of the next 5 years, $5,000 at the end of each year for the next 8 years and $6,000 at the end of each year for the final 3 years of the 16 year life of the patent. If the owner of this patent wants a lump sum settlement 3 years from now in lieu of all 16 payments, at what price would he receive equivalent value if his minimum rate of return is 8% before income taxes?

3-3 Machine "A" has an initial cost of $50,000, an estimated service period of 10 years and an estimated salvage value of $10,000 at the end of the 10 years. Estimated end-of-year annual disbursements for operation and maintenance are $5,000. A major overhaul costing $10,000 will be required at the end of 5 years. An alternate Machine "B" has an initial cost of $40,000 and an estimated zero salvage value at the end of the 10-year service period with estimated end-of-year disbursements for operation and maintenance of $8,000 for the first year, $8,500 for the second year and increasing $500 each year thereafter. Using a minimum ROR of 10%, compare the present worth costs of 10-year service from Machines "A" and "B".

3-4 A project has an initial cost of $120,000 and an estimated salvage value after 15 years of $70,000. Estimated average annual receipts are $25,000. Estimated average annual disbursements are $15,000. Assuming that annual receipts and disbursements will be uniform, compute the prospective rate of return before taxes.

3-5 A couple plans to purchase a home for $250,000. Property taxes are expected to be $1,900 per year while insurance premiums are estimated to be $700 per year. Annual repair and maintenance is estimated at $1,400. An alternative is to rent a house of about the same size for $1,500 per month (approximate using $18,000 per year) payments. If a 8.0% return before-taxes is the couple's minimum rate of return, what must the resale value be 10 years from today for the cost of ownership to equal the equivalent cost of renting? Finally, given the breakeven year 10 sale value just asked for, what is the corresponding annual price escalation or de-escalation in the house over the ten years?

3-6 An old 30 year life $1000 bond matures in 20 years and pays semi-annual interest of $40. What rate of return compounded semi-annually does the bond yield if you pay $800 for it and hold it until maturity assuming the analysis is made on the first day of a new semi-annual period. If the bond is callable 8 years from now at face value, what could an investor pay for the bond and be assured of receiving annual returns of 6% compounded semi-annually? Neglect the possibility of bankruptcy by the bond issuer.

3-7 What can be paid for the bond in problem 3-6 if a 10% return compounded semi-annually is desired and a bond call is considered a negligible probability?

3-8 An investor has $50,000 in a bank account at 7% interest compounded annually. She can use this sum to pay for the purchase of a plot of land. She expects that in 10 years she will be able to sell the land for $130,000. During that period she will have to pay $2,000 a year in property taxes and insurance. Should she make the purchase? Base your decision on a rate of return analysis and verify your conclusion with future value analysis.

3-9 A new project will require development costs of $60 million at time zero and $100 million at the end of 2 years from time zero with incomes of $40 million per year at the end of years 1, 2 and 3 and incomes of $70 million per year at the end of years 4 through 10 with zero salvage value predicted at the end of year 10. Calculate the rate of return for this project.

3-10 Equipment is being leased from a dealer for $500,000 per year with beginning of year payments and the lease expires three years from now. It is estimated that a new lease for the succeeding four years on similar new equipment will provide the same service and will cost $750,000 per year with beginning of year payments. The first payment under the new lease occurs at the beginning of year four. The equipment manufacturer is offering to terminate the present lease today and to sell the lessee new equipment for $2 million now which together with a major repair cost of $600,000 at the end of year four should provide the needed equipment service for a total of seven years, after which, the salvage value is estimated to be zero. Use present worth cost analysis for a minimum rate of return of 20% to determine if leasing or purchasing is economically the best approach to provide the equipment service for the next seven years. Verify your conclusion with ROR and NPV analysis.

3-11 A person is considering an investment situation that requires the investment of $100,000 at time zero and $200,000 at year one to generate profits of $90,000 per year starting at year two and running through year 10 (a 9 year profit period) with projected salvage value of $150,000 at the end of year 10.

A) Determine the compound interest rate of return for these discrete end of period funds. Draw the cumulative cash position diagram for time zero through the end of year three at the project rate of return.

B) Determine the continuous interest rate of return for these discrete investments assuming all dollar values represent discrete end of period funds.

C) Determine the continuous interest rate of return for this investment assuming all dollar values represent continuously flowing funds. Treat the time zero investment as a continuous flowing sum (Year 0-1) and the year 1 investment as flowing during the following year 1-2. Profits flow continuously from years 2-3 to years 10-11. Salvage flows continuously during year 11-12.

D) Determine the continuous interest rate of return for this investment assuming the year zero investment is a discrete value and all dollar values after time zero represent continuously flowing funds. The year one investment is assumed to flow from year 0-1 and profits flow beginning from year 1-2, to year 9-10. Salvage flows from year 10-11.

E) Calculate the project rate of return assuming all dollar values after time zero are discrete values realized in the middle of each compounding period. Assume the time zero investment is a discrete sum at that point.

3-12 A firm is evaluating whether to lease or purchase four trucks. The four trucks can be purchased for a total cost of $240,000 and operated for maintenance, insurance and general operating costs of $20,000 at year 0, $40,000 at year 1, $50,000 at year 2 and $30,000 at year 3 (putting operating costs at the closest points in time to where they are incurred) with an expected salvage value of $100,000 at the end of year 3. The four trucks could be leased for $120,000 per year, for the 3 years, with monthly payments, so consider $60,000 lease cost at year 0, $120,000 per year at years 1 and 2 and $60,000 at year 3, putting lease costs at the closest point in time to where they are incurred. The lease costs include maintenance costs but do not include insurance and general operating costs of $10,000 at year 0, $20,000 per year at years 1 and 2 and $10,000 at year 3. If the minimum rate of return is 15% before tax considerations, use present worth cost analysis to determine if economic analysis dictates leasing or purchasing. Verify your conclusion with ROR, NPV and PVR analysis.

3-13 500,000 lbs per year of raw material are needed in a production operation (treat as end-of-year requirements). This material can be purchased for $0.24 per pound or produced internally for operating costs of $0.20 per pound if a $40,000 machine is purchased. A major repair of $10,000 will be required on the machine after 3 years. For a 5 year project life, zero salvage value and a 30% minimum rate of return before tax considerations, determine whether the company should purchase the equipment to make the raw material.

A) Use Incremental ROR, NPV and PVR analysis.

B) Verify your result from (A) with present worth cost analysis.

3-14 Earnings per share of common stock of XYZ Corporation have grown at 12% per year over the past ten years and the price of XYZ common stock has increased proportionally at 12% per year from \$30 per share ten years ago to \$93 per share today. The common stock paid annual dividends of \$2 per share in years 1 through 5 and \$4 per share in years 6 through 10. Assume the dividends were deposited when received in a money market account yielding 8% interest per year. Determine the growth rate of return over the past decade on money invested in XYZ common stock ten years ago to today. Hint: Use an analysis basis of one share of common stock bought ten years ago.

3-15 A corporation has invested \$250,000 in a project that is expected to generate \$100,000 profit per year for years 1 through 5 plus a \$150,000 salvage value at the end of year 5. It is proposed that the profits and salvage value from this investment will be reinvested immediately each year in real estate that is projected to have a \$2,000,000 value at the end of 6 years from now. Calculate the project rate of return and growth rate of return.

3-16 A heavy equipment manufacturer plans to lease a \$100,000 machine for 30 months with an option to buy at the end of that time. The manufacturer wants to get 1% per month compound interest on the unamortized value of the machine each month and wants the unamortized value of the machine to be \$25,000 at the end of the 30th month. What uniform monthly beginning-of-month lease payments must the company charge for each of the 30 months so that these payments plus a \$25,000 option to buy payment at the end of 30 months will recover the initial \$100,000 value of the equipment plus interest? What interest is paid by the lessee during the third month of the lease? What is the unamortized investment principal after the fourth payment is made?

3-17 A 20 year loan is being negotiated with a savings and loan company. \$50,000 is to be borrowed at 8% interest compounded quarterly with mortgage payments to be made at the end of each quarter over a 20 year period. To obtain the loan the borrower must pay "2 points" at the time he takes out the loan. This means the borrower must pay 2% of \$50,000 or a \$1,000 fee at time zero to obtain the \$50,000 loan. If the borrower accepts the loan under these conditions determine the annual percentage rate (APR) the investor is paying on the loan. Calculating the annual percentage rate on a loan is based on the actual dollars available for use in purchasing a home, automobile, etc. The payments are based on the loan amount prior to points and related expenditures.

3-18 Two development alternatives exist to bring a new project into production. The first development approach would involve equipment and development expenditures of \$1 million at year 0 and \$2 million at year 1 to generate incomes of \$1.8 million per year and operating expenses of \$0.7 million per year starting in year 1 for each of years 1 through 10 when the project is expected to terminate with zero salvage value. The second development approach would involve equipment and development expenditures of \$1 million at year 0 and expenses of \$0.9 million at year 1 to generate incomes of \$2 million per year and operating expenses of \$0.9 million per year starting in year 2 for each of years 2 through 10 when the project is expected to terminate with zero salvage value. For a minimum rate of return of 15%, evaluate which of the alternatives is economically better using rate of return, net present value and present value ratio analysis techniques.

3-19 An investor is interested in purchasing a company and wants you to determine the maximum value of the company today considering the opportunity cost of capital is 20%. The company assets are in two areas. First, an existing production operation was developed by the company over the past two years for equipment and development costs of \$100,000 two years ago, \$200,000 one year ago and costs and revenues that cancelled each other during the past year. It is projected that revenue minus operating expense net profits will be \$120,000 per year at the end of each of the next 12 years when production is expected to terminate with a zero salvage value. The second company asset is a mineral property that is projected to be developed for a \$350,000 future cost one year from now with expected future profits of \$150,000 per year starting two years from now and terminating 10 years from now with a zero salvage value. Use NPV analysis to determine the value of the company on a before-tax basis.

3-20 The following data relates to a processing facility.

Costs and production are in thousands. Production is in gallons and declining due to substitution of a new product in the market.

Year	0	1	2	3	4	5
Production, (Gal.)		175	100	75	55	35
Research Expense	7,500	2,500				
Equipment		6,700				
Patent Rights	1,000					
Operating Costs		1,750	1,000	750	500	250
Selling Price, $/Gal.		80.00	80.00	80.00	80.00	80.00

Royalties are 12.5% of gross revenue.
Liquidation value in year 5 is $0.

1) Calculate the annual before-tax cash flows for years 0-5.

2) Determine the project ROR, NPV and PVR for a minimum rate of return of 15%

3) Determine the breakeven product selling price in years 1 through 5 that would provide the investor with a 15% ROR.

3-21 The following data relates to an oil and gas lease.

Costs and production are in thousands.
Production is in barrels of oil equivalent (BOE).

Year	0	1	2	3	4	5
Production, (BOE)		175	100	75	55	35
Intangibles (IDC's)	7,500	2,500				
Tangible Equipment		6,700				
Lease Bonus	1,000					
Operating Costs		1,750	1,000	750	500	250
Selling Price, $/BOE		80.00	80.00	80.00	80.00	80.00

Royalties are 12.5% of gross revenue.
Liquidation value at year 5 is $0.

1) Calculate the annual before-tax cash flows for years 0-5.

2) Determine the project ROR, NPV and PVR for a minimum rate of return of 15%

3) Determine the breakeven product selling price in years 1 through 5 that would provide the investor with a 15% ROR.

3-22 The following data relates to a mining operation.

Costs and production are in thousands.
Production is in tons.

Year	0	1	2	3	4	5
Production, (tons)		175	100	75	55	35
Mine Development	7,500	2,500				
Mining Equipment		6,700				
Mineral Acquisition	1,000					
Operating Costs		1,750	1,000	750	500	250
Selling Price, $/ton		80.00	80.00	80.00	80.00	80.00

Royalties are 12.5% of gross revenue.
Liquidation value at year 5 is $0.

1) Calculate the annual before-tax cash flows for years 0-5.

2) Determine the project ROR, NPV and PVR for a minimum rate of return of 15%

3) Determine the breakeven product selling price in years 1 through 5 that would provide the investor with a 15% ROR.

3-23 A machine in use now has a zero net salvage value and is expected to have an additional two years of useful life but its service is needed for another 6 years. The operating costs with this machine are estimated to be $4,500 for the next year of use at year 1 and $5,500 at year 2. The salvage value will be 0 in two years. A replacement machine is estimated to cost $25,000 at year 2 with annual operating costs of $2,500 in its first year of use at year 3, increased by an arithmetic gradient series of $500 per year in following years. The salvage value is estimated to be $7,000 after 4 years of use (at year 6). An alternative is to replace the existing machine now with a new machine costing $21,000 and annual operating costs of $2,000 at year 1, increasing by an arithmetic gradient of $500 each following year. The salvage value is estimated to be $4,000 at the end of year 6. Compare the economics of these alternatives for a minimum ROR of 20% using a 6 year life by:

A) Present worth cost analysis.

B) Equivalent annual cost analysis

C) Incremental NPV analysis

3-24 Discount rates on U.S. treasury bills (T-Bills) are different from normal compound interest discount rates because T-Bills interest effectively is paid at the time T-Bills are purchased rather than at the maturity date of the T-Bills. Calculate the nominal annual rate of return compounded semi-annually to be earned by investing in a 6-month $10,000 T-Bill with a 5% annual discount rate.

3-25 A company wants you to use rate of return analysis to evaluate the economics of buying the mineral rights to a mineral reserve for a cost of $1,500,000 at year 0 with the expectation that mineral development costs of $5,000,000 and tangible equipment costs of $4,000,000 will be spent at year 1. The mineral reserves are estimated to be produced uniformly over an 8 year production life (evaluation years 2 through 9). Since escalation of operating costs each year is estimated to be offset by escalation of revenues, it is projected that profit will be constant at $4,000,000 per year in each of evaluation years 2 through 9 with a $6,000,000 salvage value at the end of year 9. Calculate the project rate of return, then assume a 15% minimum rate of return and calculate the project growth rate of return, NPV and PVR.

3-26 For a desired rate of return of 15% on invested capital, determine the maximum cost that can be incurred today by an investor to acquire the development rights to a new process that is expected to be developed over the next two years for a $1.5 million cost at year 1 and a $2.0 million cost at year 2. Production profits are expected to start in year 3 and to be $1.0 million per year at each of years 3 through 10. A $3 million sale value is estimated to be realized at the end of year 10. If the current owner of the development rights projects the same magnitude and timing of project costs and revenues but considers 10% to be the appropriate minimum discount rate, how does changing the discount rate to 10% from 15% affect the valuation?

3-27 To achieve a 20% rate of return on invested capital, determine the maximum cost that can be incurred today to acquire oil and gas mineral rights to a property that will be developed 3 years from now for estimated escalated dollar (actual) drilling and well completion costs of $2,500,000 with an expected net profit of $1,500,000 projected to be generated at year 4 and declining by an arithmetic gradient of

$200,000 per year in each year after year 4 for eight years of production (evaluation years 4 through 11). Salvage value is estimated to be zero. If the oil and gas mineral rights are already owned by an investor whose minimum ROR is 20%, what range of sale values for these mineral rights would make the owner's economics of selling better than holding the property for development 3 years from now for the stated profits?

3-28 Your integrated oil and gas company is considering the purchase at time zero of a 100% working interest in a property. If you elect to develop the lease for an 87.5% net revenue interest, the following costs will be incurred: in time zero, the lease bonus cost is $100,000, intangible drilling costs are estimated at $550,000 while tangible completion costs are estimated at $300,000. Operating costs are estimated to remain constant at $8.00 per barrel (includes production costs, severance taxes and ad valorem taxes) in each of years 1, 2, 3 and 4. Oil prices are forecasted to be $50.00 per barrel in each of years 1, 2, 3 and 4. Production is summarized in the follow table. The escalated dollar minimum rate of return is 12.0%. Use net present value, present value ratio, and rate of return analysis to determine if the acquisition and development of this lease is economically viable. Finally calculate the uniform breakeven product selling price per barrel of oil equivalent that would provide the investor with a 12% rate of return on the time zero capital investments.

Year	0	1	2	3	4
Lease Cost	$100,000				
Intangible Drilling	$550,000				
Tangible Completion	$300,000				
Production, (BOE/yr)		17,500	9,000	6,500	3,000
Selling Price, $/BOE		$50.00	$50.00	$50.00	$50.00
Operating Cost, $/BOE		$ 8.00	$ 8.00	$ 8.00	$ 8.00
Royalty, % of Gross		12.5%	12.5%	12.5%	12.5%

3-29 Evaluate the economics of problem 3-28 if you were to farm out the property described in that statement based on the following terms. You would receive a 5.0% overriding royalty (5.0% of gross revenues) until the project pays out. Payout is based on undiscounted 'net revenues minus operating costs' to recover before-tax capital costs estimated at $950,000. Because of the additional overriding royalty, the producer will realize a 82.5% net revenue interest to payout. For this example, neglect any potential sale value or abandonment costs in year 4. Upon payout, your company would back in for a 25.0% working interest and a 21.875% net revenue interest (25.0% of 87.5%). After payout the 5.0% overriding royalty terminates.

3-30 A gas pipeline manager has determined that he will need a compressor to satisfy gas compression requirements over the next five years or 60 months. The unit can be acquired for a year zero investment of $1,000,000. The cost of installation at time zero is $75,000 and a major repair would be required at the end of year 3 for an estimated $225,000. The compressor would be sold at the end of year five for $300,000. The alternative is to lease the machine for a year 0 payment of $75,000 to cover installation costs and beginning of month lease payments of $24,000 per month for 60 months. Lease payments include all major repair over the term of the lease. The nominal discount rate is 12% compounded monthly. Use present worth cost analysis for annual periods to determine whether leasing or purchasing offers the least cost method of providing service. Verify this conclusion with equivalent monthly cost analysis.

3-31 A new $10,000, ten year life U.S. Treasury Bond pays annual dividends of $800 based on the 8.0% annual yield to maturity. (A) After purchasing the bond, if interest rates instantly increased to 10.0%, or decreased to 6.0%, how would the bond value be affected? (B) If the bond has a 30 year life instead of a ten year life, how do the interest rate changes to 10.0% or 6.0% affect the value? (C) If the 30 year 8.0% bond is a new $10,000 face value (yr 30 maturity value) zero coupon bond instead of a conventional bond, how is value affected by the interest rate changes?

3-32 An existing remediation system will require end of year 1 though 7 operating and maintenance costs of $50,000 each year to complete the process. An upgrade to this system is estimated to cost $75,000 today (at time zero). This investment is expected to reduce the current annual operating and maintenance costs by $15,000 each year. Further, the upgrade modifications would accelerate the remediation process with cleanup completed after just 5 years from today.

For a minimum rate of return of 9.0% per year, should the current system be retained or modified? Use present worth cost analysis and verify your results with net present value analysis.

3-33 Two remediation alternatives are currently under consideration. You have been asked to evaluate the economics of each alternative. Alternative 1 involves the installation of an active vapor extraction system with off gas treatment. This alternative has a time zero cost of $170,000 and an operating life of 5 years. Operating and maintenance costs are estimated at $35,000 at the end of each of years one through five. Estimated salvage at the end of year 5 is $50,000. Alternative 2 involves a bio-remediation process that will require 10 years of treatment with quarterly sampling estimated to cost $12,500 per quarter through the end of year ten.

For a minimum rate of return of 9.0% compounded quarterly, should Alternative 1 or Alternative 2 be selected? Use present worth cost analysis and verify your results with net present value analysis.

3-34 Evaluation of two off gas treatment options for a project with an estimated life of five years is being considered. For a minimum rate of return of 10.0% compounded monthly, use present worth cost and net present value analyses to determine which alternative is best.

Option 1 — Use a catalytic converter with a time zero capital cost of $70,000 and end of month operating and maintenance costs of $1,000 per month.

Option 2 — Install two 1,000 pound carbon canisters at a cost of $7,500 each at time zero. Replacement of the carbon is estimated to be required six times in each of years one and two, four times in year three, two times in year four and one time in at the end of month six in year five (middle of the year). The cost of carbon replacement is estimated to be $4.00 per pound.

CHAPTER 3 AUXILIARY PROBLEMS

A3-1 You have been asked to evaluate whether it is economically better to use a submersible centrifugal pump system or a down-hole positive displacement rod pump system to lift crude oil 4,000 feet in a well with an estimated producing life of 12 years. Production is assumed to be the same for both lifting alternatives. The submersible pump system's initial installed cost is $100,000 including tubing, wiring, and surface gear while the installed rod pump's cost, including sucker rods and surface gear, is $135,000. It is estimated that the submersible pump will need to be replaced every 3 years with a similar refurbished used pump for a cost of $35,000 at year 3, $45,000 at year 6 and $55,000 at year 9. Year 12 salvage value of the submersible pump is $50,000. The rod pump is estimated to need replacing every 4 years for costs of $8,000 at year 4, and $12,000 at year 8. Due to corrosion, the salvage value of the rod pump system at year 12 will be zero. The minimum ROR is 15%. Use present worth cost analysis to determine which pumping system is economically better.

A3-2 A project has costs and incomes as shown on the diagram in thousands of dollars.

	I=100	I=250	I=375	I=500	I=500	I=400
C=100	C=500	C=100	C=125	C=150	C=150	C=200
						L=100
0	1	2	3	4	5	6

"L" represents the salvage or liquidation value of the assets upon termination of the project. The investor's minimum rate of return is 15%. Calculate the before-tax cash flow (BTCF) and then determine the ROR, NPV, PVR and Growth ROR for the project using the 6-year evaluation life.

A3-3 A loader is being considered to tram coal from a stockpile to a coal load-out facility. The cost of the machine is estimated at $1,400,000 with an estimated salvage value of $425,000 at the end of year 7. Operating costs are estimated to be $320,000 per year with major repairs of $250,000 and $300,000 required at the end of the 3rd and 5th years respectively. Given the required tram distance, it is estimated the machine can move 2,900 tons of coal per day, 250 days per year. For a desired minimum rate of return of 12%, calculate the present worth cost and the equivalent annual cost of operating this machine over the next 7 years. Finally, calculate the break-even cost per ton of coal being trammed over the 7 year service life.

A3-4 Production of crude oil from a 10,000-foot deep North Sea well, with L-80 carbon steel 5 inch tubing, requires down-hole injection of chemicals to control tubing corrosion due to high temperatures, pressures and corrosive chlorides in the crude oil. It is proposed to replace the L-80 carbon steel tubing, which cost \$8.50 per foot 1 year ago, with 13% chrome stainless steel tubing costing \$30 per foot. Ten thousand feet of tubing is needed and installation costs are estimated at \$80,000. Annual cost savings in chemicals, labor and chemical injection equipment are projected to be \$100,000 in year 1 following the installation of the new tubing with savings escalating 7% per year in succeeding years. Using NPV for a 15% minimum ROR, a 6-year evaluation life, and a salvage value of 0 in year 6, determine the economic desirability of replacing the steel tubing. Assume the existing L-80 carbon steel tubing has no salvage value at time 0. What breakeven life will cause the 13% chrome tubing replacement investment to yield a 15% ROR?

A3-5 Evaluate the economic potential of purchasing mineral rights to a known deposit adjacent to your existing mine. The acquisition of this private property would be incurred now (time 0) for a \$2 million mineral rights acquisition cost. Mining equipment costs of \$7 million will also be incurred at time zero along with a mine development cost of \$4 million. An additional \$1 million will be spent on mine development at the end of year 1. Production is expected to start in year 1 with 150,000 tons of gold ore. Production in years 2, 3 and 4 is estimated at 250,000 tons of ore per year. It is estimated that the gold ore reserves will be depleted at the end of year 4. Reclamation costs will be expensed in year 5 and will total \$0.5 million. Equipment will also be sold in that year for \$1 million. All ore is estimated to contain an average grade of 0.1 ounce's of gold per ton, with metallurgical recovery estimated at 90%. The price of gold is forecasted to be uniform at \$900 per ounce each year. Operating costs are also estimated to be uniform at \$600 per ounce in each of years 1-4. Compute the project before-tax cash flow (BTCF), and then determine the project NPV, ROR, GROR and PVR for an investor seeking a 15% minimum rate of return.

A3-6 Development of a natural gas property is projected to involve production, costs and prices as follows with costs expressed in thousands of dollars and production and price in units as noted. mcf = thousand cubic feet, mmcf = million cubic feet and m$ = thousands of dollars.

Year	0	1	2	3	4
Production, mmcf/yr		300	700	500	150
Price, $/mcf		5.00	5.25	5.50	5.75
Royalties, % of Gross Revenue		12.5%	12.5%	12.5%	12.5%
Operating Cost, m$		60	70	80	90
Intangible Well Cost, m$	1,000				
Tangible Well Cost, m$	700				
Tangible Pipeline Cost, m$	450				
Mineral Acquisition Cost, m$	2,000				

Calculate the annual before-tax cash flow, and then determine the ROR, NPV, PVR and Growth ROR for a 15% minimum ROR. Assume the investor has a 100% working interest in the property and that salvage value is 0.

A3-7 Two used machines can be acquired for $60,000 per machine to provide necessary service for the next 2 years. The salvage of these machines is estimated at $20,000 per machine at the end of year 2 when the old machines will be replaced with one new machine capable of providing the same total service. The new machine would cost $350,000 at the end of year 2 and is anticipated to yield a salvage value of $170,000 at the end of year 4. Operating costs associated with the used machines are estimated at $60,000 per machine at year 1 and $70,000 per machine at year 2. Operating costs with a new machine purchased at year 2 are estimated to be $80,000 at year 3 and $85,000 at year 4. Instead of buying the old machines and replacing them at year 2, a new machine providing the necessary service can be purchased today (time 0) for a cost of $300,000. Service with either the old or new machines is needed for the next 4 years; therefore, a 4-year evaluation life should be used. It is estimated that a new machine purchased at time 0 will yield a salvage value of $80,000 at year 4. Operating costs with a new machine purchased now (time 0) are estimated at $75,000 at year 1, $80,000 at year 2, $85,000 at year 3, and $90,000 at year 4. Assuming a minimum discount rate of 15%, use a present worth cost analysis of each alternative to determine the least cost approach for providing the necessary service. Then, determine the 4 equal end-of-year revenues at years 1 through 4 for each alternative that would cover the cost of service and yield a 15% ROR to the investor.

A3-8 Suppose you want to borrow $200,000 to purchase a home. You have found terms that include a 30-year note with a (nominal) rate of 7.0% compounded monthly. The loan includes payment of 2.5 points, which will be paid out of the loan at closing. (One point is equal to 1% of the loan value).

A) Calculate the monthly mortgage payment.

B) How much interest is paid in the 2nd month's payment?

C) How much principal is paid in the 2nd month's payment?

D) Assuming the points are the only relevant closing costs associated with the loan, what is the APR on this loan?

The key concept to Case D is recognition that you will not have the full $200,000 loan value to apply against the purchase of the home, (due to the points), but you will have to pay back $200,000 in principal payments plus the accrued interest.

A3-9 Two used machines can be rebuilt for $50,000 per machine to provide necessary service for the next 2 years. The current value of each machine is $10,000 which may relate to an economic opportunity cost if the machines are kept and the sale value is foregone, or cash to help pay for a new machine (2nd alternative). If the units are rebuilt, the salvage of these machines is estimated at $30,000 per machine at the end of year 2 when the old machines will be replaced with one new machine capable of providing the same total service. The new machine would cost $340,000 at the end of year 2 and will yield a salvage value of $200,000 at the end of year 4. Operating costs associated with the used machines are $50,000 per machine at year 1 and $60,000 per machine at year 2. Operating costs with a new machine purchased at year 2 will be $80,000 at year 3 and $85,000 at year 4.

Instead of rebuilding the old machines and replacing them at year 2, a new machine providing the necessary service can be purchased today (time 0) for a cost of $300,000. Service with either the old or new machines is needed for the next 4 years; therefore, a 4-year evaluation life should be used. It is estimated that a new machine purchased at time 0 will yield a salvage value of $80,000 at year 4. Operating costs with a new machine purchased now (time 0) are estimated at $75,000 at year 1, $80,000 at year 2, $85,000 at year 3, and $90,000 at year 4. Assuming a minimum discount rate of 15%, use net present value analysis and determine the economically preferred approach for providing the necessary service.

A3-10 A small commercial airline needs to develop a maintenance program for equipment utilizing a new destination site or hub. The company has to make a decision regarding either outsourcing the necessary maintenance to a competitor with maintenance facilities already in place, or, developing their own on-site program. The anticipated end of year one cost of the outsource approach would be $8,500,000, this would increase to $9,000,000 at the end of year 2 and $9,500,000 at the end of years 3, 4 and 5.

If they choose to develop, the initial outlay would total $12,500,000 in equipment and spare parts inventory costs. Assume a zero salvage value at the end of year 5. Operating costs would be $5,000,000 in year 1, $5,500,000 in year two and $6,500,000 in each of years 3, 4 and 5. The investor's minimum rate of return is 10.0%. Use present worth cost analysis to determine which alternative is economically preferred and support those cost findings with an incremental NPV analysis.

The two five-year programs are summarized on the following diagrams in (000's):

Outsource, BTCF	0	–8,500	–9,000	–9,500	–9,500	–9,500
Year	0	1	2	3	4	5

Develop, BTCF	–12,500	–5,000	–5,500	–6,500	–6,500	–6,500
Year	0	1	2	3	4	5

A3-11 Suppose you want to acquire a computer for use during the next three years. After identifying the right machine, you are now considering whether it is economically better to purchase the unit with cash or to make beginning of month lease payments over the next 36 months (months 0–35). Sales tax is 7.0% and would apply to either the purchase price or the monthly lease payments described below. Shipping charges amount to $125 for either alternative and assume they would also be subject to sales tax. If you purchase the machine, the cost today is $2,400 and salvage is estimated at $300 at the end of the 36th month.

If you choose to lease, your payment will be $85 per month, beginning today. Neglect any option to purchase upon termination of the lease. Your minimum rate of return is a nominal 12.0% compounded monthly. Use a 36 month-life and make a nominal rate of return analysis to determine which alternative is economically preferred. This is for personal use so no federal or state income tax effects are considered relevant.

A3-12 A production facility is currently utilizing carbon steel tubing. The current process requires injection of chemicals to control tubing corrosion due to high temperatures and pressures and corrosive chlorides in the product. It is proposed to replace the carbon steel that cost $22 per foot 1 year ago, with chrome stainless steel tubing that would cost $60 per foot today, (time zero). 20,000 feet of tubing would be required and installation costs will total $500,000 (also at time zero).

Annual cost savings in chemicals, labor and chemical injection equipment are projected to be $400,000 in year 1 following the installation of the new tubing with savings escalating 7% per year in succeeding years. Use a 6-year evaluation life with a salvage value of zero at the end of year 6. Assume a 15% minimum ROR. Use NPV and ROR analyses to determine if installation of the chrome tubing is economically desirable. Assume the existing carbon steel tubing has no salvage value today, at time 0.

A3-13 An investment opportunity has projected costs and revenues as shown on the diagram in thousands of dollars.

	200	250	575	600	600	600
–450	–300	–450	–225	–150	–150	–250
0	1	2	3	4	5	6

The investor's minimum rate of return is 12% compounded annually. Calculate the project before-tax cash flow (BTCF) and then determine the ROR, NPV, PVR and Growth ROR for the project using the 6-year evaluation life. Then develop the cumulative cash position diagram to illustrate the meaning of the rate of return result. Finally, develop the cumulative NPV diagram and indicate the project maximum capital exposure, discounted payback, and NPV on your diagram.

A3-14 A manager is trying to evaluate the economics of purchasing or leasing a natural gas processing facility. It may be purchased and installed on company land for $1,600,000 or leased for $465,000 per year with beginning of year lease payments. With either alternative, the annual revenue to the plant for natural gas liquids is expected to be $3,500,000 with annual operating costs of $800,000. The life of the plant is estimated to be 8 years. If purchased, the net salvage value of the plant at the end of year 8 is estimated to be $1,000,000. For a 15% minimum rate of return, use net present value and rate of return to determine whether the manager should purchase or lease the processing facility.

A3-15 Your company has an existing fleet of eight 150-ton haul trucks and economic consideration is being given to either;

1) replace the 8 existing trucks with 6 new 200-ton trucks, or,

2) replace the existing truck beds with a new ultra light series capable of increasing the payload while maintaining the gross vehicle weight. This decision would reduce the number of operating trucks from the current 8 to 7 while maintaining current production, or,

3) repair and keep the existing 8 trucks,

The economic objective in this decision is to lower the overall cost of operations while maintaining the existing level of productivity. Listed below are the time diagrams for each alternative which includes costs for all modifications, training, repairs and operating costs for each alternative along with the relative capacities per truck. If six new trucks are purchased, all of the eight existing trucks will be sold at time zero for $200,000 per truck. If modified, only one truck will be sold for the same value of $200,000. Scenario 3 assumes that the entire existing fleet will have to be replaced at the end of year 4 with replacement costs and residual values also shown per machine.

6 New 200 Ton Trucks,
Summary of Costs & Residuals Per Truck (in 000's)

Year	0	1	2	3	4	5	6	7
Capital	(1,300)	—	—	—	—	—	—	—
Oper. Costs	—	(700)	(700)	(700)	(1,000)	(750)	(750)	(750)
Residual Value*	200	—	—	—	—	—	—	100

**In time zero this relates to before-tax value of each of the existing trucks to be sold.*

7 Modified Bed Trucks (150T to 170T),
Summary of Costs & Residuals Per Truck (in 000's)

Year	0	1	2	3	4	5	6	7
Capital	(175)	—	—	—	(210)	—	—	—
Oper. Costs	—	(750)	(730)	(730)	(825)	(775)	(775)	(775)
Residual Value*	200	—	—	—	—	—	—	50

**In time zero this relates to before-tax value of 1 existing truck that could be sold.*

8 Existing Trucks 150T Trucks,
Summary of Costs & Residuals Per Truck (in 000's)

Year	0	1	2	3	4	5	6	7
Capital	—	—	—	—	(1,200)	—	—	—
Oper. Costs	(100)	(730)	(730)	(730)	(730)	(700)	(700)	(700)
Residual Value*	—	—	—	—	100	—	—	600

The company has a before-tax, escalated (or nominal) minimum rate of return of 12%. Use present worth cost analysis and incremental net present value to determine from an economic viewpoint which alternative is best.

A3-16 You plan to purchase a vehicle that would cost $123,400 if you paid cash. That number is inclusive of all manufacturer or dealer prep fees. Instead of a cash purchase, you plan on putting 20% down ($24,680), and will borrow the balance (80%) of the cost of the vehicle. The finance office at the dealership is currently offering a 3-year, 36-month loan at a nominal 6.0% flat interest rate. Payments are $3,235.82 per month. The loan would require an additional one-time service fee due today of $1,850 to initiate the loan with this amount treated similar to points on a mortgage. The loan service fee is an additional cash cost to you, the buyer, and is not reflected in the cost of the vehicle described above. Since state laws vary, neglect all applicable sales tax and license fees which if included, could impact the economic decision.

A) Calculate the APR on the loan assuming you will borrow the money to purchase the vehicle.

B) Separate from the loan in Part A, if the residual value (sale value) of the vehicle at the end of month 36 is estimated by the dealer at $90,000; calculate the 36 beginning of month lease payments you would expect to pay starting at time zero if the relevant cost of borrowing money is a nominal interest rate of 6.0% compounded monthly?

C) If you had money earning 12% per year compounded monthly (opportunity cost of capital), calculate the present worth cost of each financial option in Parts A and B to determine which approach to financing the vehicle would provide for the use at the lowest present worth cost. Consider the $90,000 residual value to be the relevant sale value at the end of month 36 if you purchase with the borrowed money as you only plan to utilize the vehicle for the next 36 months.

A3-17 An oil lease containing an estimated 2,000,000 barrels of oil may be obtained at time zero for a lease bonus cost of $7,000,000. Additional time zero geological and geophysical (g&g) costs are estimated to total $700,000. These acquisition and g&g costs would be followed by development of the lease and would involve an end of year 1 investment of $5,000,000 in intangible drilling costs and $4,000,000 in tangible completion costs and equipment. Production in the latter half of year 1 is estimated at 150,000 barrels of oil equivalent (BOE). Year 2 production is estimated at 350,000 BOE with 275,000 in year 3 and 200,000 in year 4 when it is expected that the property would be sold for \$8,000,000 at the end of year 4. Assume a uniform selling price of \$75.00 per barrel of oil equivalent each year over the 4-year producing period. Operating costs are estimated to be \$15.00 per BOE and also forecasted to remain constant. Royalties are estimated at 12.5% of gross revenue. The investor's minimum rate of return is 15%. Calculate the project before-tax cash flows for evaluation periods 0 through 4 and determine the project rate of return, net present value, present value ratio and benefit-cost ratio.

CHAPTER 4

MUTUALLY EXCLUSIVE AND NON-MUTUALLY EXCLUSIVE PROJECT ANALYSIS

For economic analysis purposes, income-producing and service-producing alternatives must be broken into two sub-classifications which are: *(1) comparison of mutually exclusive alternatives, which means making an analysis of several alternatives from which only one can be selected, such as selecting the best way to provide service or to improve an existing operation or the best way to develop a new process, product, mining operation or oil/gas reserve; (2) comparison of non-mutually exclusive alternatives which means analyzing several alternatives from which more than one can be selected depending on capital or budget restrictions, such as ranking research, development and exploration projects to determine the best projects to fund with available dollars.* Analysis of mutually exclusive alternatives will be presented first in this chapter with non-mutually exclusive alternative analysis discussed in the latter pages of the chapter. It will be shown that valid discounted cash flow criteria such as rate of return, net present value and benefit-cost ratio are applied in very different ways in proper analysis of mutually exclusive and non-mutually exclusive alternative investments.

4.1 Analysis of Mutually Exclusive Income-Producing Alternatives Using Rate of Return, Net Value and Ratios

In any industry, classic illustration of mutually exclusive alternative analysis often involves evaluation of whether it is economically desirable to improve, expand or develop investment projects. Whenever you must make an economic choice between several alternative investment choices, and selecting one of the choices excludes in the foreseeable future being able to invest in the other choices, you are involved with mutually exclusive alternative analysis. In Chapter 3 we have already illustrated how incremental analysis of differences between alternative ways of providing the same service was the key to rate of return, net present value or ratio analysis of service producing alternatives. It will be illustrated in the following examples that *incremental analysis is the key to correct analysis of mutually exclusive income-producing alternatives with all discounted cash flow analysis techniques.* The words incremental, difference and marginal are used interchangeably by persons involved in evaluation work when referring to changes in costs or revenues that are incurred in going from one alternative to another or from one level of operation to another.

EXAMPLE 4-1 Mutually Exclusive Income-Producing Alternatives

Consider the analysis of two different ways, "A" and "B", of improving an existing process. As shown on the following time diagrams, "A" involves a small change costing $50,000 with savings and salvage as illustrated. "B" involves a much larger change costing $500,000 which includes the "A" changes with savings and salvage as shown. Assume $500,000 is available to invest and that other opportunities exist to invest any or all of it at a 15% ROR. Which, if either, of the mutually exclusive alternatives "A" and "B" should we select as our economic choice? Use ROR analysis, then verify your economic conclusions with NPV, NAV, NFV and PVR analysis.

Solution; ROR Analysis, Values in Thousands of Dollars

C = Cost, I = Savings, L = Salvage Value

A) C = 50 at 0; I = 50 at 1 . . . . I = 50 at 5; L = 50

PW Eq. $0 = -50 + 50(P/A_{i,5}) + 50(P/F_{i,5})$

By trial and error, $i = ROR_A = 100\% > i^* = 15\%$, so satisfactory

B) C = 500 at 0; I = 250 at 1 . . . . I = 250 at 5; L = 500

PW Eq. $0 = -500 + 250(P/A_{i,5}) + 500(P/F_{i,5})$

By trial and error, $i = ROR_B = 50\% > i^* = 15\%$, so satisfactory

The ROR results can also be obtained by dividing annual savings by initial cost and multiplying by 100, since initial cost equals salvage.

Many people think in terms of the project with the largest rate of return on total investment as always being economically best, but in fact, the largest rate of return project is not always the best economic choice. In this case, although "A" has a total investment rate of return of 100%, which is twice as large as the "B" rate of return, the investments differ in magnitude by a factor of ten. A smaller ROR on a bigger investment often is economically better than a bigger ROR on a smaller investment. Incremental analysis must be made to determine if the extra, (or incremental) $450,000 that will be invested in "B" over the required "A" investment, will be generating more or less profit (or savings), than the $450,000 would earn if invested elsewhere at the minimum rate of return of 15%. The incremental analysis is made for the bigger project "B" minus the smaller project "A" so that incremental cost is followed by incremental income giving:

B – A) C = 450   I = 200   I = 200   L = 450
0   1 5

PW Eq. $0 = -450 + 200(P/A_{i,5}) + 450(P/F_{i,5})$

$i = ROR_{B-A} = 44.4\% > 15\%$, Select "B."

It should be clear from an economic viewpoint that if $500,000 is available to invest, we would be better off with all of it invested in project "B". Our incremental analysis has broken project "B" into two components, one of which is like project "A", and the other is like the incremental project. Selecting project "B" effectively is equivalent to having $50,000 of the capital invested in project "A" earning a 100% ROR and $450,000 incremental investment earning a 44.4% ROR. Surely selecting "B" is better than selecting "A" which would give a 100% ROR on the $50,000 capital invested in "A" and require investing the remaining $450,000 elsewhere at the 15% minimum ROR. Incremental analysis is required to come to this correct conclusion and notice that it requires rejecting alternative "A" with the largest ROR of 100% on total investment.

Evaluation of mutually exclusive multiple investment alternatives (the situation where only one alternative may be selected from more than one investment choice) by rate of return analysis requires both total investment and incremental investment rate of return analysis. *The rate of return analysis concept for mutually exclusive alternatives is based on testing to see that each satisfactory level of investment meets two requirements as follows: (1) The rate of return on total individual project investment must be greater than or equal to the minimum rate of return, "i^*"; (2) The rate of return on incremental investment compared to the last satisfactory level of investment must be greater than or equal to the minimum ROR, "i^*". The largest level of investment that satisfies both criteria is the economic choice.* Analysis of total investment rate of return alone will not always lead to the correct economic choice because the project with the largest total investment rate of return is not always best. It is assumed that money not invested in a particular project can be invested elsewhere at the minimum rate of return, "i^*". Therefore, it is often preferable to invest a large amount of money at a moderate rate of return rather than a small amount at a large return with the remainder having to be invested elsewhere at a specified minimum rate of return. *These evaluation rules and concepts apply to growth rate of return analysis as well as regular rate of return analysis, since growth rate of return is just a special type of regular return.*

Net Value Analysis (Present, Annual, Future) of Mutually Exclusive Alternatives "A" and "B"

To illustrate the application of NPV, NAV and NFV to evaluate mutually exclusive investment alternatives these techniques will now be applied to evaluate alternatives "A" and "B" for the previously stated 15% minimum ROR.

	C	I	I	
A)	C = \$50	I = \$50	I = \$50	L = \$50
	0	1	5	
B)	C = \$500	I = \$250	I = \$250	L = \$500
	0	1	5	

$$NPV_A = 50\overset{3.352}{(P/A_{15\%,5})} + 50\overset{.4972}{(P/F_{15\%,5})} - 50 = +\$142.50$$

$$NPV_B = 250(P/A_{15\%,5}) + 500(P/F_{15\%,5}) - 500 = +\$586.60$$

$$NAV_A = 50 + 50\overset{.14832}{(A/F_{15\%,5})} - 50\overset{.29832}{(A/P_{15\%,5})} = +\$42.50$$

$$NAV_B = 250 + 500(A/F_{15\%,5}) - 500(A/P_{15\%,5}) = +\$175.00$$

$$NFV_A = 50\overset{6.742}{(F/A_{15\%,5})} + 50 - 50\overset{2.011}{(F/P_{15\%,5})} = +\$286.50$$

$$NFV_B = 250(F/A_{15\%,5}) + 500 - 500(F/P_{15\%,5}) = +\$1{,}180.00$$

We see that all the net value results are positive which consistently indicates that both alternatives "A" and "B" are satisfactory since they generate sufficient revenue to more than pay off the investments at the minimum ROR of 15%. To determine which alternative is best we must make incremental net value analysis just as we did for ROR analysis. We can get the incremental net value results either by looking at the differences between the total investment net values for the bigger investment minus the smaller, which is "B-A" in this case, or by working with the incremental costs, savings, and salvage. Exactly the same incremental net values are obtained either way.

B – A)	C = \$450	I = \$200	I = \$200	L = \$450
	0	1	5	

$$NPV_{B-A} = NPV_B - NPV_A$$
$$= 586.6 - 142.5 = +\$444.10 > 0, \text{ Select "B"}$$

$$\text{or} = 200\overset{3.352}{(P/A_{15\%,5})} + 450\overset{.4972}{(P/F_{15\%,5})} - 450 = +\$444.10$$

directly from the incremental data:

$$NAV_{B-A} = NAV_B - NAV_A = 175.0 - 42.5 = +\$132.50$$

$$NFV_{B-A} = NFV_B - NFV_A = 1{,}180.0 - 286.5 = +\$893.50$$

In each case the incremental net value results are positive, indicating a satisfactory incremental investment. The reason it is satisfactory can be shown by looking at the net value that would be received from investing the \$450,000 incremental capital elsewhere at $i^* = 15\%$.

C = \$450 at $i^* = 15\%$.

0 1 . . . . 5 $F = 450(F/P_{15\%,5}) = +\$904.95$

$$NPV = 904.95(\overset{0.4972}{P/F_{15\%,5}}) - 450 = \$0$$

Similarly, NAV = \$0 and NFV = \$0.

Money invested at the minimum ROR, "i^*", always has a zero net value. Obviously the positive incremental net value results for "B-A" are better than the zero net value that would be obtained by investing the money elsewhere at "i^*".

In summary, the net value analysis concept for evaluating mutually exclusive alternatives is based on two tests: (1) the net value on total individual project investment must be positive; (2) the incremental net value obtained in comparing the total investment net value to the net value of the last smaller satisfactory investment level must be positive. The largest level of investment that satisfies both criteria is the economic choice. This is always the alternative with the largest positive net value. This means, if you have a dozen mutually exclusive alternatives and calculate NPV, or NAV, or NFV for each, the economic choice will always be the alternative with the largest net value. When you select the mutually exclusive investment alternative with the largest net value as the economic choice, you are not omitting incremental analysis. Experience shows that incremental analysis always leads to selection of the project with the biggest net value on total investment as the economic choice. You can mathematically convert between NPV, NAV and NFV and therefore you must get the same economic conclusion using any of these techniques.

$$NPV = NAV(P/A_{i^*,n}) = NFV(P/F_{i^*,n})$$

Ratio Analysis of Mutually Exclusive Alternatives "A" and "B"

A) C = \$50   I = \$50   I = \$50

0   1 5   L = \$50

B) C = \$500   I = \$250   I = \$250

0   1 5   L = \$500

$PVR_A = NPV_A$ / PW Cost = 142.5/50 = 2.85 > 0, so satisfactory

$PVR_B = NPV_B$ / PW Cost = 586.6/500 = 1.17 > 0, so satisfactory

Project "A" has the bigger total investment ratio but the smaller project "B" ratio relates to ten times larger investment value. Getting smaller dollars of NPV per present worth cost dollar invested on larger investment often is a better mutually exclusive investment choice. Incremental analysis is the optimization analysis that answers the question concerning which of mutually exclusive alternatives "A" and "B" is the better investment. This is true with ratios the same as was illustrated earlier for ROR and net value analysis.

	C = \$450	I = \$200	I = \$200	
B – A)	0	1	5	L = \$450

$PVR_{B-A} = NPV_{B-A}$ / PW Investment
= 444/450 = 0.99 > 0 satisfactory

Accepting the incremental "B-A" investment indicates accepting project "B" over "A", even though the total investment ratio on "B" is less than "A". *As with ROR analysis, the mutually exclusive alternative with bigger ROR, PVR or Benefit Cost Ratio on total individual project investment often is not the better mutually exclusive investment. Incremental analysis along with total individual project investment analysis is the key to correct analysis of mutually exclusive choices.*

Since benefit cost ratio equals PVR plus one, it should be evident to the reader that either PVR or Benefit Cost Ratio analysis give the same conclusions, as long as the correct break-even ratios of zero for PVR and one for Benefit Cost Ratio are used.

4.2 Unequal Life Mutually Exclusive Income-Producing Alternatives and The Handling of Opportunity Costs in Evaluations

As discussed in Chapter 3, it is important to recognize that when using ROR, NAV or NFV techniques to analyze unequal life service-producing alternatives that generate no significant revenue, you must use a common evaluation life for all alternatives, normally the life of the longest life alternative. The only exception to this rule involves the evaluation of alternatives that do not have the opportunity to have revenue allocated to them, such as remediation work.

Analysis of unequal life income-producing alternatives is not a problem with NPV or ratio analysis because time zero is a common point in time for calculating NPV or ratios of either equal or unequal life alternatives. If you have unequal lives for different alternatives, the time value of money considerations are different in rate of return, annual value and future value calculations and you may choose the wrong alternative as being best if you do not get a common evaluation life. This merely means that you must calculate NFV at the same future point in time for all alternatives, or you must calculate NAV by spreading costs and revenues over the same number of years for all alternatives. *For ROR, net value or ratio analysis of unequal life income-producing alternatives, treat all projects as having equal lives which are equal to the longest life project with net revenues and costs of zero in the later years of shorter life projects.* Note that this is not the same technique presented in Chapter 3 to convert unequal life service-producing alternatives that have revenues associated with them, to equal life alternatives using either Method 1, 2 or 3. When projects have different starting dates, net present value must be calculated at the same point in time for all projects for the results to be comparable.

Incremental analysis of mutually exclusive service or income producing alternatives can also help investors understand why costs previously incurred in a project are not relevant to the decision of what is the best use of available capital budget dollars today. Money spent in the past is often defined as a sunk cost and generally, such expenditures are not economically relevant because these costs cancel in the incremental analysis, and what is left is the opportunity cost (if any). Opportunity costs are represented by the market value (or cash flow) of an asset that is passed up if that asset is kept rather than being sold. For example, if an investor keeps a building or piece of equipment and passes up selling it, an opportunity cost is incurred in the form of the revenue that is foregone, and that must be paid for from future development cash flows. Incremental analysis always properly accounts for sunk cost and opportunity cost considerations.

Actions taken by management to delay expenditures may create a negative opportunity cost, or actually add value to the property. An example involves investing additional capital in a negative profit general business unit (or an offshore petroleum platform or mining operation) in order to delay abandonment or reclamation costs. As long as the net present value of the alternatives calling for additional investment to defer abandonment has greater value than the net present value of abandonment now, deferring abandonment would be preferred from an economic viewpoint.

Finally, in analyzing either equal life or unequal life income-producing or service-producing alternatives, *changing the minimum discount rate may change the economic choice. You cannot use net value or ratio results calculated at a given discount rate such as 12% to reach valid economic decisions for a different minimum discount rate such as 25%. You must use net value and ratio results calculated using a discount rate representative of the opportunity cost of capital for consistent economic decision making.* The following examples illustrate these considerations.

Example 4-2 Analysis of Unequal Life Mutually Exclu sive Income Producing Alternatives with Sunk Costs and Opportunity Costs

Determine whether it is economically desirable to sell the development rights to a new process for $150,000 cash offer at time zero or to keep the rights and develop them using one of two development scenarios. The project net before-tax cash flows for each alternative are presented in the following time diagrams. These diagrams also reflect the money previously invested in developing this process. Use NPV, ROR and PVR analysis techniques to make this economic decision for a minimum rate of return of 15%. Then, consider the sensitivity of changing the discount rate to 20%. All dollar values are in 000's.

Year	-2	-1	0	1	2	3	4 8	9	10
(A) Develop	-100	-250	-200	-350	100	100	150 ... 150	-	-
(B) Develop	-100	-250	-300	-400	200	200	200 ... 200	200	200
(C) Sell	-100	-250	150	-	-	-	- .... -	-	-

Solution:

Example 4-1 emphasized that evaluating mutually exclusive alternatives was a two-step process: 1) evaluate individual alternatives to eliminate projects that do not achieve minimum economic objectives, 2) incremental analyses are made on the remaining projects. By challenging the smallest level of investment with the next largest investment option, you always choose the largest investment alternative satisfying both individual and incremental economic criterion. The incremental process will also prove that sunk costs are not relevant, only opportunity costs are to be considered so sunk costs are ignored in step 1 of this problem solution. Note also that the unequal lives are not an issue if the economic focus remains on the present value, rather than future or equivalent annual figures. The economic assumption is that zero cash flows will be realized in years 9 and 10 for option A, and years 1-10 if you decide to sell in option C.

Looking forward from time zero, alternative (A) yields the following economics, which are sometimes referred to as "point forward" economics:

Year	-2	-1	0	1	2	3	4	8	9	10
(A) Develop	~~100~~	~~250~~	-200	-350	100	100	150	150	-	-

NPV$_A$ @ 15% = $-200 - 350(P/F_{15\%,1}) + 100(P/A_{15\%,2})(P/F_{15\%,1})$
$+ 150(P/A_{15\%,5})(P/F_{15\%,3}) = -32.4 < 0$, reject A

ROR$_A$ = 13.2% < 15%, reject A

PVR$_A$ = $-32.5 / [\ 200 + 350(P/F_{15\%,1})\ ] = -0.06 < 0$, reject A

Note that all criteria lead to the same conclusion. Looking "point forward" in this model at time zero, there is not enough present worth positive cash flow to cover negative cash flow and add value to the investor's portfolio. Therefore, alternative (A) is rejected.

Year	-2	-1	0	1	2	3	4	8	9	10
(B) Develop	~~100~~	~~250~~	-300	-400	200	200	200	200	200	200

Once again, neglecting the previously incurred costs in year's -2 and -1, alternative (B) yields the following "point forward" economics:

NPV$_B$ @ 15% = $-300 - 400(P/F_{15\%,1}) + 200(P/A_{15\%,9})(P/F_{15\%,1})$
$= 182 > 0$, accept B

ROR$_B$ = 21.7% > 15%, accept B

PVR$_B$ = $182 / [\ 300 + 400(P/F_{15\%,1})\ ] = 0.28 > 0$, accept B

All criteria indicate that alternative (B) is economically satisfactory from this point forward compared to investing the money elsewhere at $i^* = 15\%$.

Year	-2	-1	0	1	2	3	4	8	9	10
(C) Sell	~~-100~~	~~-250~~	150	-	-	-	-.........	-	-	-

NPV_C @ 15% = 150 > 0, accept C

ROR_C = ∞% > 15%, accept C

PVR_C = 150 / 0 = ∞ > 0, accept C

Even though the projects have unequal lives, the use of present worth equations resulted in the zero cash flows having no impact. Unequal lives will require closer consideration when calculations involve measures of equivalent annual value or net future value.

Incremental analysis of those remaining satisfactory alternatives is next. Technically, we know this process will lead us to selecting alternative (B), since it has the largest individual NPV. However, alternative (C) has the largest ROR and PVR. Incremental analysis will demonstrate the consistency of each method in economic decision-making and also show how the sunk costs cancel and therefore cannot influence the economic decision. Incremental will also show what is relevant is the foregone opportunity to sell the property today which is incurred in keeping the project for continued development.

Year	-2	-1	0	1	2	3	4	8	9	10
(B-C) Dev-Sell	0	0	-450	-400	200	200	200	200	200	200

NPV_{B-C} @ 15% = $-450 - 400(P/F_{15\%,1}) + 200(P/A_{15\%,9})(P/F_{15\%,1})$

= 32 > 0, accept B over C

ROR_{B-C} = 16% > 15%, accept B over C

PVR_{B-C} = $32 / [\,450 + 400(P/F_{15\%,1})\,]$ = 0.04 > 0, accept B over C

Note how the B-C incremental diagram proves the theory that sunk costs are not relevant by removing them from the incremental time diagram. Instead of costs incurred in the past that are sunk, what is relevant is the opportunity foregone (opportunity cost) when cash flow from selling is passed up in order to keep the property and develop it. This subject matter is discussed again after tax considerations have been introduced in Section 9.3.

One final note on the economics of this example: looking at all sunk and point forward cash flows of a project is sometimes known as "life cycle" economics. In this case, while none of the overall economic alternatives would be favorable, this analysis would assess each scenario and offer the best economic scenario available from the existing conditions. This is a classic example where the financial considerations might override the economic decision and favor another alternative due to the impact of capital that might be sitting on the financial balance sheet for this project. Or, in rationing capital budget dollars, management might prefer to sell the project today and hope to add more value to the firm through other alternatives.

Analysis of Changing the Minimum Discount Rate to 20.0%:

From the individual economic analyses just completed, only Alternatives B and C have rates of return competitive with investing elsewhere at i* = 20.0%. Since the largest NPV is always the economic choice when evaluating mutually exclusive alternatives, only NPV will be illustrated here for i* = 20%.

$\mathbf{NPV_A}$ **@ 20%** = –104.8 < 0, so, reject A.

$\mathbf{NPV_B}$ **@ 20%** = + 38.5 > 0, so, B is acceptable compared to investing @ i* = 20.0%.

$\mathbf{NPV_C}$ **@ 20%** = + 150.0 > 0, so, C is the maximum NPV, select C.

The maximum project NPV is the Alternative C, which indicates the investor should sell today and invest the $150 in other opportunities where it could earn a 20.0% ROR and maximize the investor's economic value. This same sensitivity to discount rates can be expanded to a graphical format, for a range of i* values. This is often referred to as an *NPV Profile* and is illustrated in Figure 4-1.

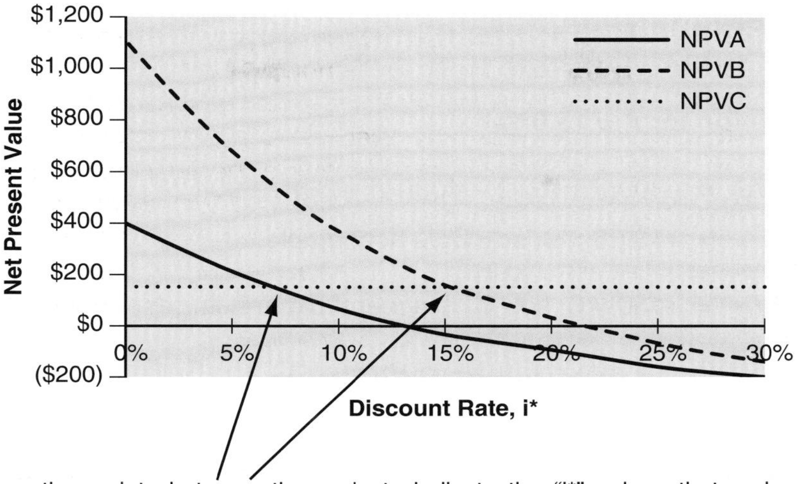

Intersection points between the projects indicate the "i*" values that make the projects a break-even. They also indicate the incremental rates of return between the respective alternatives. For example, ROR_{B-C} is equal to 15.98% as previously calculated. Since selling is a time zero value, its NPV is unaffected by the discount rate, with NPV remaining constant at $150 for all discount rates.

Figure 4-1 NPV Profile for Example 4-2, Alternatives A, B and C.

A variation of the analysis in Example 4-2 is presented to show *when mutually exclusive projects have different starting dates, you must calculate NPV for different alternatives at the same point in time for results to be comparable.*

EXAMPLE 4-3 Analysis of Mutually Exclusive Alternatives With Different Starting Dates With NPV, ROR and PVR.

Re-analyze mutually exclusive alternatives "B" and "C" as described in Example 4-2 using NPV, ROR and PVR analyses for i* = 15.0%, assuming the "B" development project starts at the end of year two, instead of time zero. All values are still in thousands.

(B) Develop	—	—	–300	–400	200	200
	0	1	2	3	4	12

(C) Sell	150	—	—	—	—	—
	0	1	2	3	4	12

Solution for i* = 15.0%:

$$NPV_B = -300(P/F_{15,2}) - 400(P/F_{15,3}) + 200(P/A_{15,9})(P/F_{15,3})$$
$$= +137.6 > 0, \text{ so, "B" is acceptable.}$$

$$NPV_C = +150 > 0, \text{ so, "C" is acceptable and largest NPV.}$$

Selecting the maximum NPV, Project "C" (or Selling) is the economic choice. This is a different economic decision than was reached for the project timing described in Example 4-2 where "B" Develop started at time zero with NPV of +182.0.

Incremental Rate of Return Analysis

(B-C) Dev-Sell	–150	—	–300	–400	200	200
	0	1	2	3	4	12

PW EQ: $0 = -150 - 300(P/F_{i,2}) - 400(P/F_{i,3}) + 200(P/A_{i,9})(P/F_{i,3})$

By calculator, ROR, i = 14.56% < 15.0% so, reject Develop, accept Sell

Incremental PVR Analysis

$$PVR_{B\text{-}C} = \text{Incremental NPV / Incremental PW Costs}$$
$$= (137.6 - 150) / \{150 + 300(P/F_{15,2}) + 400(P/F_{15,3})\}$$
$$= -12.4 / 639.83 = -0.0194 < 0$$

so, reject Develop, accept Sell

When properly applied, NPV, ROR, GROR, PVR and B/C Ratio criteria will lead to the same economic conclusion in the evaluation of mutually exclusive alternatives. If projects have different starting dates, for valid NPV analysis of mutually exclusive alternatives, project NPV's must be calculated at the same point in time before proper interpretation of the results can be made.

EXAMPLE 4-4 Mutually Exclusive Project Analysis Case Study

An existing production facility must be shut down unless an environmental capital cost of $150 million is incurred now at year 0. This improvement will enable production to continue and generate estimated profits of $60 million per year for each of the next 8 years when salvage value of the facility is projected to be zero. An alternative under consideration would combine process improvement and expansion with an environmental cost change for a cost of $200 million now at year 0, plus $150 million cost at year 1 to generate estimated project profits of $60 million in year 1 and $120 million profit per year in each of years 2 through 8. The minimum ROR is 12%. Evaluate which of these alternatives is better using ROR, NPV and PVR analysis. Then, change the minimum ROR to 25% and analyze the alternatives using the same techniques.

Solution, all values in millions of dollars:

A)

C = 150	I = 60	I = 60	I = 60	I = 60	I = 60
0	1	2	3	4	8

B)

	I = 60				
C = 200	C = 150	I = 120	I = 120	I = 120	I = 120
0	1	2	3	4	8

ROR Analysis

A) PW Eq: $150 = 60(P/A_{i,8})$, $i = ROR_A = 36.7\% > i^* = 12\%$

B) PW Eq: $200 = -90(P/F_{i,1}) + 120(P/A_{i,7})(P/F_{i,1})$

$i = ROR_B = 28.6\% > i^* = 12\%$

Both projects have acceptable economics, but incremental rate of return analysis is required to determine if the extra incremental investment in "B" generates sufficient incremental revenues to justify the additional $50 million cost at time zero and the additional $150 million cost at year one.

$$\textbf{B – A)}\quad \underset{0}{C = 50}\quad \underset{1}{C = 150}\quad \underset{2}{I = 60}\quad \underset{3}{I = 60}\quad \underset{4\,\ldots\ldots}{I = 60}\quad \underset{8}{I = 60}$$

B –A) PW Eq: $50 = -150(P/F_{i,1}) + 60(P/A_{i,7})(P/F_{i,1})$

$i = ROR_{B-A} = 21\% > i^* = 12\%$

so select "B".

Note that once again, the project with biggest ROR on total investment is not the economic choice.

NPV Analysis

$$NPV_A = 60(\overset{4.968}{P/A_{12\%,8}}) - 150 = +\$148.1$$

$$NPV_B = 120(\overset{4.564}{P/A_{12\%,7}})(\overset{0.8929}{P/F_{12\%,1}}) - 90(\overset{0.8929}{P/F_{12\%,1}}) - 200$$
$$= +\$208.7$$

Incremental analysis verifies the selection of the project with the largest total investment NPV which is "B".

$NPV_{B\text{-}A} = NPV_B - NPV_A = 208.7 - 148.1 = 60.6 > 0$, so select "B".

Incremental analysis of mutually exclusive alternatives always leads to selection of the investment project with largest NPV on total investment. Often this is not the project with the largest ROR or PVR on total investment. However, incremental analysis gives the same economic conclusion with all techniques of analysis.

PVR Analysis

$$PVR_A = \frac{NPV_A}{PW\ Cost_A} = \frac{148.1}{150} = 0.99 > 0$$

$$PVR_B = \frac{NPV_B}{PW\ Cost_B} = \frac{208.7}{200 + 90(P/F_{12\%,1})} = 0.74 > 0$$

Which alternative is better, "A" or "B"? "A" is not necessarily preferred just because it has the largest ratio on total investment. As with ROR and NPV, incremental analysis must be made and Present Worth Cost "B-A" is taken from incremental "B-A" time diagram and does not equal Present Worth Cost B minus Present Worth Cost A because of the effect of year 1 income on the year 1 total and incremental investment net costs.

$$\mathbf{PVR_{B-A}} = \frac{NPV_{B-A}}{PW\ Cost_{B-A}} = \frac{208.7 - 148.1}{50 + 150(P/F_{12\%,1})}$$

$= 0.33 > 0$, so select "B", consistent with the ROR and NPV results.

See the incremental "B-A" time diagram for verification that the incremental costs are 50 in year 0 and 150 in year 1.

Benefit cost ratio analysis gives the same conclusions following the PVR analysis procedure. Remember that benefit cost ratio equals PVR plus one, and one is the break-even ratio with benefit cost ratio analysis while zero is the break-even ratio with PVR analysis.

Change i^* to 25% :

ROR Analysis

A) $ROR_A = 36.7\% > i^* = 25\%$

B) $ROR_B = 28.6\% > i^* = 25\%$

Project ROR for each alternative is greater than the new minimum ROR, indicating acceptable economics for both. Incremental analysis is the optimization analysis that tells whether "A" or "B" is the better economic choice.

B-A) $ROR_{B-A} = 21\% < i^* = 25\%$, so reject "B"

Since the "B-A" ROR is less than "$i^* = 25\%$", the incremental year 0 and year 1 expenditures in alternative "B" over "A" are not justified. Alternative "A" becomes the correct investment choice. Recognize the critical importance of minimum ROR to project economics. Changing "i^*" from 12% to 25% switches the economic choice of investment from alternative "B" to "A". NPV and PVR analysis verify this conclusion.

NPV Analysis for $i^* = 25\%$

$$NPV_A = 60\overset{3.329}{(P/A_{25\%,8})} - 150 = +\$49.74$$

$$NPV_B = 120\overset{3.161}{(P/A_{25\%,7})}\overset{0.8000}{(P/F_{25\%,1})} - 90\overset{0.8000}{(P/F_{25\%,1})} - 200$$
$$= +\$31.46$$

At $i^* = 25\%$, alternative "A" gives the largest NPV and is therefore the correct economic choice. Incremental evaluation confirms this:

$NPV_{B\text{-}A} = 31.46 - 49.74 = -18.28$, so reject "B"

Note that you cannot use the NPV results calculated for a 12% discount rate to achieve valid economic conclusions for a 25% discount rate.

PVR Analysis for $i^* = 25\%$

$$PVR_A = \frac{NPV_A}{PW\ Cost_A} = \frac{49.74}{150} = .33 > 0$$

$$PVR_B = \frac{NPV_B}{PW\ Cost_B} = \frac{31.46}{200 + 90(P/F_{25\%,1})} = 0.116 > 0$$

$$PVR_{B-A} = \frac{NPV_{B-A}}{PW\ Cost_{B-A}} = \frac{31.46 - 49.74}{50 + 150(P/F_{25\%,1})}$$
$$= -.10 < 0, \text{ so reject "B"}$$

NPV and incremental ROR and PVR indicate that alternative "A" is the correct investment choice when the minimum rate of return is 25%. Note that NPV and PVR must be recalculated at the appropriate minimum ROR in order to make correct economic decisions. In this example, NPV and PVR at $i^* = 12\%$ cannot be used to evaluate the alternatives when the minimum rate of return has changed to 25%.

4.3 Mutually Exclusive Investment Analysis Using Growth Rate of Return and Future Worth Profit Methods

It was mentioned in the summary of the Example 4-1 ROR analysis that Growth ROR analysis is applied to evaluate mutually exclusive alternatives in the same way regular ROR analysis is applied. This means calculating Growth ROR on both total investments and incremental investments to verify that both are greater than the minimum ROR, "i^*".

Looking at future worth profit for decision purposes is just a variation of the Growth ROR or Net Future Value evaluation techniques. *The objective of all investments from an economic viewpoint is to maximize the profit that can be accumulated at any specified future point in time from a given amount of starting capital.* Instead of using analysis methods such as ROR, Growth ROR, NPV, NAV, NFV or PVR to achieve that investment objective, another valid evaluation approach is to directly calculate the future worth profit (future value) that can be generated by investing a given amount of capital in different ways and assuming the profits can be reinvested at the minimum ROR, "i^*", when the profits are received. The investment choice that gives the maximum future worth profit is the same choice we would get using ROR, Growth ROR, NPV, NAV, NFV or PVR analyses. The following example illustrates the Growth ROR and future worth profit techniques.

EXAMPLE 4-5 Growth ROR and Future Worth Profit Analysis

Use Growth ROR analysis for a minimum rate of return of 15% to determine which of the following mutually exclusive alternatives, "A" or "B", is best. Verify the result with future worth profit analysis and NPV analysis.

All Values in Thousands of Dollars, C = Cost, I = Income, L = Salvage

A) C = 200   I = 80   I = 80   L = 200
0   1 8

B) C = 300   I = 150   I = 140 Declining Gradient   L = 0
0   1   2 8

Solution:

Both Growth ROR and Future Worth Profit analysis, as well as NPV, NAV, NFV and regular ROR analysis assume that residual capital not invested in one of the projects and incomes as they are received can be invested elsewhere at the minimum ROR, which is $i^* = 15\%$ for this analysis. This gives the following Growth ROR and future worth income (profit) calculations:

Growth Rate of Return Analysis

Alternative "A":

A)	C = 200	I = 80	I = 80	L = 200
	0	1.	8	

Reinvest "I" and "L" at $i^* = 15\%$

			C = 200
—	C = 80	C = 80	F = 1,298
0	1.	8	

where $F = 80(F/A_{15\%,8}) + 200 = +1{,}298$

A + Reinvestment of Income

C = 200	—	—	F = 1,298
0	1.	8	

Growth ROR_A PW Eq: $200 = 1{,}298(P/F_{i,8})$

Growth ROR_A $i = 26.5\% > i^* = 15\%$, so satisfactory

Alternative "B":

B)	C = 300	I = 150	I = 140	declining gradient	L = 0
	0	1	2	8	

Reinvest Income at $i^* = 15\%$

—	C = 150	C = 140	declining gradient	F = 1,677
0	1	2	8	

where $F = [150 - 10(A/G_{15\%,8})](F/A_{15\%,8}) = 1{,}677$

B + Reinvestment of Income

C = 300	—	—	—	F = 1,677
0	1	2	8	

Growth ROR_B PW Eq: $300 = 1{,}677(P/F_{i,8})$

Growth ROR_B, $i = 24.1\% > i^* = 15\%$, so satisfactory

Incremental Growth ROR Analysis ("B-A")

(B–A)	C = 100	—	—	—	F = 379
	0	1	2.	8	

Growth ROR_{B-A} PW Eq: $100 = 379(P/F_{i,8})$

Growth $ROR_{B-A} = i = 18.4\% > i^* = 15\%$, indicating select "B"

Project "B" does not have the largest Growth ROR on total investment but incremental analysis indicates that "B" is the economic choice.

Future Worth Profit Analysis

Future worth profit analysis uses the future worth profit calculations from the Growth ROR analyses. If \$300 thousand is available to invest, putting \$200 thousand of it into alternative "A" and reinvesting the profits at $i^* = 15\%$ will generate a future value of \$1,298 thousand in 8 years. Investing elsewhere the \$100 thousand of our \$300 thousand that is not needed if we choose "A" gives:

(B–A)	C = 100	—	—	F = 100(F/P$_{15\%,8}$) (3.059) = \$305.90
	0	1	8	

Therefore, the total future value 8 years from now of \$200 thousand invested in project "A" and \$100 thousand elsewhere is \$1,298 thousand + \$305.9 thousand or \$1,604 thousand. This is not as great as the future worth of "B" calculated to be \$1,677 thousand, so select "B". This is the same conclusion reached with Growth ROR analysis. NPV analysis indicates select "B" as follows:

$$NPV_A = -200 + 80(\overset{4.487}{P/A_{15\%,8}}) + 200(\overset{0.3269}{P/F_{15\%,8}}) = +\$224$$

$$NPV_B = -300 + [150 - 10(\overset{2.781}{A/G_{15\%,8}})](\overset{4.487}{P/A_{15\%,8}}) = +\$248$$

Ordinary compound interest ROR analysis cannot be used on this problem and many similar problems because of difficulties encountered with the incremental ROR analysis. Evaluation of ordinary compound interest ROR on total investment shows that the rates of return on projects "A" and "B" are satisfactory. Incremental analysis gives the following time diagram:

(B-A)	C = 100	I = 70	I = 60 . . . . . I = 0	L = –200
	0	1	2 8	

This time diagram has incremental cost followed by incremental income followed by negative incremental salvage value which is the same as incremental cost. This is the type of analysis situation that generates the dual ROR problem discussed later in this chapter. Regular ROR analysis cannot be used in this situation for reasons that will be given later. This is why it is important to be familiar with other techniques of analysis such as Growth ROR, Future Worth Profit, NPV, NAV, NFV or PVR.

4.4 Changing the Minimum Rate of Return with Time

The minimum rate of return (opportunity cost of capital or hurdle rate) represents the rate of return that we think we could get by investing our money elsewhere, both now and in the future for the period of time covered by the project evaluation life. There is little reason to expect that our other opportunities will remain uniformly the same over a long period of time. While other opportunities for the investment of capital now may be at $i^* =$ 10%, we may expect a major project with a projected 20% ROR to be developed starting three years from now which could absorb all of our available capital and raise "i^*" to 20%. *For analyses with minimum rates of return that change with time, NPV, NFV, PVR and Future Worth Profit analysis are recommended as the best and really the only usable analysis methods.* Regular ROR and Growth ROR are not always consistent decision criteria if you do not have a single minimum ROR to which you can compare them. Similarly, you cannot calculate NAV with different minimum rate of return values at different points in time. For analysis simplification reasons, most investors including major companies assume their minimum ROR is uniform and equal over project evaluation lives. However, changing the minimum rate of return is illustrated in the following example to demonstrate proper economic analysis techniques for this situation.

EXAMPLE 4-6 Effect of Changing the Minimum Rate of Return With Time

Compare the economic potential of mutually exclusive investments "A" and "B" using NPV and rate of return analysis. Assume the minimum rate of return is 30.0% in years one and two, changing to 12.0% in years three through ten. Then re-evaluate the investments using a 12.0% minimum rate of return over the entire ten year project life and then again using a 30.0% minimum rate of return over the entire ten year project life. Comparison of these results emphasizes the importance of the minimum rate of return in investment decision-making from an economic viewpoint.

A)	C=20	I=10	I=10	I=10	I=10	L=20
	0	1	2	3.	10	
B)	C=30	I=12	I=12	I=12	I=12	L=30
	0	1	2	3.	10	

Solution, All Values in Thousands of Dollars:

Net Present Value, Changing i* From 30% in Years 1 & 2 to 12% Over Years 3 to 10

$$NPV_A = -20 + 10(P/A_{30,2}) + 10(P/A_{12,8})(P/F_{30,2}) + 20(P/F_{12,8})(P/F_{30,2}) = +27.78$$

$$NPV_B = -30 + 12(P/A_{30,2}) + 12(P/A_{12,8})(P/F_{30,2}) + 30(P/F_{12,8})(P/F_{30,2}) = +28.78$$

These results indicate virtual break-even economics between "A" and "B" with a very slight one thousand dollar present value advantage to "B." However, if we consider the minimum rate of return to be uniform and equal over time at either 12.0% or 30.0%, as most investors usually do, we get different results.

Net Present Value, i* = 12% Over the Entire Project Life

$NPV_A = -20 + 10(P/A_{12,10}) + 20(P/F_{12,10}) = +42.94$

$NPV_B = -30 + 12(P/A_{12,10}) + 30(P/F_{12,10}) = +47.46$

Select B with Largest NPV

Net Present Value, i* = 30% Over the Entire Project Life

$NPV_A = -20 + 10(P/A_{30,10}) + 20(P/F_{30,10}) = +12.37$

Select A with Largest NPV

$NPV_B = -30 + 12(P/A_{30,10}) + 30(P/F_{30,10}) = +9.27$

Assuming uniformly equal discount rates of 12.0% or 30.0% has given different economic conclusions than the break-even economic conclusion reached by changing the discount rate with time in the initial analysis. Most companies do not want to get involved in the additional level of confusion involved with changing the discount rate with respect to time. Therefore, even though a company knows they have other opportunities for investing capital at a relatively high rate of return such as 30.0% for the next several years, followed by an assumed lower rate such as 12.0% , they simplify the analysis by using a 12.0% rate of return over the entire evaluation life. This example shows that such a simplifying assumption, with respect to the evaluation discount rate, can have an effect on economic investment decision-making.

Rate of Return Analysis

PW Eq $_A$ $0 = -20 + 10(P/A_{i,10}) + 20(P/F_{i,10})$
By Trial and Error, $i = ROR_A = 50.0\% > i^* = 30.0\%$ or 12.0%, so satisfactory

PW Eq $_B$ $0 = -30 + 12(P/A_{i,10}) + 30(P/F_{i,10})$
By Trial and Error, $i = ROR_B = 40.0\% > i^* = 30.0\%$ or 12.0%, so satisfactory

Incremental rate of return analysis is needed now to determine the optimum choice since both "A" and "B" have satisfactory total investment rates of return compared with investing money elsewhere at either $i^* = 30.0\%$ or $i^* = 12.0\%$.

B-A)	C=10	I=2	I=2	I=2...........	I=2	L=10
	0	1	2	3...........	10	

PW Eq $_{B\text{-}A}$ $0 = -10 + 2(P/A_{i,10}) + 10(P/F_{i,10})$

By Trial and Error, $i = ROR_{B\text{-}A} = 20.0\% < i^* = 30.0\%$ but $> 12.0\%$

The investor cannot tell with rate of return analysis whether the incremental "B-A" investment is satisfactory or not relative to investing elsewhere at 30.0% over the next two years and at 12.0% over the following eight years. The fact that rate of return analysis of projects often breaks down and cannot be used when discount rates that vary with time possibly is one of the main reasons that changing the discount rate with time is not more commonly applied in industry practice. A large majority of companies emphasize rate of return analysis over the other techniques of analysis and that cannot be done if discount rates are changed with time. Notice that for a uniform minimum discount rate of either 12.0% or 30.0% over all ten years, incremental rate of return analysis gives economic conclusions consistent with NPV analysis conclusions. Select "B" if $i^* = 12.0\%$, select "A" if $i^* = 30.0\%$.

Finally, if firms are utilizing a discount rate based on financial cost of capital, that number is very likely to be changing over project lives the same as opportunity cost of capital changes. Once again however, rather than trying to forecast those future changes, most companies use a financial cost of capital calculated today, as reflecting the average financial cost of capital over the project life. We do not advocate the use of financial cost of capital unless unlimited financing is assumed to exist so that financial cost of capital equals opportunity cost of capital. Remember that it is always opportunity cost of capital that is relevant for valid discounted cash flow analysis of investments.

4.5 Differences Between Net Value Analysis and Cost Analysis

There is a tendency for people to get confused concerning the difference between Present Worth (PW), Annual Worth (AW), or Future Worth (FW) cost analysis of service-producing alternatives and Net Present Value (NPV), Net Annual Value (NAV) and Net Future Value (NFV) analysis of income-producing alternatives or differences between service-producing alternatives. They are similar but very different because of sign convention differences. *Cost analysis is used to evaluate service-producing investments. When costs carry a positive sign and any revenues or salvage values are negative, the net cost (present, annual or future, discounted at "i^*") is a positive number. With this sign convention for analyzing alternative ways of providing a service, the minimum cost option is selected. Net value analysis, however, is used to assess either income-producing projects or incremental differences between service-producing projects using conventional cash flow analysis sign convention where costs are negative and revenues are positive, so the alternative yielding maximum net value is selected.*

To utilize cost analysis in the evaluation of service-producing alternatives, you work with the given or estimated costs for each individual alternative way of providing a service. To utilize net value analysis in service evaluations, you must work with incremental savings that incremental costs will generate. Incremental analysis identifies the mutually exclusive investments to which NPV may be applied. Proper application of ROR requires an incremental analysis of mutually exclusive alternatives to consistently achieve the same economic conclusions reached by NPV alone. This concept of incremental analysis is demonstrated in Example 4-7.

EXAMPLE 4-7 A Comparison of Present Worth Cost and Net Present Value Analysis Criteria

Economic analysis of the optimum thickness of insulation for a steam line needs to be made for an investor with a minimum rate of return, i* = 12.0%. Engineering has arrived at the following estimates for installed insulation costs and the annual heat loss costs resulting for the different amounts of insulation. This data is summarized in the following table:

Insulation Thickness	Initial Investment	Cost of Annual Heat Loss (Per Year)
0″	$ 0	$40,000
1″	$ 60,000	$20,000
2″	$ 85,000	$10,000
3″	$118,000	$ 6,000

Assume the insulation and project life are eight years with zero salvage value and base your analysis results on both present worth cost analysis and net present value analysis. The 0" option represents the current situation, so in calculating net present value, compare the current situation with the other amounts of insulation.

Solution: Present Worth Cost Analysis

0″ Insulation $40{,}000(P/A_{12,8}) = \$198{,}704$

1″ Insulation $20{,}000(P/A_{12,8}) + 60{,}000 = \$159{,}352$

2″ Insulation $10{,}000(P/A_{12,8}) + 85{,}000 = \$134{,}676$* Minimum Cost

3″ Insulation $6{,}000(P/A_{12,8}) + 118{,}000 = \$147{,}805$

* Selecting two inches of insulation will minimize the present worth cost. This is illustrated in Figure 4-2.

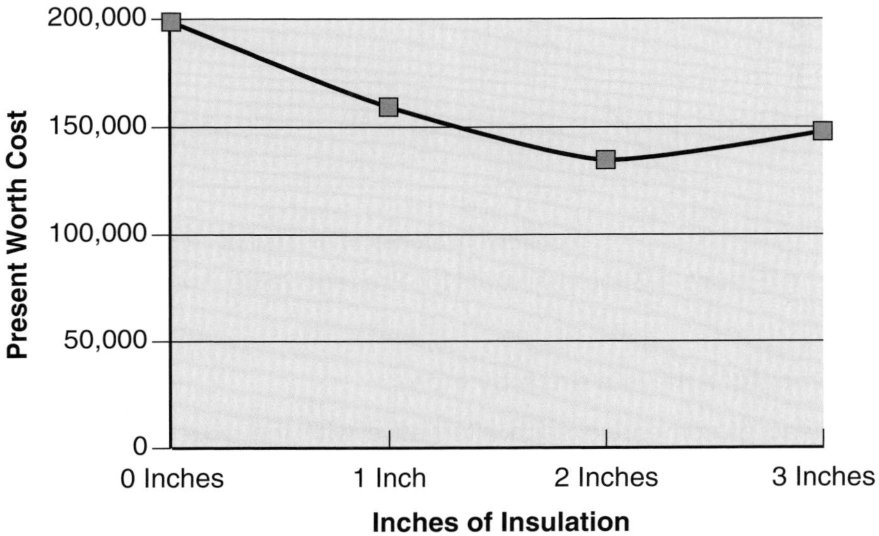

Figure 4-2 Present Worth Cost Analysis

Net Present Value (Incremental Analysis)

For NPV analysis, calculate the incremental savings for one, two and three inches of insulation compared to the current situation of no insulation. In other words, if $60,000 is spent today for one inch of insulation, the investor can save $20,000 in annual heat loss costs –20,000 – (–40,000) = +20,000 savings

$$1''\text{–}0'' \quad 20{,}000(P/A_{12,8}) - 60{,}000 = \$39{,}352$$
$$2''\text{–}0'' \quad 30{,}000(P/A_{12,8}) - 85{,}000 = \$64{,}028 \text{ * Maximum NPV}$$
$$3''\text{–}0'' \quad 34{,}000(P/A_{12,8}) - 118{,}000 = \$50{,}899$$

* Selecting two inches of insulation now maximizes the net present value obtainable from these mutually exclusive investment alternatives. This is illustrated in Figure 4-3.

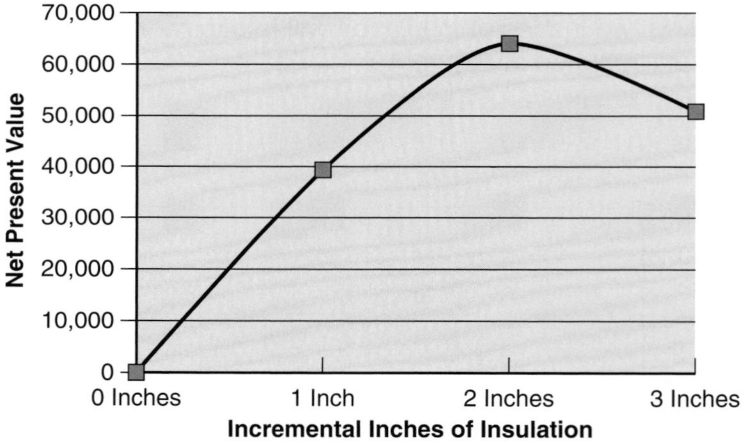

Figure 4-3 Incremental Net Present Value Analysis

Incremental Analysis (Inch by Inch)

Instead of comparing each alternative with the current scenario of zero inches, each additional one-inch of insulation investment could be thought of as representing mutually exclusively income producing (savings) alternatives. These alternatives range from doing nothing (0″ option) to spending the money for 3″ of insulation. When the alternatives are compared with the current "do nothing" scenario, the individual economics were determined. Next, the inch-by-inch incremental analysis for each of these mutually exclusive alternatives is presented.

1″–0″ 20,000($P/A_{12,8}$) – 60,000 = \$39,352

As discussed in previous examples in Chapter 4, the incremental NPV of \$39,352 tells us that 1″ is better than doing nothing. Therefore, the next level of initial capital investment is compared to the last satisfactory level, as follows:

2″–1″ 10,000($P/A_{12,8}$) – 25,000 = \$24,676

So, 2″ add value over the 1″ option.
Note also that the NPV2″ – NPV 1″ gives the same result:

\$64,028 – \$39,352 = \$24,676

Comparing the next level of investment to the last satisfactory level gives:

3″–2″ 4,000($P/A_{12,8}$) – 33,000 = –\$13,129

Select the largest level of investment for which incremental economics are satisfactory. This is two inches of insulation as determined by the earlier incremental NPV analysis.

The inch by inch incremental process would be more essential had rate of return analysis been asked for in this problem as investors can't expect individual total investment rates of return to consistently determine which alternative is best. In this example, the results would be the same by relying on individual ROR criteria, but this is not always the case.

Alternative	ROR
1" – 0"	29%
2" – 0"	31%
3" – 0"	23%

This analysis of mutually exclusive options using rate of return alone does correctly suggest that each option is preferred to doing nothing and luckily, that the 2" option is preferred. But this analysis and conclusion are by chance since we don't always select the mutually exclusive alternative with the largest individual ROR. Therefore, incremental analysis of those alternatives is key when using ROR, Ratios or Growth ROR:

Alternative	ROR	
1" – 0"	29%	1" is preferred to doing nothing
2" – 1"	37%	2" is preferred to the 1" option
3" – 2"	-1%	2" is preferred to the 3" option

The 2" option is the largest level of investment satisfying both the individual and incremental economic criteria and is the economic choice.

4.6 Effect of Evaluation Life on Economic Analysis Results

Because of the time value of money, cash flow realized 15 or 20 years in the future has less impact on project economics than cash flow realized in the first 10 years of project life. For shorter life projects with evaluation lives under 10 years, the evaluation life used can affect the economic choice significantly. For example, sometimes the life over which we choose to evaluate a process improvement is very arbitrarily chosen due to the uncertainty associated with projecting savings in certain process analyses. The following illustration shows how evaluation life can affect economic results in this relatively short evaluation life situation.

EXAMPLE 4-8 Effect of Evaluation Life on Comparison of Two Alternatives

Evaluate two different levels of improvement being considered for an existing process. The new equipment costs and projected annual savings in labor and materials are as follows:

	Equipment Cost	Projected Annual Savings
Level 1	$200,000	$125,000
Level 2	$350,000	$180,000

For a minimum ROR of 20% evaluate Levels 1 and 2 using NPV analysis assuming zero salvage value for (A) a 3 year evaluation life, and (B) a 5 year evaluation life. (C) For what evaluation life would there be no economic differences between the alternatives?

Solution, All Values in Thousands of Dollars:

A) 3 Year Life

$$NPV_1 = 125(\overset{2.106}{P/A_{20\%,3}}) - 200 = +\$63.25 \quad \text{Select Maximum NPV}$$

$$NPV_2 = 180(\overset{2.106}{P/A_{20\%,3}}) - 350 = +\$29.08$$

B) 5 Year Life

Increasing the evaluation life enhances the economics of both alternatives. However, the economics of bigger initial cost alternatives are always enhanced relatively more rapidly than smaller initial cost alternatives by lengthening evaluation life (or lowering the minimum discount rate). In this case the economic choice switches to selecting Level 2 for a 5 year life whereas Level 1 was preferred for a 3 year life.

$$NPV_1 = 125(\overset{2.991}{P/A_{20\%,5}}) - 200 = +\$173.88$$

$$NPV_2 = 180(\overset{2.991}{P/A_{20\%,5}}) - 350 = +\$188.38 \quad \text{Select Maximum NPV}$$

C) Break-even Life "n"

When there are no economic differences between the alternatives, NPV_1 will equal NPV_2. If we write an equation setting NPV_1=NPV_2 for an unknown life "n", we can solve for the break-even life "n".

$$125(P/A_{20\%,n}) - 200 = 180(P/A_{20\%,n}) - 350$$

$$\text{or, } 150 = 55(P/A_{20\%,n})$$

$$(P/A_{20\%,n}) = 150/55 = 2.727$$

By interpolation in the $P/A_{i,n}$ factor column of the 20% tables we get n = 4.34 years. Select Level 2 for an evaluation life greater than 4.34 years. Select Level 1 for an evaluation life less than 4.34 years.

4.7 Investment Analysis When Income or Savings Precedes Costs

When income or savings precedes cost, ROR analysis leads to the calculation of "i" values that have rate of reinvestment requirement meaning instead of rate of return meaning. These results must be used very differently than ROR results since "rate of reinvestment requirement" results greater than the minimum ROR are unsatisfactory (instead of satisfactory with regular ROR). This is illustrated in Examples 4-9 and 4-10.

EXAMPLE 4-9 Analysis of Mutually Exclusive Alternatives When Income Precedes Cost

Consider the following problem. Evaluate the following two mutually exclusive alternatives using ROR, Growth ROR, Future Worth Profit, NPV and PVR. The minimum rate of return $i^* = 10\%$.

A) C = $100,000 (year 0); — (year 1 . . . . 5) —; L = $305,200 (year 5)

B) C = $100,000 (year 0); I = $41,060 (year 1 . . . . 5) I = $41,060; L = $0 (year 5)

Rate of Return Analysis

A) PW Eq: $0 = -100{,}000 + 305{,}200(P/F_{i,5})$, $i = ROR_A = 25\%$

B) PW Eq: $0 = -100{,}000 + 41{,}060(P/A_{i,5})$, $i = ROR_B = 30\%$

Since the initial costs of projects "A" and "B" are equal, many people conclude there are no incremental differences in the projects, so, "B" is the choice, since "B" has the larger ROR on total investment. This is incorrect! Looking at "A-B" so incremental cost is followed by incremental revenue we get the following: (remember negative incremental income is equivalent to cost)

A–B) C = $0 (year 0); C = $41,060 (year 1 . . . . 5) C = $41,060; L = $305,200 (year 5)

A-B) PW Eq: $0 = -41{,}060(P/A_{i,5}) + 305{,}200(P/F_{i,5})$

$ROR_{A\text{-}B}$, $i = 20.0\% > 10.0\%$ so, accept "A"

Even though project "B" has the largest ROR on total investment, project "A" is the economic choice from incremental analysis. Differences in the distribution of revenues to be realized cause incremental differences in the projects that must be analyzed.

The year one through five incremental costs of $41,060 per year are referred to as "opportunity costs" by many people since they result from the following rationale. Selecting project "A" causes the investor to forgo realizing the project "B" revenues each year. Revenues or savings foregone are lost opportunities or "opportunity costs", so selecting "A" causes opportunity costs of $41,060 in each of years one through five.

If you look at "B-A", you get incremental income followed by incremental cost so the following rationale applies:

B–A) C = 0 ——— I = $41,060 ——— I = $41,060 C = $305,200
0 ——— 1 5

B-A) PW Eq: $0 = 41{,}060(P/A_{i,5}) - 305{,}200(P/F_{i,5})$

$i = 20.0\% > 10.0\%$ so, reject "B"

(*This B-A "i" value does not have rate or return meaning. Instead, it represents the rate at which funds must be reinvested to cover the year five future cost of $305,200. See the following discussion*)

The incremental numbers and trial and error "i" value obtained, are the same for "A-B". However, note that *on the "B-A" time diagram incremental income is followed by cost. It is physically impossible to calculate rate of return when income is followed by cost. You must have money invested (cost) followed by revenue or savings to calculate rate of return. When income is followed by cost you calculate an "i" value that has "rate of reinvestment requirement" meaning.* The "B-A" incremental "i" value of 20% means the investor would be required to reinvest the year one through five incremental incomes at 20% to accrue enough money to cover the year five cost of $305,200. If the minimum ROR of 10% represents investment and reinvestment opportunities thought to exist over the project life, as it should, then a reinvestment requirement of 20% is unsatisfactory compared to reinvestment opportunities of 10%, so reject "B" and select "A". This is the same conclusion that the "A-B" ROR analysis gave.

Summarizing several important considerations about the ROR analysis for this problem, for the incremental ROR analysis of alternatives "A" and "B" we discussed the need to subtract alternative "B" from alternative "A" so that we had incremental costs followed by incremental revenues. Then we discussed what happens if you incorrectly subtract alternative "A" from "B" as follows:

B–A) C = $0 ——— I = $41,060 ——— I = $41,060 C = $305,200
0 ——— 1 5

Incremental “B-A” incomes of $41,060 each year precede the $305,200 incremental “B-A” cost at the end of year five. When income precedes cost, the “i” that we calculate is the interest rate that must be obtained through the reinvestment of the income each period, for the final value of the cumulative incomes and compound interest to equal the cost at that time. A required reinvestment rate greater than the minimum ROR is unsatisfactory, whereas an ROR greater than the minimum ROR is satisfactory. Figure 4-4 shows the cumulative cash position diagram for this situation. Note that the cumulative cash position in this example is positive during the entire project life. Whenever the cumulative cash position is positive, no investment is involved and the interest rate “i” means the rate at which money must be reinvested and not the rate of return on investment.

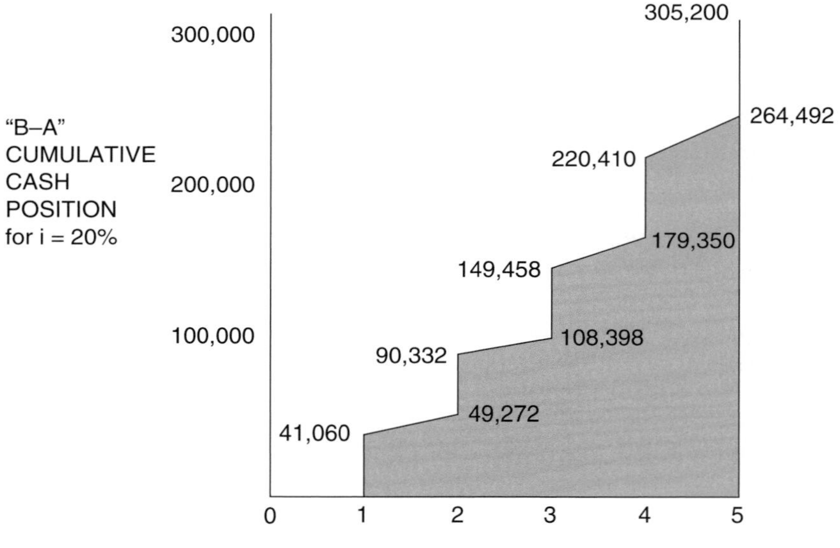

Figure 4-4 Cumulative Cash Position for Income Preceding Cost

Given that the minimum ROR is 10%, do we accept alternative “A” or “B” for the example just discussed? As previously mentioned, if investment preceded income, we would accept alternative “A” because an incremental 20% ROR is better than investing elsewhere at a 10% ROR. However, if "B-A" incremental income precedes cost, we would be rejecting project "B", because the "B-A" rate of reinvestment required at 20% exceeds the other opportunities we have to invest capital which is assumed to be 10%.

Future Worth Profit Analysis from $100,000 Initial Investment

A) FW Profit = $305,200

$$\text{B) FW Profit} = \$41{,}060(\overset{6.105}{F/A_{10\%,5}}) = \$250{,}671$$

Select Project "A" to maximize future profit.

Since the $100,000 initial investment is the same for both "A" and "B", maximum future profit (value) on total investment is desired.

Growth Rate of Return Analysis

A) Growth ROR_A is equal to the regular $ROR_{A,}$ = 25%

B) Growth $ROR_{B,}$ PW Eq: $0 = -100{,}000 + 250{,}671(P/F_{i,5})$
$GROR_B = i = 20.2\%$

Since the same $100,000 initial investment is involved with both "A" and "B", we want the alternative with the largest Growth ROR, "A". Incremental analysis gives the same conclusion.

A-B) GROR PW Eq: $0 = 54{,}529(P/F_{i,5})$
$GROR_{A\text{-}B}$ $i = \infty\% > 10.0\%$ so, select "A" over "B"

Net Present Value (NPV) Analysis

$$NPV_A = 305{,}200(\overset{0.6209}{P/F_{10\%,5}}) - 100{,}000 = +\$89{,}500$$ ← Select "A" With Max. NPV

$$NPV_B = 41{,}060(\overset{3.791}{P/A_{10\%,5}}) - 100{,}000 = +\$55{,}700$$

$NPV_{A-B} = 89{,}500 - 55{,}700 = +\$33{,}800$ Therefore, Select "A", consistent with selecting the project with the largest NPV.

Present Value Ratio (PVR) Analysis

$PVR_A = 89{,}500 / 100{,}000 = .895 > 0$, acceptable

$PVR_B = 55{,}700 / 100{,}000 = .557 > 0$, acceptable

$$PVR_{A-B} = (89{,}500 - 55{,}700)/41{,}060\overset{3.1699}{(P/A_{10\%,4})}$$

$$= 33{,}800/130{,}155 = 0.26 > 0, \text{ so select "A".}$$

When each of these evaluation methods is properly applied you consistently come to the same economic conclusion. You only need to utilize one method to make a proper evaluation. Here, as in other examples throughout this text, multiple criteria solutions are presented to illustrate the consistent results obtained with any of the evaluation methods. Proper incremental analysis is the key to the evaluation of mutually exclusive alternatives where only one alternative may be selected.

EXAMPLE 4-10 Rate of Return, Net Present Value and Rate of Reinvestment in Analyses When Income Precedes Cost

Your company has been asked to consider a proposal to accept a payment of $12 million today and $25 million at the end of one year from now in order to handle disposal of a waste product from a facility for each of the next 10 years, (end of years one through ten). Your estimated costs for disposal of this material include a time zero capital investment of $5 million with end of year one through ten operating costs of $4 million per year. The minimum rate of return is 15.0%. Use ROR and NPV analysis to determine if the company should accept this opportunity?

Income:	12.0	25.0		
Costs:	–5.0	–4.0	–4.0	–4.0
Year	0	1	2	10
Net CF:	**7.0**	**21.0**	**–4.0 ....**	**–4.0**

NPV @ 15.0%: $7.0 + 21(P/F_{15,1}) - 4.0(P/A_{15,9})(P/F_{15,1})$
$= \$8.66 > 0$, acceptable

This analysis has income preceding costs, so the meaning of the calculated "i" value that makes NPV equal zero is *rate of reinvestment requirement*, not rate of return. Therefore, a required investment rate that is less than our minimum rate of return, (reflecting other available investment opportunities) is acceptable. A required rate of reinvestment greater than i* = 15.0% would be an unacceptable project.

PW EQ: $0 = 7.0 + 21(P/F_{i,1}) - 4.0(P/A_{i,9})(P/F_{i,1})$

Rate of Reinvestment = i = 5.06% < 15.0%, acceptable.

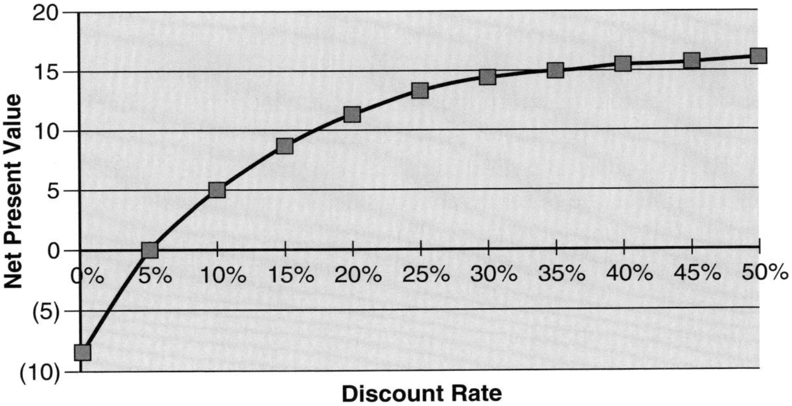

Figure 4-5 NPV vs i* with Rate of Reinvestment Meaning

As illustrated in Figure 4-5, when NPV increases with a correspondingly higher discount rate it is generally the result of income preceding costs and the presence of rate of reinvestment meaning associated with each i* value. *This situation could be thought of in two different ways; First, larger discount rates always diminish the present value of future cash flows more rapidly than smaller discount rates. Second, as other opportunities for the use of capital increase, the money received up front at time zero and year one can generate more future value creating more profit relative to the estimated down stream costs.*

Once again note that the "i" calculated when investment precedes income has completely different meaning than when income precedes investment. Difficulty arises if these two types of projects are mixed in incremental analysis because the interest "i" has two different meanings in the same equation. Techniques for analyzing this type of investment project situation are presented in the following section. It will be shown that the cumulative cash position diagram is a useful tool in the evaluation of this type of problem.

4.8 Alternating Investment, Income, Investment: The Dual Rate of Return Situation

In the last section, examples 4-9 and 4-10 illustrated situations where income preceded costs. Discussion then focused on how the meaning of the calculated "i" value was not rate of return, but the rate at which the revenues (or positive cash flow) must be reinvested to assure sufficient revenues exist to cover future costs. When this occurs, the resulting rates of reinvestment that are less than the investor's minimum rate of return are considered economically satisfactory.

Extending this concept, when a time diagram contains cash flows with an initial investment, followed by income and then more investment(s), the related present worth equation will yield multiple "i" values. These "i" values will always contain a combination of meaning related to both rate of return on the initial investment as well as rate of reinvestment requirement related to economically covering the cost(s) in the future years. These "i" values are often referred to as "Dual Rates of Return" and generally speaking, are not significant in assessing the economic potential of a project. This is due to the fact that despite the label, "Dual Rate of Return," neither solution has pure "rate of return" meaning. Instead, as mentioned previously, the results contain a combination of rate of return and rate of reinvestment meaning, which may be good part of the time, but unsatisfactory part of the time. This forces investors to consider other criteria such as NPV or a modified form of rate of return illustrated in the following examples.

Cash flows containing investment-income-investment timing may occur in a variety of investment situations. One such case involves the incremental analysis of mutually exclusive alternatives that have different project lives. This is often defined as an acceleration problem and is common to oil and gas as well as mining investments. In depleting a finite, resource, the decision to accelerate the production rate through immediate capital expenditure(s) will shorten the life of the project. The incremental analysis of these alternatives creates the classic investment-income-investment situation.

Alternating investment, income, investment analysis situations occur in a variety of situations. The most common, which is illustrated in the next example, occurs from looking at incremental differences between unequal life alternatives where the bigger investment alternative has bigger period revenues and shorter project life. This is the classical acceleration problem mentioned previously common to mineral and petroleum development type projects where a given mineral or petroleum reserve can be depleted more rapidly by making a bigger initial investment. This evaluation situation also commonly occurs with acceleration type investments in many different types of general industry situations. Other examples of cost, income, cost include (1) An investment in a building or project that generates income for several years after which the building or project must be razed or restored to different condition; (2) Mining projects that generate income followed by significant reclamation costs; (3) Forest planting investments followed by clear-cutting which generates income but must be followed by forest replanting costs where environmental laws or company policy require it; (4) Offshore platform development for petroleum production that must be followed by significant platform reclamation costs.

EXAMPLE 4-11 Analysis of Mutually Exclusive Unequal Life Acceleration Type Projects

Investments "A" and "B" are mutually exclusive ways of developing a project. Which is best if the investor desires a minimum rate of return of 20%? Make a valid ROR analysis using either Growth ROR or one of two present worth cost modifications known as the "Escrow Approach" or "Year by Year Approach." Verify those conclusions with NPV.

Solution, All Values in Thousands of Dollars:

I = Revenue, L = Salvage Value, C = Cost

A)	C = 182	I = 100	I = 100	I = 100
	0	1	2	3

B)	C = 250	I = 184	I = 184
	0	1	2

Get equal life alternatives by assuming the life of "B" is 3 years with net revenue and cost of zero at year 3.

Rate of Return Analysis, (ROR)

By trial and error the ROR_A = 30% and ROR_B = 30% both of which exceed the 20% minimum rate of return required for the investment of capital. The investments and project lives are unequal so it is difficult to tell intuitively if "A" or "B" is best for i^* = 20%. Projects with equal total investment rates of return are not necessarily economically equivalent. Incremental analysis gives:

B–A)	C = 68	I = 84	I = 84	C = 100
	0	1	2	3

ROR PW Eq: $68 + 100(P/F_{i,3}) = 84(P/A_{i,2})$

or, in NPV format: $84(P/A_{i,2}) - 100(P/F_{i,3}) - 68 = 0$

i = 0% : 84(2.000) – 100(1.0000) – 68 = 0

i = 10% : 84(1.736) – 100(0.7513) – 68 = +2.69

i = 15% : 84(1.626) – 100(0.6575) – 68 = +2.83

i = 20% : 84(1.528) – 100(0.5787) – 68 = +2.48

i = 30% : 84(1.361) – 100(0.4552) – 68 = +0.80

i = 40% : 84(1.224) – 100(0.3644) – 68 = –1.62

i=0% and i=33.3% are dual rates of return by trial and error.

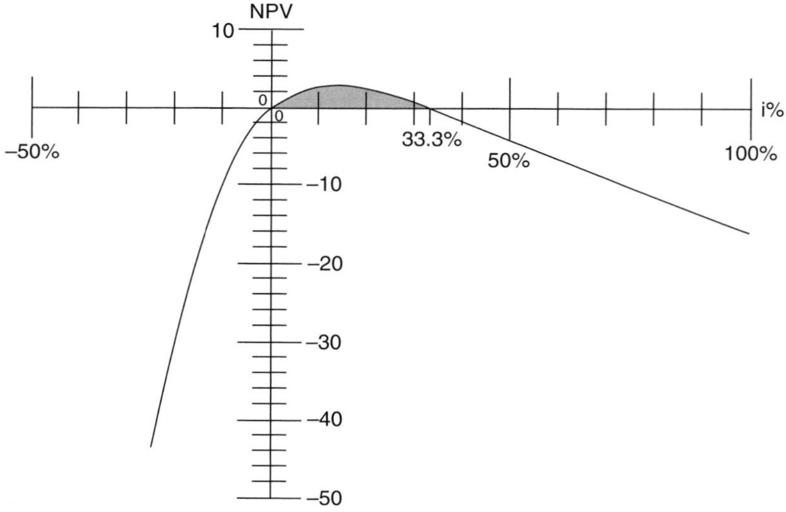

Figure 4-6 NPV vs Discount Rate For Cost, Income, Cost

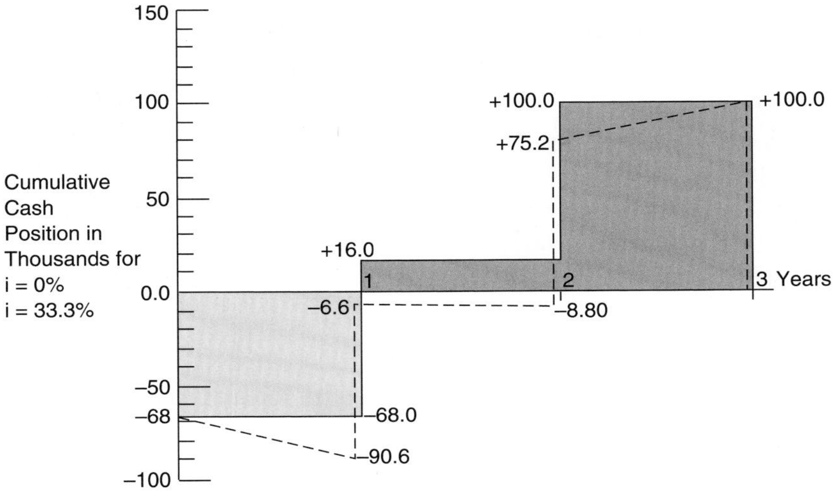

Figure 4-7 Cumulative Cash Position Diagram and The Meaning of Dual "i" Values

A graph of NPV versus the discount rate "i" as illustrated in Figure 4-6 emphasizes the parabolic variation in NPV with the discount rate changes for this cost, income, cost situation. This is very different from the declining exponential variation for NPV versus "i" when cost is followed by income as illustrated earlier in Chapter 3, Example 3-21. However, *the term "dual rates of return" is really a misnomer because neither "i" value means rate of return. Both "i" values have a combination rate of return, rate of reinvestment meaning as the Figure 4-7 cumulative cash position diagram shows.* Note that a 0% rate of return is bad compared to i^* = 20% percent whereas a reinvestment rate of 0% is good compared to 20% reinvestment opportunities. Similarly, a 33% rate of return is good but a 33% rate of reinvestment requirement is bad. Both dual ROR values are good part of the time and bad part of the time.

Looking at Figure 4-7, whenever you are in a negative cumulative cash position, the meaning of "i" is rate of return. On the other hand, whenever you are in a positive cumulative cash position, the meaning of "i" is rate of reinvestment requirement. Using the cumulative cash position diagram, it becomes evident that the dual "i" values have different meaning at different points in time. Therefore, an analysis method other than regular rate of return should be utilized. If the investment decision must be based on a compound interest rate of return measure, several modifications can be made to eliminate the cost-income-cost sequence in the cash flows. These methods will be introduced and include Growth ROR, the Escrow Approach and the Year-by-Year Approach. The last two approaches are sometimes referred to as "Present Worth Cost Modifications." NPV may also be utilized if an alternative to ROR analysis is acceptable. The net value techniques are valid alternative analysis techniques that avoid the "dual ROR" problem.

Net Present Value Analysis, (NPV)

For $i^* = 20\%$, time zero is a common time for all projects.

$$NPV_A = 100(P/A_{20\%,3}) - 182 = +\$28.6 \quad [P/A_{20\%,3} = 2.106]$$

$$NPV_B = 184(P/A_{20\%,2}) - 250 = +\$31.1 \leftarrow \text{Select "B", Largest NPV} \quad [P/A_{20\%,2} = 1.528]$$

Growth Rate of Return Analysis

There is no need to calculate Growth ROR for the "A" and "B" total investments. We already know that "A" and "B" are satisfactory from total investment ROR analysis, so we only need to apply Growth ROR analysis to the incremental investments. Note that the Growth ROR reinvestment step eliminates the alternating investment, income, investment situation and gets us back to incremental investment followed by incremental revenue, the ROR analysis situation.

B–A)	C = \$68	I = \$84	I = \$84	C = \$100
	0	1	2	3

Reinvesting incremental year 1 and 2 incomes at $i^* = 20\%$:

—	C = \$84	C = \$84	—	
0	1	2	3	F = +\$221.8

$$\text{where } F = 84(F/A_{20\%,2})(F/P_{20\%,1}) = +\$221.8 \quad [F/A_{20\%,2} = 2.200,\ F/P_{20\%,1} = 1.200]$$

B–A + Reinvesting incremental income:

B–A)	C = $68	—	—	—	F = +$121.8
	0	1	2	3	

PW Eq: $68 = 121.8(P/F_{i,3})$, i = Growth $ROR_{B\text{-}A}$=21.4% > 20%
Select "B"

Growth Rate of Return Analysis;
Excel™ Modified Internal Rate of Return or MIRR Approach:

MIRR is always based on a single present worth equivalent investment at time zero growing to a single future value at the end of the project life. The MIRR definition requires an additional step in manually solving for a Growth ROR using this function. For our example, reinvestment of positive cash flows is the same:

B-A	C = 68	I = 84	I = 84	C = 100
	0	1	2	3

Reinvesting incremental year 1 and 2 incomes at 20%

B-A	—	C = 84	C = 84	—	F = 221.8
	0	1	2	3	

Where $F = 84(F/A_{20,2})(F/P_{20,1}) = 221.8$

Next compute the present worth equivalent investment of all negative cash flow. This measure is not based on maximum capital exposure.

PW Equivalent Cost: $68 + 100(P/F_{20,3}) = 125.9$

B-A	C=125.9	—	—	—	F = 221.8
	0	1	2	3	

MIRR PW Eq: $0 = -125.9 + 221.8(P/F_{i,3})$

i = MIRR or Mod. Growth $ROR_{B\text{-}A}$ = 20.8% > 20%, Select B

ROR Using the Escrow Approach

Another modification for ROR analysis that many individuals and companies use to eliminate the alternating investment, income, investment situation is a present worth modification of the final cost. By discounting the final cost at the minimum ROR, you convert the problem to a regular cost followed by income type of evaluation. Working with the incremental "B-A" diagram, discount the final year 3 cost of $100 thousand at $i^* = 20\%$, giving the following modified time diagram:

	0.5787			
B–A)	$C = \$68+\$100(P/F_{20\%,3})$	I = $84	I = $84	—
	0	1	2	3

Modified PW Eq: $0 = -125.87 + 84(P/A_{i,2})$

$i = 21.6\% > 20\%$, Select "B"

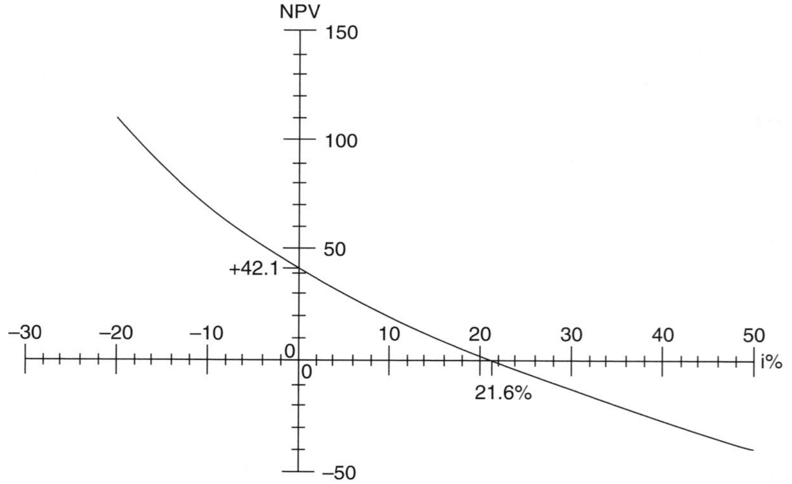

Figure 4-8 NPV vs. Discount Rate For Modified PW Cost Analysis

Explanation of the Escrow Approach

This present worth cost modified ROR analysis really involves adding an outside investment earning at the minimum discount rate to the initial cost, income, cost project. By selecting the magnitude of the outside investment so it will generate income in the later years equal to costs following income in the initial project, cost following income is eliminated.

B–A)	C = \$68	I = \$84	I = \$84	C = \$100
	0	1	2	3
+				
An Outside Investment	C = \$57.87	—	—	I = \$100
at $i^* = 20\%$	0	1	2	3

where "C" at time 0 = 57.87= $100(P/F_{i^*=20\%,3})$ (0.5787)

= Total	C = \$125.87	I = \$84	I = \$84	—
	0	1	2	3

Modified Present Worth Equation:

$0 = -125.87 + 84(P/A_{i,2})$ i = 21.6% PW Cost Modified ROR

ROR Using the Year-by-Year Modification

It is not necessary to present worth costs following income all the way to time 0 to eliminate costs following income. It is only necessary to bring costs following revenue back one year at a time until they are offset by income, as the following illustrates.

B–A)	C = \$68	I = \$84	I = \$84	C = \$100
	0	1	2	3
+				
An Outside Investment	—	—	C = \$83.3	I = \$100
at $i^* = 20\%$	0	1	2	3

where C at year 2 = $100(P/F_{20\%,1})$ = \$83.33 (0.8333)

= Total	C = \$68	I = \$84	I = \$0.7	—
	0	1	2	3

Modified PW Eq.: $0 = -68 + 84(P/F_{i,1}) + 0.7(P/F_{i,2})$

i = 24.4% PW Cost Modified ROR

Adding an outside investment of 83.3 at year 2 to the "B-A" project does not weight the PW Modified ROR as low as adding the investment of 57.87 at time zero. However, note that the 24.4% modified ROR result relates to very different unamortized investment values each year than the time zero 21.6% PW Modified ROR relates to. Both results are economically equivalent even though different in magnitude. The modification that eliminates cost following revenue and modifies the analysis as little as possible is felt by many people to be the most desirable modification to use, so the latter year 2 modification often finds use in industry practice.

All of the analysis methods utilized for this example, other than regular ROR, have selected alternative "B" consistently. Any of these techniques can and should be used in place of regular rate or return analysis when the investment, income, investment type of analysis is encountered. The combination rate of return, rate of reinvestment meaning associated with cost, income, cost dual rates of return is what makes the dual ROR results useless for valid economic decisions. The existence of dual rates is algebraically caused by the sign changes in cost, income, cost equations. This can be illustrated for incremental "B-A" analysis in this example.

B–A)	C = $68	I = $84	I = $84	C = $100
	0	1	2	3

PW Eq: $0 = -68 + 84(P/F_{i,1}) + 84(P/F_{i,2}) - 100(P/F_{i,3})$

Mathematically:

$$0 = -68 + 84(1/(1+i)) + 84(1/(1+i))^2 - 100(1/(1+i))^3$$

Substitute $X = (1/(1+i))$:

$$0 = -68 + 84X + 84X^2 - 100X^3$$

This is a "third order polynomial equation" as a function of X. Algebraic rules indicate that polynomial equations may have as many positive roots as sign changes, two in this case. Solving for X: X = 1, and X = 3/4 gives i = 0% and i = 33.3%. These are the same dual ROR results obtained earlier by trial and error.

EXAMPLE 4-12 Reclamation Costs Can Cause the Dual ROR Problem

An investment project requires the initial investment of $70,000 to generate a projected stream of positive $40,000 per year cash flows in each of years one through five. However, a reclamation cost of $140,000 is expected to be required at year 6 (the year 6 reclamation cost could relate to restoration of surface land to original contours for an open pit mining operation, reclamation of an offshore platform for an offshore petroleum production project, or reclamation costs for land cleanup from chemical contamination, to name several possibilities). The minimum ROR is 20%. Analyze the economic potential of this project using both NPV and ROR analysis.

Solution, All Values in Thousands of Dollars:

C = 70	I = 40	I = 40	I = 40	I = 40	I = 40	C = 140
0	1	2	3	4	5	6

When cost follows revenue, correct ROR analysis requires use of one of the modified ROR analysis techniques introduced in Example 4-11 (Escrow Approach, Year-by-Year Approach, or Growth Rate of Return). In this example, the sum of the positive cash flows is $200 while the negative cash flows total $210. Clearly, some of the early cash flows will be utilized to pay off the initial investment, providing a return on that investment, while the remaining positive cash flows will have to be reinvested at an interest rate if enough cash is to be generated to cover the future obligation. This illustrates the rate of return and rate of reinvestment meaning associated with all dual “i” values.

ROR Analysis Using an NPV Type of Equation

PW Eq: $40(P/A_{i,5}) - 140(P/F_{i,6}) - 70 = 0$

$i = 0\%$: $40(5.000) - 140(1.0000) - 70 = -10.0$

$i = 5\%$: $40(4.329) - 140(0.7462) - 70 = -1.3$

$i = 8\%$: $40(3.993) - 140(0.6302) - 70 = +1.5$

$i = 15\%$: $40(3.352) - 140(0.4323) - 70 = +3.6$

$i = 20\%$: $40(2.991) - 140(0.3349) - 70 = +2.7$

$i = 25\%$: $40(2.689) - 140(0.2621) - 70 = +0.9$

$i = 30\%$: $40(2.436) - 140(0.2072) - 70 = -1.6$

Note that due to the "parabolic variation" of the NPV type equation results versus "i", by interpolation, NPV = 0 for the dual rates of return of 6.40% and 26.78%. Each of these rates makes the cumulative cash position zero at the end of project life. Both rates involve a combination meaning of rate of return on investment in early project life and rate of reinvestment rate in the later project years. These dual rates cannot be used directly for decision making purposes as ROR results. However, the dual rates do provide some useful information because they bracket the range of minimum rate of return values for which project net present value is positive. This tells the range of "i^*" for which the project is satisfactory. Whenever dual rates exist, it is easiest to rely on NPV analysis for decision purposes. However, going to Growth ROR analysis or present worth cost modified ROR analysis is equally valid, but generally more work. NPV calculated at "i^*" always leads to correct economic decision in this situation, whereas the dual rates problem makes ROR analysis more confusing.

$$\text{NPV @ } 20\% = 40(\overset{2.991}{P/A_{20\%,5}}) - 140(\overset{0.3349}{P/F_{20\%,6}}) - 70 = +\$2.754 > 0$$

The NPV analysis is quick and simple to make and the positive NPV result tells us the project investment is satisfactory, although the NPV of +2.754 is only slightly greater than zero compared to the magnitude of costs that generated it, so project economics effectively are a break-even with investing elsewhere at 20%.

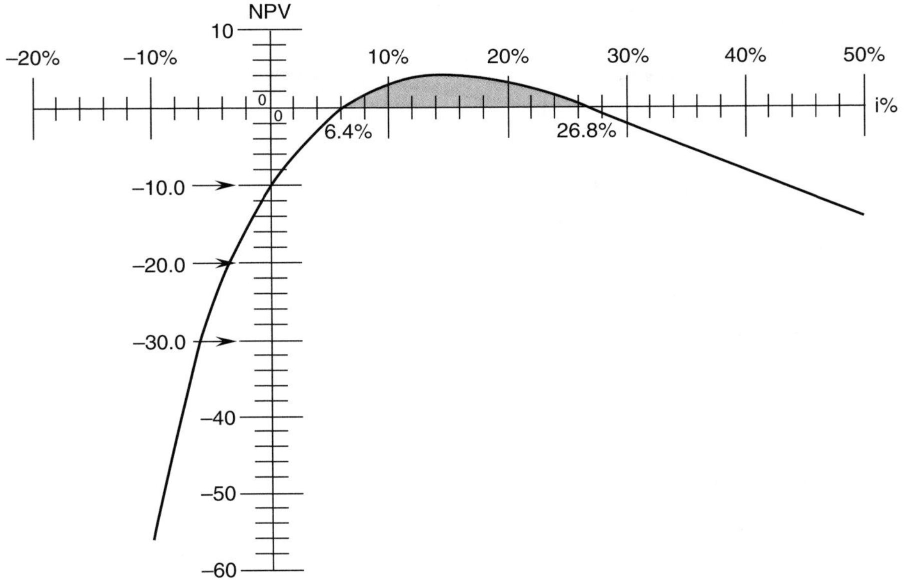

Figure 4-9 NPV vs Discount Rate for Cost, Income, Cost

Now before getting into the details of the modified ROR analysis, note that NPV at i = 0% is negative for this example, which has dual positive rate values of 6.4% and 26.78%. Whenever the NPV at i = 0% is negative for an investment, income, investment situation, due to the parabolic variation of NPV with changes in "i", dual positive "i" values exist if any real interest rate solutions exist for the NPV equation. If NPV at i = 0% is positive, dual rate values exist with one being negative and the other positive. This test of NPV at i = 0% tells an investor where to look for the dual rates if it is deemed desirable to determine them.

Before presenting the modified ROR analysis calculations, note that in calculating the dual rates at the beginning of this solution that as "i" increased from 0% to 15% that NPV increases rather than decreases. This is a unique result of cost following revenue in the cost, income, cost analysis situation. Whenever you find NPV increasing with increasing interest rates (rather than decreasing as it always does for cost, income analyses) it is the author's experience that this is caused by cost following revenue in the analysis.

ROR Using the Escrow Approach

To eliminate this investment, income, investment situation, present worth the final cost or costs at the minimum ROR to an equivalent present value, giving the following diagram:

$$\begin{array}{llll} C = \$70 + \$140(\overset{0.3349}{P/F_{20\%,6}}) & I = \$40 & I = \$40 & — \\ \hline 0 & 1 \ldots\ldots\ldots\ldots & 5 & 6 \end{array}$$

PW Cost Modified ROR PW Eq: $116.88 = 40(P/A_{i,5})$

Modified ROR = i = 21.1% > 20%, so satisfactory. Since this modified ROR result is based solely on income following cost, it is valid for economic decision-making purposes as a rate of return result. Discounting the year 6 cost modifies the magnitude of our ROR result but not its validity for comparison to $i^* = 20\%$ for the economic decision.

Growth ROR

Combine reinvestment of revenue at "i^*" with the initial project to eliminate cost following revenue as follows:

Initial Project

$$\begin{array}{llll} C = \$70 & I = \$40 & I = \$40 & C = \$140 \\ \hline 0 & 1 \ldots\ldots\ldots\ldots & 5 & 6 \end{array}$$

Reinvest Revenues @ i^*=20%

$$\begin{array}{lllll} — & C = \$40 & C = \$40 & — & \\ \hline 0 & 1 \ldots\ldots\ldots\ldots & 5 & 6 & F = \$357.20 \end{array}$$

where, $F = 40(\overset{7.442}{F/A_{20\%,5}})(\overset{1.200}{F/P_{20\%,1}}) = \$357.2$

Combine Initial + Reinvestment Revenues

$$\begin{array}{lllll} C = \$70 & — & — & C = \$140 & \\ \hline 0 & 1 \ldots\ldots\ldots\ldots & 5 & 6 & F = \$357.2 \end{array}$$

Growth ROR PW Eq: $70 = 217.2(P/F_{i,6})$

Growth ROR = i = 20.9% > 20%, so satisfactory.

Both the present worth cost modified ROR analysis and Growth ROR analysis have given the same economic conclusion, which is in this case and in general always consistent with NPV analysis economic conclusions. The key to correct ROR analysis of cost, income, cost analysis situations is to modify the analysis to eliminate cost following revenue before making the ROR analysis. The present worth cost and Growth ROR modifications are the two basic approaches used to eliminate cost following revenues. However, there are several variations in the way different people apply these modifications. One in particular is worth noting.

In applying the escrow approach it is not necessary to bring costs following revenue all the way to year 0. It really is only necessary to present worth costs following revenue year by year until those costs are offset by project revenue. This gives the following modification referred to as the "Year by Year Modification."

ROR Using the Year-by-Year Modification

Discount the year 6 cost year by year until offset by project income.

3		4		5		6
C=19.90	← P/F 20,1 ←	C=63.88	← P/F 20,1 ←	C=116.66	← P/F 20,1 ←	C=140
I=40.00		I=40.00		I= 40.00		
Net I=20.10		Net C=23.88		Net C= 76.66		

New Modified Diagram

C = 70	I = 40	I = 40	I = 20.1	—	—	—
0	1	2	3	4	5	6

PW Eq: $0 = -70 + 40(P/A_{i,2}) + 20.1(P/F_{i,3})$

i = Modified ROR = 22.75% > $i^* = 20\%$ so satisfactory

This modified ROR result is several percent bigger than the initial present worth cost modified result. This is because the two modified ROR results relate to very different initial year 0 investments. The results are really equivalent and give the same economic conclusion when compared to the 20% minimum ROR. Remember that you cannot and should not look at the magnitude of ROR results and think big is best. A project with a big ROR that relates to a given investment and stream of income may not be as desirable as a project with a smaller ROR that relates to bigger investment and a different stream of income.

EXAMPLE 4-13 A Petroleum Infill Drilling Acceleration Problem Involving Dual Rates of Return

A producing oil field has wells drilled on 160 acre centers. It is proposed to infill drill wells on 80 acre centers to accelerate petroleum production and give more efficient drainage of the petroleum reservoir. Present and proposed costs and net revenues are shown on the following time diagrams with values in thousands of dollars:

Present	C=0	I=900	I=700	I=550	I=410	I=280	I=150
	0	1	2	3	4	5	6

Accelerate	C=735	I=1,750	I=1,150	I=600	I=100	I=0	I=0
	0	1	2	3	4	5	6

For a minimum ROR of 12%, use rate of return analysis to determine if the acceleration drilling program investment is satisfactory from an economic viewpoint.

Solution:

The "present" producing project is clearly satisfactory since costs for development have already been incurred (so they are sunk). For no additional costs to be incurred, the "present" project revenues are projected to be generated. This relates to an infinite percent return on zero dollars invested in the present project, an economically satisfactory project. The accelerated project total investment ROR is 200%. However, this ROR does not need to be calculated because knowing the present project is satisfactory, we can go to incremental analysis to determine if incremental investment dollars spent on the accelerated production infill drilling program are justified economically by incremental revenues. The incremental diagram involves cost, income, cost as follows because the negative incremental incomes in years 4, 5 and 6 are effectively costs as follows:

Incremental Rate of Return Analysis

	C=735	I=850	I=450	I=50	C=310	C=280	C=150
Accelerated – Present	0	1	2	3	4	5	6

If you write a conventional present worth equation for the incremental diagram values, you get dual rates as follows:

$$\text{PW Eq: } 0 = -735 + 850(P/F_{i,1}) + 450(P/F_{i,2}) + 50(P/F_{i,3})$$
$$- 310(P/F_{i,4}) - 280(P/F_{i,5}) - 150(P/F_{i,6})$$

Trial and error, dual "i" values of 17% and 25% result. An investor that treats either of these results as rate of return compared with the minimum ROR of 12% would conclude that the incremental project economics are satisfactory. This turns out to be an incorrect conclusion. Both of the dual rates of 17% and 25% have rate of reinvestment meaning as well as rate of return meaning at different points in time. Required rates of revenue reinvestment of 17% and 25% compared with 12% reinvestment opportunities indicated by the minimum ROR indicate a very unsatisfactory incremental investment whereas rates of return of 17% and 25% compared to the 12% minimum ROR look satisfactory. The unsatisfactory rate of reinvestment meaning is stronger than the rate of return meaning as the following NPV and Escrow ROR analysis results show.

Net Present Value Analysis

$$\text{NPV} = -735 + 850(P/F_{12\%,1}) + 450(P/F_{12\%,2}) + 50(P/F_{12\%,3})$$
$$- 310(P/F_{12\%,4}) - 280(P/F_{12\%,5}) - 150(P/F_{12\%,6})$$
$$= -13.6 < 0, \text{ so slightly unsatisfactory.}$$

Escrow Approach ROR Analysis

$$\text{Mod. Yr 0 Cost} = 735 + 310(P/F_{12\%,4}) + 280(P/F_{12\%,5})$$
$$+ 150(P/F_{12\%,6}) = \$1{,}166.90$$

$$\text{Mod. PW Eq: } 0 = -1{,}166.9 + 850(P/F_{i,1}) + 450(P/F_{i,2}) + 50(P/F_{i,3})$$

Trial and error:

i = Modified ROR = 11% < i^* = 12%, so unsatisfactory

Note that any investor who treats either of the positive dual rates of 17% and 25% as rate of return comes to the wrong economic conclusion in this analysis. When cost follows revenue, you must modify the analysis to eliminate cost following revenue before you can make ROR analysis.

EXAMPLE 4-14 Cost, Income, Cost from Incremental Service Producing Analysis

It is necessary to evaluate whether an asset should be replaced today for a $20,000 cost or two years from today for a $25,000 cost with operating costs and salvage values as shown on the diagrams for a six year evaluation life. Use incremental ROR analysis for a 15% minimum ROR to reach the economic decision. All values are in thousands of dollars on the diagrams.

Replace Now (A)	C=20	OC=1	OC=2	OC=3	OC=4	OC=5	OC=6	L=4
	0	1	2	3	4	5	6	

Replace Later (B)	C=0	OC=6	C=25 OC=8	OC=1	OC=2	OC=3	OC=4	L=9
	0	1	2	3	4	5	6	

Solution:

Analyze "A-B" to get incremental cost followed by incremental savings. However, it is impossible to avoid having incremental costs and negative incremental salvage (effectively cost) in years 3 through 6, giving the dual ROR problem.

R = incremental savings which are equivalent to revenue.

A–B)	C = 20	R = 5	R = 31	C = 2	C = 2	C = 2	C = 2	L = -5
	0	1	2	3	4	5	6	

A modified ROR analysis is needed to eliminate cost following revenue or savings. There is little value obtained from calculating the dual rates of return except to satisfy curiosity, but the dual rates for this analysis are +22.32% and –13.03%.

ROR Using the Escrow Approach

$$\text{Mod. Cost} = 20 + 2\overset{2.8550}{(P/A_{15\%,4})}\overset{0.7561}{(P/F_{15\%,2})} + 5\overset{0.4323}{(P/F_{15\%,6})} = 26.48$$

$$\text{PW Eq: } 0 = -26.48 + 5(P/F_{i,1}) + 31(P/F_{i,2})$$

$$i = \text{incremental investment modified ROR} = 18.05\% > i^* = 15\%$$

Accept the incremental investment in "A" and reject "B" (replace later). Incremental NPV analysis verifies this modified ROR analysis conclusion.

$$NPV_{A-B} = 5\overset{0.8696}{(P/F_{15\%,1})} + 31\overset{0.7561}{(P/F_{15\%,2})} - 2\overset{2.855}{(P/A_{15\%,4})}\overset{0.7561}{(P/F_{15\%,2})}$$

$$- 5\overset{0.4323}{(P/F_{15\%,6})} - 20 = +1.31 > 0, \quad \text{so accept "A", reject "B"}$$

To complete our discussion of the investment, income, investment situations, it is important to point out and emphasize that *if income follows the second investment, a dual ROR situation may not exist. This means that investment, income, investment, income analysis situations may not give the dual ROR problem but investment, income, investment always does. Look at the project cumulative cash position diagram for the positive "i" value calculated to test whether combination rate of return, rate of reinvestment meaning is associated with the "i" value at different points in time.* Remember, if the cumulative cash position does not go positive at any time, rate of reinvestment meaning does not exist and the meaning of "i" is rate of return for the entire project evaluation life. The following example illustrates this important analysis consideration.

EXAMPLE 4-15 An Investment, Income, Investment, Income Situation Where Conventional ROR Analysis is Valid

Diagram values in thousands of dollars.

		C = 100			
C = 50	I = 30	I = 30	I = 60	I = 60	I = 60
0	1	2	3	4	5

A development project will require investments of \$50,000 at time zero and \$100,000 of the end of year 2 as shown on the time diagram, with incomes of \$30,000 at the end of years 1 and 2, and \$60,000 at the end of years 3, 4 and 5. For a minimum rate of return of 20%, use ROR analysis to evaluate the economic desirability of this project. Is the "i" value that you calculate meaningful for economic decision making as ROR? Does NPV analysis verify your conclusion?

Solution, All Values in Thousands of Dollars:

NPV Eq: $30(P/A_{i,2}) + 60(P/A_{i,3})(P/F_{i,2}) - 100(P/F_{i,2}) - 50 = 0$

Since the NPV at i = 0% is positive, only one positive "i" exists that will make NPV = 0. By trial and error, i = 27.46% makes NPV = 0. Is this "i" value of 27.46% a rate of return result or is it one of a pair of "dual rates of return" that have combination rate of return, rate of reinvestment requirement meaning at different points in time? If a companion dual rate of return exists, it would be negative. However, it is possible to avoid the search for the possible companion dual ROR by testing to see if rate of reinvestment meaning is associated with 27.46% "i" value at any point in time. *Dual rates of return always have combined rate of return, rate of reinvestment meaning at different point in time. If rate of reinvestment meaning does not exist at any time, then dual rates of return do not exist for this problem and the 27.46% "i" value can be treated as ROR for decision purposes.*

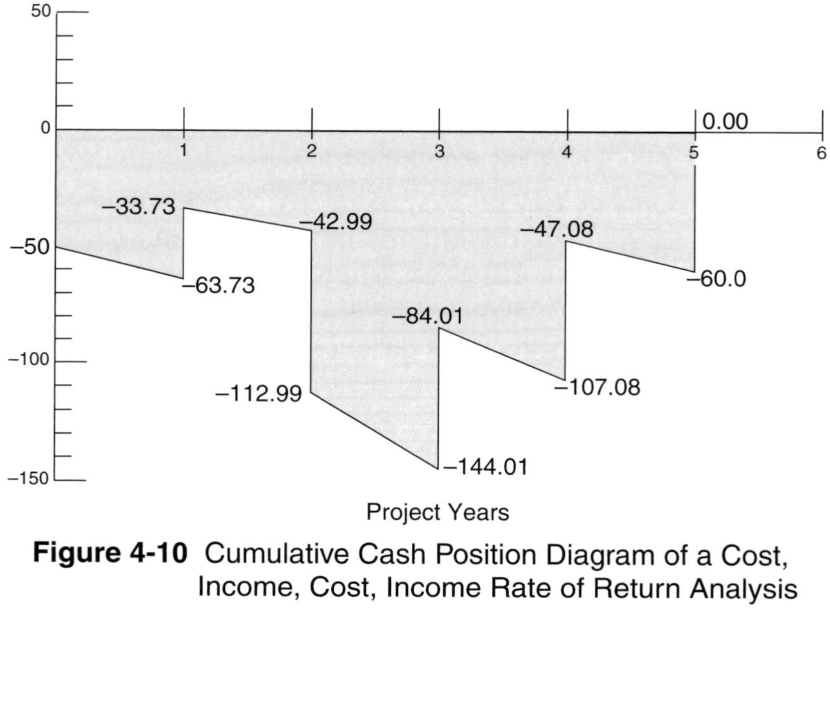

Figure 4-10 Cumulative Cash Position Diagram of a Cost, Income, Cost, Income Rate of Return Analysis

Evaluation of the cumulative cash position diagram for this project at the project "i" value of 27.46% does show that the cumulative cash position never goes above zero at any time during the project life. Therefore, the "i" of 27.46% means "rate of return" over the entire project life and never means rate of reinvestment. Only when the cumulative cash position goes positive does "i" have the rate of reinvestment meaning.

4.9 Alternating Income, Investment, Income Situations

For the situation when you have alternating income, investment, income on the time diagram, dual rates of return occur for the opposite conditions described in the previous section for the investment, income, investment situation. For income, investment, income situations, dual "i" values that are both positive will exist if NPV at i = 0% is positive, and positive dual "i" values will not exist if NPV at i = 0% is negative. Analysis rules are similar to those given in the last section. However, note that for income, investment, income situations, a project is acceptable for an "i^*" greater than the largest project positive dual "i" value because this is the region of positive net present value. When dual rates exist, a project is acceptable only for "i^*" values outside the region between the dual rates, because this is the range of "i^*" values that makes NPV positive. Figure 4-11 in Example 4-16 illustrates those considerations.

EXAMPLE 4-16 Income, Cost, Income and Rate of Return Analysis

As a variation to Example 4-10, a company has been asked to consider a proposal to accept two payments of $12 million, one at time zero and the second at the end of year one, along with a payment for $23 million at the end of ten years from now when the project is to be completed. These payments are to provide for the cost to your company in disposing of waste product from a processing facility for each of the next 10 years, (end of years one through ten). Your estimated costs for disposal of this material include a time zero capital investment of $7 million with end of year one through ten operating costs of $4 million per year. The minimum rate of return is 15.0%. Use ROR and NPV analysis to determine if the company should accept this opportunity?

Solution: All Values in Millions of Dollars

Income:	12.0	12.0	—	. . . . —	23.0
Costs:	–7.0	–4.0	–4.0	. . . . –4.0	–4.0
Year:	0	1	2	 9	10
Net CF:	**5.0**	**8.0**	**–4.0**	**. . . . . –4.0**	**19.0**

NPV @ 15.0%: $5.0 + 8(P/F_{15,1}) - 4.0(P/A_{15,8})(P/F_{15,1}) + 19(P/F_{15,10})$

$= \$1.04 > 0$, acceptable, but close to break-even

This analysis has income preceding costs, followed by more income, which is another dual "i" value situation with 0% and 8.6% being the dual "i" values. In this analysis, *the meaning of the calculated "i" value is rate of reinvestment requirement in the early years as initial positive cash flows pay off the negative cash flows in some of the early years of the project. In the later years, the meaning of "i" switches to rate of return as the remaining costs are paid off by the positive cash flow in year 10.* This analysis requires a cash flow modification to eliminate the multiple sign changes in the present worth equation. The same procedures used in cost-income-cost situations must be employed here, giving an initial investment generating positive cash flow. Such a modification is presented below in the form of Growth ROR. In this analysis, all positive cash flows are taken forward to the end of the project, while negative cash flows are discounted to time zero.

Net CF:	5.0	8.0	–4.0	. . . . –4.0	19.0
Year:	0	1	2	 9	10

Time Zero Modified Cost: $-4.0\overset{4.4873}{(P/A_{15,8})}\overset{0.8696}{(P/F_{15,1})} = -15.61$

End of Year 10 Future Value: $5\overset{4.0456}{(F/P_{15,10})} + 8\overset{3.5179}{(F/P_{15,9})} + 19 = 67.37$

PW Eq: $0 = -15.61 + 67.37(P/F_{i,10})$,

GROR = i = 15.75% > 15.0%, acceptable

The following diagram illustrates that when income-cost-income exists, the analysis relationship between NPV and i* is inverted when compared to cost-income-cost.

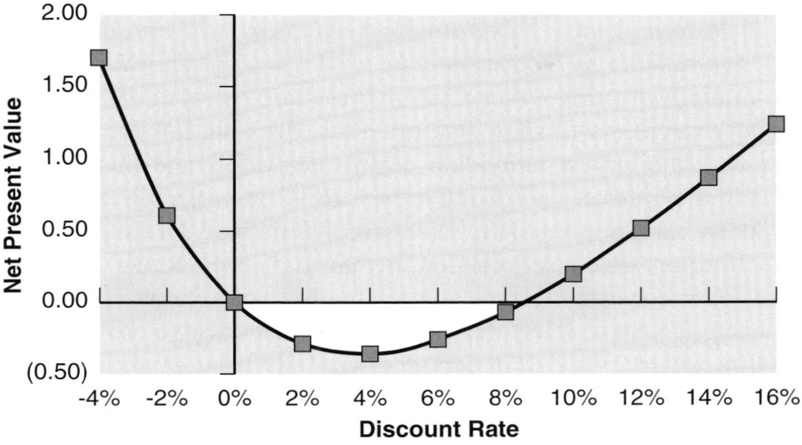

Figure 4-11 NPV vs i* for Income-Cost-Income

As illustrated in Figure 4-11, the parabolic relationship between NPV and the discount rate in this income-cost-income analysis tends to vary in an inverse fashion to that in a cost-income-cost situation. Once again, to get valid rate of return results, you must modify the analysis to have dollars invested initially followed by income in later years to provide a return on the invested capital.

4.10 Evaluation of Non-Mutually Exclusive Investments

Non-mutually exclusive investments are investment alternatives from which more than one choice can be selected depending on available capital or budget restrictions, such as selecting research, development or exploration projects from many alternatives. The ranking of drilling prospects in the petroleum industry is a classic example of non-mutually exclusive alternative analysis. The objective in analyzing non-mutually exclusive projects is to maximize the cumulative profitability that can be generated from the available investment dollars.

To maximize the cumulative profitability that can be generated by investing available investment capital in several non-mutually exclusive alternatives, select the combination of projects that will maximize cumulative net value or cumulative future worth profit. Use of any of these methods requires looking at all the different possible combinations of projects to determine the group of projects that is best for a given budget.

To rank non-mutually exclusive projects in the order that you will want to select them to maximize cumulative net value or future profit for a given budget, two ranking techniques may be used. They are growth rate of return and ratio analysis using either PVR or B/C Ratio as calculated earlier. The following examples will show that often this does not involve selecting the project with the largest individual project net value, and that ranking the projects in the order of decreasing regular ROR on project investments does not properly rank non-mutually exclusive alternatives. Of the basic evaluation techniques discussed earlier in this text, only Ratio analysis and Growth ROR consistently rank non-mutually exclusive alternatives in the order that you want to select them to maximize cumulative profitability.

If a true opportunity cost of capital is used as the minimum discount rate, all projects with positive NPV will be accepted for investment and there is no need for ranking independent non-mutually exclusive alternatives. However, investors usually do not have an exactly correct opportunity cost of capital, so under conditions of rationed capital (limited budget dollars), the ranking of independent or non-mutually exclusive projects is necessary.

EXAMPLE 4-17 Evaluation of Non-Mutually Exclusive Alternatives Compared to Mutually Exclusive Alternatives With Net Present Value

Consider the following four investment alternatives which all have a 5 year life and zero salvage value. Assume that $i^* = 20\%$ before taxes.

Alternative	Investment, $	Operating Cost Savings Per Year, $
1	10,000	6,000
2	25,000	10,000
3	35,000	15,000
4	50,000	17,000

A) If $50,000 is available to invest and alternatives 1, 2, 3 and 4 are mutually exclusive (only one alternative can be chosen), which alternative should be selected?

B) If \$35,000 is available to be invested, and the alternatives are non-mutually exclusive, should we choose alternative 3 or alternative 1 plus 2? We do not have enough money to finance alternative 4 so for financial reasons (rather than economic reasons) it must be left out of this analysis.

Solution:

A) Mutually Exclusive Alternatives

NPV analysis will be presented here because it is generally the simplest method to use to evaluate mutually exclusive projects.

$$NPV_1 = 6{,}000\overset{2.991}{(P/A_{20\%,5})} - 10{,}000 = +\$7{,}946$$

$$NPV_2 = 10{,}000(P/A_{20\%,5}) - 25{,}000 = +\$4{,}910$$

$$NPV_3 = 15{,}000(P/A_{20\%,5}) - 35{,}000 = +\$9{,}865$$

$$NPV_4 = 17{,}000(P/A_{20\%,5}) - 50{,}000 = +\$847$$

Alternative 3 has the largest NPV at $i^* = 20\%$, so for mutually exclusive alternatives, alternative 3 is the economic choice.

B) Non-Mutually Exclusive Alternatives

If we were to proceed as we did in part (A) and pick the largest NPV, we would select alternative 3 for this analysis also. However, it should be very obvious that if these alternatives are not mutually exclusive, we can make better use of our \$35,000 by selecting alternatives 1 plus 2, rather than 3, since this gives us \$16,000 in savings each year for the \$35,000 investment, rather than the \$15,000 savings obtained form alternative 3. Cumulative NPV for alternatives 1 + 2 is \$12,856 compared to NPV_3 = \$9,865. Therefore, note that the project with biggest NPV is not involved in the economic choices. Only with mutually exclusive alternatives is the biggest NPV project always best.

When a small group of alternatives is being considered, cumulative NPV is usually the easiest approach utilized to determine optimal value for a limited budget. However, when the number of alternatives increases, the use of ranking techniques such as ratios can help evaluators rank alternatives in the economic order of selection to maximize cumulative NPV.

EXAMPLE 4-18 Ranking Non-Mutually Exclusive Projects Using Growth ROR Analysis and PVR Analysis

Determine whether a manager should spend $50,000 on project 1 or projects 2 and 3 if the projects are non-mutually exclusive for a minimum ROR 10%.

1) ROR = 40%

C = $50,000	I = $20,000	I = $20,000	L = $50,000
0	1	2	

2) ROR = 33%

C = $30,000	I = $10,000 . . . . . . I = $10,000	L=$30,000
0	1 5	

3) ROR = 25%

C = $20,000	I = $5,000. . . . . I = $5,000	L=$20,000
0	1 7	

Solution:

Maximize Cumulative NPV

$$NPV_1 = 20{,}000(\overset{1.736}{P/A_{10\%,2}}) + 50{,}000(\overset{.8264}{P/F_{10\%,2}}) - 50{,}000 = +\$26{,}033$$

$$NPV_2 = 10{,}000(\overset{3.791}{P/A_{10\%,5}}) + 30{,}000(\overset{.6209}{P/F_{10\%,5}}) - 30{,}000 = +\$26{,}535$$

$$NPV_3 = 5{,}000(\overset{4.868}{P/A_{10\%,7}}) + 20{,}000(\overset{.5132}{P/F_{10\%,7}}) - 20{,}000 = +\$14{,}605$$

Maximum Cumulative NPV = $NPV_2 + NPV_3 = +\$41{,}140$

Note that ranking by regular ROR or NPV does not give the correct answer. However, ranking the alternatives by Growth ROR or PVR does rank the projects correctly as is illustrated in the following calculations.

Growth Rate of Return

Use a common evaluation life of 7 years for each alternative assuming net revenues and costs of zero in the later years of shorter life alternatives “1” and “2”.

1) C = \$50,000 | I = \$20,000 | I = \$20,000 | L=\$50,000
0 | 1 | 2

Rein-vest: — | C = \$20,000 | C = \$50,000, C = \$20,000 | F = +\$148,210
0 | 1 | 2 7

where, $F = 20{,}000(F/P_{10\%,6}) + 70{,}000(F/P_{10\%,5}) = +\$148{,}210$, with $F/P_{10\%,6} = 1.772$ and $F/P_{10\%,5} = 1.611$

1+ Rein-vest: C = \$50,000 | — | — | F = +\$148,210
0 | 1 7

Growth ROR PW Eq: $0 = -50{,}000 + 148{,}210(P/F_{i,7})$,
Growth ROR = i = 17%

2) C = \$30,000 | I = \$10,000 | I = \$10,000 | L=\$30,000
0 | 1 5

Rein-vest: — | C = \$10,000 | C=\$30,000, C = \$10,000 | — | F=+\$110,170
0 | 1 . . . . 5 | 7

where, $F = [10{,}000(F/A_{10\%,5}) + 30{,}000](F/P_{10\%,2}) = +\$110{,}170$, with $F/A_{10\%,5} = 6.105$ and $F/P_{10\%,2} = 1.21$

2+ Rein-vest: C = \$30,000 | — | — | F=+\$110,170
0 | 1 7

Growth ROR Eq: $0 = -30{,}000 + 110{,}170(P/F_{i,7})$,
Growth ROR = i = 20.4%

3) C = \$20,000 | I = \$5,000 | I = \$5,000 | L=\$20,000
0 | 1 7

Rein-Vest: C = \$5,000 | C=\$20,000, C = \$5,000 | F=\$67,430
0 | 1 7

where, $F = 5{,}000(F/A_{10\%,7}) + 20{,}000 = \$67{,}430$, with $F/A_{10\%,7} = 9.487$

3+ Rein-Vest	C = \$20,000	— ... —	F=\$67,430
	0	1 7	

Growth ROR Eq: $0 = -20{,}000 + 67{,}430(P/F_{i,7})$,
Growth ROR = i = 19.1%

Alternatives 2 and 3 with the largest and next largest Growth ROR values are the economic choices for the available investment budget of \$50,000. Ratio analysis verifies these choices as follows:

$PVR = NPV\ @\ i^* / PW\ Cost\ @\ i^*$	B/C Ratio = PVR + 1
$PVR_1 = 26{,}033/50{,}000 = 0.52$	$B/C\ Ratio_1 = 1.52$
$PVR_2 = 26{,}535/30{,}000 = 0.88$	$B/C\ Ratio_2 = 1.88$
$PVR_3 = 14{,}605/20{,}000 = 0.73$	$B/C\ Ratio_3 = 1.73$

Both PVR and B/C Ratio results indicate projects 2 and 3 are the economic choices consistent with Growth ROR and cumulative NPV results. Properly calculated ratios and Growth ROR results will always rank non-mutually exclusive alternatives in exactly the same correct order.

It is instructive to note that a higher minimum ROR such as $i^* = 25\%$ causes the choice to switch to alternative 1. When you have good reinvestment opportunities, the short life high ROR project 1 is economically more desirable than when reinvestment opportunities are poor.

NPV for i^* = 25%

$$NPV_1 = 20{,}000(\overset{1.440}{P/A_{25\%,2}}) + 50{,}000(\overset{.6400}{P/F_{25\%,2}}) - 50{,}000 = +\$10{,}800$$

$$NPV_2 = 10{,}000(\overset{2.689}{P/A_{25\%,5}}) + 30{,}000(\overset{.3277}{P/F_{25\%,5}}) - 30{,}000 = +\$6{,}700$$

$$NPV_3 = 5{,}000(\overset{3.161}{P/A_{25\%,7}}) + 20{,}000(\overset{.2097}{P/F_{25\%,7}}) - 20{,}000 = +\$0$$

Maximum Cumulative NPV = NPV_1 = +\$10,800, so select project 1.

Growth ROR for $i^* = 25\%$

Growth ROR calculations for $i^* = 25\%$ verify that project 1 is best based on the following results: Growth $ROR_1 = 28.6\%$, Growth $ROR_2 = 28.6\%$, Growth $ROR_3 = 25\%$. Although the Growth ROR results for projects 1 and 2 are equal, with a $50,000 budget we can either do project 1 with a 28.6% Growth ROR or the combination projects 2 and 3 which have Growth ROR results of 28.6% and 25% respectively. Intuitively you know that the Growth ROR of 28.6% on $30,000 invested in projects 2 and the Growth ROR of 25% on $20,000 invested in project 3 has to be less desirable than the Growth ROR of 28.6% on all $50,000 in project 1, so select project 1 as the economic choice.

PVR for $i^* = 25\%$

$PVR_1 = 10{,}800 / 50{,}000 = 0.22$

$PVR_2 = 6{,}700 / 30{,}000 = 0.22$

$PVR_3 = 0 / 20{,}000 = 0.00$

Since the Growth ROR results for projects 1 and 2 were equal, we expect the ratios to be equal. Once again, as with growth ROR, two mutually exclusive choices exist for spending $50,000 on non-mutually exclusive projects 1, 2 and 3. We can either invest in project 1, or in the combination of projects 2 and 3.

$PVR_1 = 0.22$

$PVR_{2+3} = (6{,}700 + 0) / (30{,}000 + 20{,}000) = 0.13$

Since the same $50,000 would be invested either way, select the maximum PVR which is project 1. This is consistent with Growth ROR results and conclusions. With both PVR and Growth ROR results, the projects were put in the desired selection order but the budget constraint caused us to analyze several mutually exclusive choices before making the final investment decision.

The next example has a primary objective of emphasizing the necessity of netting together all inflows and outflows of money and working with the resultant net cash flow each compounding period in either Growth ROR or Ratio calculations.

EXAMPLE 4-19 Ranking Non-Mutually Exclusive Projects Using PVR and Growth ROR

Rank the following non-mutually exclusive alternatives using PVR for $i^* = 15\%$.

A)

	I = \$110	I = \$110	I = \$110
C = \$100	C = \$200	OC = \$0	OC = \$0
0	1	2	8

B)

		I = \$150	I = \$150
C = \$100	C = \$90	OC = \$40	OC = \$40
0	1	2	8

Solution: All Values in Dollars
Net Present Value (NPV)

$$NPV_A = 110(\overset{4.487}{P/A_{15\%,8}}) - 200(\overset{.8696}{P/F_{15\%,1}}) - 100 = +\$219.60$$

$$NPV_B = [110(\overset{4.160}{P/A_{15\%,7}}) - 90](\overset{.8696}{P/F_{15\%,1}}) - 100 = +\$219.60$$

The rates of return for projects A and B are both 43.35%

These two projects are identical economically and financially from an out-of-pocket cost viewpoint. To rank them equally with PVR (or Growth ROR) you must first net costs and incomes together that are at the same points in time and work with resultant net costs in the denominator of PVR.

Present Value Ratio (PVR)

$$PVR_A = 219.6 / [100 + (200 - 110)(\overset{.8696}{P/F_{15\%,1}})] = +1.23$$

$$PVR_B = 219.6 / [100 + 90(\overset{.8696}{P/F_{15\%,1}})] = +1.23$$

If you incorrectly do not net the project “A” year 1 cost of \$200 against the revenue of \$110 before calculating the ratio denominator, you calculate

$$PVR_A = 219.6 / [100 + 200(\overset{.8696}{P/F_{15\%,1}})] = 0.80 = \text{incorrect } PVR_A$$

This ranks project “A” as economically inferior to project “B” which is not the case.

Growth Rate of Return

To use Growth ROR as a ranking technique, project net costs must be discounted at the minimum ROR to a common time zero before making the Growth ROR calculations for a common evaluation life. This makes the cost basis for Growth ROR calculations identical to the PVR denominator.

A) C = \$100 NetC = \$90 I = \$110 I = \$110

0 1 2 8

Reinvest Income @ i^*=15%: C = \$110 C = \$110

0 1 2 . . . . 8 F=\$1,217.40

$$\text{where, } F = 110(F/A_{15\%,7}) = \$1{,}217.40 \quad [11.067]$$

A+ Reinvest Income @ i^*=15%: C = \$100 C = \$90 — —

0 1 2 . . . . 8 F=\$1,217.40

To properly rank projects using Growth ROR, bring the net costs beyond time zero back to time zero by discounting at the minimum ROR, which is 15% for this analysis. This enables us to calculate rate of growth of a single year 0 sum of money which will always be identical to the denominator of a properly calculated PVR or B/C Ratio. By calculating Growth ROR on year 0 single sums of money, it is clear that projects with the largest Growth ROR are our choices. Those projects must generate the greatest future value possible from available investment dollars.

$$\text{Growth ROR PW Eq: } 100 + 90(P/F_{15\%,1}) = 1{,}217.4(P/F_{i,8}) \quad [0.8696]$$

Growth ROR = i = 27.14%

Since the net costs and incomes on the "B" diagram are identical to the "A" diagram, Growth ROR_B = Growth ROR_A = 27.14%

As with PVR analysis, it should be evident that if the year 1 costs and revenues for project "A" are not netted together, a Growth ROR is calculated based on year 0 cost of \$100 and year 1 cost of \$200 and the 23.79% Growth ROR_A result would rank "A" inferior to "B". This is not a valid result.

Finally, *if costs such as major repair, reclamation or expansion costs occur in project years after positive net income has been realized for one or more years, only the resultant present worth net cost that is not covered by the present worth of net income from the early project years goes into the denominator of PVR calculations or as part of the cost basis for Growth ROR calculations.*

When investments have different starting dates, whether they are mutually exclusive or non-mutually exclusive, it is necessary to use a common evaluation time for NPV or PVR results that lead to valid economic decisions as the following variation of Example 4-19 illustrates.

EXAMPLE 4-19a Analysis of Mutually Exclusive or Non-Mutually Exclusive Alternatives With Different Starting Dates

Re-evaluate alternatives A and B in Example 4-18, first as mutually exclusive alternatives and second as non-mutually exclusive alternatives, considering that investment alternative B starts closer to year 1 than year 0 for i* equal to 15%.

		I = \$110	I = \$110	I = \$110	—
A)	C = \$100	C = \$200	OC = \$0	OC = \$0	—
	0	1	2	8	9

				I = \$150	I = \$150
B)	—	C = \$100	C = \$90	OC = \$40	OC = \$40
	0	1	2	3	9

Solution:

If you incorrectly calculate NPV and PVR results at the start of each project, you get the results shown in Example 4-19 which lead to break-even economic conclusions whether the alternatives are mutually exclusive alternatives with equal NPV results of \$219.60 or non-mutually exclusive alternatives with equal PVR results of +1.23. When projects have different start dates, for valid analysis, you must calculate NPV and PVR results at a common evaluation date, so we arbitrarily select year zero for this analysis.

Net Present Value (NPV)

$$NPV_A = 110\overset{4.487}{(P/A_{15\%,8})} - 200\overset{0.8696}{(P/F_{15\%,1})} - 100 = +\$219.60$$

$$NPV_B = 110\overset{4.160}{(P/A_{15\%,7})}\overset{0.7561}{(P/F_{15\%,2})} - 90\overset{0.7561}{(P/F_{15\%,2})}$$

$$- 100\overset{0.8696}{(P/F_{15\%,1})} = +\$190.98$$

If A and B are mutually exclusive, the maximum NPV (alternative A) is the economic choice. This is a different economic result than the break-even economic conclusion reached in Example 4-19 where the same projects were assumed to have the same starting dates. Therefore, project start date affects mutually exclusive alternative analysis conclusions. If the alternatives are non-mutually exclusive, rank them with PVR as follows.

Present Value Ratio (PVR)

$$\text{Year 0 } PVR_A = +219.6/[100+(200 - 110)\overset{0.8696}{(P/F_{15,1})}] = +1.23$$

$$\text{Year 0 } PVR_B = +190.98/[100\overset{0.8696}{(P/F_{15,1})} + 90\overset{0.7561}{(P/F_{15,2})}] = +1.23$$

The alternatives are economically break-even non-mutually exclusive investments as was concluded for the equal starting date investment alternatives in Example 4-19. Notice that since PVR is the ratio of NPV divided by present worth net cost not offset by revenue, PVR results calculated at any year are the same, because discounting or compounding both the numerator and denominator of PVR (or benefit cost ratio) the same number of years has no impact on the PVR result. However, the numerator and denominator of PVR must both be at the same evaluation time.

The following example concerns ratio analysis ranking of non-mutually exclusive alternatives. It has been shown in numerous earlier examples that changing the minimum rate of return can and often will change economic choices, which emphasizes the need to use a minimum rate of return in all analysis situations that represents other opportunities thought to exist for the investment of capital. Straying from this requirement causes inconsistent and often incorrect economic decision-making. Similarly, with ratio analysis it is necessary to use break-even cutoff rates of zero for PVR and one for B/C Ratio. You will not get economic decisions that are consistent with results from other valid techniques if you raise the ratio cutoff rate to say, 0.25 for PVR or 1.25 for B/C Ratio as an alternative to raising the minimum ROR and leaving the cutoff at zero for PVR and one for B/C Ratio. The following example illustrates considerations related to these points.

EXAMPLE 4-20 Ratio Analysis Considerations Related to Net Present Value and Rate Of Return

Alternatives "A" and "B" may be either mutually exclusive or non-mutually exclusive investments. Discuss the analysis of these alternatives for either situation using NPV, PVR, B/C Ratio, ROR and Growth ROR for minimum ROR values of 12%, 15% and 20%. Analyze some of the effects of changing the PVR cutoff value as an alternative to changing minimum ROR.

A) C = \$100   I = \$34.67   I = \$34.67
0   1 5

B) C = \$100   I = \$16.67   I = \$16.67
0   1 20

Solution:

By Trial and Error, ROR_A = 21.7%, ROR_B = 16.0%

Decision Criteria	i^* = 12%	i^* = 15%	i^* = 20%
NPV_A	+25.00	+16.20	+ 3.70
NPV_B	+25.00	+ 4.80	–18.50
PVR_A	+ .25	+ .16	+ .04
PVR_B	+ .25	+ .05	– .18
B/C $Ratio_A$	+ 1.25	+ 1.16	+ 1.04
B/C $Ratio_B$	+ 1.25	+ 1.05	+ .82
Growth ROR_A	13.1%	15.6%	20.1%
Growth ROR_B	13.1%	15.2%	18.4%

For i^* = 12%, alternatives "A" and "B" are economically equivalent whether they are mutually exclusive or non-mutually exclusive alternatives. Raising "i^*" to 15% or 20% causes the economic choice to shift to favoring "A" over "B" with all techniques. Note NPV_A is greater than NPV_B for both i^* = 15% and i^* = 20%; we know "A" is better than "B" if we consider the alternatives to be mutually exclusive. Explicit incremental analysis calculations must be done to verify that conclusion with PVR, B/C Ratio, ROR and Growth ROR, but all techniques give the same economic conclusion.

If "A" and "B" are considered to be non-mutually exclusive alternatives, PVR, B/C Ratio, and Growth ROR, are the valid ranking techniques and all indicate "A" is better than "B" for i^* = 15% and 20%.

Now let's analyze the effect of using i^* = 12% to handle time value of money in ratio calculations, but effectively increase "i^*" by raising the cutoff for acceptable projects from zero to 0.25 with PVR and from 1.0 to 1.25 with B/C Ratio. This is an evaluation approach sometimes used in industry practice. Notice it leads to the conclusion in this case that "A" and "B" are equivalent, whether they are mutually exclusive or non-mutually exclusive. Actually raising "i^*" to 15% or 20% shows clear economic advantage to "A" for the higher "i^*" values with all standard techniques of analysis. Also notice that for i^* = 12%, all methods show the alternatives are equivalent. This means incremental ROR analysis ("B-A" to get incremental costs followed by incremental revenues) will give the incremental "B-A" ROR to be 12%. Treating alternatives "A" and "B" as economically equivalent is the conclusion given by ratio calculations at i^* = 12% with increased cutoff values of 0.25 for PVR or 1.25 for B/C Ratio. This explicitly means that a 12% incremental ROR on "B-A" is satisfactory. This is a misleading conclusion if other opportunities really exist to invest dollars at an ROR greater than 12%, which raising the cutoff rates on PVR to 0.25 and B/C Ratio to 1.25 implies. Since this approach involves inconsistencies in economic conclusions, it seems undesirable to use it. However, it can be argued that the differences in results from increasing the ratio cutoff instead of increasing "i^*" are small and not significant. Regardless, it is important to be aware that this approach may give economic results and conclusions that are inconsistent with other standard evaluation techniques.

4.11 Summary of Mutually Exclusive and Non-Mutually Exclusive Alternative Analysis

Mutually Exclusive Alternative Analysis

Evaluating mutually exclusive alternatives was described in this Chapter as a two-step process: 1) evaluate individual alternatives to make sure all projects meet the minimum economic objectives (sometimes this is described as "weeding out the bad apples from a basket of opportunities"). 2) Evaluate the economic potential of additional capital invested in more capital-intensive alternatives using incremental analysis. Challenge the smallest satisfactory investment with the next largest initial investment. If the larger investment is economically satisfactory, challenge it with the next largest level of initial investment. The largest investment meeting each criterion will be the economic choice. This is always the project with the largest Net Present Value (NPV).

Incremental analysis demonstrates why sunk costs are not relevant in economic decision-making. What is relevant is the opportunity foregone, i.e. the revenue or cash flow passed up when a different investment course of action was selected. An incremental analysis properly accounts for both sunk cost and opportunity cost considerations.

Rate of Return or Growth Rate of Return. With either regular ROR or Growth ROR analysis of mutually exclusive alternatives you must evaluate both total investment ROR and incremental investment ROR, selecting the largest investment for which both are satisfactory. Use a common evaluation life for Growth ROR analysis of unequal life alternatives, normally the life of the longest life alternative, assuming net revenues and costs are zero in the later years of shorter life alternatives.

Net Value Analysis. With NPV, NAV or NFV analysis you want the mutually exclusive alternative with the largest net value because this is the alternative with the largest investment that has both a positive total investment net value and a positive incremental net value compared to the last satisfactory smaller investment. When using NAV or NFV to evaluate unequal life alternatives you must use a common evaluation life, normally the life of the longest life alternative, assuming net revenues and costs are zero in the later years of shorter life alternatives as with ROR analysis.

Ratio Analysis. With ratio analysis of mutually exclusive alternatives using either PVR or B/C Ratio, it is necessary to evaluate both total investment ratios and incremental investment ratios. Analogous to ROR analysis, the mutually exclusive alternative with the biggest total investment ratio often is not the best economic choice. A bigger investment with a somewhat smaller ratio often is a better mutually exclusive alternative choice.

Future Worth Profit Analysis. Calculate the FW Profit that can be generated by each alternative project if profits and salvage are reinvested at the minimum rate of return, "i^*". Select the project that maximizes FW profit for the investment money available to invest. With this method you must compare the FW profit for the same investment dollars in all cases, by assuming the budget money not required in one project will be invested elsewhere at "i^*".

Dual-i-Values

Dual-i-values relate to the multiple solutions that occur when cash flows result in investments generating revenue that are followed by more investments. All dual-i-values contain a combination of rate of reinvestment and rate of return meaning, which makes them useless for ROR analysis in terms of being used to reliably assess economic profitability. If a compound interest ROR measure of economic value is desired, three modifications to the cash flows were described including Growth ROR, the Escrow Approach and the Year-by-Year Approach. In each present worth modification, cash flows are adjusted at the minimum rate of return to eliminate the existence of cost-income-cost. Each of the present worth modifications results in the same NPV. This means that even though the approaches generate modified ROR results of varying magnitudes, the economic conclusions will always be consistent with NPV.

Non-Mutually Exclusive Alternatives

Rate of Return or Growth Rate of Return. Regular ROR analysis cannot be used to consistently rank non-mutually exclusive alternatives. Use Growth ROR and rank the alternatives in the order of decreasing Growth ROR. This will maximize profit from available investment capital. Use a common evaluation life for Growth ROR analysis of unequal life alternatives, normally the life of the longest alternative.

Net Value Analysis. With NPV, NAV or NFV analysis of non-mutually exclusive projects, select the group of projects that will maximize cumulative net value for the dollars available to invest. This does not necessarily involve selecting the project with largest net value on individual project investment. When using NAV or NFV to evaluate unequal life alternatives you must use a common evaluation life, normally the life of the longest life alternative.

Ratio Analysis. Ranking projects in the order of decreasing present value ratio (PVR) or B/C Ratio is the easiest way of selecting non-mutually exclusive projects to maximize cumulative NPV for available investment dollars.

Future Worth Profit Analysis. Calculate the FW Profit that can be generated by each alternative project if profits and salvage are reinvested at the minimum rate of return, "i^*". Use a common evaluation life equal to the longest life alternative if unequal life projects are involved. Select the group of investment projects that will maximize the cumulative FW Profit for the money available to invest, analogous to the way NPV and NFV are applied. Assume that any odd dollar amounts can be invested elsewhere at "i^*", the same as with other techniques of analysis.

Remember, with all of these evaluation methods, the minimum rate of return, "i^*", is the rate of return that represents the other opportunities which are felt to exist for the use of available investment capital. This term is sometimes called the hurdle rate, discount rate, opportunity cost of capital or just cost of capital.

If you use a valid minimum ROR and apply the discounted cash flow analysis techniques as described in this chapter and summary, you will reach correct economic decisions for your cost, revenue, and timing of cost and revenue project data and assumptions. It is always important to recognize that economic analysis calculation results are just a direct reflection of the input data and analysis assumptions. With any techniques of analysis, economic evaluation conclusions are only as good and valid as the data and assumptions on which they are based.

PROBLEMS

Excel solutions at Stermole.com

4-1 If a time zero cost of $300,000 is incurred for equipment replacement, an existing project "A" is expected to maintain the generation of $450,000 before-tax profits each year for year one through year 10. Two alternatives are being considered for improvement (project "B") and improvement combined with expansion (project "C") with projected costs and revenues as shown on the time diagrams. All dollar values are expressed in thousands of dollars.

A)

C = 300	I = 450	I = 450	I = 450
0	1	2	10

B)

C = 900	I = 550	I = 550	I = 550
0	1	2	10

C)

	I = 750		
C = 1,200	C = 800	I = 850	I = 850
0	1	2	10

For a minimum rate of return of 15% and considering the alternatives to be mutually exclusive, determine whether project "A", "B" or "C" is economically best using ROR, NPV and PVR. Then increase the minimum ROR to 25% from 15% over the entire 10 year evaluation life and re- evaluate the alternatives using any valid analysis.

4-2 A company is analyzing the economics of leasing a parcel of land over the next 6 years for time zero lease payment of $80,000. The land would be used as a product marketing center requiring construction of a $200,000 building on the land in time zero and it is estimated that it would generate annual revenues of $290,000 and annual operating costs of $160,000 at the end of years one through five. The lease contract stipulates that at the end of year six the building must be torn down and the property restored to its initial conditions and this is estimated to cost $360,000 at the end of year six. Use rate of return analysis to determine if this project is economically viable for a 20% minimum ROR. Verify your results with NPV.

4-3 A double pipe heat exchanger with steam in the shell is to be insulated to reduce heat loss to surroundings. The thickness of insulation, initial cost and projected annual cost of heat loss are given in the following table. If the minimum ROR is 20% before taxes, determine the optimum thickness of insulation for an insulation life of six years with a zero salvage value.

Insulation Thickness (Inches)	Initial Cost, $	Annual Heat Loss Cost, $
0	0	1400
1	1200	800
2	1800	600
3	2500	500
4	3500	400

Base your results on Present Worth Cost Analysis and verify that result with incremental NPV and ROR calculations.

4-4 You have been asked to make rate of return analysis to support or reject the economic viability of project development that has the estimated potential of generating $450,000 revenue per year and operating costs of $310,000 per year for each of the next 10 years (assume end-of-year one through 10 values). A company has agreed to construct and finance the project for deferred payments of $50,000 per year at the end-of-year two, three and four with final lump sum purchase cost of $1,450,000 to be made at the end of year five. The year ten salvage value is estimated to be $300,000. Make rate of return analysis to evaluate project economics for minimum rates of return of (a) 5%, (b) 15% and (c) 50%. Do NPV results support your conclusions?

4-5 To achieve labor cost savings on a manufacturing process, a company will install one of two possible equipment automation changes. New capital equipment costs and projected savings are as follows:

	Equipment Cost	Projected Annual Savings
Change 1	$150,000	$ 80,000
Change 2	$230,000	$115,000

(A) For a six year evaluation life, which change, if any, should be selected if i* = 40% before tax? Use Net Present Value Analysis and assume zero salvage values.

(B) Is there any evaluation life other than six years that would switch the economic evaluation result found in (A)? If yes, what is the break-even life for which there are no economic differences between the alternatives?

4-6 Rank non-mutually exclusive alternatives "A" and "B" using PVR Analysis for i* = 15%.

A)

	C = $200		C = $230	
C = $100	I = $110	I = $110	I = $110	I = $110 I = $110
0	1	2	3	4. 8

B)

	C = $200		C = $180	
C = $100	I = $110	I = $20	I = $110	I = $110 I = $110
0	1	2	3	4. 8

4-7 Two mutually exclusive unequal life investment alternatives, "A" and "B", must be evaluated to determine the best economic choice for i* = 20%. The investments, "C", and incomes, "I", and salvage values, "L", are shown on the time diagrams in thousands of dollars.

A)

C = 100	I = 40	I = 40	I = 40	I = 40	I = 40	L=100
0	1	2	3	4	5	

B)

C = 150	I = 60	I = 60	I = 60	L=150
0	1	2	3	

i) Determine the dual rates of return that result from a direct incremental ROR Analysis of "B-A".

ii) Evaluate the projects using NPV Analysis.

iii) Evaluate the projects using incremental Growth ROR Analysis.

iv) Evaluate the projects using PW Cost Modified ROR Analysis.

v) Is the economic choice affected by reducing the minimum ROR to 10% from 20%?

4-8 A friend offers to give you 10 payments of \$1000 at annual time periods zero through 10 except year three if you give him \$9000 at year three as shown on the time diagram. All values are in dollars.

I = 1000	I = 1000	I = 1000	C = 9000	I = 1000	I = 1000
0	1	2	3	4.	10

Evaluate this income, investment, income opportunity shown on the time diagram for before-tax minimum rates of return of 10% and 20%.

A) Use Net Present Value Analysis.
B) Analyze the project using Present Worth Cost Modified ROR.

4-9 A new process can be developed and operated at Levels "A" or "B" with capital costs, sales and operating costs as shown. All values are in thousands of dollars.

		Sales = 75	Sales = 75
A)	C = 100	Op. Costs = 35	Op. Costs = 35
	0	1	5

		Sales = 100	Sales = 100
B)	C = 150	Op. Costs = 45	Op. Costs = 45
	0	1	5

If i* = 20%, which level of investment should be selected? Use NPV Analysis and verify your results with ROR and PVR Analysis. If the minimum ROR is reduced to 12%, what is the economic choice? If the minimum ROR is 12% for years one and two and 20% for years three, four and five, what is the economic choice?

4-10 Improvement and expansion of a production facility are under consideration. At the present time profits are \$450,000 per year, and in the future escalation of operating costs each year is expected to exactly offset escalation of revenue, so profit margins are projected to remain constant at \$450,000 per year for each of the next years one through 10. Two alternatives for improvement and improvement combined with expansion are being considered with projected costs and revenues as shown on the time diagrams following this problem statement, with all dollar values expressed in thousands of dollars.

A)

—	I = 450	I = 450	I = 450
0	1	2.	10

B)

C = 800	I = 700	I = 700	I = 700
0	1	2.	10

C)

C = 1,300	I = 850 C = 900	I = 1,050	I = 1,050
0	1	2.	10

For a minimum rate of return of 15%, and considering the alternatives to be mutually exclusive, determine whether the present "A", improvement "B", or improvement plus expansion project "C" is economically best using ROR, NPV and PVR. Then increase the minimum ROR to 25% from 15% over the entire 10 year evaluation life and re-evaluate the alternatives using both ROR and NPV analysis. Then assume that the minimum ROR is increased from 15% to 25% for evaluation years one and two and then, starting in year three, the minimum ROR reverts to 15% again through year 10.

4-11 An ethylene plant manager is considering the investment of $32,000,000 today (time zero) to integrate heavy duty industrial single shaft gas turbines to reduce energy costs for a 750,000 metric ton per year liquids cracker. The time zero investment is expected to generate energy operating cost savings of $12,000,000 at the end of each of years one through five. An alternative is to consider using aero-derivative turbines (based on jet engines) that cost $34,000,000 but require an additional $4,000,000 time zero investment in design modifications. These turbines are slightly more efficient and generate annual energy savings of $14,000,000 but also require additional maintenance of $500,000 per year at the end of each of years one through five. If the desired minimum rate of return is 15%, use rate of return analysis to determine which of these two alternatives should be the economic choice. Verify your conclusion with NPV analysis.

4-12 Use ROR analysis to compare project "A" involving the investment of $240,000 to generate a series of equal end-of-year revenues of $50,000 per year for five years plus a salvage value of $240,000 at the end of year five and project "B" involving the investment of $240,000 to generate a series of equal end-of-year revenues of $98,500 per year for 5 years with zero salvage value. The projects are mutually exclusive and the minimum ROR is 10%. Verify your results with NPV Analysis.

4-13 Determine the best economic way for a research manager to allocate $500,000 in the following non- mutually exclusive projects if i* = 20%.

A) C = $200,000 I = $90,000. . . . . I = $90,000 L = 0
0 1 6

B) C = $500,000 I = $300,000 . . . . . I = $300,000 L = 0
0 1 3

C) C = $300,000 I = $120,000 . . . . I = $120,000 L = $100,000
0 1. 5

Use NPV Analysis and verify the results with Growth ROR Analysis and PVR Analysis

4-14 If alternatives "A" and "B" are mutually exclusive projects, use ROR Analysis to determine which is economically best if i* = 15%.

A) C = $20,000 I = $12,000 . . . . . I = $12,000 L = $20,000
0 1 12

B) C = $28,000 I = $14,000 . . . . . I = $14,000 L = $28,000
0 1 12

Verify the ROR Analysis results with NPV and PVR Analysis.

4-15 Three unequal life investment alternatives with costs, profits and salvage values as shown on the time diagrams are being considered.

A) C = \$160,000   I = \$150,000 . . . . . . I = \$150,000   L = \$50,000
0   1 5

B) C = \$320,000   I = \$275,000. . . . . . I = \$275,000   L = \$70,000
0   1 4

C) C = \$480,000   I = \$500,000 . . . . . I = \$500,000   L = \$100,000
0   1 3

Assume \$480,000 is available to invest and other opportunities exist to invest all available dollars at a 20% ROR. Use NPV Analysis to determine how the \$480,000 should be spent from an economic viewpoint if the alternatives are non-mutually exclusive. Then use NPV Analysis to determine which of the alternatives, "A", "B" or "C", is best if the alternatives are mutually exclusive. Verify these results with PVR Analysis.

4-16 For an investor with a minimum rate of return of 20.0%: (1) Rank the following non-mutually exclusive alternatives. (2) For a time zero budget of \$500, which of these projects would you select? Consider that year one or later year budgets will cover costs in year one or later years not covered by project revenues in earlier years. (3) Develop the "Cumulative NPV" Diagram for alternative "D" and indicate the point on this diagram that represents the investor's maximum capital exposure.

Yr	**0**	**1**	**2**	**3**	**4**	**5**
A)	–200	60	100	–200	300	300
B)	–300	–90	100	200	300	400
C)	–300	250	250	250	250	–600
D)	–300	100	150	–350	400	400

4-17 Improvement to a coal mine haul road is being considered to shorten the overall haul distance and reduce truck cycle times thereby increasing the total number of cycles per day. The cost of the improvements is estimated to be $6,000,000 at time zero. Currently, the trucks make 16 cycles per day from the mine pit to a port load out facility which translates into 2,000,000 tons of coal being hauled each year. If the road improvement is made, the number of cycles is anticipated to increase by 25% to 20 cycles per day which translates into an additional 500,000 tons of annual production from the mine. Total mine reserves are estimated to be 14,000,000 tons and the coal is sold at an average selling price of $32.00 per ton with operating costs of $12.00 per ton. If the haul road improvement is made, the life of the mine will be shortened from seven to six years due to the accelerated production schedule. With the modified haul road, total production in years one through five would be 2,500,000 tons per year with year six production of 1,500,000 tons.

For this acceleration problem, use rate of return analysis to determine if the investment in the haul road improvement should be made today. The minimum acceptable rate of return is 15%.

4-18 Improvement to a mine haul road is being considered to shorten the overall haul distance and reduce truck cycle times, thereby increasing the total number of cycles per day. The cost of the improvements is estimated to be $6,000,000 at time zero. Currently, the trucks make 16 cycles per day from the mine pit to a crushing facility which, given the truck performance, capacities and haul distance, translates into 2,000,000 tons of ore being hauled each year. If the road improvement is made, the number of cycles is anticipated to increase by 25% to 20 cycles per day which translates into an additional 500,000 tons of annual production from the mine. Total mine reserves are estimated to be 14,000,000 tons. If the haul road improvement is made, the life of the mine will be shortened from seven to six years due to the accelerated production schedule. With the modified haul road, total production in years one through five would be 2,500,000 tons per year with year six production totaling 1,500,000 tons at which time the reserves would be depleted. For each alternative, the average ore grade is 0.09 ounces per ton with a 0.85 recovery rate. The average selling price is $350.00 per ounce while the operating costs are $190.00 per ounce beginning in year 1. The minimum acceptable rate of return is 15.0%.

For this acceleration problem, use rate of return analysis to determine if the haul road improvement can be economically justified. Then verify your findings with a net present value analysis.

4-19 Two alternatives exist for you to invest $250,000 as shown on the following time diagrams. Consider risk to be identical for each investment. Assuming your minimum discount rate is 15.0%, determine the economically better choice using the rate of return, net present value, present value ratio, growth rate of return and future worth profit.

A)	–250	115.32 . . . . 115.32	
	0	1 6	
B)	–250	— . . . . —	1,206.7
	0	1 6	

4-20 A proposed investment has the following projected net cash flow stream from development cost and product sale profits, and abandonment costs. Use rate of return analysis to determine if this investment is satisfactory for a minimum discount rate of 12.0%. All cash flows are in thousands.

BTCF	–1,470	+1,705	+897	+103	–617	–559	–294
	0	1	2	3	4	5	6

4-21 A natural gas distribution company is evaluating the economic desirability of replacing or repairing existing gas mains in a small town. At the present time, with the existing gas mains, it is estimated that 100,000 Mcf of gas is being lost per year and that this gas could be sold to corporate customers at $8.00 per Mcf. The cost of replacing the gas mains is estimated to be $4,000,000 at time zero. Replacement of the mains would effectively eliminate all gas loss for the next 10 years. The cost of repairing the gas mains is estimated to be $1,600,000 which would reduce annual gas loss to 25,000 Mcf at year one (allocate to the end of the year), with gas loss increasing by a constant gradient of 6,000 Mcf per year in years following year one. Use present worth cost analysis for a 10 year evaluation life and i* = 15.0% to determine from an economic viewpoint if the gas mains should be replaced, repaired, or left in the present condition. Verify your cost analysis results with incremental NPV.

CHAPTER 4 AUXILIARY PROBLEMS

A4-1 Two used engines are not utilized in an airline's fleet, but instead, are being leased to another company for average annual end of year income totaling $400,000 for both engines. Average annual operating costs to maintain both engines total $100,000 per year. These numbers are believed to be sustainable for the next 2 years, after which, a total modification cost of $250,000 for both engines will be required (assume an end of year 2 cost). This modification will allow the engines to generate total lease income of $500,000 per year for the next 3 years (end of years 3, 4 & 5). Assume total operating costs will be $100,000 in each of those years. To simplify the analysis, assume the engines will be scrapped for spare parts totaling $200,000 at the end of year 5. The company is considering selling the engines for $1,200,000 today. For a minimum rate of return of 12%, would you recommend selling or keeping the engines and leasing them for the next 5 years?

A4-2 An existing mineral operation is expected to generate annual before-tax cash flow (revenue – operating costs) of $100 million per year at each of years 1, 2, 3, and 4. An alternative to the present scenario is the purchase of the mineral rights in an adjacent property for $40 million now (time 0) with the expectation that $50 million would be spent on development and equipment at year 1, and another $55 million at year 2. This expansion would make the total project revenue minus operating costs $100 million at year 1 (same as present scenario), $140 million at year 2, $150 million at year 3, $160 million at year 4, and $65 million in each of years 5 through 10. Equipment will need to be repaired or replaced for an expected cost of $65 million at the end of year 6 with a salvage value at the end of year 10 of $40 million. Make before-tax NPV analysis to determine whether the project expansion is economically justifiable, given a minimum ROR of 15%. Verify your NPV conclusion using before-tax ROR and PVR analyses. Note, the $100 in years 1 through 4 is reflected in the time diagrams for each alternative.

PRESENT:	—	100	100	100	100	0	0	0	0	0	0
Year	0	1	2	3	4	5	6	7	8	9	10
		100	140	150	160	65	65	65	65	65	65
EXPAND:	–40	–50	–55	—	—	—	–65	—	—	—	40
Year	0	1	2	3	4	5	6	7	8	9	10

A4-3 Two mutually exclusive alternatives exist to invest $100,000 as shown on the following time diagrams.

A) –100,000 — — ...... — 627,500
0 1 2 ...... 6 7

B) –100,000 44,190 44,190 44,190
0 1 2 7

Assuming a minimum ROR of 15%, determine the economically better choice using: ROR, NPV, PVR, Growth ROR, and Future Worth Profit.

A4-4 A mineral property is producing at a rate that will generate $5 million in annual operating profit (revenue minus operating costs) during the next year (assume end of year 1). Escalation of operating costs is expected to be offset by sales escalation in future years, so that annual end-of-year operating profit will remain constant at $5 million each year until mineral reserves are depleted. At the current production rate, mineral reserves will be depleted at the end of 10 years from now. An increase in the annual production rate is being considered by incurring a $2 million equipment and development cost now (time 0) and a $4 million equipment and development cost a year from now (year 1). These expansion costs would permit increasing mineral production to give projected total operating profit of $6 million at year 1 and $8 million per year at years 2 through 8 when reserves will be depleted at the increased production rate. The alternatives are summarized below as the present and expand diagrams. Use NPV analysis to evaluate the economic desirability of the expansion investments for a minimum ROR of 20%. Verify your NPV findings by making a valid ROR analysis and PVR analysis of these mutually exclusive alternatives.

PRESENT:	—	5	5	5	5	5
	0	1	2	8	9	10
		6				
EXPAND:	–2	–4	8	8	0	0
	0	1	2	8	9	10

A4-5 A production facility is currently utilizing carbon steel tubing. The current process will require injection of chemicals to control tubing corrosion due to high temperatures and pressures and corrosive chlorides in the transported product. It is proposed to replace the carbon steel that cost \$12 per foot with an installation cost of \$125,000 both incurred 1 year ago, with chrome stainless steel tubing that would cost \$68 per foot today, (time zero). 20,000 feet of tubing would be required and installation costs are estimated to total \$500,000 (also at time zero).

Annual cost savings in chemicals, labor and chemical injection equipment are projected to be \$550,000 in year 1 following the installation of the new tubing with savings escalating at an annually compounded rate of 7% per year in succeeding years beginning in year 2. For simplicity, use a 6-year evaluation life with a salvage value of zero at the end of year 6. Assume a 15% minimum ROR. Identify the two mutually exclusive service alternatives in time diagram format and evaluate each with present worth cost analysis. Support your cost findings using incremental NPV and ROR analyses to determine if installation of the chrome tubing is economically desirable. Assume the existing carbon steel tubing has no salvage value today, at time 0.

A4-6 An existing operation is producing annual before-tax cash flows (BTCF) of \$125 million per year (assume end-of-year values) expected to be realized over the next 4 years (years 1–4). However, if environmental improvements are not made, the property will have to be shut down in year 5. Assume the cash flow from year five will be used to cover all shutdown costs in that period (therefore zero cash flow would be realized in year 5 and beyond).

An alternative to a plant shutdown is to make the necessary environmental improvements to the property. These improvements would include expenditures of $50 million now (time zero) with the expectation that $125 million would be spent in year 1 and another $95 million cost incurred at the end of year 2. In addition to maintaining the existing cash flow, these expenditures would extend the life of the plant and increase the cash flow from operations to the separate figures identified on the "expand" diagram below. An equipment repair/replace expenditure of $75 million has been charged to the project at the end of year 6. Terminal value is estimated to total $50 million at year 10. The investor's minimum rate of return is 15% per year, compounded annually. Evaluate these mutually exclusive alternatives using NPV, ROR and PVR.

Values in millions;

CURRENT

BTCF	0	125	125	125	125	0	0	0	0	0	0
Year	0	1	2	3	4	5	6	7	8	9	10

EXPAND (Includes the Current BTCF)

Oper Profit	0	125	140	160	175	75	75	75	75	75	75
Capital	–50	–125	–95	—	—	—	–75	—	—	—	50
BTCF	–50	0	45	160	175	75	0	75	75	75	125
Year	0	1	2	3	4	5	6	7	8	9	10

A4-7 Your company is currently considering an acceleration program to enhance the timing of production and quantity of reserves from an existing lease. The before-tax cash flows for the two alternatives are summarized below in thousands of dollars.

Current	—	3,600	2,800	2,200	1,640	1,120	600
	0	1	2	3	4	5	6
Proposed	–2,940	7,000	4,600	2,400	400	0	0
	0	1	2	3	4	5	6

The investor's before-tax minimum rate of return is 12.0%. Use rate of return analysis to evaluate the economics of this acceleration program and support those findings with NPV analysis.

A4-8 Rank these non-mutually exclusive alternatives if other opportunities exist to earn a before-tax minimum rate of return of 10%. Values are in thousands of dollars.

A)

		100	550			
–300	–200	–250	–300	600	600	600
0	1	2	3	4	5	6

B)

–500	300	–150	350	450	550
0	1	2	3	4	5

C)

–200	150	–500	600	600
0	1	2	3	4

A4-9 Rank these non-mutually exclusive alternatives for a 20% opportunity cost of capital. Values are given in thousands of dollars.

A)

	I=100	I=150				
C=100	C=200	C=250	I=300	I=300	I=300	I=300
0	1	2	3	4	5	6

B)

		I=200			
—	C=300	C=150	I=250	I=250	I=250
0	1	2	3	4	5

C)

C=200	I=170	C=200	I=350	I=350	I=350	C=100
0	1	2	3	4	5	6

A4-10 A chemical company wants you to analyze whether it is better economically to sell patent rights to a new chemical process for $300,000 cash now (time 0) or whether it would be better to keep the patent rights and develop them using one of two development scenarios for which projected costs and incomes are given on the following time diagrams. All dollar values are in thousands of dollars.

A)

	I=100	I=420	....	I=420
C=700	C=300	C=200	....	C=200
0	1	2	....	9

B)

		I=670	....	I=670
C=500	C=800	OC=250	....	OC=250
0	1	2	....	9

Use ROR analysis to determine whether it is better to sell, or develop with the "A" or "B" scenario, assuming a minimum ROR of 15%. Verify your results with NPV and PVR analyses. If the minimum ROR is raised to 25%, use any valid analysis to determine the economic choice.

A4-11 A deep water-flood project has been on line for 2 years. Engineering calculations indicate that the producing wells are each capable of 750 barrels of oil equivalent per day (BOE), but problems with the existing artificial lift system has limited production to 400 BOE per well. The project engineer has to decide whether to (1) reduce the injection rates to match the artificial lift capabilities, or (2) maintain injection and modify the artificial lift equipment to lift larger volumes of fluid (750 BOE). Production for each alternative is provided in the following table.

YEAR	REDUCED INJECTION Production (MBOE)	MODIFIED LIFT Production (MBOE)
1	1200	1500
2	1300	1700
3	1500	2200
4	1700	2150
5	1400	1700
6	1300	1500
7	1200	1300
8	1100	750
9	1000	350
10	750	100
11	400	0

The time 0 cost of the upgraded artificial lift facility is estimated at \$7 million, with operating costs of \$2.5 million more per year relative to the present operation beginning in year 1. Working interest is 100%, the net revenue interest is 80%, and oil price per barrel is \$44. Assume escalation of incremental operating expenses exactly offsets escalation of incremental revenues. Determine whether it is economically preferable to reduce the injection rates or to redesign and modify the lift system if the minimum acceptable before-tax ROR is 15%. M = 1,000.

A4-12 A coal mining project has been on line for 2 years. Engineering mine plan calculations indicate that the present mine production can be increased to the accelerated coal mining production schedule shown below, by changing the mine plan and acquiring additional new equipment. The project engineer has to decide whether to (1) maintain current production rates, or (2) accelerate production by purchasing the additional mining equipment necessary to increase coal production.

YEAR	PRESENT PRODUCTION (Tons in 000's)	ACCELERATED PRODUCTION (Tons in 000's)
1	1200	1500
2	1300	1700
3	1500	2200
4	1700	2150
5	1400	1700
6	1300	1500
7	1200	1300
8	1100	750
9	1000	350
10	750	100
11	400	0

The time 0 cost of the accelerated coal mining production equipment is estimated at \$7 million with operating costs of \$2.5 million more a year relative to the current operation. Working interest is 100%, net revenue after royalties is 80%, and coal price per ton is \$44.00. Assume escalation of incremental operating expenses exactly offsets escalation of incremental revenues. Is it economically desirable to maintain present coal mining production rates or to accelerate production? The minimum acceptable before-tax ROR is 15%.

A4-13 Development of a natural gas well is projected to involve the annual production, costs and prices summarized below. All capital and operating costs are in dollars while the production is summarized in thousands of cubic feet (Mcf). Pricing is in \$/Mcf. The investor has a 100% working interest and an 87.5% net revenue interest.

Year	0	1	2	3	4
Production (Mcf)	-	300,000	700,000	500,000	150,000
Price, \$/Mcf	-	5.00	5.25	5.50	5.75
Operating Costs	-	60,000	70,000	80,000	90,000
Intangible Drilling	1,000,000				
Tangible Completion	700,000				
Gathering Line	450,000				
Lease Bonus	2,000,000				

A) Calculate the before-tax cash flows for this scenario and using a minimum rate of return of 15%, evaluate the economics of drilling now using NPV, ROR and PVR.

B) Consider the economic implications of delaying the start of drilling this project for four years to take advantage of anticipated escalation in the price of natural gas. Assume the lease bonus would remain at time zero, but all other costs in drilling and connecting the well will be delayed to the end of year 4. During the next four years, capital and operating costs will both escalate 5% per year. That means the year 4 intangible drilling cost would be $1{,}000{,}000(1.05)^4 = 1{,}215{,}506$ while the year 5 operating expense in the first year of production would be $60{,}000(1.05)^4 = 72{,}930$. The price of natural gas is estimated at \$6.50/Mcf in year 5 with that amount escalating 10% per year in each of years 6, 7 and 8. Therefore, the year 8 price would be $\$6.50(1.1)^3 = \$8.65$. For a minimum rate of return of 15%, compute the project before-tax cash flows (BTCF) and evaluate the opportunity of deferring development using NPV, ROR and PVR.

C) Evaluate which alternative is best by making an incremental analysis with the described criteria.

A4-14 An engineer received a drilling proposal from the operator of a property in which his company was a working interest owner. The economic alternatives involved entering into a joint venture with a 50% working interest and a 50% net revenue interest for a time zero $1.6MM investment (50% share), or not join and retain a 12.5% overriding royalty interest (no capital investment). The net present value for the join case was $744M with a discounted profitability index (DPI, benefit-cost-ratio) of 1.50. The NPV for the nonparticipation case was $574M, with an infinite DPI since there is no investment. Incremental NPV analysis indicates the join case to be best with a $170M incremental NPV. The incremental DPI analysis gives a 1.11 for the joint venture case. The company uses DPI as the metric for making economic decisions and the minimum acceptable DPI is 1.20.

Here in is the problem and there are two schools of thought on the results of this analysis management was debating:

- The joint venture case is not acceptable because the incremental analysis DPI is 1.11 (less than the 1.20 required), therefore that $1.6MM of capital would be used for some other, higher DPI projects, in our portfolio
- The other school of thought is that the incremental DPI is used only for a go/no-go decision on comparing the two alternatives for this single proposal only, which says join, as does the incremental NPV analysis; and that the "real" DPI will then be the DPI of 1.50 for the joint venture case.

Please point management in right direction and describe the issues at hand here and the evaluation method they should employ.

A4-15 Development of a natural gas well is projected to involve the annual production, costs and prices summarized below. All capital and operating costs are in dollars while the production is summarized in thousands of cubic feet, (Mcf). Pricing is in $/Mcf. The investor has a 100% working interest and an 87.5% net revenue interest.

Year	0	1	2	3	4
Production (Mcf)	-	300,000	700,000	500,000	150,000
Price, $/Mcf	-	5.00	5.25	5.50	5.75
Operating Costs	-	60,000	70,000	80,000	90,000
Intangible Drilling	1,000,000	-	-	-	-
Tangible Completion	700,000	-	-	-	-
Gathering Line	450,000	-	-	-	-
Lease Bonus	2,000,000	-	-	-	-
Site Reclamation	-	-	-	-	600,000

For an investor seeking a minimum rate of return of 15%, make a valid rate of return analysis of this drilling opportunity.

CHAPTER 5

ESCALATED AND CONSTANT DOLLARS

5.1 Inflation and Escalation in Economic Analysis

Many people use the terms inflation and escalation interchangeably but generally, as used in this textbook they have different meaning. The term inflation is often associated with increases in prices for goods and services that is the result of "too many dollars chasing too few goods," and is commonly measured by various indexes, the most common of which is the Consumer Price Index or CPI. A more refined definition of inflation might be, "a persistent rise in the prices associated with a basket of goods and services that is not offset by increased productivity." Deflation could be defined as an overall decline in prices for a similar basket of goods and services. *Escalation on the other hand refers to a persistent rise in the price of specific commodities, goods or services due to a combination of inflation, supply/demand and other effects such as environmental and engineering changes. Note that escalation deals with specific goods and services, while inflation is concerned with a basket of goods and services, so inflation involves average change.* Inflation is just one of several factors that contributes to cost or price escalation and it should be evident that escalation is what affects the actual costs and revenues that will be realized for a project. Therefore, escalation of costs and revenues is the consideration that must be accounted for in economic evaluation of investments. Figure 5-1 enumerates these considerations.

Items	
Inflation Supply/Demand Technological Changes Market Changes Environmental Effects Political Effects Miscellaneous Effects	Items Affecting Escalation

Figure 5-1 Items Related to "Escalation"

The importance of cost and price escalation and the pyramiding effect it can have on the escalation of investment costs and revenues has been driven home forcefully to investment decision makers around the world in the 1970's and 1980's. Examples are innumerable. To cite one, in 1969 the Alaskan pipeline was estimated to have a cost of $900 million while in 1977 the final cost estimate was close to $8 billion, or about a 900% escalation from the initial estimate. Certainly not all of this cost escalation was due to inflation. Supply/demand effects on labor and materials and other factors such as environmental and engineering changes caused very significant escalation of the project costs. Fortunately, crude oil price escalation prior to the 1986 price decline was sufficient to cover the escalated costs. This example helps emphasize the very significant differences between inflation rates and escalation rates and that in economic evaluation work we are concerned with the effects of escalation of costs and revenues rather than inflation effects alone. However, inflation often has such a significant effect on escalation rates for specific goods and services that we should digress and discuss some of the causes and effects of inflation before later proceeding to present two explicit approaches for handling inflation and escalation properly in economic analyses.

Literally millions of words have been written on the subject of inflation in the past decade. We discussed in Chapter 2 that 6% compound interest will double capital in twelve years but have you thought about the fact that 6% inflation will cut the purchasing power of currency in half in twelve years? The same compound interest factors that work for us with savings apply inversely when accounting for the effect of inflation on purchasing power. Who benefits and who gets hurt most by inflation? There is no firm answer to this question but generally individuals and governments with large amounts of borrowed money benefit to some degree from inflation because they are able to pay off their debt with inflated future dollars that have lower purchasing power than the dollars originally borrowed. On the other hand people on fixed incomes with little or no debt clearly are hurt by inflation because the purchasing power of their income or capital decreases each year approximately proportional to the annual inflation rate. It is necessary to discuss how inflation rates are derived to amplify the meaning of the last statement.

As previously mentioned, in most countries the quoted inflation rate is derived from the change in an index, made up of the weighted average of prices for a "basket of goods and services." In the United States, the broadest measure of this index is known as the Consumer Price Index or CPI. As currently defined the CPI can be broken down into 8 major categories including food and beverages, housing, apparel, transportation, medical care, recreation, education and other items including the cost of hair cuts, cosmetics and bank fees. Approximately 80,000 items in total may be surveyed each month. The CPI may be calculated regionally or by other socio-economic parameters. The later categories include an index for all Urban Consumers known as the CPI_u and a similar index for all Wage Earners known as the CPI_W. A survey of the buying habits of more than 29,000 families in these different categories forms the basis for the items selected each month. For more information check out the Bureau of Labor Statistics website at http://stats.bls.gov/cpi/.

It is important to note that an increase in the level of one price, or group of prices does not constitute inflation. If the prices of crude oil, iron ore, and uranium rise while the prices of automobiles, wheat and beef fall, we can not be certain whether there has been inflation. In other words, it may not be certain whether the average level of prices has risen or fallen. Lower prices in one set of goods may have offset higher prices of other. An increase in the price of one individual commodity is just that, an individual price increase. It may be due to inflation, excess demand or short supply or a combination of both. This further emphasizes why in economic evaluation work that escalation of costs and revenues for specific goods and services is relevant to the analysis rather than a given inflation rate.

Even if inflation is diminished to 1% from 4% levels over an extended period of time, different financial instruments such as indexed bonds and the more traditional non-indexed variety do exist in the financial marketplace today and require unique consideration to make a proper economic comparison. Further, although escalated dollar evaluations are the most common approach we find utilized in the United States, some U.S. companies and many foreign companies prefer to utilize constant dollars. Therefore, it is important to understand how inflation can influence project evaluations and the various assumptions that investors make on this subject.

There are two basic evaluation techniques that can be used with equal validity to handle inflation and escalation properly in economic analyses. They are escalated dollar analysis and constant dollar analysis. The economic conclusions that are reached are always identical with either approach. *Escalated dollar values refer to actual dollars of revenue or cost that will be realized or incurred at specific future points in time. Elsewhere in the literature you find escalated dollars referred to by the terms current dollars, inflated dollars, nominal dollars, and dollars of the day. Constant dollar values refer to hypothetical constant purchasing power dollars obtained by discounting escalated dollar values at the inflation rate to some arbitrary point in time, which often is the time that corresponds to the beginning of a project but may be any point in time. Constant dollars are referred to as real dollars or deflated dollars in many places in the literature.* Figure 5-2 relates the definitions of escalated dollars and constant dollars to a variation of Figure 5-1 used earlier to illustrate how inflation and escalation are related.

Constant Dollar Items		Escalated Dollar Items
	Inflation Supply/Demand Technological Changes Market Changes Environmental Effects Political Effects Miscellaneous Effects	

Figure 5-2 "Constant Dollar" Items That Relate to "Escalated Dollar" Items

Constant dollar analysis advocates take the point of view that since escalated dollars have different purchasing power at different points in time it is necessary to convert all dollar values to some hypothetical constant purchasing power value before making an economic analysis. Constant dollar analysis is a valid analysis approach but it is no better than making the analysis directly in terms of escalated dollars and the constant dollar calculations require extra work and chance for error. It must be remembered that the purpose of economic analysis is to compare alternative opportunities for the investment of capital to select the investment alternatives that will maximize the future profit that can be accumulated at some future point in time. If you stop to think about it, the alternatives that will maximize your future profit in escalated dollars must be exactly the same alternatives that will maximize your future profit expressed in terms of constant purchasing power dollars referenced to some earlier date. The key to proper analysis and consistent, correct economic evaluation conclusions lies in recognizing that you cannot mix escalated dollar analyses and constant dollar analyses. To do so is analogous to comparing apples and oranges. You must either compare all alternatives using escalated dollars or you must compare all alternatives using constant dollars; and you must remember that the minimum ROR must be expressed in relation to other escalated dollar investment opportunities for escalated dollar analyses while the minimum rate of return must be expressed in relation to other constant dollar investment opportunities for constant dollar analysis. A very common constant dollar analysis mistake is for an evaluator to calculate constant dollar rate of return for a project and then compare it to other escalated dollar investment opportunities such as a bank interest rate, attainable bond interest rates or another escalated dollar ROR opportunity.

Consider how escalated and constant dollar estimates for costs and revenues are obtained. The evaluation of projects starts by estimating project costs and revenues in today's prices or values. This establishes what the project costs and revenues would be if the project occurred today. Next, since projects do not occur instantaneously, today's dollar values may be adjusted to project the actual or escalated values that will be realized. If the increase can be described on a percentage basis, single payment compound amount factors, $(F/P_{i,n})$ can be used to determine the actual value anticipated at the future point in time. The escalation rate is used as a substitute value for i. This approach is utilized in many text examples, but may not be appropriate in actual evaluations depending on the forecasting techniques utilized. Also note, if you think values may decline, negative escalation rates might also be used. The actual values anticipated to be realized over the project life form the basis for the escalated dollar evaluation.

Many investors choose to utilize the anticipated inflation over future years as an approximation for escalation. This is one forecast of the future, but there is no reason evaluations cannot be based on as many separate escalation or de-escalation rates as there are parameters that make up the model. Commodity prices, the price for construction equipment, steel, concrete, labor and energy to name a few, may not move in direct correlation with the rate of inflation. The use of inflation as a proxy for escalation is addressed in more detail later in the chapter concerning the use of today's dollar values in evaluations.

If a constant dollar analysis is desired, the escalated dollar cash flows for a project must be adjusted to have the anticipated inflation removed from each value over the project life. Remember that escalation includes inflation. Inflation can be removed from escalated dollar cash flows by multiplying each escalated dollar value by the single payment present worth factor $(P/F_{f,n})$, at the assumed inflation rate "f" for the number of periods needed to bring each value to its equivalent constant purchasing power.

Note that escalation rates and inflation rates are treated just like compound interest rates. As previously indicated, this means that the factor, $(F/P_{e,n})$ where e represents the annual rate of escalation, and $(P/F_{f,n})$ where f represents the annual rate of inflation can be utilized in the same manner but for different objectives than accounting for the time value of money.

So, if the selling price of a product was \$260 per unit this year (today's dollar value is \$260) and the value was expected to escalate 5.0% next year, the actual selling price one year from today would be:

$$\text{Escalated \$ Yr 1 Price} = \$260(F/P_{5\%,1}) = \$273$$

If inflation is 3.0% during the same period, the real or constant purchasing power price of the product would be:

$$\text{Time 0 Constant \$ Price} = \$273(P/F_{3\%,1}) = \$265$$

This is still a year one price, but now expressed in terms of time zero constant dollars. Many investors will approximate this value by taking a shortcut. This approach would argue that if prices escalate 5% and inflation is 3%, then approximately, there should be a 2% real or constant dollar increase in the price of the product.

$$\text{Constant \$} \cong \text{Today's \$} * (1 + (\text{Escalation-Inflation}))$$
$$\text{Constant \$} \cong \$260 * (1.02) \cong \$265$$

When escalation and inflation are low, the approximation is very close for those wanting to work with constant dollars. However, this approximation is not utilized in the text examples and problems due to confusion that can develop when working with after-tax cash flows. After-tax cash flows reflect the impact of various tax deductions, which often (but not always) are escalated deductions. Improper mixing of dollar values only dilutes the quality of the economics so the more precise, longer winded approaches are utilized throughout the text.

As a final introduction, gold has often been thought of as a good hedge against the long-term impact of inflation. Looking back to 1980, the average gold price for that year was $612 per ounce. At the beginning of 2013, the price had risen to $1,693. During that same time period, U.S. inflation (as measured by the CPI_U) averaged approximately 3.58%. Had gold increased in value at the average annual rate of inflation, the average value in 2013 would have been:

$$\$612(F/P_{3.58\%,33}) = \$1{,}954 \text{ per ounce}$$

with 3.1923 printed above the factor.

Since August 2012, when the price was $1,775, the value of gold has declined, representing a period of negative escalation, or de-escalation in its value. The price of gold is impacted by a variety of factors such as inflation, central banks, regulatory environments, the strength of the U.S. dollar or other currencies, speculation in markets, economic stability, and a multitude of other considerations.

Using the early 2013 gold price of $1,693 per ounce as an average value for the year, and investment in an ounce of gold in 1980 would have produced an average annual rate of return of:

$$\text{PW Eq: } 0 = -612 + 1{,}693(P/F_{i,33}) \quad \text{ROR, } i = 3.13\% \text{ per year}$$

After adjusting for an actual 3.58% annual inflation rate, the real rate of return on the investment would be a negative 0.43% per year over the specified time period. Pick any time frame and analysts marketing gold or any commodity can create a desired rate of return effect, positive or negative. The calculations related to this real or constant dollar measure of economic performance is addressed in Examples 5-1 and 5-2.

It is worth noting that the term "constant purchasing power" has nothing to do with the price remaining constant each year. Instead, it has to do with the relative purchasing power of that money over time. Obviously more than inflation is influencing the price of gold and other parameters that make up our economic evaluation models.

Finally, it is also important to note that inflation can have the same impact on interest rates as that just described in terms of cash flow or the price of a product. Further, discount rates are influenced in the same manner as is introduced in Example 5-1:

Consider the following investment analysis example to illustrate how today's dollar values are the starting basis to get both escalated dollar values and constant dollar values and the corresponding rates of return.

EXAMPLE 5-1 Escalated and Constant Dollar ROR Analysis

Today's Dollar Values, C=Cost, I=Income

$$\underset{0}{C_0 = \$100} \qquad \underset{1}{C_1 = \$150} \qquad \underset{2 \text{ years}}{I_2 = \$400}$$

Convert today's dollar values to escalated dollar values assuming cost escalation of 20% per year and income escalation of 10% per year. Calculate the escalated dollar rate of return. Then assume inflation is 15% per year and calculate the constant dollar project ROR.

Solution:

Use single payment compound amount factors ($F/P_{i,n}$ factors) at the appropriate escalation rates to convert today's dollars to escalated dollars as shown on the following diagram.

Escalated Dollar Value Determination

$$\underset{0}{C_0 = \$100} \qquad \underset{1}{C_1 = \$150(\overset{1.200}{F/P_{20\%,1}}) = \$180} \qquad \underset{2}{I_2 = \$400(\overset{1.210}{F/P_{10\%,2}}) = \$484}$$

Escalated Dollar ROR Analysis

When escalated costs and revenues have been obtained, they are the basis for the time value of money calculation to determine the desired evaluation criterion, which in this analysis is ROR.

PW equation: $0 = -100 - 180(P/F_{i,1}) + 484(P/F_{i,2})$

i = Escalated Dollar ROR = 47.7% by trial and error

This escalated dollar ROR is compared to the escalated dollar minimum ROR to determine if the project is economically satisfactory.

Constant Dollar Value Determination

Now convert the escalated dollar values to constant dollar values assuming an annual inflation rate of 15%. This is achieved by discounting the escalated dollars from the previous analysis at the rate of inflation to express all dollar values in terms of time zero purchasing power. Use the single payment present worth factor ($P/F_{i,n}$ factor) for the assumed inflation rate as illustrated on the following diagram:

$C_0 = \$100 \quad C_1 = \$180(P/F_{15\%,1}) = \$156 \quad I_2 = \$484(P/F_{15\%,2}) = \$366$

0 1 2

The meaning of the constant dollar costs and revenues is as follows: \$156 at year 0 would purchase the goods and services that \$180 would purchase at year 1, if inflation is 15% per year, and \$366 at year 0 would purchase the goods and services that \$484 would purchase at year 2, if inflation is 15% per year. The meaning of these constant purchasing power dollars is only valid when related to purchasing the average goods and services that make up the inflation index that was used to project 15% inflation per year.

Constant Dollar ROR Analysis

PW equation: $0 = -100 - 156(P/F_{i',1}) + 366(P/F_{i',2})$

i' = Constant Dollar ROR = 28.5% by trial and error

This constant dollar ROR is compared to the constant dollar minimum ROR to determine if the project is economically satisfactory. Either escalated or constant dollar analysis of this project, or any other, will give the same economic decision. *To reach a decision concerning the economic viability of this project using either the escalated or constant dollar analysis results we must know the other opportunities that exist for the use of our money and whether these other opportunities are expressed in escalated or constant dollars.* For illustration purposes consider that other opportunities exist to have our money invested at an escalated dollar ROR of 35%. Comparing the project's escalated dollar ROR of 47.7% to the minimum rate of return of 35% we conclude that the project is economically satisfactory. If we compared the project's constant dollar ROR of 28.5% to the other escalated dollar opportunities we would be making an invalid comparison. We cannot compare constant dollar results with other escalated dollar project results. All results must be calculated on the same consistent basis before comparison is made. To make a constant dollar analysis result comparison, we must convert the escalated dollar minimum ROR of 35% to the corresponding constant dollar minimum rate of return, which we then compare to the project constant dollar ROR of 28.5%. Mathematically, for escalated dollar ROR analysis, the factor $P/F_{i,n}$ does the job that the product of factors $P/F_{f,n} \times P/F_{i',n}$ does for constant dollar analysis of the same starting escalated dollar values where "i" equals escalated dollar ROR, "i′" equals constant dollar ROR and "f" equals the inflation rate.

$P/F_{i,n} = P/F_{f,n} \times P/F_{i',n}$, gives:

$1/(1 + i)^n = 1/(1 + f)^n \times 1/(1 + i')^n$, or:

$$1 + i = (1 + f)(1 + i') \qquad \text{5-1}$$

giving $i' = [(1 + i)/(1 + f)] - 1$

This mathematical proof is known as "Fisher's Rule" for the economist Irving Fisher who lived from 1867 to 1947.

Equation 5-1 and its rearranged form are equally valid for the calculation of project rates of return and minimum rates of return. This means the value of the escalated dollar project rate of return, "i," can be replaced by "i*," the escalated dollar minimum rate of return, and the constant dollar project rate of return "i'," may be replaced by the constant dollar equivalent minimum rate of return "i*'." For this example, the escalated dollar minimum ROR, i* = 35%, the inflation rate f = 15%, so this gives a value for i*' as follows:

$i^{*'} = [(1 + .35)/(1 + .15)] - 1 = .174$ or 17.4%

Comparing the project's constant dollar ROR of 28.5% to other constant dollar ROR opportunities of 17.4% leads to the economic conclusion that the project is satisfactory, consistent with the escalated dollar analysis conclusion based on comparing the 47.7% project escalated dollar ROR to the 35% escalated dollar minimum ROR. Note that if our other opportunities were represented by an escalated dollar bond investment ROR of 10%, for 15% annual inflation, the corresponding constant dollar minimum ROR would be negative.

$i^{*'} = [(1 + .10)/(1 + .15)] - 1 = -.043$ or –4.3%

Money earning a 10% escalated dollar ROR in a 15% per year inflation climate is losing average purchasing power at a 4.3% rate per year. Yet, if that is the best other opportunity that exists, it is better than doing nothing with the money and losing the average purchasing power at a 15% rate per year.

EXAMPLE 5-1a Today's Dollars Equal Escalated Dollars Assumption: Escalation = 0%

When escalation is predicted to be 0% per year on all costs and revenues over the life of a project, today's dollar values equal escalated dollar values. To illustrate, consider 0% escalation per year of the Example 5-1 today's dollar costs and revenues and calculate escalated dollar project ROR.

Solution: Escalated Dollar Values for 0% Escalation Per Year

$$\begin{array}{ccc} & 1.000 & 1.000 \\ C_0 = 100 & C_1 = 150(F/P_{0\%,1}) = \$150 & I_2 = 400(F/P_{0\%,2}) = \$400 \\ \hline 0 & 1 & 2 \end{array}$$

That the F/P factors at 0% equal 1.0 is clearly seen in the mathematical format, where

$$F/P_{0\%,1} = (1 + i)^n = (1 + 0)^1 = 1.0 \text{ and } F/P_{0\%,2} = (1 + 0)^2 = 1.0.$$

Escalated Dollar Analysis

PW Eq: $0 = -100 - 150(P/F_{i,1}) + 400(P/F_{i,2})$

i = Escalated Dollar ROR = 38.6% by trial and error

This 38.6% escalated dollar ROR is different in magnitude from the 47.7% escalated dollar ROR result from Example 5-1 because the cost and revenue escalation assumptions are completely different. Assuming that all costs and revenues escalate at 0% per year in this Example 5-1a is very different than assuming that all costs escalate at 20% per year and revenues escalate at 10% per year as was assumed in Example 5-1.

EXAMPLE 5-1b Today's Dollars Equal Constant Dollars Assumption: Escalation = Inflation

When escalation is predicted to equal the inflation rate per year on all costs and revenues over the life of the project, today's dollar values equal constant dollar values. To illustrate, consider 15% per year escalation of the Example 5-1 today's dollar costs and revenues (15% is the assumed annual inflation rate for Example 5-1) and calculate escalated dollar ROR and constant dollar ROR. Then use Equation 5-1 to verify the interchangeable character of the results.

Solution: Escalated Dollar Values for Escalation Equal to 15% Inflation Per Year

$C = \$100 \quad C = \$150(F/P_{15\%,1}) = \$172.5 \quad I = \$400(F/P_{15\%,2}) = \$528.8$

0 1 2

Escalated Dollar Analysis:

PW Eq: $0 = -100 - 172.5(P/F_{i,1}) + 528.8(P/F_{i,2})$

i = Escalated Dollar ROR = 59.4% by trial and error.

This result is different from either the Example 5-1 or Example 5-1a results, because the cost and revenue escalation assumptions are different.

Constant Dollar Values:

$C=\$100 \quad C = \$172.5(P/F_{15\%,1}) = \$150 \quad I = \$528.8(P/F_{15\%,2}) = \$400$

0 1 2

Escalating all values at the rate of inflation (15% in this example) and then discounting all values at the same rate of inflation for the same number of periods makes project constant dollar values equal to the original today's dollar values. This occurs because $P/F_{f,n} = 1/(1+f)^n$ is the reciprocal of $F/P_{f,n} = (1+f)^n$.

Constant Dollar Analysis:

PW Eq: $0 = -100 - 150(P/F_{i',1}) + 400(P/F_{i',2})$

i′ = Constant Dollar ROR = 38.6% by trial and error.

The constant dollar ROR is numerically the same as the Example 5-1a escalated dollar ROR result, but the 38.6% constant dollar ROR result must be compared to a minimum ROR expressed in constant dollars whereas the Example 5-1a escalated dollar ROR result must be compared to a minimum ROR expressed in escalated dollars, analogous to the decision-making discussion near the end of Example 5-1.

Once the escalated dollar ROR has been calculated, when inflation is assumed to be uniformly the same rate each year, Equation 5-1 can be used to calculate constant dollar ROR instead of discounting escalated dollars at the inflation each year and then calculating constant dollar ROR by trial and error from a proper constant dollar present worth equation.

To prove this approach for this example:

i = escalated dollar ROR = 59.4%

f = inflation rate = 15.0%

From Equation 5-1, $1 + i = (1 + f)(1 + i')$ so

$i' = [(1 + i)/(1 + f)] - 1$, therefore;

$i' = [(1.594)/(1.15)] - 1 = 0.386$ or 38.6%

A simplification of Equation 5-1 often used by bankers, brokers, economists and evaluation people alike is as follows:

$$1 + i = (1 + f)(1 + i') = 1 + f + i' + fi'$$

Neglecting the fi′ interaction term and rearranging gives the following approximation:

$$i - f \approx i' \qquad 5\text{-}2$$

For Example 5-1b, escalated ROR of 59.4% minus the inflation rate of 15.0% is approximately a 44.4% constant dollar ROR. The difference in the approximate 44.4% constant dollar ROR and the actual 38.6% result is 5.8% approximation error from dropping the fi′ interaction term which equals (.15)(.386) or 0.058 or 5.8%.

A diagram explanation of the relationship between escalated dollar present worth calculations and constant dollar present worth calculations is shown in Figure 5-3 which follows.

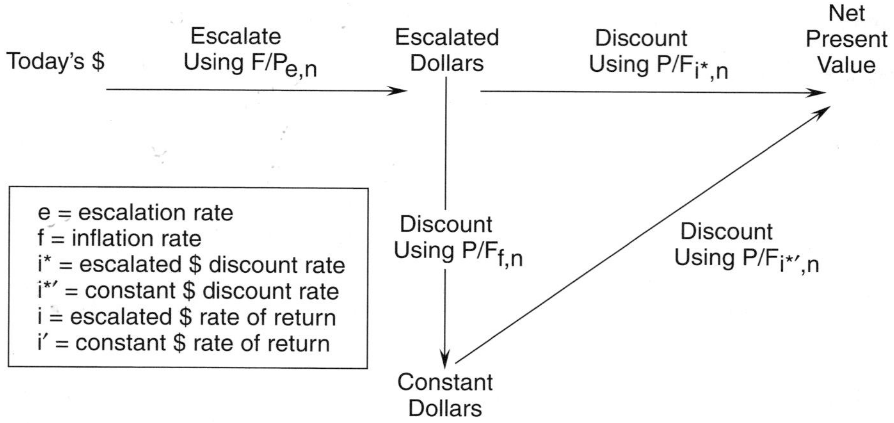

Figure 5-3 Equivalent Escalated Dollar and Constant Dollar Present Value Calculations

EXAMPLE 5-2 Escalated and Constant Dollar ROR and NPV Analysis

A proposed investment has the following projected today's dollar costs and revenues:

		Rev = \$70,000	Rev = \$70,000	
C_0 = \$20,000	C_1 = \$40,000	OC = \$20,000	OC = \$20,000	L=0
0	1	2	3	

Use ROR and NPV analysis to evaluate the economic potential of this investment project for the following evaluation assumptions. For escalated dollar analysis assume the escalated dollar minimum ROR is 15%. Use Equation 5-1 to calculate the equivalent constant dollar minimum ROR for constant dollar analysis.

A) Assume year 1 development cost will escalate 7% per year. Year 2 and 3 revenues will escalate 8% per year. Operating costs will escalate 9% per year. Make escalated dollar analysis.

B) For the part (A) escalation assumptions and given escalated dollar minimum ROR of 15%, make constant dollar analysis of the project for assumed inflation of 6% per year over the project life.

C) Use the given today's dollar cost and revenue estimates to evaluate the project and discuss the implicit escalation and inflation rate assumptions involved.

Solution, All Values in Thousands of Dollars:

A) Escalated Dollar Analysis

		2	3
		1.166	1.260
		Rev=70$(F/P_{8\%,2})$=81.62	70$(F/P_{8\%,3})$=88.2
		1.188	1.295
		OC=20$(F/P_{9\%,2})$=23.76	20$(F/P_{9\%,3})$=25.9
C_0=20	C_1=40$(F/P_{7\%,1})$=42.8	Net Rev =57.86	=62.3
0	1	2	3

The today's dollar costs and revenues are converted to escalated dollar values using single payment compound amount factors calculated at the escalation rates. Note that the uniform series compound amount factor, $F/A_{i,n}$, has not been utilized to escalate the uniform revenues and operating costs. The uniform series factor would give cumulative revenue or operating cost at year 3, rather than year by year calculation of the desired escalated dollar costs and revenues. Therefore, the uniform series factors are not useful for escalation calculations.

$$\text{Escalated \$ NPV} = -20 - 42.8\overset{.8696}{(P/F_{15\%,1})} + 57.86\overset{.7561}{(P/F_{15\%,2})}$$

$$+ 62.3\overset{.6575}{(P/F_{15\%,3})} = +27.49 > 0, \text{ accept the project}$$

Escalated \$ ROR = 42.5%; this is the "i" value that makes escalated dollar NPV = 0.

$42.5\% > i^* = 15\%$, accept the project

B) Constant Dollar Analysis

The escalated dollar costs and net revenues from part (A) are the basis for the constant dollar calculations.

Constant Dollar Values

$C_0=20$	$C_1=42.8\overset{.9434}{(P/F_{6\%,1})}$ = 40.38	$R_2=57.86\overset{.8900}{(P/F_{6\%,2})}$ = 51.49	$R_3=62.3\overset{.8396}{(P/F_{6\%,3})}$ = 52.30
0	1	2	3

Constant dollar values are obtained by discounting escalated dollars at the rate of inflation of 6% per year. For constant dollar NPV analysis we must convert the 15% escalated dollar minimum ROR to the equivalent constant dollar minimum ROR for the assumed 6% per year inflation rate. Use Equation 5-1 for this calculation as follows:

$$i^{*\prime} = [(1 + i^*)/(1 + f)] - 1 = (1.15/1.06) - 1 = 0.0849 \text{ or } 8.49\%$$

$$\text{Constant \$ NPV} = -20 - 40.38\overset{.9217}{(P/F_{8.49\%,1})} + 51.49\overset{.8496}{(P/F_{8.49\%,2})}$$

$$+ 52.30\overset{.7831}{(P/F_{8.49\%,3})} = +27.48 > 0, \text{ so accept}$$

or

$$\text{Constant \$ NPV} = -20 - 40.38(1/1.0849)^1 + 51.49(1/1.0849)^2$$

$$+ 52.30(1/1.0849)^3 = +27.48 > 0, \text{ so accept}$$

Note that the constant dollar NPV is identical to the escalated dollar NPV within round-off error calculation accuracy. Constant dollar NPV equations are mathematically equivalent to escalated dollar NPV equations, so of course give the same results. The mathematical equivalency follows:

Escalated \$ Calculations = Constant \$ Calculations

$(\text{Escalated \$ Value})(P/F_{i^*,n}) = (\text{Escalated \$ Value})(P/F_{f,n})(P/F_{i^{*\prime},n})$

since $P/F_{i^*,n} = (P/F_{f,n})(P/F_{i^{*\prime},n})$

as discussed earlier in the development of Equation 5-1. For this analysis in year 2:

$$P/F_{15\%,2} = 0.7561 = (P/F_{6\%,2})(P/F_{8.49\%,2})$$
$$= (0.8900)(0.8496) = 0.7561$$

Constant \$ ROR = 34.4%; this is the "i" value that makes constant dollar net present value equal to zero.

$34.4\% > i^{*\prime} = 8.49\%$, accept the project

C) Today's Dollar Analysis

Using today's dollars as the basis for evaluation calculations involves one of two different assumptions. Either you assume that today's dollars equal escalated dollar values or you assume that today's dollars equal constant dollar values (see Ex. 5-1a and 5-1b).

Today's Dollars Equal Escalated Dollars

Assuming that today's dollars equal escalated dollars explicitly assumes that costs and revenues in the future will be the same as they would be today. This implicitly involves the assumption that costs and revenues will escalate at 0% per year over the evaluation life. This is an escalated dollar assumption similar to, but different from the part "A" assumptions, so an escalated dollar minimum ROR must be used in NPV calculations and for ROR analysis decisions. The "today's dollar values equal escalated dollar values" analysis follows:

$$NPV = -20 - 40(P/F_{15\%,1}) + 50(P/F_{15\%,2}) + 50(P/F_{15\%,3})$$
$$= +15.9 > 0 \text{ accept}$$

$ROR = 32.2\% > i^* = 15\%$, accept

Note these escalated dollar NPV and ROR results are significantly different from the part "A" escalated dollar analysis results. There are an unlimited number of different ways that escalated costs and revenues can be projected. Assuming today's dollars are equal to escalated dollars is just one specific escalation assumption. It is important to understand specific escalation assumptions used in analyses because they will affect evaluation results.

A variation of the today's dollar equal escalated dollars assumption is to escalate all capital costs (such as acquisition and development costs) at specified rates and to assume that the escalated dollar net revenues or profits in the income generating years will equal today's dollar net revenues or profits. This is often called "the washout assumption" since it assumes that any escalation of operating costs each year will be offset (washed out) by the same dollar escalation of revenue. Note there are no revenues in the development years, so costs must be escalated in pre-revenue years. The washout assumption only applies to revenues and operating costs in the revenue generating years.

Today's Dollars Equal Constant Dollars

Since constant dollar values are obtained by discounting escalated dollars at the rate of inflation, the only way today's dollars can equal constant dollars is if all today's dollar values escalate each year at the rate of inflation. Escalating each cost and revenue at the rate of inflation and then discounting the resulting escalated dollars at the rate of inflation to get constant dollars brings the dollar values back to the starting today's dollar values. This is a constant dollar analysis assumption, so a constant dollar minimum ROR (8.49% for this analysis) must be used in the constant dollar NPV calculations and for the economic decision with constant dollar ROR results. The today's dollars equal constant dollars NPV and ROR results follow:

$$NPV = -20 - 40(P/F_{8.49\%,1}) + 50(P/F_{8.49\%,2}) + 50(P/F_{8.49\%,3})$$
$$= +24.8 > 0, \text{ so accept}$$

$$ROR = 32.2\% > i^{*\prime} = 8.49\%, \text{ so accept}$$

Note the today's dollars equal escalated dollars NPV result is significantly different from the today's dollars equal constant dollars

NPV result. Although the ROR results are 32.2% for both cases, different minimum rates of return are used for the economic decision with ROR in the two cases. These two today's dollar analysis cases are very different and can lead to different investment decisions. Obviously, understanding the escalated dollar or constant dollar inflation and escalation assumptions being made is very important for correct economic decision making.

EXAMPLE 5-3 Escalated and Constant Dollar Cost Analysis of Service Producing Alternatives

Compare two alternatives that provide a service using escalated and constant dollar analysis. Consider alternative "A" to be capital intensive, requiring the expenditure of $100,000 at time zero and no operating costs in years one or two to provide a service for two years while alternative "B" is labor intensive, requiring end-of-year one and two escalated dollar operating costs of $60,000 and $72,000 respectively. Salvage is zero in both cases. Make present worth cost analysis for an escalated dollar minimum rate of return of 30%, then for $i^* = 20\%$, then for $i^* = 10\%$. Assume inflation of 20% per year for all constant dollar calculations. Verify the present worth cost results with incremental NPV analysis.

Solution, All Values in Thousands of Dollars:

Escalated Dollar Diagrams

(A)	C = 100	—	—
	0	1	2

(B)	—	OC = 60	OC = 72
	0	1	2

Solution:

Escalated Dollar PW Cost Analysis

1) for $i^* = 30\%$, remembering $P/F_{i^*,n} = (1/1+i^*)^n$

$PW_A = 100$
$PW_B = 60(1/1.3) + 72(1/1.3)^2 = 88.75$, Select "B"

2) for i* = 20%

$PW_A = 100$
$PW_B = 60(1/1.2) + 72(1/1.2)^2 = 100$

Results indicate break-even economics.

3) for i* = 10%

$PW_A = 100$, select smaller Present Worth Cost, "A"
$PW_B = 60(1/1.1) + 72(1/1.1)^2 = 114$

Constant Dollar Diagrams for Inflation Rate, f = 20%

(A) C = 100 — —
0 1 2

(B) — OC = $60(P/F_{20\%,1})$ = 50 OC = $72(P/F_{20\%,2})$ = 50
0 1 2

Constant Dollar PW Cost Analysis:

1) for an escalated dollar minimum ROR, i* = 30%, the corresponding constant dollar minimum ROR, $i^{*\prime}$ is 8.33%

$PW_A = 100$
$PW_B = 50(1/1.0833) + 50(1/1.0833)^2 = 88.75$, Select Smaller, "B"

2) for i* = 20%, constant dollar $i^{*\prime}$ is 0

$PW_A = 100$ Break-even
$PW_B = 50(1/1.0) + 50(1/1.0)^2 = 100$

Results indicate break-even economics

3) for i* = 10%, constant dollar $i^{*\prime}$ is -8.33%

$PW_A = 100$, Select Smaller, "A"
$PW_B = 50(1/.9166) + 50(1/.9166)^2 = 114$

Note that not only do escalated and constant dollar analysis give the same conclusion, but those conclusions are based upon identical present worth costs. If we look at the incremental difference between "A" and "B", we can show that incremental NPV analysis gives the same result for escalated or constant dollar analysis.

Incremental Escalated Dollar Diagram

$$\text{(A–B)}\quad \frac{C = 100 \qquad\qquad \overset{\text{Savings}}{60} \qquad\qquad 72}{0 \qquad\qquad\qquad 1 \qquad\qquad\qquad 2}$$

Escalated Dollar Incremental NPV Analysis

i^*=30%, $NPV_{A-B} = 60(1/1.3) + 72(1/1.3)^2 - 100 = -11.25 < 0$, select "B"

i^*=20%, $NPV_{A-B} = 60(1/1.2) + 72(1/1.2)^2 - 100 = 0$, break-even

i^*=10%, $NPV_{A-B} = 60(1/1.1) + 72(1/1.1)^2 - 100 = +14.0 > 0$, select "A"

Incremental Constant Dollar Diagram

$$\text{A–B)}\quad \frac{C = 100 \qquad\qquad \overset{\text{Savings}}{50} \qquad\qquad 50}{0 \qquad\qquad\qquad 1 \qquad\qquad\qquad 2}$$

Constant Dollar Incremental NPV Analysis

For $i^* = 30\%$ and f=20%, equivalent $i^{*\prime} = 8.33\%$

$NPV_{A-B} = 50(1/1.0833) + 50(1/1.0833)^2 - 100$
$= -11.25$, select "B"

For $i^* = 20\%$ and f=20%, equivalent $i^{*\prime} = 0\%$

$NPV_{A-B} = 50(1/1.0) + 50(1/1.0)^2 - 100 = 0$, break-even

For $i^* = 10\%$ and f=20%, equivalent $i^{*\prime} = -8.33\%$

$NPV_{A-B} = 50(1/.9166) + 50(1/.9166)^2 - 100 = 14.0$, select "A"

Note the identical incremental NPV results for both escalated and constant dollar analysis, so of course the same economic decision results either way.

Now that we have established that either escalated or constant dollar analysis properly handled gives the same economic analysis conclusions, are there reasons for preferring one method over the other? In general it takes two present worth calculations in constant dollar analysis to achieve the same result that can be obtained with one present worth calculation in escalated dollar analysis. Fewer calculations means fewer chances for math errors, a point in favor of escalated dollar analysis. To make proper after-tax analysis, tax calculations must always be made in escalated dollars as must borrowed money principal and interest payments. For constant dollar analysis, this requires careful diligence to avoid improper mixing of escalated and constant dollars. With escalated dollar analysis all values are in escalated dollars so this is not a problem, another point in favor of escalated dollar analysis. From a practical and ease of calculation viewpoint, there is little to be said for constant dollar analysis that cannot be said more favorably for escalated dollar analysis. However, for those evaluation people who want to make constant dollar analysis rather than escalated dollar analysis, the following steps should be followed:

1) Determine the escalated dollar values for all project costs and revenues.
2) Convert all escalated dollar values to the corresponding constant dollar values for the assumed inflation rates each year.
3) Convert the escalated dollar minimum ROR, "i^*", to the corresponding constant dollar value, "$i^{*\prime}$", if the minimum ROR is initially expressed in terms of escalated dollars.
4) Calculate constant dollar NPV using $i^{*\prime}$, or calculate constant dollar ROR, "i'", and compare to $i^{*\prime}$ for the economic decision.

One situation that can give constant dollar analysis a potential intangible advantage over escalated dollar analysis is in evaluation of a project to determine and negotiate the break-even selling price that a purchaser may be willing to pay for a product. Since in inflationary times a given constant dollar minimum rate of return is always less than the equivalent escalated dollar minimum rate of return, it may be easier to convince a buyer to accept paying the price needed for you to get a 15% constant dollar ROR than a higher but equivalent escalated dollar ROR for a given rate of inflation. This is a potential marketing or negotiation advantage rather than an economic analysis advantage. The following example shows that break-even analysis economic calculations (such as break-even selling price) will be exactly the same with either escalated dollar analysis or constant dollar analysis.

EXAMPLE 5-4 Break-even Selling Price Analysis in Escalated and Constant Dollars.

The investment of $30,000 today is estimated to produce 100 product units each year for the next two years when the product is expected to become obsolete. Year 2 salvage value is expected to be zero. Today's dollar operating costs for years 1 and 2 are estimated to be $8,000 per year. Inflation is expected to be 7.0% per year for each of the next two years. If product selling price is projected to escalate 8% per year and operating costs escalate 10% per year, calculate the year 1 and 2 escalated dollar selling price that will give the investor a desired 15% constant dollar ROR on invested dollars.

Solution, All Values in Dollars:

Let X = Today's Dollar Selling Price Per Unit

	Year 1	Year 2
Escalated $ Sales	$X(100)(F/P_{8\%,1}) = 108.0X$	$X(100)(F/P_{8\%,2}) = 116.6X$
Escalated $ OC	$8000(F/P_{10\%,1}) = 8{,}800$	$8000(F/P_{10\%,2}) = 9{,}680$
Escalated $ Profit	$108.0X - 8{,}800$	$116.6X - 9{,}680$
Constant $ Profit	$(108.0X - 8{,}800)(P/F_{7\%,1})$	$(116.6X - 9{,}680)(P/F_{7\%,2})$

As shown, today's dollar revenues and operating costs are converted to escalated dollar values using the selling price and operating cost escalation rates of 8% and 10% respectively. If you want to work in escalated dollars you use the resultant escalated dollar profits shown, which are a function of the unknown today's dollar selling price per unit, X. If you prefer to work in constant dollars you present worth escalated dollar profit at the 7% per year rate of inflation to convert escalated dollars to constant dollars.

Escalated Dollar Present Worth Equation Calculations

To write an escalated dollar present worth equation we must use escalated dollar values and handle the time value of money at the escalated dollar minimum ROR that is equivalent to the desired 15% constant dollar minimum ROR for assumed 7% per year inflation. Using Equation 5-1:

$$i^* = (1 + f)(1 + i^{*\prime}) - 1 = (1.07)(1.15) - 1 = .2305 \text{ or } 23.05\%$$

$$30{,}000 = (108.0X - 8{,}800)\overset{.81268}{(P/F_{23.05,1})} + (116.6X - 9{,}680)\overset{.66045}{(P/F_{23.05,2})}$$

Solving for X = $264.26/units = Today's Dollar Selling Price

$264.26(F/P_{8\%,1})$ = $285.40/unit = Year 1 Escalated $ Selling Price

$264.26(F/P_{8\%,2})$ = $308.24/unit = Year 2 Escalated $ Selling Price

Constant Dollar Present Worth Equation Using Constant Dollar Profits

Handle the time value of money using the 15% constant dollar minimum ROR:

$$30{,}000 = (108.0X - 8{,}800)(P/F_{7\%,1})(P/F_{15\%,1}) + (116.6X - 9{,}680)(P/F_{7\%,2})(P/F_{15\%,2})$$

solving for X = \$264.26/units = Today's Dollar Selling Price

$264.26(F/P_{8\%,1})$ = \$285.40/unit = Year 1 Escalated \$ Selling Price

$264.26(F/P_{8\%,2})$ = \$308.24/unit = Year 2 Escalated \$ Selling Price

The same break-even selling prices result from either escalated or constant dollar analysis.

To conclude the inflation and escalation discussion, a few words should be said about forecasting escalation rates for different commodities or segments of industry. The past often is a good indicator of the future, so analysis of past cost trends for a particular commodity or asset is one way to get an indication of what the future might hold. This approach was very poor in the 1973-1980 period due to the significant increase in energy costs around the world, but no method of analysis is going to predict consistently the effects of that kind of upset to the world economy. The U.S. Bureau of Labor Statistics publishes 70 or more price indices for commodities and materials, 5 or more indices or wage rates and an index of engineering costs which can be obtained to give past trends. "Chemical Engineering" consolidates these Bureau of Labor Statistics into the CE Plant Cost Index published on a bi-monthly basis as a measure of the cost of typical chemical plants. "Chemical Engineering" also presents the Marshall and Swift equipment cost index bi-monthly. No one has a crystal ball to forecast the future accurately, but the use of available indices can be helpful in determining cost and price trends and rates of change of these trends needed to forecast meaningful escalation rates for costs and revenues needed for investment analyses.

In summary, proper evaluation of investments in various escalated dollar or constant dollar analyses requires understanding how to apply the following three different kinds of rates:

1. **Escalation Rates:** used to convert today's dollar values to escalated dollar values.

2. Inflation Rates: used to convert escalated dollar values to constant dollar values.

3. Time Value of Money Rates: used to account for the time value of money using "i" or "i^*" in escalated dollar analyses, and "i′" or "$i^{*\prime}$" in constant dollar analyses.

These rates are all used in the following example illustrating general escalated and constant dollar analysis calculations involving different escalation rates and inflation rates each year.

EXAMPLE 5-5 ROR and NPV Analysis With Changing Escalation and Inflation Rates Each Year

A cost of $100,000 today is projected to generate today's dollar incomes of $75,000 per year at the end of each of years 1, 2 and 3 with today's dollar operating costs of $25,000 per year at years 1, 2 and 3. Salvage value is zero at year 3. Incomes and operating costs are projected to escalate 10% in year 1, 12% in year 2, and 15% in year 3, so net income minus operating cost escalates at the same given rate each year. Calculate the project escalated dollar ROR and NPV assuming the minimum ROR for each of the 3 years is 15% in escalated dollars. Then assume inflation rates will be 10% in year 1, 8% in year 2 and 6% in year 3, and calculate constant dollar ROR and NPV.

Solution:

Today's Dollar Values (In Thousands of Dollars)

C = 100	Net I_1 = 50	Net I_2 = 50	Net I_3 = 50
0	1	2	3

Escalated Dollar Values

C = 100	Net I_1 = 55	Net I_2 = 61.6	Net I_3 = 70.84
0	1	2	3

where,

$$\text{Net } I_1 = 50(F/P_{10\%,1}) = 55.0 \quad [F/P_{10\%,1} = 1.100]$$

$$\text{Net } I_2 = 50\overset{1.100}{(F/P_{10\%,1})}\overset{1.120}{(F/P_{12\%,1})} = 61.60$$

$$\text{Net } I_3 = 50\overset{1.100}{(F/P_{10\%,1})}\overset{1.120}{(F/P_{12\%,1})}\overset{1.150}{(F/P_{15\%,1})} = 70.84$$

Escalated Dollar Present Worth Equation for ROR Analysis

$100 = 55(P/F_{i,1}) + 61.6(P/F_{i,2}) + 70.84(P/F_{i,3})$

i = Escalated Dollar ROR = 37.4% by trial and error

37.4% > 15%, so satisfactory

Escalated Dollar Net Present Value

$$NPV = -100 + 55\overset{.8696}{(P/F_{15\%,1})} + 61.6\overset{.7561}{(P/F_{15\%,2})} + 70.84\overset{.6575}{(P/F_{15\%,3})}$$

$= +\$41.0 > 0$, so satisfactory

Constant Dollar Values

C = 100	Net I_1 = 50	Net I_2 = 51.85	Net I_3 = 56.25
0	1	2	3

where escalated dollars discounted at the annual inflation rates give the following constant dollar net incomes:

$$\text{Net } I_1 = 55\overset{.9091}{(P/F_{10\%,1})} = 50.0$$

$$\text{Net } I_2 = 61.6\overset{.9091}{(P/F_{10\%,1})}\overset{.9259}{(P/F_{8\%,1})} = 51.85$$

$$\text{Net } I_3 = 70.84\overset{.9091}{(P/F_{10\%,1})}\overset{.9259}{(P/F_{8\%,1})}\overset{.9434}{(P/F_{6\%,1})} = 56.25$$

Constant Dollar Present Worth Equation for ROR Analysis

$100 = 50(P/F_{i',1}) + 51.85(P/F_{i',2}) + 56.25(P/F_{i',3})$

i' = Constant Dollar ROR = 26.3% > $i^{*'}$ values shown in next section, so satisfactory.

Constant Dollar Net Present Value Analysis

For constant dollar NPV analysis we must calculate the constant dollar minimum ROR each year that is equivalent to the 15% escalated dollar minimum ROR for the assumed inflation rates of 10% in year 1, 8% in year 2 and 6% in year 3 using a rearranged version of Equation 5-1.

$i^{*\prime} = \{(1 + i^*)/(1 + f)\} - 1$

Year 1, $i^{*\prime} = (1.15/1.10) - 1 = 4.54\%$

Year 2, $i^{*\prime} = (1.15/1.08) - 1 = 6.48\%$

Year 3, $i^{*\prime} = (1.15/1.06) - 1 = 8.49\%$

$$NPV = -100 + 50\overset{.9566}{(P/F_{4.54\%,1})} + 51.85\overset{.9566}{(P/F_{4.54\%,1})}\overset{.9391}{(P/F_{6.48\%,1})}$$

$$+ 56.25\overset{.9566}{(P/F_{4.54\%,1})}\overset{.9391}{(P/F_{6.48\%,1})}\overset{.9217}{(P/F_{8.49\%,1})}$$

$= +\$41.0 > 0$, so satisfactory

Note the equivalence of constant dollar NPV and escalated dollar NPV results. Even with different escalation and inflation rates each year, correct analysis gives the same escalated and constant dollar NPV results, so of course the same economic conclusions from either analysis. Similarly, with ROR analysis results in either escalated or constant dollars, as long as you compare project ROR to the minimum ROR expressed in the same kind of dollars (escalated or constant), you get the same economic conclusions from either escalated or constant dollar ROR analysis.

5.2 Exchange Rate Effects on Escalation and Cash Flow Analysis

Whenever project costs and revenues involve more than one currency, exchange rates must be projected for each evaluation period to permit analysis of the project in terms of one currency. Economic analysis results tend to be very sensitive to exchange rate projections. In general, exchange rate changes often reflect current changes (or perceived future changes) in relative inflation rates between countries. However, this is not always the case. Differences in country interest rates and balance of payment deficits can be major factors that affect exchange rates. In 1995 the U.S. dollar declined 15% to 20% against both the Japanese yen and the German mark although U.S. inflation was relatively low at 3% per year or less. Usually however, devaluation of a country currency against the U.S. dollar, Japanese yen, or European currencies is caused by current or projected future inflation rate differences between the countries. Therefore, exchange rate projections often implicitly account for future inflation effects on escalated dollar analysis. The following example illustrates the mechanics of handling exchange rates in cash flow analysis as well as the sensitivity of evaluation results to exchange rate effects.

EXAMPLE 5-6 Exchange Rate Analysis Variations

A company is considering investing $1,000 in Country "Z" whose time zero (now) currency exchange rate is 100 Z Units per $1.00 U.S. The following time diagram gives the relevant cost, production, selling price and exchange rate data, with values in today's U.S. dollars.

Production = 10,000 units in years one and two
Selling Price = $0.06/unit in years one and two
Operating Costs = $0.01/unit in years one and two

		$600 Revenue	$600 Revenue	
Cost =	$1,000	$100 Op. Costs	$100 Op. Costs	
	0	1	2	Salvage = $400

Analyze the following evaluation cases:

Case A) Evaluate the project ROR and NPV @ i* = 10% using a U.S. dollar analysis assuming zero percent escalation of all values per year.

Case B) Evaluate the project ROR and NPV @ i* = 10% using Country Z currency analysis assuming zero percent escalation of all values per year.

Case C) Change the Case B analysis to reflect projected 50% per year devaluation of Country Z currency against the U.S. dollar. Assume all project costs, revenues, and salvage values are incurred or realized in U.S. dollars, but do the analysis in terms of Z units. (This could be a Country Z mining or petroleum project where product is sold internationally in U.S. dollars.)

Case D) Re-work Case C assuming sales revenue is realized by selling product (such as electric power) in country Z at the uniform selling price of 6.0 Z units {(100Z/$1.00) ×

($0.06/Unit)} per product unit each year. In other words, product is being sold to the country Z general population and the economy of the country will not permit passing inflation effects through currency devaluation on to the consumer. For simplicity, also assume salvage value is unaffected by exchange rate changes. However, operating costs are assumed to be affected by exchange rate changes.

Case E) Re-analyze Case B using U.S. dollar financial borrowed money leverage assuming $800 U.S. (8,000 Z units) are borrowed at year 0 at 10% annual interest to be repaid with year 1 and 2 mortgage payments of $200 U.S. loan principal plus accrued interest plus a balloon (lump sum) loan principal payment of $400 at the end of year 2 to pay off the loan when the project is sold. Sales in Country Z currency units are converted to U.S. dollars to pay off the loan.

Case F) Re-analyze Case D using the leveraged borrowed money conditions described in Case E.

Solutions:

Case A) U.S. Dollars Analysis

10,000 units/yr ($0.06/unit) = $600 revenue/yr
–10,000 units/yr ($0.01/unit) = –$100 operating cost/yr

Before-Tax Cash Flow/yr = $500 + $400 Salvage at year 2

–$1,000	$500	$500+$400 Salv.
0	1	2

ROR = 23.11%
NPV @ 10% = $198.35 U.S.

Case B) Country Z Currency Analysis (100 Z Units = $1.0 U.S.)

–100,000Z	50,000Z	50,000Z + 40,000Z Salv.
0	1	2

ROR = 23.11%
NPV @ 10% = 19,835 Z Units

Case C) Country Z Currency Analysis With Exchange Rate Changes

Year 0 100 Z Units = \$1.0 U.S.
Year 1 150 Z Units = \$1.0 U.S.
Year 2 225 Z Units = \$1.0 U.S.

Z Currency Unit Cash Flow:

Year	0	1	2
Revenue	—	90,000*	225,000
– Operating Costs	—	–15,000**	–22,500
– Capital Costs	–100,000	—	—
Cash Flow	–100,000	+75,000	+202,500

* \$600 U.S.(150Z Units / \$1.00 U.S.) = 90,000Z Units
** –\$100 U.S.(150Z Units / \$1.00 U.S.) = –15,000Z Units

ROR = 84.66%
NPV @ 10% = 135,537 Z Units

The devaluation effects have worked for the investor and given better economic results for the assumption that revenue escalates proportional to devaluation. This would relate to an export project such as mining or oil and gas production project where product is sold internationally in U.S. dollar prices. Often it is very difficult or impossible to pass on to domestic consumers price escalation due to currency devaluation effects. The domestic consumer may not have the financial means to pay higher prices. Case D shows that this assumption gives very different economic results.

Case D) Z Currency Unit Cash Flow Analysis as in Case C, No Revenue Escalation

Year	0	1	2
Revenue	—	60,000	100,000
– Operating Costs	—	–15,000	–22,500
– Capital Costs	–100,000	—	—
– Cash Flow	–100,000	45,000	77,500

ROR = 13.36%
NPV @ 10% = +4,958 Z Units

These results are economically less desirable than the "no devaluation" Case B results, because devaluation is assumed to negatively affect operating costs but to have no off-setting positive effect on revenue. When leveraged money is involved, currency devaluation can have much greater effects as the following two cases show.These cases relate to borrowed money analysis considerations introduced in Chapter 11, but applied here to illustrate the significant impact of exchange rate changes on leveraged evaluations. Refer to Chapter 11, Example 11-1 if the handling of borrowed money (leverage) in this analysis is not clear.

Case E) Z Currency Analysis With Borrowed U.S. Dollars, No Exchange Rate Changes

Year	0	1	2
Revenue	—	60,000	100,000
– Operating Costs	—	–10,000	–10,000
– Interest	—	–8,000	–6,000
– Loan Principal	—	–20,000	–20,000
– Balloon Principal	—	—	–40,000
+ Borrowed Dollars	+80,000	—	—
– Capital Costs	–100,000	—	—
Leveraged CF	–20,000	+22,000	+24,000

Leveraged ROR = 77.58%
Leveraged NPV @ 10% = 19,835 Z Units

This leveraged ROR result is much better than the 23.11% ROR for cash investment Case B. However, note the NPV for Case B is the same as for Case E because the cost of borrowed money which is the 10% interest rate is the same as the 10% opportunity cost of capital minimum discount rate.

Case F) Z Currency Analysis With Borrowed U.S. Dollars, Exchange Rate Changes Affect Operating Costs, Loan Principal and Interest, Not Revenue

Year	0	1	2
Revenue	—	60,000	100,000
– Operating Costs	—	–15,000	–22,500
– Interest	—	–12,000	–13,500
– Loan Principal	—	–30,000	–135,000
+ Borrowed Dollars	+80,000	—	—
– Capital Costs	–100,000	—	—
Leveraged CF	–20,000	+3,000	–71,000

Since the cumulative negative cash of 91,000 exceeds the 3,000 positive cash flow, it is evident that the leveraged ROR for this Case is negative.

Leveraged ROR = negative infinity
Leveraged NPV @ 10% = –75,950 Z Units

The effects of devaluation of currency can be devastating economically on a leveraged project using a U.S. dollar loan (or another hard currency loan) to be repaid with the devalued currency. Unless revenue in terms of the devalued currency escalates at a rate proportional to the currency devaluation rate, the economics of leveraged investments deteriorate.

5.3 Summary

Escalated values are also defined as actual, current, then current or nominal dollars. They are always inclusive of the effects of inflation and other parameters including technological, environmental, market and related issues.

Constant values are escalated values that have had the effects of inflation discounted from them to a base period in time which typically is time zero, but it could be any point. Constant dollars are also referred to as real or deflated dollars.

The only difference between escalated and constant values is the inflation rate each year related to the host currency.

Previous variables introduced in Chapters 2 and 3 are now defined more explicitly to reflect the proper handling of inflation, they include:

e = escalation rate
f = inflation rate

i* = escalated $ discount rate
i*′ = constant $ discount rate

i = escalated $ rate of return
i′ = constant $ rate of return

Escalated dollar and constant dollar project rates of return and minimum rates of return can be explicitly related for any uniform annual inflation rate using Equation 5-1, which was developed in Example 5-1.

Eq 5-1: $1+i = (1+f)(1+i')$

Rearranged: $i' = \{(1+i)/(1+f)\} - 1$

A commonly used approximation to Equation 5-1 is the following:

$i' \approx i - f$

PROBLEMS

Excel solutions at Stermole.com

5-1 Consider the following "today's dollar" cash flows.

		Rev=600
C=100	C=200	OC=100
0	1	2

For cases A, B, C and D below, assume the escalated dollar minimum rate of return is 15.0% and:

A) Calculate the project escalated dollar NPV if revenue escalates at 10.0% per year, and all costs escalate at 6.0% per year.

B) Using the escalated dollar results from Case A, calculate the project constant dollar NPV if inflation is 5.0% per year and escalation of costs and revenues is the same as in Case A. For evaluation consistency, adjust the escalated dollar minimum discount rate of 15.0% using text Equation 5-1 to calculate the equivalent constant dollar minimum discount rate for use in this constant dollar NPV analysis.

C) Calculate the project escalated dollar NPV assuming today's dollar values equal escalated dollar values. State the explicit cost and revenue escalation assumption built into this analysis.

D) Calculate the project constant dollar NPV assuming today's dollar values equal constant dollar values. State the explicit cost and revenue escalation assumption built into this analysis.

5-2 In 1988, the U.S. gross domestic product (GDP) increased to $4.90 trillion at year end, from the 1987 year end level of $4.54 trillion in actual escalated dollar values. In the same year, the consumer price index rose approximately 4%. What was the escalated (current) dollar percent increase in GDP? What was the constant (real) dollar percent increase in GDP?

5-3 An investment related to developing a new product is estimated to have the following costs and revenues in "today's" or "time zero" dollars.

		I=$200,000	I=$200,000
C_0=$50,000	C_1=$150,000	OC=$100,000	OC=$100,000
0	1	2	5

A) Evaluate the project escalated dollar ROR if both capital costs and operating costs are estimated to escalate at 15% per year from time zero with income escalating at 10% per year.

B) Make constant dollar ROR Analysis of Case "A" assuming the rate of inflation for the next 5 years will be 10% per year.

C) Use escalated dollar ROR Analysis to analyze the investment assuming a washout of escalation of income and operating costs with a 15% escalation of capital costs in year one.

5-4 A product that sells today for $100 per unit is expected to escalate in price by 6% in year one, 8% in year two and 10% in year three. Calculate the escalated dollar year three product selling price. If inflation is expected to be 5% in year one, 9% in year two and 12% in year three, determine the year three constant dollar product selling price.

5-5 An investor has an opportunity to buy a parcel of land for $100,000. He plans to sell it in two years. What will the sale price have to be for the investor to get a 25% constant dollar before-tax ROR with inflation averaging 10% annually? What escalated dollar annual rate of increase in land value will give the needed sale price?

5-6 Determine the break-even escalated dollar selling price per unit required in each of years one and two to achieve a 15% constant dollar project ROR, assuming a 12% per year inflation rate. All dollar values are today's dollar values.

	Sales=$X(1000)	Sales=$X(1000)
C=$100,000	OC=$50,000	OC=$50,000
0	1	2

Selling price escalation is 10% per year from time zero when selling price is $X per unit. Operating Cost (OC) escalation is 15% per year from time 0. 1,000 units are to be produced and sold each year.

5-7 What can be paid now (today) to acquire a property that will be developed 2 years from now and which engineers estimate will have today's dollar costs and revenues shown on the following time diagram. All values are in thousands of today's dollars.

			Rev=$150	Rev=$150	Rev=$150
C_{Acq}=?	—	C=$200	OC=$50	OC=$50	OC=$50
0(now)	1	2	3	4	5

Starting from now, it is projected that inflation will be 7% per year. The escalated dollar minimum ROR is 15%. Evaluate the acquisition cost that can be paid now to acquire this property for the following five cases:

Case 1. Make the analysis using today's dollar costs and revenues assuming they are a reasonable projection of escalated dollar capital costs, operating costs and revenues to be incurred (this assumption effectively assumes zero percent escalation of all costs and revenues each year or that escalation of all capital costs and operating costs will be offset by escalation of revenues so that escalation of costs and revenues will have zero effect on economic analysis results).

Case 2. Make the analysis using the today's dollar costs and revenues assuming they represent constant dollar values. (This assumption is valid if you assume that all capital costs, operating costs and revenues will escalate at the same rate of inflation each year. Discounting these escalated dollar values at the same rate of inflation to get constant dollar values gives the original today's dollar values for this assumption.)

Case 3. Use escalated dollar analysis assuming capital cost (C) escalation will be 12% per year, operating cost (OC) escalation will be 10% per year and revenue (Rev) escalation will be 10% per year.

Case 4. Make constant dollar analysis for the Case 3 escalation assumption assuming 7% inflation as given.

Case 5. Use the escalated dollar analysis assuming capital costs escalate at 12% per year and escalation of operating costs is exactly offset by a like-dollar escalation of revenues each year which gives uniform profit margins each year. This commonly is called "the washout assumption".

5-8 An investor has paid $100,000 for a machine that is estimated to produce 5000 product units per year for each of the next three years when the machine is estimated to be obsolete with a zero salvage value. The product price is the 'unknown' to be calculated, so it is estimated to be $x per unit in year one escalated dollars and to increase 10% per year in year two and 6% in year three. Total operating costs are estimated to be $8000 in year one escalated dollars and to increase 15% in year two and 8% in year three. The annual inflation rate is estimated to be 7%. What must be the year one, two and three escalated dollar product selling price if the investor is to receive a 12% annually compounded constant dollar ROR on invested dollars?

5-9 Reclamation costs on a project are expected to be incurred over a 30 year period from 27 to 56 years in the future from now. Reclamation costs are estimated to escalate 5.0% per year in the future. Using a 5.0% annual discount rate as representative of annual reclamation cost escalation, the year 0 present worth of the 27 to 56 year future reclamation costs is estimated to be $1.0 million. It is assumed that money today and in the future over the 56 year life of this analysis can be invested in U.S. Treasury Bonds paying 9.0% interest per year. Determine the magnitude of year 0 investment that an investor needs to make in U.S. Treasury Bonds paying 9.0% annual interest to cover the year 27 through 56 future reclamation costs.

5-10 The following time diagram before-tax cash flows are today's dollar values. The investor has a constant dollar minimum rate of return of 10.0% and annual inflation is forecasted to be 3.0% over the project life beginning in year 1. All values are in millions.

–100	–200	150	150	150	150
0	1	2	3	4	5

A) Assuming the rate of escalation for all cash flows is equal to the inflation rate, calculate the escalated dollar project NPV and ROR.

B) Based on your calculations in part A, determine the constant dollar equivalent cash flows and resulting constant dollar NPV and ROR.

C) Neglecting A and B, if the rate of escalation was forecasted to be 0% per year over the project life, calculate the corresponding escalated dollar NPV and ROR. Inflation is still forecast to be 3.0% per year.

D) Again, neglecting A and B, if the rate of escalation was forecasted to be 0% per year over the project life, but inflation is still forecast at 3.0% per year, calculate the corresponding constant dollar NPV and ROR.

CHAPTER 5 AUXILIARY PROBLEMS

A5-1 A proposed project has today's dollar costs and revenues as follows:

	Rev=300	Rev=300
C=200	OC=100	OC=100
0	1	2

For cases A through D, assume an escalated dollar i* of 12.0%:

A) Calculate the project escalated dollar NPV at time zero for revenue escalation of 5.0% in year 1 with the year 1 value compounding an additional 6.0% in year 2. Cost escalation will be 8.0% in year 1 with the resulting value then escalating an additional 10.0% in year 2.

B) Calculate the project constant dollar NPV assuming 7.0% inflation per year and escalation of costs and revenue will be as defined in Part A.

C) Calculate the project escalated dollar NPV assuming the today's dollar values equal escalated dollar values. State the explicit cost and revenue escalation assumption built into this analysis.

D) Calculate the project constant dollar NPV using the assumption that today's dollar values equal constant dollar values. Use the same 7.0% annual inflation rate. State the explicit cost and revenue escalation assumption built into this analysis.

A5-2 An investor has an opportunity to buy a parcel of land for $200,000. He plans to sell it in two years. What will the land sale price have to be for the investor to get a 20% constant dollar before-tax ROR with inflation averaging 8% annually? What escalated dollar annual rate of increase in land value will give the needed sale price?

A5-3 An investor has paid $200,000 for a machine that is estimated to produce 2,000 product units per year for each of the next three years when the machine is estimated to be obsolete with a zero salvage value. The product price is the 'unknown' to be calculated, so it is estimated to be $x per unit in year one escalated dollars and to increase 5% in year two above the year 1 value and an additional 8% in year three. Total operating costs are estimated to be $15,000 in year one escalated dollars with this amount increasing 10% in year two and an additional 8% in year three. The annual inflation rate is estimated to be 5%. What must be the year one, two, and three escalated dollar product selling price if the investor is to receive a 12% annually compounded constant dollar ROR on invested dollars?

A5-4 The price of copper at mid-year 1977 was $0.60 per pound and at mid-year 2008, it was $3.80 per pound.

A) What was the escalated dollar annually compounded copper price escalation rate during this period?

B) For assumed average annual inflation of 4% per year during this period, what was the annual constant dollar copper price escalation rate during this period?

A5-5 In 2008, the mid-year price of crude oil was at $126.00 per barrel. In 1980, the mid-year price of crude oil traded at $39.50 per barrel. During that same period, the average rate of inflation was 3.7% per year.

A) Calculate the 1980 constant dollar equivalent price of crude oil being sold in 2008.

B) Calculate the 2008 equivalent price of 1980 crude oil if oil escalated annually at the average rate of inflation.

C) From 1980 to 2008, what was the average annual rate of escalation in the price of crude oil?

CHAPTER 6

UNCERTAINTY AND RISK ANALYSIS

6.1 Introduction

In this age of advancing technology, successful managers must make informed investment decisions that determine the future success of their companies by drawing systematically on the specialized knowledge, accumulated information, experience and skills of many people. In evaluating projects and making choices between investment alternatives, every manager is painfully aware that he cannot and will not always be right. Management pressure is increased by the knowledge that a company's future depends on the ability to choose with a high degree of consistency those investment and market opportunities that have a high probability of success even though the characteristics of future events are seldom precisely known.

In the previous chapters in the text investment analyses all were considered to be made under "no-risk" conditions. That is, the probability of success was considered to be 1.0 for each investment evaluated. This means that by expressing risk and uncertainty quantitatively in terms of numerical probabilities or likelihood of occurrence, where probabilities are decimal fractions in the range of zero to 1.0, we implicitly considered that the probability of achieving projected profits or savings was 1.0 for investment situations evaluated. We are all aware that due to risk and uncertainty from innumerable sources, the probability of success for many investments is significantly different than 1.0. When faced with decision choices under uncertain conditions, a manager can use informal analysis of the risk and uncertainty associated with the investment or he can analyze the elements of risk and uncertainty in a quantitative manner. Informal analysis relies on the decision makers experience, intuition, judgement, hunches and luck to determine whether or not a particular investment should be made. The quantitative analysis approach is based on analyzing the effects that risk and uncertainty can have on an investment situation by using a logical and consistent decision strategy that incorporates the effects of risk and uncertainty into the analysis results. Use of the quantitative analysis approach should not be considered to imply that the informal analysis considerations of experience, intuition and judgement are not needed. On the contrary, the purpose of quantitative analysis of risk and uncertainty is to provide the decision maker with as much quantitative information as possible concerning the risks and uncertainties associated with a particular investment situation, so that the decision maker has the best possible information on which to apply experience, intuition and good judgment in reaching the final decision. The objective of investment decision making from an economic viewpoint under conditions of uncertainty is to invest available capital where we have the highest probability of generating the maximum possible future profit. The use of quantitative approaches to incorporate risk and uncertainty into analysis results may help us be more successful in achieving this objective over the long run.

No matter how comprehensive or sophisticated an investment evaluation may be, uncertainty still remains a factor in the evaluation. Even though rate of return or some other economic evaluation criterion may be calculated for a project with several significant figures of accuracy using the best available cost and income data, the decision maker may still feel uneasy about the economic decision indicated because he or she knows the assumptions on which the calculations are based are uncertain. If the economic evaluation method used does not reflect this uncertainty then every assumption built into an economic analysis is a "best guess" and the final economic result is a consolidation of these values. Making decisions on the basis of such "best guess" calculations alone can be hazardous. Consider a manager who may select investment alternative "A" with a 20% ROR over investment "B" which has a 15% ROR based on the "best guess" ROR calculation approach. Would this decision be justifiable if the probability of success of alternative "A" was 50% (or one chance in two) compared with a probability of success of alternative "B" of 90%? It is evident that the manager needs some measure of the "risk" involved in each alternative in addition to the "best guess" or most likely rate of return results.

There are several different approaches that can be used to quantitatively incorporate risk and uncertainty into analyses. These include sensitivity analysis or probabilistic sensitivity analysis to account for uncertainty associated with possible variation in project parameters, and expected value or expected net present value or rate of return analysis to account for risk associated with finite probability of failure. The use of sensitivity analysis is advocated for most economic analyses and the use of expected value analysis is advisable if finite probability of project failure exists. Sensitivity analysis is described in the first half of this chapter and expected value analysis is described in the second half.

Sensitivity analysis is a means of evaluating the effects of uncertainty on investment by determining how investment profitability varies as the parameters are varied that affect economic evaluation results. Sensitivity analysis is a means of identifying those critical variables that, if changed, could considerably affect the profitability measure. In carrying out a sensitivity analysis, individual variables are changed and the effect of such a change on the expected rate of return (or some other decision method) is computed. Once all of the strategic variables have been identified, they can be given special attention by the decision maker. Some of the typical investment parameters that often are allowed to vary for sensitivity analysis include initial investment, selling price, operating cost, project life, and salvage value. If probabilities of occurrence are associated with the various levels of each investment parameter, sensitivity analysis becomes probabilistic sensitivity analysis.

It may now be evident to the reader that the term "uncertainty" as used in this text refers to possible variation in parameters that affect investment evaluation. *"Risk" refers to the evaluation of an investment using a known mechanism that incorporates the probabilities of occurrence for success and failure and/or of different values of each investment parameter.* Both uncertainty and risk influence almost all types of investment decision, but especially investment involving research and development for any industry and exploration for minerals and oil or gas.

6.2 Sensitivity Analysis to Analyze Effects of Uncertainty

As described in the previous section, sensitivity analysis refers to analysis of how investment profitability is affected by variation in the parameters that affect overall profitability. For a case where rate of return is the economic criterion used to measure profitability, sensitivity analysis involves evaluation of how rate of return varies with parameters such as initial investment, profit per year, project life, and salvage value. It is frequently used to determine how much change in a variable would be necessary to reverse the decision based on average-value or best-guess estimates. It usually does not take into consideration the likelihood of variation. The rate of change in the total outcome relative to the rate of change in the variable being considered will indicate the significance of this variable in the overall evaluation.

Example 6-1 will introduce a single variable sensitivity analysis. It is important for the reader to keep in mind that in this analysis, no downstream effects are considered relevant to the evaluation. In other words, each parameter is independent of the other so changing the magnitude of the capital investment will have no impact on any other operations or the magnitude of project operating costs, etc. To further illustrate, when the years of income are reduced, there is no adjustment in the residual value of the assets. Such numbers may increase or decrease but again, are neglected here to simplify the introduction of this evaluation procedure.

EXAMPLE 6-1 Single Variable Sensitivity Analysis

Annual Before-Tax Positive Cash Flows (BTCF) of $67,000 are shown on the time diagram for this $240,000 investment case with an expected salvage value of $70,000 after five years. Evaluate the sensitivity of project ROR to plus or minus 20% and 40% variations in initial investment, annual profit, project life and salvage value.

–$240,000	$67,000	$67,000	$67,000	$67,000	$67,000 $70,000
0	1	2	3	4	5

Solution:

Using the most expected cost and revenue parameters gives:

PW Eq: $240{,}000 = 67{,}000(P/A_{i,5}) + 70{,}000(P/F_{i,5})$

The "most expected" project ROR is 18%. How will this "most expected" 18% ROR vary as parameters are changed?

A) Initial Investment Sensitivity Analysis

Initial Investment	Change in Prediction	ROR	Percent Change in 18.0% ROR Prediction
144,000	–40	42.0	133.3
192,000	–20	27.5	52.9
240,000	0	18.0	0
288,000	+20	11.2	–37.9
336,000	+40	5.8	–67.7

The percent variations in the ROR from changes in initial investment costs are very significant. In general, changes in parameters close to time zero (such as initial investment and annual BTCF) have a much more significant effect on investment ROR than changes in parameters many years in the future from time zero (such as salvage value).

B) Project Life Sensitivity Analysis

Project Life	Change in Prediction	ROR	Percent Change in 18.0% ROR Prediction
3	–40	5.6	–68.8
4	–20	13.4	–25.5
5	0	18.0	0
6	+20	20.9	16.3
7	+40	22.9	27.1

Note that this sensitivity analysis really involves changes in total cash flow as well as project life. If project life was longer (say 10 years or more), changes in life would have a less sensitive effect on ROR.

C) Annual BTCF Sensitivity Analysis

Annual BTCF	Change in Prediction	ROR	Percent Change in 18.0% ROR Prediction
40,200	–40	3.6	–80.2
53,600	–20	11.0	–39.0
67,000	0	18.0	0
80,400	+20	24.8	37.9
93,800	+40	31.5	74.8

Percent variations in ROR due to changes in annual BTCF are very significant because the changes start occurring close to time zero. Individual parameters such as selling price, production rates and operating costs affect profit.

D) Salvage Value Sensitivity Analysis

Salvage Value	Change in Prediction	ROR	Percent Change in 18.0% ROR Prediction
42,000	–40	15.9	–11.9
56,000	–20	16.9	– 6.0
70,000	0	18.0	0
84,000	+20	19.0	5.4
98,000	+40	20.0	10.8

Sensitivity analysis shows that accuracy of salvage value is the least important of all the parameters that go into this ROR analysis because salvage value occurs far in the future from time zero. Also, in this case, cumulative salvage dollar value is small compared to cumulative profit. In some evaluations this is not the case and salvage value has a much more sensitive effect.

Graphically, an approach used to summarize these type of findings is often described as a Tornado Diagram. With this methodology the variation in each parameter is plotted relative to the economic measure of performance. By stacking the parameters in descending order of range of results a visual presentation of the parameters making the biggest economic impact is presented as follows:

Example 6-1 Tornado Diagram

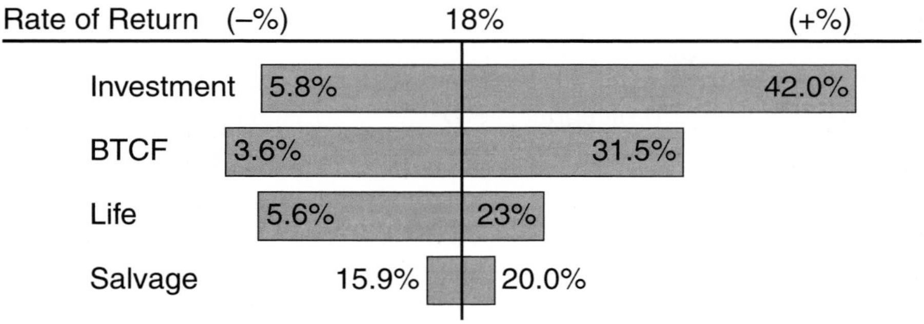

6.3 The Range Approach to Sensitivity Analysis

The range approach involves estimating the most optimistic and most pessimistic values (or the best and worst) for each factor in addition to estimating most expected values. This approach will make investment decision making easier for the cases where (1) a project appears desirable even when pessimistic values are used and therefore obviously should be adopted from an economic viewpoint, (2) when a project appears to be undesirable even when optimistic values are used and therefore rejection is dictated on economic grounds. When a project looks good with optimistic values but bad with pessimistic values further study of the project and the risk and uncertainty surrounding the project should be made. Application of this method is shown in Example 6-2.

EXAMPLE 6-2 Range Approach Sensitivity Analysis

Use the range approach to evaluate the investment described in Example 6-1 for best and worst case sensitivity analysis using the plus or minus 20% parameter variations with a five year life and a minimum rate of return of 15%.

Solution:

	Best Case	Expected Case	Worst Case
Investment	192,000	240,000	288,000
Annual BTCF	80,400	67,000	53,600
Salvage	84,000	70,000	56,000
Project Life in yrs.	5	5	5
ROR, %	36.4	18.0	3.7

The results indicate that the project is satisfactory for the best and most expected conditions but unsatisfactory for the worst conditions. More information is needed on the expected probability of occurrence of the worst case conditions to reach a valid and meaningful decision.

The best, worst and most expected sensitivity analysis results give very useful information that bracket the range of project ROR results that can reasonably be expected. This is the type of information that managers need to reach investment decisions. It is very important to recognize that although a project ROR greater than the minimum rate of return is predicted for the most expected parameters, the result is based on parameters which are subject to variation. This variation should be analyzed over the full range of possible results utilizing the best engineering and management judgments of people involved with a project.

6.4 Probabilistic Sensitivity Analysis

The application of probability distributions to relate sales volume and prices, operating costs and other parameters to probability of occurrence permits "probabilistic analysis" by the Monte Carlo simulation technique. A brief description of the method follows, then the method will be illustrated.

A weakness of traditional techniques for the evaluation of projects is an inability to combine information from a number of sources into a straightforward and reliable profitability indicator. The major factor in this problem is the large number of variables that must be considered. An additional factor is that it is not possible to obtain accurate single-valued estimates of many of the variables.

Probability theory is the study of the uncertainty of events. A basic tool of probability theory is the use of a range of values to describe variables that cannot adequately be quantified by single value estimates. For example, the determination of the least, greatest and most likely values of a variable will more accurately quantify the variable than will the average value.

The distribution and relative possibilities of values assigned to a given variable will remain characteristic of that variable if factors affecting the variable remain constant. Figure 6-1 illustrates three possible distributions of values. The values are plotted on the horizontal axis and the respective probabilities of their occurrence on the vertical axis. Analysis of the three examples indicates that the uncertainty of the parameter described in Example 3 is much greater than that in Example 2. The uncertainty of Example 3 is indicated by the wide range of values.

A majority of the parameters in real evaluations often give an intermediate range of parameter values as illustrated by Example 1. Ideally we would like to have a very small range for all parameters as illustrated by Example 2. In practice we get a combination of small, intermediate and large ranges of parameter value variation for different parameters in actual evaluation situations.

The distributions in Figure 6-1 all have their values symmetrically distributed around the most likely value (the familiar bell-shaped curve is an example of this distribution). A distribution of this type is called the normal distribution. If the most likely value is shifted to either side of the center of the distribution, then it is referred to as a skewed distribution. *The normal distribution and the skewed distribution are both special types of a general class of curves known as density functions. In the remainder of this discussion normal distributions will be referred to as such and the term density function will be used to describe probability distributions that are not normal.* The shape of the distributions will be determined by the nature of the variables they describe.

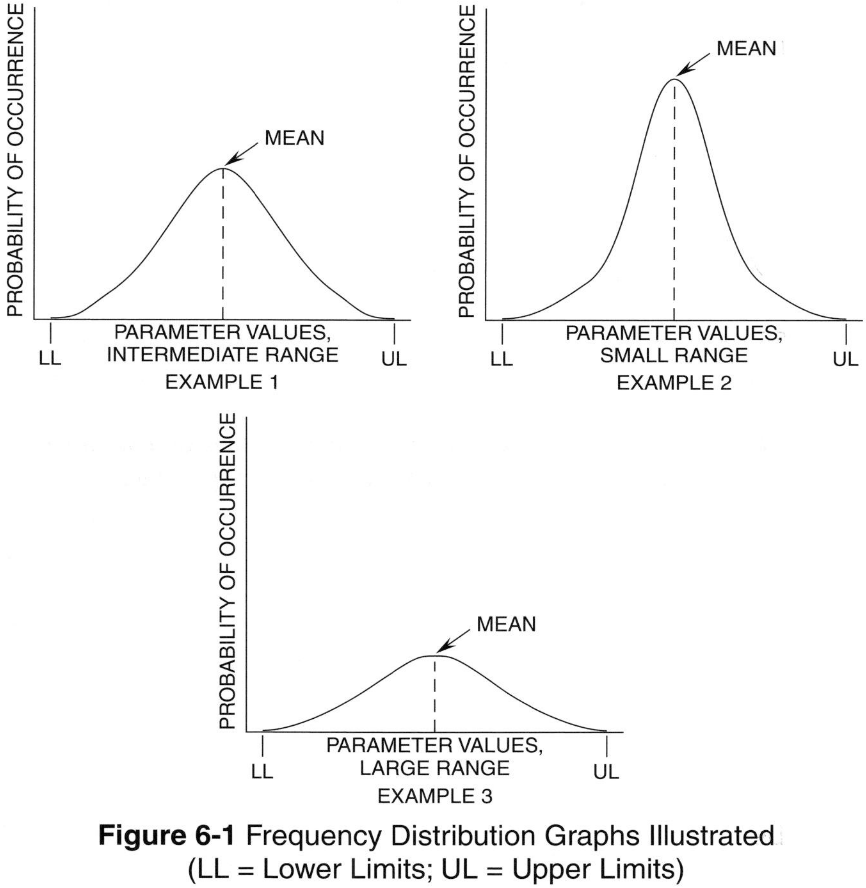

Figure 6-1 Frequency Distribution Graphs Illustrated
(LL = Lower Limits; UL = Upper Limits)

In principle, a relative frequency distribution graph is converted to the equivalent cumulative frequency distribution graph by moving from the left end of the distribution to the right end and computing the total area that is less than or equal to corresponding values of the parameter within the range evaluated. The cumulative area to the left of a given parameter value divided by the total area under the curve is the cumulative probability that a random parameter value will be less than or equal to the given parameter value.

Figure 6-2 illustrates typical cumulative frequency distribution graphs that would result from converting the relative frequency graphs shown in Figure 6-1 to the corresponding plots. Note that Example 3 with a large range of parameter values has a much flatter cumulative probability curve than Example 2 which has a small range of parameter values. Example 2 has a much higher percentage of the parameter values in a given range of cumulative probability of occurrence compared to Example 3.

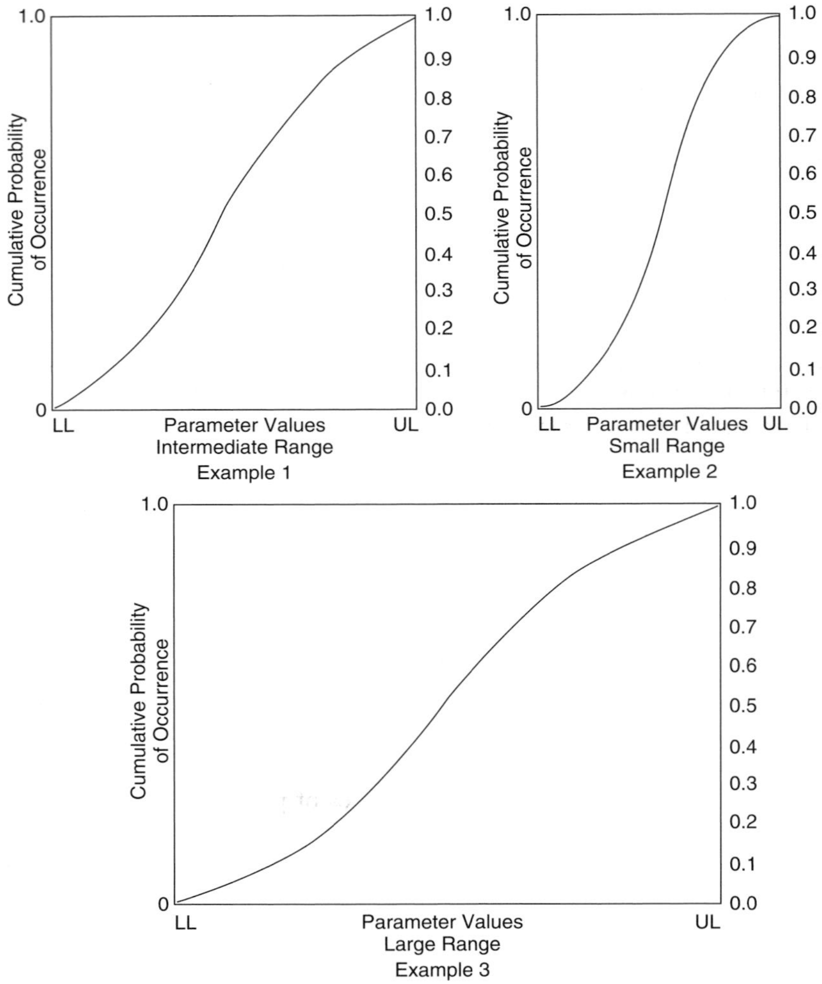

Figure 6-2 Cumulative Frequency Distribution (LL = Lower Limit, UL = Upper Limit)

Now to describe the probabilistic sensitivity analysis approach, consider that we are about to evaluate a new development project. We might be interested in the effect on our economic evaluation criterion of changes in project parameters such as initial investment, product selling price per unit, production rate or sales projections, operating costs, project life and salvage value. For each of these variables and/or other variables to be investigated, a frequency distribution plot of probability of occurrence versus parameter value similar to the examples in Figure 6-1 is prepared by the person or persons most familiar with and capable of projecting future values of the parameter involved. These frequency distribution data are then converted to cumulative probability of occurrence versus parameter value graphs similar to the examples in Figure 6-2. When these graphs are available for each parameter that is considered to vary, the use of Monte Carlo simulation is applied. This generally involves curve-fitting a mathematical expression to describe each cumulative probability of occurrence versus parameter value so that picking a random number between 0.0 and 1.0 analogous to the cumulative probability of occurrence will automatically fix the parameter at the corresponding value. Different random numbers are selected to fix each of the different parameters being varied. Then using the randomly selected parameter values, the economic analysis criterion such as rate of return is calculated. Then you iterate and do the same thing over again picking a new set of random numbers to determine a new set of parameters used to calculate rate of return. This process is generally repeated for at least a 1,000 iterations dependent somewhat upon the complexity of the model. A Histogram (or frequency distribution) can then be developed for the desired economic measures such as rate of return, net present value, ratios, etc. While rate of return is a valid economic measure, its use in statistical modeling is often minimized. This is due to variation in meaning that can occur should the randomly generated parameters result in a cash flow stream where income precedes costs and the "i" value has rate of reinvestment meaning that is likely to be inconsistent with other measures. It is easy to create other problem areas such as the generation of cost-income-cost in a cash flow stream that might lead to dual solutions and inconsistent measures of performance. For all these reasons, it is recommended that the economic focus with Monte Carlo be based on NPV or ratios, which do not rely on an iterative process in the various solutions to be accumulated.

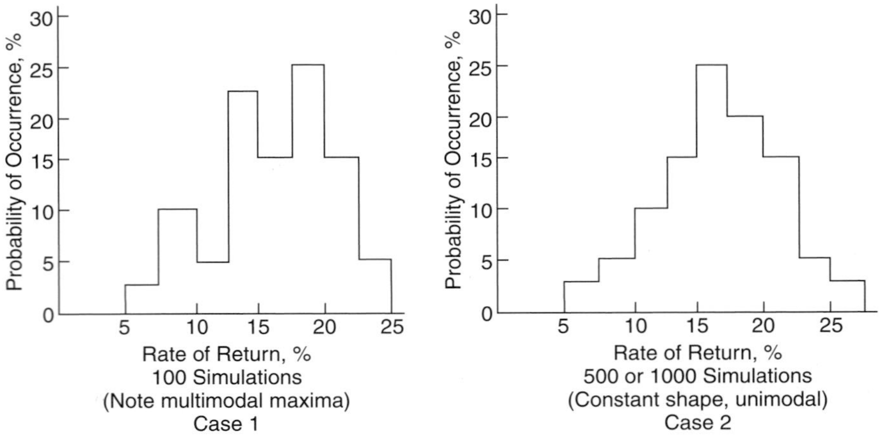

Figure 6-3 Frequency Distribution of ROR for Varying Simulations

The histogram for case 1 has multi-modal (more than one maxima) peaks indicating that statistically we have not made enough simulations to get a rate of return frequency distribution with constant shape. If the input data frequency distribution is unimodal (having one peak as illustrated in Figure 6-1) the output rate of return frequency distribution plot should be unimodal. Case 2 demonstrates for this hypothetical situation that if we go to 500 or 1000 simulations we get a unimodal graph with the same shape indicating that 500 simulations are sufficient for analyzing this hypothetical investment using probabilistic sensitivity analysis.

An important thing to note about probabilistic sensitivity analysis results is that you do not get a single result, but instead you get a range over which the results vary as a function of probability of occurrence and also you get a most expected result. In many investment situations the shape of this curve is more important than the most expected value. For example a project with a most expected ROR of 25% with a range of possible results from negative ROR to positive 40% might be considered less desirable than a project with a most expected ROR of 18% and a range of possible results from 10% to 25% because the certainty associated with the 18% most expected ROR investment is greater than the certainty associated with the other investment. Probabilistic sensitivity analysis enables the decision maker to get a firmer feeling concerning the effects of risk and uncertainty on economic analysis results than any other analysis approach gives.

The weak point of the probabilistic analysis method lies in the subjective assigning of probabilities of occurrence to the levels of parameters that go into the analysis. However, it is generally considered to be best to specifically state the probabilities of occurrence based on the best judgement of people involved with a project and then to base the analysis on these estimates even though they are subjective in nature. In the final analysis any evaluation technique is only as good as the estimates of the input parameters and must be used in conjunction with good engineering logic and managerial judgement. Assigning probabilities to parameter estimates is just one more step in quantifying the assumptions that are made. These techniques provide management with additional tools to aid in the decision-making process.

Following is a simplified example that illustrates the principles of applying probabilistic analysis to project ROR sensitivity analysis.

EXAMPLE 6-3 A Simple Probabilistic Sensitivity Analysis

A new product to be produced by one of two different processes. It is felt that there is a 60% probability that the process selected will have initial cost of $50,000, a life of five years and zero salvage value. There is a 40% probability that an improved process will be selected with initial cost of $40,000, a life of five years and zero salvage value. With either process there is a 50% probability that annual profit will be $20,000 for the five year project life and a 25% probability that the annual profits will be $15,000 or $25,000 per year. Plot project ROR versus probability of occurrence assuming the parameter values are independent of each other.

Solution:

The following table presents the possible combinations of different investment costs, annual profits, probabilities of occurrence and ROR.

Investment	Annual Profit	Probability of Occurrence	$P/A_{i,5}$	ROR (%)
50,000	15,000	(.6)(.25) = .15	3.334	15.2
50,000	20,000	(.6)(.50) = .30	2.500	28.7
50,000	25,000	(.6)(.25) = .15	2.000	41.1
40,000	15,000	(.4)(.25) = .10	2.667	25.4
40,000	20,000	(.4)(.50) = .20	2.000	41.1
40,000	25,000	(.4)(.25) = .10	1.600	56.0
		1.00		

The most probable project ROR is 41.1% with a 35% probability of occurrence. In Figure 6-5, the cumulative probability diagram shows a cumulative probability of 75% that the ROR will be 28.7% or higher.

Instead of mathematically determining the probability of occurrence of the various ROR results for this problem we could have used the general Monte Carlo simulation technique to get the same results. The general idea of this method as described earlier is to first develop curves for cumulative probability of occurrence versus the economic parameter similar to Figure 6-4. Then random numbers between zero and one are related to cumulative probability of occurrence so that selection of a random number fixes the initial investment for a calculation. Selection of another random number selects the cash flow for that calculation. ROR is then calculated using these values. This procedure is then repeated several hundred or maybe a thousand times until the shape of the ROR versus probability of occurrence curve does not change with additional calculations. For a large number of Monte Carlo simulations the results using this technique for Example 6-3 will be identical to those given in Figure 6-5. The Monte Carlo simulation data are evaluated by forming a histogram from the ROR results. For instance, if one thousand runs are made then approximately three hundred of the ROR results should be 28.7%, since we know the mathematical probability of occurrence of this result is .30.

In general, the variations in input data such as selling price, operating cost, production rate, borrowed money interest rate and so forth that are evaluated will be continuous functions of cumulative probability of occurrence rather than the step functions illustrated in Figure 6-4. Continuous input data give a continuous ROR versus probability of occurrence histogram graph for Monte Carlo simulation in general.

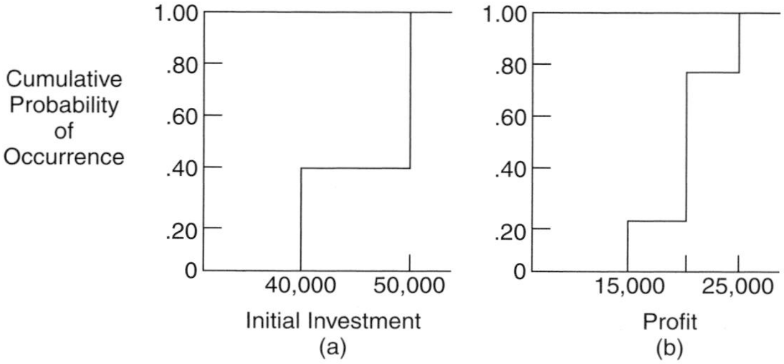

Figure 6-4 Cumulative Probability Diagram

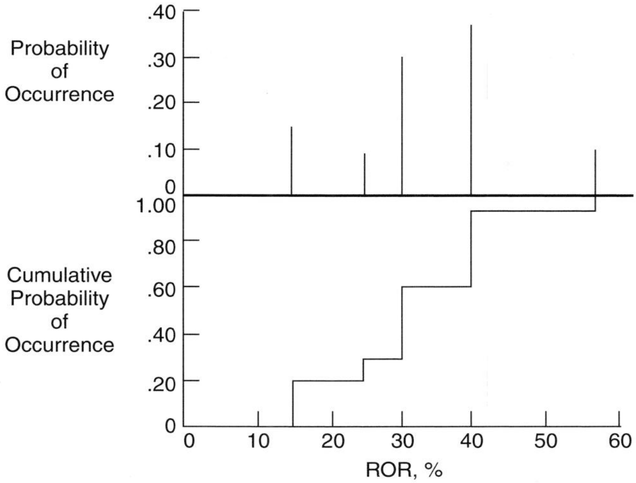

Figure 6-5 Cumulative Probability of Occurrence

6.5 Expected Value Analysis (Economic Risk Analysis)

Expected value is defined as the difference between expected profits and expected costs. Expected profit is the probability of receiving a certain profit times the profit and expected cost is the probability that a certain cost will be incurred times the cost. If you define cost as negative profit and keep the signs straight, you can do as some text authors do and define expected value as the algebraic sum of the expected value of each possible outcome that could occur if the alternative is accepted. Either definition leads to the same expected value result, which sometimes is called a "risk adjusted" result. Several examples of expected value analysis when time value of money considerations are not relevant or significant will be presented first. Then time value of money related examples will be illustrated.

EXAMPLE 6-4 Expected Value Analysis of a Gambling Game

A wheel of fortune in a gambling casino has 54 different slots in which the wheel pointer can stop. Four of the 54 slots contain the number 9. For $1 bet on hitting a 9, the gambler wins $10 plus return of the $1 bet if he or she succeeds. What is the expected value of this gambling game? What is the meaning of the expected value result?

Solution:

Probability of Success = 4/54
Probability of Failure = 50/54

Expected Value = Expected Profit – Expected Cost

= (4/54)($10) – (50/54)($1) = –$0.185

The meaning of the -$0.185 expected value result is that it is the average monetary loss per bet of this type that would be realized if the gambler made this bet over and over again for many repeated trials. It is important to recognize that the gambler is not going to lose $0.185 on any given bet. Over a large number of bets, however, the loss per bet would average $.185. This result should make it evident then that a positive expected value is a necessary condition for a satisfactory investment, but not a sufficient condition as will be discussed later.

EXAMPLE 6-5 Expected Value Analysis of a Simplistic Drilling Venture

If you spend $500,000 drilling a wildcat oil well, geologists estimate the probability of a dry hole is 0.6 with a probability of 0.3 that the well will be a producer that can be sold immediately for $2,000,000 and a probability of 0.1 that the well will produce at a rate that will generate a $1,000,000 immediate sale value. What is the project expected value?

Solution, All Values in Thousands of Dollars:

Expected Value = Expected Profits – Expected Costs

= 0.3(2,000 – 500) + 0.1(1,000 – 500) – 0.6(500)

= +$200

or rearranging:

Expected Value = 0.3(2,000) + 0.1(1,000) – 1.0(500) = +$200

Over the long run, investments of this type will prove rewarding, but remember that the +$200,000 expected value is a statistical long-term average profit that will be realized over many repeated investments of this type. The expected value of an investment alternative is the average profit or loss that would be realized if many investments of this type were repeated. In terms of Example 6-5 this means if we drilled 100 wells of the type described, we expect statistics to begin to work out and assuming our probabilities of occurrence are correct, we would expect about 60 dry holes out of 100 wells with about 30 wells producing a $2,000,000 income and about 10 wells producing a $1,000,000 income. This makes total income of $70,000,000 from 100 wells drilled costing a total of $50,000,000 leaving total profit of $20,000,000 after the costs, or profit per well of +$200,000, which is the expected value result for Example 6-5.

Certainly if you have enough investments of this type in which to invest and enough capital to invest, statistics are very favorable to you, and you would expect to come out ahead over the long run if you made many investments of this type. However, if the loss of the $500,000 drilling investment on a dry hole would break you, you would be foolish to invest in this type of project because there is only a 40% chance of success on any given try. Only if you can stick with this type of investment for many times can you expect statistics to work in your favor. This is one important reason why most large companies and individuals carry insurance of various types even though in nearly all cases the expected profit from self-insuring is positive and therefore favorable to the company or individual. If a disaster from fire can break a company or individual financially, that company cannot afford to self-insure. This is why insurance companies spread large policies over many insurance companies. If disaster does strike a large policy holder, the loss will be distributed over several companies, lessening the likelihood of financial disaster for any one company. It is also the reason most individuals carry fire insurance, homeowners or tenant insurance, and car insurance. The direct financial loss or lawsuit loss potential is so great that most of us cannot afford to carry that risk alone even though expected value is favorable to us if we self insure. The conclusion is that *a positive expected value is a necessary but not a sufficient condition for a satisfactory investment.*

It should now be evident that although expected value has deterministic meaning only if many trials are performed, if we consistently follow a decision-making strategy based on selecting projects with positive expected values, over the long run statistics will work for us and income should be more than sufficient to cover costs. On the other hand, if you consistently take the gambler's ruin approach and invest or bet on investments or gambling games with negative expected values, you can rest assured that over the long run, income will not cover your costs and if you stick with negative expected value investments long enough, you will of course, lose all your capital. This is exactly the situation that exists with all of the gambling games in places such as Las Vegas, Reno and Atlantic City. The odds are always favorable to the house, meaning the gambling house has a positive expected value and therefore the gambler has negative expected value. The gambler has absolutely no realistic hope for success over the long run under these negative expected value conditions. He will lose all the money set aside to gamble with if he sticks with the games long enough.

The reader should notice that in Example 6-5, two different, but equivalent equations were used to calculate expected value as follows:

Let P = probability of success, 1 – P = probability of failure

$$\text{Expected Value} = (P)(\text{Income} - \text{Cost}) - (1 - P)(\text{Cost}) \qquad 6\text{-}2$$

$$\text{or} \qquad = (P)(\text{Income}) - (1.0)(\text{Cost}) \qquad 6\text{-}2a$$

6.6 Expected NPV, Expected PVR, and Expected ROR Analysis

When time value of money considerations are significant, expected NPV, PVR and ROR analysis are methods of including the probabilities of success and failure in analyses when costs and revenues occur at different points in time. If we use appropriate time value of money present worth factors to convert costs and profits at different points in time to lump sum values at time zero or some other chosen time, the expected value analysis approach can be applied to determine if this type of investment would be suitable over the long run for many repeated investments of the same type. With expected NPV and PVR we are, of course, looking for alternatives with a positive expected value. With expected ROR analysis we calculate the expected ROR value, "i", that will make the expected NPV equation equal to zero. An acceptable expected ROR must be greater than the minimum ROR.

EXAMPLE 6-6 Expected Value Applied to ROR, NPV and PVR Analysis

A research and development project is being considered. The project is expected to have an initial investment cost of $90,000 and a probability of 0.4 that annual profits of $50,000 will be realized during the 5 year life of the project with a probability of 0.6 of failing. Salvage value is expected to be zero for success or failure. Assume the minimum discount rate is 10% on a risk-free basis.

Should the project be done? Compare expected value, expected net present value, expected rate of return and expected present value ratio analysis with corresponding non-risk adjusted evaluation results.

Solution, Values in Dollars:

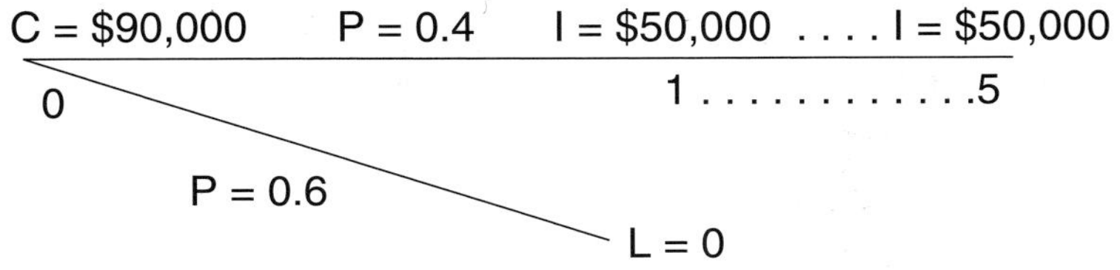

A) Expected Value and Chance Factor Approach

$$EV = 0.4(50{,}000\overset{3.7908}{(P/A_{10\%,5})} - 90{,}000) - .6(90{,}000) = -\$14{,}184$$

The negative expected value indicates reject investing in the project.

The expected value approach is most useful when statistically more complex models are utilized. In many of these cases, the various outcomes that are possible in a model are defined, and an associated chance factor is derived for each branch. In this example two outcomes exist which can be labeled "success" and "failure." By calculating the NPV for each outcome separately, the chance factors (in this model just the probability of success and failure) can be applied to the appropriate outcomes to determine the identical expected value (EV) as shown:

Expected Value Per Outcome = (NPV of Outcome)(Chance Factor)

Summing all of the project's expected values per outcome gives the overall project expected value.

EV Success	$= \{50{,}000\overset{3.7908}{(P/A_{10\%,5})} - 90{,}000\}(0.4)$	= 39,816
EV Failure	$= (-90{,}000)(0.6)$	= −54,000
Project Expected Value		= −14,184

The same calculation was introduced in the expected value solution to this problem.

B) Expected Net Present Value

This analysis is identical to the (A) analysis, except we generally use Equation 6-2a to determine Expected NPV. This is just a rearranged form of the Expected Value equation from part "A".

$$\text{ENPV} = 0.4(50{,}000)\overset{3.7908}{(P/A_{10\%,5})} - 1.0(90{,}000) = -\$14{,}184$$

Since the ENPV is negative, we should not invest in the project from an economic viewpoint. Note the expected value analysis in part (A) accounting for the time value of money at 10% per year gave a result identical with the EV result from Case A.

For these statistically simplistic models, another approach for calculating the ENPV is to first, risk adjust the cash flows, and then, calculate ENPV using the same present worth equation format previously developed. This approach is helpful in making expected value calculations on a hand calculator but again, it should be emphasized that the resulting cash flow stream does not represent the expected cash flows for any single investment. Instead, the calculated values reflect the average cash flows that might be expected after many repeated investments of this type with success occurring 40% of the time and failure occurring 60% of the time.

	0	1 5
Cash Flows	–\$90,000(1.0)	50,000(0.4) . . . . 50,000(0.4)
Risk Adjusted Cash Flows	–\$90,000	20,000. 20,000

$$\text{ENPV} = -90{,}000 + 20{,}000\overset{3.7908}{(P/A_{10\%,5})} = -14{,}184$$

This approach can be more difficult to apply to more complex statistical models than summing the expected values for all outcomes.

If you look at non-risk adjusted NPV (risk free NPV) which implicitly assumes 100% probability of success, the project economics look very acceptable.

$$\text{Risk Free NPV} = (50{,}000)\overset{3.798}{(P/A_{10\%,5})} - (90{,}000) = +\$99{,}540 > 0$$

Obviously adjusting for risk of failure or not adjusting for risk of failure has a very significant impact on economic results and conclusions.

C) Expected Rate of Return

Expected ROR is the "i" value that makes Expected NPV equal 0.

Expected Present Worth Income @ "i" – Present Worth Cost @ "i" = 0

$50{,}000(P/A_{i,5})(.4) - 90{,}000 = 0$

by trial and error, "i" = Expected ROR = 3.6% < i^* = 10% so reject

Non-risk adjusted or risk free rate of return analysis gives a different conclusion:

$50{,}000(P/A_{i,5}) - 90{,}000 = 0$

by trial and error, "i" = ROR = 47.6% > i^* = 10% so accept

This result is much greater than the 10% minimum ROR indicating very acceptable economics. As a variation of expected ROR analysis, some people account for risk by increasing the minimum ROR by what they consider to be an appropriate amount. The difficulty with this approach is that there is no consistent, rational way to adjust the minimum ROR appropriately to account for risk in different projects. For this example, the risk free ROR is about 47.6% (based on probability of success of 1.0 instead of 0.4) compared to the expected ROR of 3.6%. Expected ROR of 3.6% compared to risk free minimum ROR of 10% indicates the project is economically unsatisfactory. To get the same conclusions based on comparison of risk free ROR and risk adjusted minimum ROR results requires increasing the minimum ROR to about 132% (where 10%/3.6% = X/47.6%, therefore X = 132%). A majority of people who attempt to compensate for risk by adjusting the minimum ROR end up significantly under-compensating for risk. For this example many people will propose increasing the minimum ROR inversely proportional to probability of success (1/0.4) from 10% to 25% when as previously discussed the increase should be from 10% to about 130%. However, there is no way to know this without making an expected ROR type of analysis. Expected value analysis using ROR, NPV or PVR is the preferred approach to incorporate risk into economic analysis calculations.

D) Expected Present Value Ratio Analysis

EPVR = ENPV / Expected PW Cost = –14,184/90,000 = –0.16

The negative expected PVR indicates the project economics are unsatisfactory for the project parameters built into this analysis.

Risk Free PVR = +99,540/90,000 = +1.11

Consistent with the other criteria, the risk free PVR indicates very acceptable economics which is the opposite conclusion reached with expected PVR.

Expected value analysis in general involves constructing a diagram showing investment costs and all subsequent chance events and dollar values that are anticipated. Standard symbolism uses circles to designate chance nodes from which different degrees of success and failure may be shown to occur. The sum of the probabilities of occurrence on the different branches emanating from a chance node must add up to 1.0. *These "expected value diagrams" are sometimes called "decision tree diagrams"* because decision options concerning whether to proceed in one or more different ways or to terminate the project always exist prior to each chance node where different degrees of success or failure may occur. These diagrams often have multiple branches and look very much like a drawing of a tree, which has led to the name "decision tree analysis" being used in industry practice to refer to this type of analysis. In typical decision tree analyses, at different stages of projects, probabilities of success and failure change. As you progress from the research or exploration stage of a project to development and production, risk of failure changes significantly. This is illustrated in the following two examples.

EXAMPLE 6-7 Expected Value Analysis of a Petroleum Project

Use Expected NPV analysis for a minimum ROR of 20% to evaluate the economic potential of buying and drilling an oil lease with the following estimated costs, revenues and success probabilities. The lease would cost $100,000 at time 0 and it is considered 100% certain that a well would be drilled to the point of completion one year later for a cost of $500,000. There is a 60% probability that well logs will look good enough to complete the well at year 1 for a \$400,000 completion cost. If the well logs are unsatisfactory an abandonment cost of \$40,000 will be incurred at year 1. If the well is completed it is estimated there will be a 50% probability of generating production that will give \$450,000 per year net income for years 2 through 10 and a 35% probability of generating \$300,000 per year net income for years 2 through 10, with a 15% probability of the well completion being unsuccessful, due to water or unforeseen completion difficulties, giving a year 2 salvage value of \$250,000 for producing equipment.

Solution, in Thousands of Dollars:

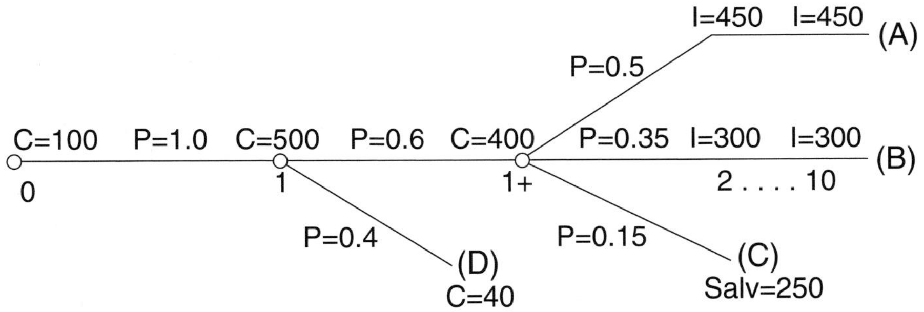

Times 1 and 1+ are effectively the same point in time, the end of year 1. Normally drilling and completion time are separated by weeks or months which puts them at the same point in time with annual periods. Times 1 and 1+ are separated on the diagram to make room for the probabilities of occurrence associated with different events.

Expected Value

Determine the possible different outcomes and the subsequent NPV for each. Apply the probability of each outcome to the calculated NPV's giving ENPV per outcome. Summing each gives the project's overall ENPV.

There are four (4) possible outcomes:

A) Successful Development leading to incomes of \$450 per year.
B) Successful Development leading to incomes of \$300 per year.
C) Failure with a salvage of \$250 at the end of year two.
D) Failure with an abandonment cost of \$40 at year one.

For Case A, the chance factor is; (0.6)(0.5)
For Case B, the chance factor is; (0.6)(0.35)
For Case C, the chance factor is; (0.6)(0.15)

A)	$[-100 - 900(P/F_{20,1}) + 450(P/A_{20,9})(P/F_{20,1})]\,(0.30)$	$= +198.48$
B)	$[-100 - 900(P/F_{20,1}) + 300(P/A_{20,9})(P/F_{20,1})]\,(0.21)$	$= +33.13$
C)	$[-100 - 900(P/F_{20,1}) + 250(P/F_{20,2})]\,(0.09)$	$= -60.87$
D)	$[-100 - 540(P/F_{20,1})]\,(0.4)$	$= -219.99$
	Project Expected Net Present Value (ENPV)	$= -49.26$

Expected Net Present Value (ENPV) at 20%

$$\{[450\overset{4.031}{(P/A_{20,9})}(.5) + 300\overset{4.031}{(P/A_{20,9})}(.35) + 250\overset{.8333}{(P/F_{20,1})}(.15) - 400](.6)$$

$$- 40(.4) - 500\}\overset{.8333}{(P/F_{20,1})} - 100 = -49.26$$

This result is only slightly less than zero compared to the total project costs of $1 million, therefore, slightly unsatisfactory or breakeven economics are indicated.

Alternate Form of (ENPV) Equation

$$450\overset{4.031}{(P/A_{20,9})}(.5)\overset{.8333}{(P/F_{20,1})}(.6) + 300\overset{4.031}{(P/A_{20,9})}(.35)\overset{.8333}{(P/F_{20,1})}(.6)$$

$$+250\overset{.6944}{(P/F_{20,2})}(.15)(.6) - 400\overset{.8333}{(P/F_{20,1})}(.6) - 40\overset{.8333}{(P/F_{20,1})}(.4)$$

$$-500\overset{.8333}{(P/F_{20,1})}(1.0) - 100 = -49.26$$

Risk Adjusting the Cash Flows

		−500(1.0)	450(0.6)(0.5)	450(0.6)(0.5)
		−400(0.6)	300(0.6)(0.35)	300(0.6)(0.35)
CF(Prob.)	−100(1.0)	−40(0.4)	250(0.6)(0.15)	—
Year	0	1	2	3–10
Risk Adj CF	−100	−756	220.5	198

$$\text{ENPV} = -100 - 756(P/F_{20,1}) + 220.5(P/F_{20,2})$$
$$+ 198(P/A_{20,8})(P/F_{20,2})$$

$$\text{ENPV} = -49.26$$

EXAMPLE 6-8 Expected Value Economics of a New Process

Use Expected NPV and PVR analysis for a minimum rate of return of 20.0% to evaluate the economic potential of buying and developing the rights to a new process with the following estimated costs, revenues and success probabilities. The process rights would cost \$100,000 at time zero, and, it is considered 100% certain that experimental development pilot plant work will be done one year later for a cost of \$500,000. There is a 60.0% probability that the experimental development results will look good enough to take the project to production for a \$400,000 capital cost at year one. (This capital cost is estimated to be incurred in the first six months of year one which is closer to year one than year 2.) If the experimental development results are unsatisfactory, a pilot plant abandonment cost of \$40,000 will be incurred at year one. If the project is taken to production, it is estimated there will be a 50.0% probability of generating production that will give \$450,000 per year net positive cash flow for years two through ten, a 35.0% probability of generating \$300,000 per year net positive cash flow for years two through ten with a 15.0% probability of the project development being unsuccessful due to unforeseen technical difficulties giving a year two salvage value of \$250,000 for production equipment.

Solution, in Thousands of Dollars:

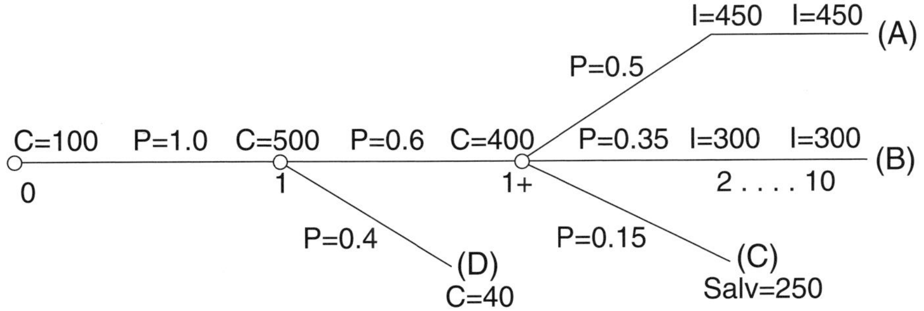

Expected Value

Determine the possible different outcomes and the subsequent NPV for each. Apply the probability of each outcome to the calculated NPV's giving ENPV per outcome. Summing each gives the project's overall ENPV.

There are four (4) possible outcomes:

A) Successful Development leading to incomes of $450 per year.
B) Successful Development leading to incomes of $300 per year.
C) Failure with a salvage of $250 at the end of year two.
D) Failure with an abandonment cost of $40 at year one.

For Case A, the chance factor is; (0.6)(0.5)

$$A)\ [-100 - 900(P/F_{20,1}) + 450(P/A_{20,9})(P/F_{20,1})]\ (0.30) = +198.48$$
$$B)\ [-100 - 900(P/F_{20,1}) + 300(P/A_{20,9})(P/F_{20,1})]\ (0.21) = +33.13$$
$$C)\ [-100 - 900(P/F_{20,1}) + 250(P/F_{20,2})]\ (0.09) = -60.87$$
$$D)\ [-100 - 540(P/F_{20,1})]\ (0.4) = -219.99$$

Project Expected Net Present Value (ENPV) = −49.26

Risk Adjusting the Cash Flows

		−500(1.0)	450(0.6)(0.5)	450(0.6)(0.5)
		−400(0.6)	300(0.6)(0.35)	300(0.6)(0.35)
CF(Prob.)	−100(1.0)	−40(0.4)	250(0.6)(0.15)	—
Year	0	1	2	3–10
Risk Adj CF	−100	−756	220.5	198

$$ENPV = -100 - 756(P/F_{20,1}) + 220.5(P/F_{20,2}) + 198(P/A_{20,8})(P/F_{20,2})$$

$$ENPV = -49.26$$

Expected Net Present Value (ENPV) at 20%

$$\{[450\overset{4.031}{(P/A_{20,9})}(.5) + 300\overset{4.031}{(P/A_{20,9})}(.35) + 250\overset{.8333}{(P/F_{20,1})}(.15) - 400](.6)$$

$$- 40(.4) - 500\}\overset{.8333}{(P/F_{20,1})} - 100 = -49.26$$

This result is only slightly less than zero compared to the total project costs of $1 million, therefore, slightly unsatisfactory or break-even economics are indicated.

Expected Present Value Ratio (EPVR)

$$EPVR = -49.26 \,/\, 100+[500 + 400(.6) + 40(.4)](P/F_{20,1}) = -0.07$$

The small negative EPVR result indicates the same slightly unsatisfactory or break-even economics shown earlier with ENPV analysis.

EXAMPLE 6-9 Expected NPV Analysis

Calculate the Expected NPV of a project which will cost $270,000 at time zero. This investment has a 60.0% probability of generating downstream development and equipment costs at the end of year one estimated to total $500,000. If the second expenditure at the end of year one is successful, there is a 90.0% probability it would lead to the generation of net cash flows totaling $400,000 per year at the end of each of years two through ten. Failure from the time zero investment would result in no additional cost or benefit to the investor. However, should the project fail after the year one cost, a net cost of $250,000 would be realized at the end of year two from dismantlement costs and salvage of equipment. Should this project be accepted? Use a minimum rate of return of 12.0%.

Solution: All Values in Thousands.

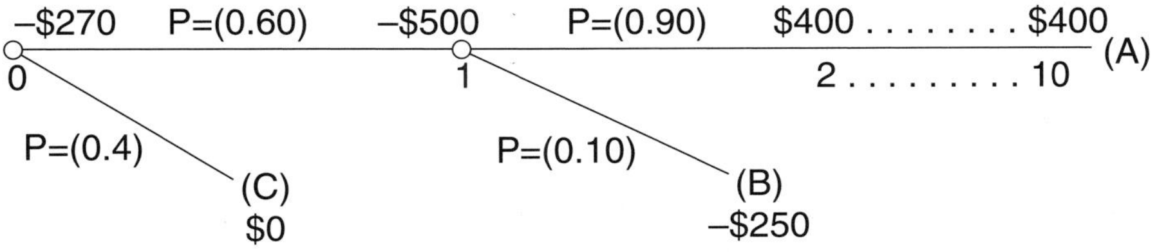

Expected Value

There are three (3) possible outcomes in this solution:

A) Successful Development, Chance Factor,
   P = (0.6)(0.9) = (0.54)

B) Failure at Year 2, Chance Factor, P = (0.6)(0.1) = (0.06)

C) Failure at Time Zero, Chance Factor, P = (0.40)

EV_A) $[-270 - 500(P/F_{12,1}) + 400(P/A_{12,9})(P/F_{12,1})]\ (0.54) = +640.71$

EV_B) $[-270 - 500(P/F_{12,1}) - 250(P/F_{12,2})]\ (0.06) = -54.94$

EV_C) $[-270]\ (0.40) = -108.00$

Project Expected Net Present Value (ENPV) = +477.77

Risk Adjusted Cash Flows

Year	0	1	2	3-10
CF(Prob.)	–270(1.0)	–500(0.6)	400(0.6)(0.9) –250(0.6)(0.1)	400(0.6)(0.9)
Risk Adj CF	–270	–300	201	216

$$ENPV = -270 - 300(P/F_{12,1}) + 201(P/F_{12,2}) + 216(P/A_{12,8})(P/F_{12,2})$$
$$= +477.77 > 0, \text{ accept}$$

Expected Net Present Value

$$\textbf{ENPV @ 12.0\%} = 400\overset{5.32825}{(P/A_{12,9})}(0.9)\overset{0.89286}{(P/F_{12,1})}(0.6)$$
$$- 250\overset{0.79719}{(P/F_{12,2})}(0.1)(0.6) - 500\overset{0.89286}{(P/F_{12,1})}(0.6)$$
$$- 270 = +477.77 > 0, \text{ ok}$$

Example 6-9A

Utilizing the data from Example 6-9, what additional cost could be incurred at time zero for either research or geological/geophysical data and give the investor the same risk adjusted NPV of $477.77? Assume the additional time zero cost will increase the probability of success in year 1 from 0.6 to 0.8. Therefore, the probability of failure in the same period will be reduced from 0.4 to 0.2.

Solution:

Let X equal the additional cost to be incurred at time zero.

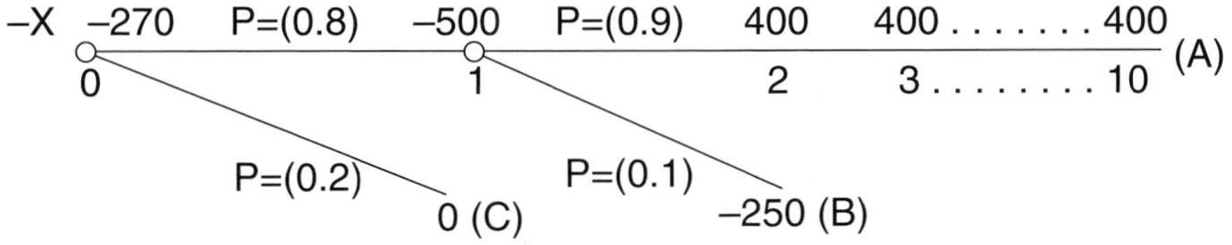

ENPV Approach:

Economically equivalent, mutually exclusive alternatives will always have equal net present values. Therefore, this solution looks at equating the current project NPV with the NPV of the revised probabilities based on the new investment, X at time zero as follows:

$$477.77 = [400(P/A_{12\%,9})(0.9) - 500](P/F_{12\%,1})(0.8) - 250(P/F_{12\%,2})(0.1)(0.8) - 270 - X$$

$$477.77 = [400(5.32825)(0.9) - 500](0.89286)(0.8) - 250(0.79719)(0.1)(0.8) - 270 - X$$

$$477.77 = 1012.98 - 15.94 - 270 - X$$

$$X = 249.27$$

Risk Adjusted Cash Flow Approach, ENPV:

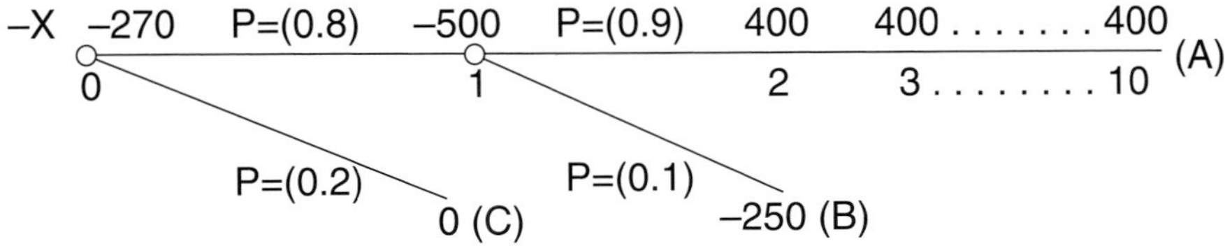

Risk Adjusted Cash Flow Calculations:

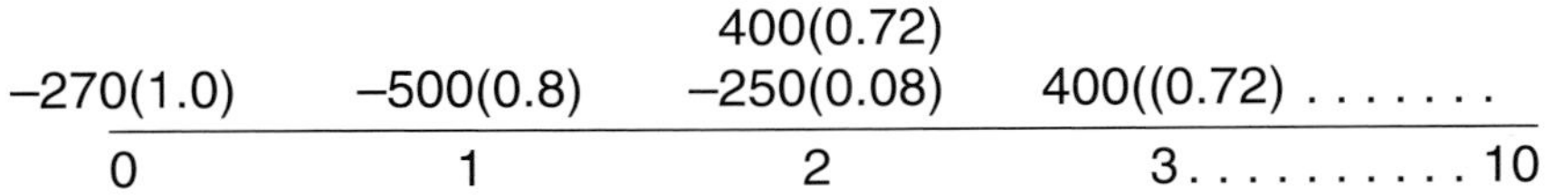

Risk Adjusted Cash Flows:

–270	–400	268	288 288
0	1	2	3. 10

$$ENPV = -270 - 400\overset{0.89286}{(P/F_{12\%,1})} + 268\overset{0.79719}{(P/F_{12\%,2})}$$

$$+ 288\overset{4.9676}{(P/A_{12\%,8})}\overset{0.79719}{(P/F_{12\%,2})}$$

$$ENPV = 727.02$$

The difference between the New ENPV of 727.02 and the Original ENPV of 477.77 is 249.25 which represents the additional cost that could be incurred at time zero and allow the investor to obtain the desired ENPV of 477.77.

It was emphasized earlier in this section that expected value represents the average gain or loss per investment that an investor would realize over many repeated investments of the type being analyzed. Whether we work with expected value, expected NPV, expected PVR or expected ROR, the average meaning of results is similar. A common misconception that some people have about expected value analysis is that it often is not valid because investors seldom repeat the same type investments over and over. These people have missed the basic expected value analysis premise that even though each specific investment decision relates to a uniquely different investment, if we consistently select investment alternatives having positive expected value, ENPV or EPVR, (or having expected ROR greater than the minimum ROR), over the long run our average rate of return on invested capital will be greater than the minimum ROR. Similar to material presented earlier in Chapter 4 for risk free analysis, to rank non-mutually exclusive alternatives using risk adjusted results, you must use either expected PVR or expected Growth ROR results. To evaluate mutually exclusive alternatives with risk adjusted results based on any valid analysis technique, incremental analysis is the key to correct economic decision making. These rules hold true even though each investment decision relates to a different investment prospect with different probabilities of success and failure at different stages of each project.

6.7 Probability of Survival (Financial Risk Analysis)

Probability of survival refers to the probability that you will not go bankrupt with a given amount of capital to invest in projects with estimated probabilities of success. This concept is a financial risk analysis consideration rather than specifically relating to economic risk analysis. A project with a large positive expected value and a small probability of success may economically look better than all other investment opportunities under consideration. However, if failure of the project would lead to bankruptcy, the project most likely will be considered financially unacceptable due to the financial risks. The italicized statement preceding Example 6-6 says "a positive expected value is a necessary but not a sufficient condition for a satisfactory investment." This means that a positive expected value indicates an economically satisfactory investment but not necessarily a financially satisfactory investment. Small investors in the oil and gas drilling business usually attempt to reduce their financial risk of total failure (bankruptcy) by taking a small interest in a large number of projects rather than large interests in a few projects. This diversified investment portfolio approach gives the probability of success a better chance to be realized over time as the following example illustrates.

EXAMPLE 6-10 Probability of Survival Applied to Exploration

Consider an exploration manager who is faced with the task of determining whether to invest $1,000,000 of a small company's money in 10 independent exploration projects which will each cost $100,000 with a 10% probability of achieving a $5,000,000 profit above cost. If the company will go bankrupt if not successful on at least 1 exploration project (or if the exploration manager will lose his job), discuss their probability of survival.

Solution:

Expected Value = 5,000,000(.10) – 100,000(.9) = +$410,000

The positive expected value is economically satisfactory and is a necessary but not a sufficient condition for this investment to be satisfactory. The question to be answered now is what is the probability of survival, or stated another way, what is the probability of getting at least 1 success out of 10 tries. This relates to the financial acceptability of the project.

Probability of at Least One Success = 1 – Probability of Zero Successes

Probability of Zero Successes = $(.9)^{10}$ = .3485

Therefore, probability of survival = 1-.3485 = .6515 or 65.15% which is certainly considerably less than a sure thing (100% probability of success). Note that ten projects each having a 10% chance of success do not give a 100% probability of overall success.

Companies often get together in joint ventures on large exploration projects to have more capital available so that enough exploration projects can be made to make the probability of survival higher than it would be if they operated alone. If in Example 6-10 a sum of $2,000,000 is available to invest in 20 projects, the probability of survival increases to 1-.1214 = .8786 and if $3,000,000 is available the probability of survival is .9577. Joint ventures can increase survival probabilities to very tolerable levels when exploration work is being done in areas where enough geological and geophysical work has been done to predict reasonable probabilities of success on any given try.

The same type of reasoning can be applied to research and development projects in all types of industries, but it is very difficult to come up with truly meaningful probabilities of success. However, if these probabilities are not estimated explicitly, managers will base a decision implicitly on "gut feel" for data, and these authors feel it is better to explicitly state the bases upon which decisions are made.

The statistical basis of the probability of survival calculations just presented is the binomial distribution for mutually exclusive alternatives. The general binomial distribution equation is:

Probability of Exactly "r" successes from "n" tries = $C_r^n P^r(1-P)^{n-r}$

where C_r^n = Combination of "n" things taken "r" at a time.

$$= \frac{n!}{r!(n-r)!} = \frac{\text{n factorial}}{\text{r factorial times (n-r) factorial}}$$

$n! = n(n-1)(n-2) - - - - (3)(2)(1)$

$0! = 1$ by definition

P = Probability of success on a given try.

1–P = Probability of failure on a given try.

Note that for Example 6-10, the probability of zero success from 10 tries is:

$$C^{10}_{0}(.1)^{0}(.9)^{10} = \frac{10!}{0!10!}(1)(.9)^{10} = (.9)^{10} = 0.3485$$

6.8 Risk Due to Natural Disaster

Another type of risk to be considered is that due to natural disaster. The following example illustrates the evaluation of data using probabilistic expected value concepts for this type of problem.

EXAMPLE 6-11 Optimum Investment to Minimize Flood Damage Costs

A manufacturing company plans to build a plant on low land near a river that floods occasionally. It is considered necessary to build a levee around its facilities to reduce potential flood damage. Four different sizes of levees that give different levels of protection are being considered and the plant manager wants to know which size levee will minimize total expected annual cost to the company from the sum of (1) amortization of the levee cost over 20 years for a before tax "i^*" of 15%: plus (2) maintenance costs, plus (3) expected damage to the plant and levee if the levee is not high enough or strong enough to hold back flood water. Analyze the following data to determine the optimum levee size.

Levee Size	Levee Cost	Probability of a Flood Exceeding Levee Size During Year	Expected Damage if Flood Exceeds Levee Size	Annual Maintenance
1	$120,000	.20	$ 80,000	$4,000
2	140,000	.10	110,000	5,000
3	160,000	.05	125,000	6,000
4	200,000	.025	150,000	7,000

Solution:

Levee Size	Annual Levee Cost +	Expected Damage Per Year +	Total Annual Maint. =	Expected Annual Cost
	0.1598			
1	$120{,}000(A/P_{15,20}) = 19{,}180$	16,000	4,000	$39,180
2	140,000(0.1598) = 22,370	11,000	5,000	38,370
3	160,000(0.1598) = 25,570	6,250	6,000	37,820
4	200,000(0.1598) = 31,960	3,750	7,000	42,710

Levee Size number 3 is the optimum selection to minimize expected equivalent annual cost.

6.9 Option Pricing Theory Related to ENPV

Patent rights to new technology, land and mineral rights to mineral properties often sell at prices significantly higher than the NPV of the said property. Those calculations are based on the most expected production rates, product prices and operating costs over the project life. Some of the reason for the differences may be described as an option pricing effect. The option pricing effect may be related to capturing potential incremental value that may occur if actual production rates or product prices turn out to be higher than the most expected production rates and prices (or the actual operating costs turn out to be lower than the most expected values). But option pricing may also relate to the decision to delay production to try and capture a greater product price in the future, or realize greater reserves than what is known at the time of a sale or acquisition. The potential increase or decrease in the incremental value often is referred to as an option pricing effect because of its direct relationship to call options on assets.

Options are referred to as either puts or calls. A general review of each follows, but more precise definitions and examples are presented in Chapter 12 of this textbook. This section will not attempt to explain the details of option pricing, for that, reader may want to check out John C. Hull's book entitled, Options, Futures and Other Derivatives or Black-Scholes and Beyond by Neil A. Chriss.

Sticking to the basics, a call option gives the buyer the right to buy a specified amount of some asset (such as stock, land, or in commodities maybe ounces of gold, pounds of copper, barrels of oil, etc.) at a specified price (known as a strike price) for a specifiec period of time. The ability to execute an option is generally limited to a specified period referred to by the option expiration date. When a call option strike price is less than the current market price of the asset, the call is said to be "in-the-money." The difference between the market value of the asset and the option strike price is often referred to as "intrinsic value." When a call option strike price is greater than the current market value of an asset, the value of the option is said to be "out-of-the-money" since it has no intrinsic value. Therefore, the value is based solely on speculation of a future price movement. The overall value of any option is referred to as a premium and all premiums may contain two components known as intrinsic and speculative value.

Typically, investors are willing to pay a premium for out-of-the-money call options on common stock to own the right to buy the stock at the strike price and make a profit, if the stock price moves above the strike price. Based on either today's prices or the most expected future prices, a patent or mineral property may have much smaller NPV value compared to the value based on higher potential future prices and or lower future production costs. This potential additional value can be captured with either of two approaches. First, a mathematical formula called the Black Scholes equation usually is used to value common stock options. Modification of the Black-Scholes model can make it applicable to valuing patents and mineral rights. Most people consider this approach to be very mathematically sophisticated, and therefore, often difficult to explain and sell to management. The second approach to capturing the call option value of a patent or mineral right type of asset is to use expected net present value (ENPV) analysis. We have seen in previous examples that ENPV can measure both uncertainty concerning the probability of failure and uncertainty concerning the magnitude of a parameter and the timing when that parameter might be incurred.

Advocates of the option pricing analysis (real-options analysis) technique often state several perceived disadvantages associated with discounted cash flow (DCF) valuation of investments using NPV. Four of these commonly perceived disadvantages follow:

1. DCF analysis tends to under value investments because use of average production and product prices and costs may not capture value associated with possible higher future production, prices and productivity or lower future costs.

2. Use of today's expectation of investment future cash flow is not indicative of the true value of an investment and prohibits accounting for the embedded investment opportunities in long-lived assets.

3. Traditional DCF analysis fixes the knowledge base today for determining future cash flow over the life of a project, which prohibits accounting for large investments occurring in stages.

4. DCF analysis constrains investment timing by assuming that investments cannot be deferred, so investment decisions must be based on today's information.

The authors of this text disagree with these perceived DCF analysis disadvantages and feel they represent misperceptions of the assumptions and calculations upon which proper DCF analysis should be based. If you based DCF analysis on the assumptions given in the four DCF disadvantage statements, then DCF analysis would be improper and disadvantageous. Following are our rebuttals to the perceived disadvantages:

1. Economic analyses of all types require projecting the future. Assuming today's production rates, prices and costs will stay the same over a project life typically is a very weak economic analysis assumption. You must project the actual future production rates, product prices, and costs by projecting escalation rates for the parameters realized over the project life. If different future cash flow scenarios are felt to be possible, probabilities of occurrence must be projected for the different scenarios so that the cumulative probabilities equal 1.0

2. Investors do not need to use today's dollars and probably should not use today's dollars as the basis for most DCF analyses. New project and development or expansion options can be built into any year of an evaluation. There is no reason to feel that DCF analysis precludes you from accounting for possible future changes in production, product prices, costs, productivity and other evaluation parameters. You must project the future possibilities at the time you do the analysis for either DCF analysis or option pricing analysis. And the future assumptions that you make will have a very significant impact on your analysis results with either DCF analysis or the option pricing methodology.

3. DCF analysis does not have to assume that project development will start today. With ENPV analysis you can build development and expansion into analyses over unlimited years, taking advantage of new technology and product pricing information available at different stages.
4. Investments can be deferred to future times with DCF analysis the same as with options-pricing analysis. Evaluation results with any method of analysis reflect the input data and the assumptions applied to the input data such as timing, escalation rates and tax effects in after-tax analyses. ENPV analysis can be done today for a project expected to be developed several years in the future. In Example 6-12, the development occurs today at time zero, but development could easily be deferred several years with similar analysis procedures.

Example 6-12 ENPV Analysis to Capture Call Option Value

Consider that you are interested in acquiring the rights to develop a project. To minimize calculations needed, assume the project has a four-year life with expected production, prices per unit, operating costs per unit and capital costs shown in the following table. Calculate the project NPV for minimum discount rates of 10% and 20%.

All values in 000's except selling price
Assuming a 100% Probability of Occurrence, Most Expected!

Year	0	1	2	3	4
Production, Units		100	100	100	100
Selling Price, $/Unit		20	22	24	26
Gross Revenue, $		2000	2200	2400	2600
Operating Costs, $		–1200	–1400	–1600	–1800
Capital Costs, $	–2400				
BTCF	–2400	800	800	800	800

NPV @ 10% = +136
NPV @ 20% = –329

Based on these valuations, an investor satisfied with a 10% rate of return on invested dollars could pay $136 at time zero to acquire the project rights and an investor desiring a 20% rate of return on invested dollars would need to be paid $329 at year zero to take the project rights and just get a 20% ROR.

Next, instead of using average or most expected values, assume there is a 60% probability of the scenario just described actually occurring. Further, there is a 10% probability of a worse case scenario and a 30% probability of a better scenario as summarized below:

Assuming a 60% Probability of Most Expected Values

Year	0	1	2	3	4
Production, Units		100	100	100	100
Selling Price, $/Unit		20	22	24	26
Gross Revenue, $		2000	2200	2400	2600
Operating Costs, $		–1200	–1400	–1600	–1800
Capital Costs, $	–2400				
BTCF	–2400	800	800	800	800

NPV @ 10% = +136
NPV @ 20% = –329

Assuming a 10% Probability of Worst Case Occurrence

Year	0	1	2	3	4
Production, Units		100	90	90	90
Selling Price, $/Unit		20	20	20	20
Gross Revenue, $		2000	1800	1800	1800
Operating Costs, $		–1200	–1500	–1800	–2100
Capital Costs, $	–2400				
BTCF	–2400	800	300	0	–300

NPV @ 10% = –1730
NPV @ 20% = –1770

Assuming a 30% Probability of Best Case Occurrence

Year	0	1	2	3	4
Production, Units		100	130	160	190
Selling Price, $/Unit		22	25	30	35
Gross Revenue, $		2200	3250	4800	6650
Operating Costs, $		–1200	–1300	–1400	–1500
Capital Costs, $	–2300				
BTCF	–2300	1000	1950	3400	5150

NPV @ 10% = +6293
NPV @ 20% = +4339

Combining these results with the probability of occurrence yields the project ENPV as follows:

Expected Value at 10%		
Expected	136(0.6) =	82
Worst	−1730(0.1) =	−173
Best	6293(0.3) =	1888
Expected Value	=	1797

Expected Value @ 20%		
Expected	−329(0.6) =	−197
Worst	−1770(0.1) =	−177
Best	4339(0.3) =	1302
Expected Value	=	928

The ENPV at 10% indicates an investor could pay thirteen times as much ($1797 vs $136), for the project as was determined by the initial expected value analysis based on average expected values. At a 20% discount rate, the ENPV is $928 versus –$329 with the average or most expected value analysis. These differences reflect the idea in "option pricing effects" which were discussed earlier. The ENPV captures this concept, but the average or most expected value analysis alone did not.

The 100% probability of occurrence NPV results based on average or most expected values may be best for making a "develop" versus "do nothing" decision. However, the ENPV results capture the "option pricing value" by accounting for the 30% probability of realizing higher production and prices and lower costs. An investor may not want to base a develop decision based on 30% probability of occurrence data, but the same investor may be willing to pay a higher price to acquire and hold the project to realize the opportunity to profit from the best case scenario if it occurs.

6.10 Summary

Sensitivity analyses are a means of identifying those critical variables that if changed, could considerably impact the profitability measure such as rate of return or net present value. Three types of sensitivity were addressed including:

1. Single Variable
2. Multi-Variable or Best Case – Worst Case
3. Probabilistic Sensitivity (Monte Carlo)

Two software models that address the probabilistic sensitivity (Monte Carlo) are known as @Risk and Crystal Ball. These template programs interact with most spreadsheets providing users with a low cost methodology to these approaches.

Risk analyses identify the likelihood of project failure and the subsequent cost to the investor. In this text the subject of project risk was addressed utilizing the decision theory approach based on expected value, (EV) which is defined as:

EV = Expected Profit – Expected Cost

Examples then illustrated several approaches that could be used with equal validity for the level of complexity presented in the textbook examples and problems. These approaches included:

1. Chance Factor, (Expected Value)
2. Expected NPV, (Incorporated the probabilities of success and failure directly into present worth equation)
3. Risk Adjusted Cash Flows, (By applying probabilities of occurrence directly to the expected values each compounding period, one risk adjusted cash flow results which can then be manipulated in a manner consistent with examples and problems prior to Chapter 6.

Of these methods, the Chance Factor, Expected Value methodology offers the broadest range of acceptability for the more statistically complex models.

An alternative method sometimes used to measure financial or political risk involves adjusting the discount rate, i* for greater chances of failure. While common in industry practice, it is not a preferred approach. This is due to the difficulties that arise when comparing projects that might be competing for limited capital. Discussion in the expected rate of return solution to Example 6-6 provided further amplification on this topic.

For more information on these and related topics, see; "Decision Analysis for Petroleum Exploration," by Paul D. Newendorp, or, "Mineral Exploration Decisions," by Deverle P. Harris.

PROBLEMS

Excel solutions at Stermole.com

6-1 A roulette wheel has 38 different stopping slots numbered from 1 to 36 plus 0 and 00. Eighteen numbers are red, 18 are black. with 0 and 00 green. Calculate the expected value for the following situations where the term "payoff" means in addition to return of the bet or "profit above all costs."

A) The payoff is $35 for a $1 bet on any number.

B) The payoff is $17 for a $1 bet on any line between two numbers (meaning the bettor wins if either number hits).

C) The payoff is $8 for a $1 bet on any corner between four numbers.

D) The payoff is $1 for a $1 bet on red or black or odd or even.

6-2 Due to uncertainty in development costs, the cost of a new manufacturing process is considered to have the following possibilities:

Cost ($)	Probability of Occurrence
5,000	0.10
8,000	0.30
10,000	0.40
14,000	0.20

What is the expected cost of the new process?

6-3 An electronics manufacturer is considering entering into a research and development venture. The research and development investment requires $100,000 at time 0 and, if successful, generates $80,000 in profit each year for 5 years. Salvage value is estimated to be zero. Experience suggests that such projects have a 40% probability of success. If the before-tax minimum rate of return is 20%, should the manufacturer undertake the project? Use expected NPV and expected ROR analysis.

6-4 If you bet $5 on the outcome of 3 football games, you can win $25 total (not above the bet cost) if you correctly pick all 3 winners. If the odds are considered even in each game or if point spreads are specified that are considered to make each game an even odds bet, what is the expected value of your bet if you neglect tie game situations?

6-5 An initial investment of $50,000 is projected to generate cash flows over a three year project life as follows:

Year	Cash Flow	Probability of Occurrence
1	$25,000	.40
	18,000	.60
2	30,000	.50
	20,000	.50
3	35,000	.70
	25,000	.30

Evaluate the expected NPV of this investment for a minimum rate of return of 15%.

6-6 A research and development manager associates a probability of success of 60% (0.6) with a research investment at time zero being successful and generating the need for an additional $300,000 development investment at the end of year one which is estimated to have a probability of 90% (0.9) of successfully generating profits of $200,000 per year for year two through 10, assuming a washout of escalation of operating costs and sales revenue. If failure occurs after the time zero research investment a reclamation cost of $100,000 will be realized at the end of year one. If failure occurs after the year one investment, the salvage value will be $250,000 at the end of year two for equipment salvage. To achieve a before-tax expected ROR of 25% in this investment, use expected NPV analysis to determine how much money can be spent on research at time zero assuming the year 10 salvage value is zero? What is the risk free project NPV valuation?

6-7 Calculate the expected net present value of a project which will cost $70,000 at time zero, considering there is a 50% chance that the investment at time zero will be successful, which will require an additional investment of $120,000 at year one. There is a 70% chance of success of the year one investment yielding profits over a six year period (years 2 to 7) equal to $125,000 per year. Failure after incurring the time zero investment will result in a year 1 abandonment cost of $10,000. Should failure occur after the year 1 investment of $120,000, a net salvage value of $50,000 will be realized at the end of year 2. Should this project be considered from an economic viewpoint if the minimum rate of return is 20%? Compare your expected NPV result with risk-free NPV. If you could acquire additional geological or geophysical data that would improve the initial year 1 probability of success from 50% to 80%, without impacting the subsequent probabilities, how much could be spent in acquiring the data and still allow the investor to realize an Expected NPV of $2,000 for the same risk free minimum rate of return of 20%?

6-8 A project that would have a time zero cost of $170,000 is estimated to have a 40% probability of generating net income of $60,000 per year for each of years one through 10 with a zero salvage value, a 30% probability of generating net income of $50,000 per year for each of years one through 10 with a zero salvage value, a 20% probability of generating net incomes of $40,000 per year for each of years one through 10 with a zero salvage value and a 10% probability of failing and generating a $20,000 salvage value at year one. For a minimum rate of return of 20% calculate the project expected NPV. What is the project expected ROR?

6-9 Two years ago, a petroleum company acquired the mineral rights to a property for which an offer of $1 million cash has been received now at year 0. Development of the property is projected to generate escalated dollar cash flow in millions of dollars of –1.5 in time zero, and +1.0, +1.8, +1.2, +0.8 and +0.4 in years one through five respectively. If the minimum DCFROR is 20%, should the company keep and develop the property or sell if there is considered to be a 60% probability of development generating the year one through five positive cash flow and 40% probability of failure generating zero cash flow in years one through five?

6-10 Two alternatives are being considered for the development of an investment project. Alternative 'A' would start development now with estimated development and equipment costs of $10 million at time zero and $20 million at year one to generate net revenues of $6 million in year one and $12 million per year uniformly at years two through 10 with a zero salvage value. Alternative 'B' would start development two years from now for estimated development and equipment costs of $15 million at year two and $30 million at year three to generate net revenues of $9 million in year three and $18 million per year uniformly at years four through 12 with a zero salvage value. Use NPV Analysis for a minimum ROR of 20% to determine the economically better alternative and verify the NPV results with PVR Analysis assuming:

A) 100% probability of success is associated with all investments.

B) Alternative 'A' has a 60% probability of success associated with year 0 cost and 100% probability of success associated with the year 1 cost, with zero net salvage value to be realized if failure occurs at year 0. Alternative'B' has an 80% probability of success associated with the year 2 cost and a 100% probability of success associated with the year 3 cost, with a zero net salvage value to be realized if failure occurs at year 3.

6-11 An investor has paid $100,000 for a machine that is estimated to have a 70% probability of successfully producing 5000 product units per year for each of the next 3 years when the machine is estimated to be obsolete with a zero salvage value. The product price is the unknown to be calculated, so it is estimated to be $X per unit in year 1 escalated dollars and to increase 10% in year 2 and 6% in year 3. Total operating costs are estimated to be $8,000 in year 1 escalated dollars and to increase 15% in year 2 and 8% in year 3. The annual inflation rate is estimated to be 7%. What must be the year 1, 2 and 3 escalated dollar product selling price if the investor is to receive a 12% annually compounded constant dollar expected DCFROR on invested dollars? Consider zero cash flow to be realized the 30% of the time the project fails. This assumes that equipment dismantlement costs will exactly offset any salvage value benefits.

6-12 A plant operation is scheduled to be developed for a time zero capital cost of $400 million with year 1 through 10 revenues of $200 million per year less operating costs of $100 million per year with a zero salvage value. Assume a washout of escalation of operating costs and revenue each year. "Washout" means any operating cost escalation is offset by the same dollar escalation of revenue (not the same percent escalation) so profit remains uniform at the today's dollar value profit.

A) Evaluate the project ROR and analyze the sensitivity of the result to changing project life to 5 years or 15 years.

B) Evaluate the sensitivity of project ROR to increasing the time zero capital cost to $600 million and $800 million for the 10 year project life.

CHAPTER 6 AUXILIARY PROBLEMS

A6-1 Calculate the expected net present value of a project which will cost $100,000 at time zero, considering there is a 60% chance that the investment at time zero will be successful, which will require an additional investment of $200,000 at year one. There is a 90% chance of success of the year one investment yielding profits over a six year period (years 2 to 7) equal to $175,000 per year. Failure at time zero will result in an abandonment cost of $80,000 at year one and failure at year one will result in a salvage value of $150,000 at year two. Should this project be considered from an economic viewpoint if the minimum rate of return is 15%? Compare your expected NPV result with risk-free NPV.

A6-2 A project that would have a time zero cost of $400,000 is estimated to have a 30% probability of generating net income of $300,000 per year for each of years 1 through 10 with a zero salvage value, a 20% probability of generating net income of $200,000 per year for each of years 1 through 10 with a zero salvage value, a 20% probability of generating net incomes of $140,000 per year for each of year 1 through 10 with a zero salvage value, and a 30% probability of failing and generating a $100,000 abandonment cost at year 1. For a minimum rate of return of 20%, calculate the project expected NPV. What is the project expected ROR?

A6-3 Two years ago, a petroleum company acquired the mineral rights to a property for which an offer of $2 million cash has been received now at year 0. Development of the property is projected to generate escalated dollar cash flow in millions of dollars of –1.5 in time zero, and +2.0, +2.4, +1.6, +1.0, and +0.5 in years 1 through 5 respectively. If the minimum DCFROR is 20%, should the company keep and develop the property or sell if there is considered to be a 70% probability the time zero development cost will generate the positive cash flows in years 1 through 5, and a 30% probability of failure generating zero cash flow in years 1 through 5.

A6-4 An investor has paid \$200,000 for a machine that is estimated to have a 70% probability of successfully producing 2,000 product units per year for each of the next 3 years when the machine is estimated to be obsolete with a zero salvage value. The product price is the 'unknown' to be calculated, so it is estimated to be \$x per unit in year 1 escalated dollars. The year 1 price is forecast to increase 5% in year 2 and 8% in year 3. Total operating costs are estimated to be \$15,000 in year 1 escalated dollars with the year 1 value increasing 10% in year 2 and an additional 8% in year 3. The annual inflation rate is estimated to be 5% each year. What must be the year 1, 2 and 3 escalated dollar product selling price if the investor is to receive an annually compounded constant dollar expected DCFROR of 12% on invested dollars? Consider a zero cash flow will be realized the 30% of the time to the project fails. This assumes that equipment dismantlement costs will exactly offset any salvage value benefits.

CHAPTER 7

DEPRECIATION, DEPLETION, AMORTIZATION, AND AFTER-TAX CASH FLOW

7.1 Introduction

Every country raises revenue through some sort of tax. Prior to the passing of the 16th Amendment to the Constitution, the United States raised revenue through tariffs, war taxes, tobacco taxes, and spirit taxes among other similar methods. In 1913, Congress passed the 16th Amendment making the federal income tax permanent, thereby giving Congress legal authority to tax income from both individuals and corporations. The combination of all laws related to taxation is known as Title 26 and more commonly referred to as "The Code". Laws governing taxation that are passed by Congress are enforced by the Treasury Department, specifically the Internal Revenue Service (IRS), which has the task of interpreting what Congress writes into law. These interpretations are called Regulations, or "Regs".

The tax code is constantly evolving but there have been three major revisions throughout history with the first in 1939, the second in 1954, and the last in 1986. The 1986 revision of the code is organized into 11 main sections as follows:

Number	Section Name	Code Sections
1	Income Taxes	1-1564
2	Estate and Gift Taxes	2001-2801
3	Employment Taxes	3101-3510
4	Miscellaneous Excise Taxes	4001-5000
5	Alcohol, Tobacco, and other Excise Taxes	5001-5891
6	Procedure and Administration	6001-7874

Number	Section Name	Code Sections
7	The Joint Committee on Taxation	8001-8023
8	Financing of Presidential Elections	9001-9042
9	Trust Fund Code	9500-9722
10	Coal Industry Health Benefits	9701-9722
11	Group Health Plan Requirements	9801-9834

In 1913 when the 16th Amendment was passed, the code was encapsulated in 400 pages. In 2012 this had expanded to approximately 73,600 pages. By comparison, the Bible, the world's number one best selling book over the century, contains approximately 1,190 to 1,701 pages depending on the version. Individual and corporate taxpayers constantly take positions on their tax returns challenging the code and related regulations. These positions may go through the court system and end up as court rulings that then become law in that district or circuit.

The US Federal Tax system is very complex and this textbook will cover only the basics of the oil and gas, mining and non-resource industries. The tax code is constantly changing and for every rule that is presented there is most likely a list of exceptions and further guidelines. For these reasons, investors should always consult a tax professional before making any economic or financial decisions in an after tax model.

Depreciation, depletion, and amortization are means of recovering in before-tax dollars your investment in certain types of property used in your trade or business, or held for the production of income. The basis upon which depreciation, depletion, and amortization are calculated is normally the cost of the property, although property acquired as a gift, or in other manners, may have a basis other than cost. The cost of buildings, machinery, equipment, and trucks are examples of business property costs that may be recovered by depreciation over the useful life of the asset. Acquisition costs and lease bonus costs paid for mineral rights for natural resources such as oil and gas, minerals, and standing timber are examples of investment property costs that may be recovered by depletion. Numerous other business costs such as the cost of acquiring a business lease, research and development expenses, trademark expenses, and pollution control equipment costs may be recovered by amortization. Depreciation, depletion, and amortization all achieve essentially the same thing, that is, recovery of the cost or other basis of investments in before-tax dollars through allowable tax deductions over a specified period of time or over the useful life of the investment. If depreciable property is sold, all or a portion of any extra depreciation claimed in prior years may have to be recaptured as taxable income. This concept is addressed in Chapter 8.

BEFORE and AFTER-TAX CASH FLOW CALCULATION:

Revenue
– Operating Costs
– Capital Costs

Before-Tax Cash Flow (BTCF)
– Income Tax

After-Tax Cash Flow (ATCF)

EXPANDED AFTER-TAX CASH FLOW CALCULATION:

Revenue
– Operating Costs
– Depreciation
– Depletion
– Amortization
– Write-offs
(non-cash capital cost deductions)

Taxable Income
– Income Tax (Fed. & State)

Net Income
+ Depreciation
+ Depletion
+ Amortization
+ Write-offs
– Capital Expenditures

After-Tax Cash Flow (ATCF)

Figure 7-1 Before-Tax and After-Tax Cash Flow

Figure 7-1 shows that the only difference between before-tax cash flow and after-tax cash flow is state and federal income tax. To calculate income tax, you must properly calculate taxable income. This requires reducing revenue by both operating expenses and "non-cash deductions" for depreciation, depletion, amortization and write-offs, as appropriate. "Non-cash deductions" get their name because they do not represent physical cash costs. Depreciation, depletion, amortization and write-offs are permitted by tax law to enable investors to recover their out-of-pocket cash "capital costs" in before-tax dollars over the deduction period of time prescribed in the tax law. The term "capital cost" means the cost is deducted for tax purposes over more than one year by depreciation, depletion, amortization (D, D & A) or write-off deductions rather than being "expensed" or deducted from revenue in the year the cost is incurred. Tax laws of countries dictate costs that can be expensed versus those that must be capitalized and deducted over a specified number of years by D, D & A or write-off deductions. Chapter 7 covers the details of business costs that may be "expensed" for tax deduction purposes (Section 7.3, 7.6, and 7.9) and costs that must be capitalized and depreciated (Section 7.4 and 7.5), depleted (Section 7.7) or amortized (Section 7.8). Write-off of costs not previously deducted is addressed in Example 7-3b and Chapter 8, Sections 8.5, 8.9 and 8.10. Write-offs generally relate to deductions for the remaining undepreciated, unamortized or undepleted value of capital costs or to the original costs for land or working capital costs which generally are not deductible by depreciation, depletion or amortization under the tax laws of any western world country.

Tax information in the following sections of this chapter and Chapter 8 is based on U.S. Internal Revenue Service (IRS) Publication 34, the "Tax Guide for Small Business" and IRS Publication 17, "Tax Guide for Individuals." These are free publications available by calling or writing any local U.S. Internal Revenue Service office or on line at www.irs.gov.

7.2 After-Tax Cash Flow in Equation Form

Figure 7-1 illustrates two alternative ways of calculating after-tax cash flow. In equation form, these after-tax cash flow calculations may be expressed as follows in accordance with the right column of Figure 7-1:

After-Tax Cash Flow = Net Income + Non-Cash Deductions
– Capital Costs

= Net Income + Depreciation + Depletion
+ Amortization + Write-offs - Capital Costs 7-1

Alternatively, in accordance with the left column of Figure 7-1, the same after-tax cash flow results may be obtained from calculating revenue minus all out-of-pocket expenditures.

After-Tax Cash Flow = Sales Revenue – Operating Costs
– Income Taxes – Capital Costs 7-2

Cash flow represents revenue or savings minus all costs, no matter what procedure you use to calculate it. Therefore, for any operating period, after-tax cash flow is the after-tax money that is available to an investor (individual or corporate) to invest in new projects, pay out in dividends, pay off old debt, or retain for future investment purposes. It is imperative that after-tax cash flow calculated as described here be the basis for the correct after-tax analysis of all types of investments.

EXAMPLE 7-1 Calculating Cash Flow

An ongoing project is expected to generate revenues of $100,000 next year with operating costs of $30,000 and income taxes totaling $24,000 for the same period. Further, capital costs totaling $20,000 for equipment are also expected to be incurred during the year. Calculate the anticipated project cash flow for next year.

Solution: (Using Equation 7-2)

Cash Flow = $100,000 – $30,000 – $24,000 – $20,000 = +$26,000

Or, Cash flow may be determined as follows:

Gross Revenue	100,000
–Operating Costs	– 30,000
Taxable Income	70,000
–Income Taxes	– 24,000
Net Income	46,000
–Capital Costs	–20,000
After-Tax Cash Flow	26,000

Of these four values (revenues, operating costs, capital costs and income taxes) the only value that is different from determining before-tax cash flow is the income tax. The remainder of this chapter and Chapter 8 will examine deductions from revenue, both "out-of-pocket" and "non-cash" deductions including depreciation, depletion, amortization, loss carry forwards and write-offs of book values that allow us to determine our taxable income and the appropriate income tax to be paid or tax savings to be realized. Obviously, failure to recognize the tax component in Example 7-1 would have a very significant impact on the value of the anticipated cash flow and resulting economic analysis calculations.

EXAMPLE 7-2 Before-Tax and After-Tax Rate of Return Analysis of a Bank Account

An investor deposits $10,000 in a bank account certificate of deposit and will receive 12% interest at the end of each year for the next three years and will receive maturity value of $10,000 at the end of year three to recover the initial investment. Assume the investor is in the 40% income tax bracket and calculate before-tax ROR and after-tax ROR on the investment.

Solution:

Before-Tax Time Diagram, C = Cost, I = Income, L = Salvage

C=$10,000	I=$1,200	I=$1,200	I=$1,200 L=$10,000
0	1	2	3

Before-tax ROR is 12.0%

There are no allowable tax deductions on bank account, bond or debenture type investments. Bank account deposit investments are neither depreciable, amortizable nor depletable. The deposit cost is deductible against the maturity or salvage value which results in zero gain or loss on the salvage value in this analysis. Interest income each year is fully taxable whether withdrawn from the account or not. 40% of the interest income of $1,200 per year goes to taxes, so $720 = ($1,200)(1-.40 tax rate) is the after-tax cash flow from interest each year. The year three maturity value of $10,000 just recovers the initial cost so it is cash flow, that is, none of it is paid out in income tax.

CF=–$10,000	CF=$720	CF=$720	CF=$720 CF= $10,000
0	1	2	3

Therefore, using Equation 3-2, since initial cost (or negative cash flow) equals final salvage (or positive cash flow) the after-tax ROR is 7.2% compared to the before-tax ROR of 12%; a significant difference. It is important to account for income tax considerations.

If you want to compare the economics of leaving your money in a bank to investing in real estate, minerals or petroleum, it makes a difference whether you compare before-tax or after-tax results. Investments in general involve costs that are either depreciable, amortizable, depletable, expensed, or not deductible at all except against liquidation or salvage value, as in the case of land or bank account deposits. This makes the relationship between before-tax and after-tax economic analysis results uniquely different for each investment situation analyzed. This necessitates comparing the economics of investments on an after-tax basis to properly and fairly evaluate the economic potential of different investments from the viewpoint of tax-paying individuals or organizations.

7.3 Business Costs That May be Expensed

For tax purposes, the fastest method of deducting costs is to "expense" or deduct them in full in the year incurred. Investors would prefer to treat all costs in this manner because the faster you get tax deductions, the faster you get the tax benefits from your deductions, and this improves project economics. However, tax law does not permit "expensing" all costs so we need to enumerate some of the important costs that can be "expensed" as opposed to those costs that must be "capitalized" and deducted for tax purposes over a period of time greater than a year.

Operating Costs that may be expensed include costs for direct labor, indirect labor, materials, parts and supplies used for product produced and sold. Only costs associated with product actually sold may be deducted. This introduces the reader to the subject of working capital which involves dollars tied up in product inventory, spare parts inventory, accounts receivable, required cash on hand, etc., that are not deductible for tax purposes until such items are actually used up or sold, as in the case of product and spare parts inventory. A more complete discussion of working capital and the accounting methods that affect its value is presented in Chapter 8. Some other common costs in the operating expense category include utilities, freight and containers, borrowed money interest paid, royalties, severance taxes, sales taxes, ad valorem taxes and certain excise taxes. The calculation and determination of some of these later items is expanded upon in Section 7.9.

Research and Experimental Costs including labor, supplies, etc., are considered to be the equivalent of operating costs and may be expensed in the year incurred. Alternatively, an investor may elect to amortize these costs straight line over five years, but this election is seldom made because slower tax deductions give slower tax savings and less desirable project economics.

Mining Exploration costs are expenditures required to delineate the extent and quality of an ore body and may include core drilling, assaying, engineering fees, geological fees, exploratory shafts, pits, drifts, etc. *Exploration costs may be either capitalized into the cost depletion basis (as dis-*

cussed later in this chapter) or expensed in the full amount in the year incurred by individual taxpayers. However, with the exception of Subchapter S corporations, corporations may expense only 70% of mining exploration costs in the year incurred with the remaining 30% deducted using straight line amortization over a 60 month period, with the first year deduction proportional to the month such costs are paid or incurred.

If exploration expenditures associated with successful ventures have been deducted by the expense option, these deductions are subject to recapture as follows: The taxpayer may elect to forego taking depletion deductions until the cost basis of exploration charges is fully recovered, or the taxpayer may restore a dollar amount equal to the previously expensed exploration charges as income. If the later option is elected, the taxpayer may add the additional income amount to the cost depletion basis for the property. Recapture may be avoided by not expensing exploration charges but instead, adding such charges to the cost depletion basis of the property.

Mining Development costs are defined as expenditures incurred after the determination has been made that an ore body is economically viable and the decision has been made to develop the property. Development costs may include exploration type costs after the decision has been made to develop a mine. Mining development costs typically include costs for overburden stripping, underground shafts, drifts, tunnels, raises, adits, etc. *Mining development costs are not subject to recapture at any point in time and may be expensed in the full amount in the year incurred by individual taxpayers and, analogous to mining exploration costs, corporations (except Subchapter S corporations) may expense only 70% of mining development costs in the year incurred with the remaining 30% deducted straight line over a five year, 60 month period, with the first year deduction prorated from the month such costs are paid or incurred.* As an alternative to expensing all or 70% of mining development cost, tax law gives investors the option of capitalizing these costs and deducting them by units of production depreciation over the producing life of the mine.

Development expenditures end when a mine reaches a level of full production. Then, costs that previously were mine development costs are treated as operating expenses from that time forward.

Petroleum Intangible Drilling Costs (IDC's) are defined as the cost of drilling oil and gas wells to the point of completion and may include:

Costs of agreements with operators and drilling contractors.
Survey and seismic work related to location of a well.
Road cost to well location to be used during drilling.
Dirt work on location for pits, etc.
Rig transportation and set-up costs.
Drilling costs including fuel, water, drilling mud, etc.
Cost of technical services including engineers, geologists, logging and drill stem test services.
Cost of swabbing, fracturing and acidizing.
Cementing of surface casing and main casing (not the cost of casing).
Reclamation of well site.

Similar to mining development costs, *intangible drilling costs may either be capitalized into the cost depletion basis (as discussed later in this chapter) or expensed in full amount in the year incurred by individuals or corporations that are not "integrated" producers. (An "integrated" petroleum producer refines more than 75,000 barrels of crude oil per day for average daily production over a year, or has retail sales of oil and gas products exceeding $5,000,000 per year.) "Integrated" petroleum producers may only expense 70% of intangible drilling costs in the year incurred and are required to amortize the remaining 30% of their intangible drilling costs straight line over a five year or 60 month period* beginning in the month the costs are paid or started to be incurred. This provision does not affect the option to expense dry hole intangible drilling costs in the year the dry hole is incurred by both integrated and non-integrated producers. Non-integrated producers often are referred to as independent producers.

7.4 Depreciation

The term depreciation is used in a number of different contexts. Some of the most common are:

1. Tax deduction for computing taxable income
2. Cost of an operation
3. A method of funding financing for a plant replacement
4. Measure of falling value

In the first context, annual taxable income is reduced by an annual depreciation deduction or allowance that reduces the annual amount of income tax payable. The annual depreciation charge is merely a paper or "book" transaction and does not involve any expenditure of cash. In the second context, depreciation is considered to be a manufacturing cost in the same way as labor or raw materials are out of pocket cash costs. This is a common application of depreciation for internal company cost accounting purposes. In the third context, depreciation is considered as a means of providing for plant replacement. However, in rapidly changing modern industries, it is doubtful that many plants will ever be replaced because the processes are likely to have become obsolete during operation, so this approach is outdated. In the fourth context, a plant or a piece of equipment may have a limited useful life, so deducting cumulative depreciation from initial value gives a measure of the asset's falling value, usually called book value or adjusted basis.

In this text, the term depreciation is usually used in the context of a tax allowance. Depreciation is a tax deduction comprising, "a reasonable allowance for the exhaustion, wear and tear and obsolescence of property used in a trade or business, or of property held by a tax payer for the production of income." Land, however, may not be depreciated. The basis or value that would be used to find investment gain or loss if property were disposed of is the basis that should be used for determining depreciation. The first step in computing depreciation is to determine the estimated useful life of the asset or its allowable depreciable life. No average useful life is applicable to all depreciable assets in different types of businesses and the allowable depreciable life is often different from the expected economic life.

The question of whether certain expenditures are repair expenses (deductible in the year incurred as an operating expense) or a capital expenditure deductible through annual depreciation deductions often is important in relation to the tax deduction handling of equipment and major facility repair/rebuild type costs. The distinction between repairs and capital expenditures is not always clear but here is a useful guide: A repair is an expenditure for the purpose of keeping property in an ordinary efficient operating condition. It does not add to the value or life of the property. It merely keeps the property in an operating condition over its probable useful life for the uses for which it was acquired. Repair costs may be expensed as operating costs for tax deduction purposes. On the other hand, capital expenditures are alterations, additions or improvements that increase the asset useful life or value or make it adaptable for a different use. Capital expenditures must be depreciated rather than expensed using the depreciation life of an equivalent new asset.

Depreciable property generally is tangible while amortizable property generally is intangible. Tangible property generally is any physical property that can be seen or touched. Intangible property generally is paper-type assets such as a copyright, patent or franchise. Depreciable property may be personal or real. Personal property is property such as machinery or equipment that is not real estate. Real property is land and generally anything that is erected on, growing on, or attached to land such as buildings. However, land itself is never depreciable, so land is non-depreciable real property whereas buildings are depreciable real property.

Property is depreciable if it meets these requirements:

1) It must be used in business or held for the production of income.
2) It must have a determinable life and that life must be longer than one year.
3) It must be something that wears out, decays, gets used up, becomes obsolete, or loses value from natural causes.
4) It is placed in service or is in a condition or state of readiness and available to be placed in service.

In general, if property does not meet all four of these conditions, it is not depreciable.

Finally, the method of financing the purchase of assets has no effect on depreciation deductions. Whether you pay cash or borrow all the money to acquire an asset, you get the same depreciation deductions. Interest on borrowed money is the only tax deduction that is different with project analyses involving borrowed money instead of cash investments as is discussed in Chapter 11.

7.5 Depreciation Methods

Depreciation of tangible property placed in service after 1986 is based on using Modified Accelerated Cost Recovery System (MACRS) depreciation for: (1) the applicable depreciation method, (2) the applicable recovery period (depreciation life), and (3) the applicable first year depreciation convention. MACRS depreciation calculations relate to the following three depreciation methods:

1) Straight Line
2) Declining Balance
3) Declining Balance Switching to Straight Line

A fourth method used to a lesser extent for tax deduction purposes but to a greater extent for public company shareholder reporting purposes is:

4) Units of Production

The following sections 7.5a through 7.5e illustrate the application of these different methods. The MACRS depreciation method is addressed in section 7.5e. Prior to introducing depreciation methods, several timing conventions that affect the first year depreciation deduction need to be addressed.

Under the current U.S. tax law, there are three applicable conventions that have an effect on the allowable depreciation deduction in the first year. These conventions apply to the MACRS method, the straight line MACRS method (which is straight line depreciation for the recovery period allowed by MACRS depreciation) and the alternative ACRS method (which applies longer depreciation lives for straight line depreciation of special categories of assets such as foreign tangible property or tax exempt use or bond financed property). The recovery period begins when an asset is placed in service under the applicable first year deduction convention. The terms recovery period and recovery property are tax terms meaning depreciation period and depreciable property.

Personal Property First Year Depreciation Conventions

1. Half-Year Convention in First Year

Under the half-year convention, applicable to personal property which is recovery property other than residential rental and non-residential real property, all property is deemed to be placed in service in the middle of the year. Therefore, one half of the first year normal depreciation is allowed in the year that the property is placed in service, regardless of when the property is placed in service during the year. In industry practice, the half-year convention usually is assumed to be applicable in evaluations involving depreciable personal property so this convention is emphasized in text examples and problems.

2. Mid-Quarter Convention in First Year

If more than 40% of annual depreciable property costs in a given depreciation life (recovery period) category are incurred in the last 3 months of a tax year, the taxpayer must use the mid-quarter depreciation convention. Under the mid-quarter convention, all property placed in service during any quarter of a tax year is treated as placed in service at the quarter's midpoint. This has the effect of increasing your depreciation deduction for property placed in service in the first two quarters of the tax year and decreasing your deduction for property placed in service in the last two quarters. Instead of deducting 50% of a full year's depreciation for all property placed in service during the year, the mid-quarter convention gives you an 87.5% deduction for property placed in service in the first quarter (which equals 10.5 mo./12mo. x 100), 62.5% deduction for second quarter property, 37.5% for third quarter property and 12.5% for fourth quarter property.

Real Property First Year Depreciation Convention

Mid-Month Convention

For residential and non-residential real property the mid-month first year convention applies. Under this convention, qualifying property is deemed to be placed in service during the middle of the month. The allowable deduction is based on the number of months the property was in service. Therefore, for a calendar tax year, assets placed in service in January of that year would receive a first year deduction equal to the fraction 11.5/12 times the calculated year one depreciation. Thus, one half month's cost recovery (depreciation) is allowed for the month the property is placed in service with full month deductions in subsequent months.

7.5a Straight Line Depreciation

Straight line depreciation is the simplest method of computing depreciation in all countries but, unfortunately, it also is the slowest method of depreciation. The faster you get depreciation tax deductions, the faster you get the tax benefits from the deductions if income exists against which to use the deductions, and the better the economics of any project will be. Therefore, straight line depreciation is generally not desirable for tax deduction purposes if faster methods are allowable.

With the straight line method, depreciation per year is determined by multiplying the cost basis of a property times a straight line depreciation rate which is one divided by the allowable depreciation life, "n" years. In equation form:

Straight Line Depreciation Per Year = (Cost)(1/n) 7-3

EXAMPLE 7-3 Illustration of Straight Line Depreciation

Assume you purchase a new machine for $100,000 in January of a tax year that corresponds to a calendar year. Assume the asset is placed into service in August of the same tax year. The estimated life of the machine is eight years when salvage value is estimated to be $30,000. Determine the annual allowable depreciation deductions by the straight line method assuming the machine is in the five year depreciation life category and that the half-year convention is applicable in the first year.

Solution, All Values in Dollars:

The actual estimated asset use life and salvage value have no effect on depreciation calculations under current tax law.

			Depreciation
Year 1	: ($100,000)(1/5)(1/2)	=	$10,000
Years 2 to 5	: ($100,000)(1/5)	=	$20,000
Year 6	: ($100,000)(1/5)(1/2)	=	$10,000
Cumulative Depreciation		=	$100,000

Note that because of the half-year one convention, it takes six years to fully depreciate the asset. The six annual depreciation deductions are related to cash flow calculations in the next example.

EXAMPLE 7-3a Straight Line Depreciation Related to Cash Flow

Assume the $100,000 cost asset in Example 7-3 is incurred in evaluation time zero and generates annual incomes and operating costs of $80,000 and $50,000 respectively in years one through eight, assuming a wash-out of annual operating cost and income escalation. Year eight salvage value is projected to be zero. Since the asset goes into service closer to evaluation year one than zero, start depreciation in year one. Use an effective income tax rate of 40% and calculate the after-tax investment DCFROR.

Solution, All Values in Dollars:

Year	0	1	2–5	6	7–8
Revenue	—	80,000	80,000	80,000	80,000
–Operating Costs	—	–50,000	–50,000	–50,000	–50,000
–Depreciation	—	–10,000	–20,000	–10,000	—
Taxable Income	—	20,000	10,000	20,000	30,000
–Income Tax @40%	—	–8,000	–4,000	–8,000	–12,000
Net Income	—	12,000	6,000	12,000	18,000
+Depreciation	—	10,000	20,000	10,000	—
–Capital Cost	–100,000				
ATCF	–100,000	22,000	26,000	22,000	18,000

PW Eq: $0 = -100{,}000 + 22{,}000(P/F_{i,1}) + 26{,}000(P/A_{i,4})(P/F_{i,1})$
$+ 22{,}000(P/F_{i,6}) + 18{,}000(P/A_{i,2})(P/F_{i,6})$

After-Tax Rate of Return, "i" by Calculator = DCFROR = 16.82%

Comparing this after-tax DCFROR result to the corresponding before-tax ROR gives:

Before-Tax PW Eq: $0 = -100{,}000 + 30{,}000(P/A_{i,8})$
Before-Tax Rate of Return, "i" by Calculator = ROR = 24.95%

The before-tax ROR is about 50% larger than the after-tax DCFROR indicating the significance of tax considerations in a proper analysis. It is worth noting that after-tax cash flow is the $30,000 operating profit reduced by the appropriate income tax. In time zero, the capital cost must be considered as well. Gross Revenue less all cash costs always yields the same after-tax cash flow as adjusting net income for the non-cash depreciation and other similar deductions less the cash capital expenditures.

Capital costs such as land and working capital are not depreciable under the tax law of the United States and virtually all other countries. Working capital investments typically represent money tied up in raw material and product sale accounts receivable. Chapter 8, Section 8.10 gives a more detailed explanation of working capital. Land and working capital investments are deducted for tax purposes as lump sum deductions equal to the original investment cost in the year of sale or disposal of the assets. These deductions commonly are called “write-offs.” Sale value, if any, from liquidation of land or working capital assets is treated as income in the year that a write-off is taken. Example 7-3b illustrates these considerations as a variation of Example 7-3a.

EXAMPLE 7-3b Non-Depreciable Cost Variation of Example 7-3a

Re-work Example 7-3a with an additional time zero non-depreciable cost of $20,000 for surface land (or working capital to cover inventory and accounts receivable costs). Land and working capital costs are not depreciable but are deducted by lump sum deductions called “write-offs” against the sale (liquidation) value which is assumed to be $30,000 at the end of year 8. Assume the final sale value is treated as ordinary income for income tax purposes.

Solution: All Values in Dollars

Year	0	1	2–5	6	7	8
Revenue*	—	80,000	80,000	80,000	80,000	110,000
– Operating Costs	—	–50,000	–50,000	–50,000	–50,000	–50,000
– Depreciation	—	–10,000	–20,000	–10,000	—	—
– Write-off**	—	—	—	—	—	–20,000
Taxable Income	—	20,000	10,000	20,000	30,000	40,000
–Inc. Tax @ 40%	—	–8,000	–4,000	–8,000	–12,000	–16,000
Net Income	—	12,000	6,000	12,000	18,000	24,000
+ Depreciation	—	10,000	20,000	10,000	—	—
+ Write-off**	—	—	—	—	—	20,000
–Equipment	–100,000	—	—	—	—	—
–Land or W.C.	–20,000	—	—	—	—	—
ATCF	–120,000	22,000	26,000	22,000	18,000	44,000

*Year 8 Revenue includes sale value of $30,000
**Non-Cash Deduction for Land or Working Capital Investment

DCFROR = 13.62% after-tax
Before-Tax ROR = 20.54%

Note that money tied up in land and working capital has a negative effect on both the before-tax and after-tax economics of this project when compared to Example 7-3a with no land or working capital investment.

7.5b Declining Balance Depreciation

Declining balance depreciation by itself is not currently allowed in the United States, but it is the main form of depreciation in Canada and other countries. Declining balance depreciation applies a depreciation rate from the straight line rate of 1/n to 2/n to a declining balance each year. Many governments specify applicable declining balance rates for different assets such as .1, .2 or .3, to be multiplied by the adjusted cost basis. Others specify the depreciation lives and type of declining balance depreciation, such as 150% or 200% declining balance rates now applicable under U.S. tax law, and require the investors to calculate their own rates. For example with 150% declining balance, 1.5/n, (where n is the depreciation life), is the depreciation rate. 200% declining balance is often referred to as double declining balance since the rate is twice the straight-line rate or, 2/n. The declining balance rate is applied to a "declining balance" or "adjusted basis" each year as shown in Equation 7-4.

Declining Balance Depreciation Per Year

= (Declining Balance Rate)(Adjusted Basis) 7-4

where, for any depreciation method:

Adjusted Basis = Cost or Other Basis
– Cumulative Depreciation Previously Taken 7-5

The term "book value" or "tax book value" often is used interchangeably with "adjusted basis." The terms "diminishing balance" and "written down value" have interchangeable meaning with "adjusted basis" in Canada and Australia. All these terms represent the remaining undepreciated value of a depreciable asset.

EXAMPLE 7-4 Illustration of Declining Balance Depreciation

Assume the $100,000 cost in Example 7-3 is to be depreciated using 200% declining balance for a five year depreciation life and that the half-year convention is applicable in the first year. Determine the annual depreciation deductions.

Solution: All Values in Dollars

The 200% Declining Balance 5-Year Rate is 2/5, or 40%

Year	200% DB Rate (2/5 = 40%)	x Adjusted Basis	= 200% DB Depreciation
1	0.40 x (1/2)*	100,000	20,000
2	0.40	80,000	32,000
3	0.40	48,000	19,200
4	0.40	28,800	11,520
5	0.40	17,280	6,912
6		10,368	
Cumulative Depreciation After 5 Years			$89,632

*Half Year Convention in First Year of Depreciation

Note that the adjusted basis is not fully depreciated in five years. This is a problem with declining balance depreciation. It literally takes infinite years to fully depreciate a given adjusted basis with declining balance depreciation. Switching from declining balance to straight line depreciation enables an investor to fully depreciate an asset in the depreciation life plus one year as shown in the next section.

7.5c Declining Balance Switching to Straight Line Depreciation

In the U.S., all depreciation rates for the MACRS depreciation of personal property are based on either 150% or 200% declining balance switching to straight line. *It is desirable to switch to straight line from declining balance in the year when you will get an equal or bigger deduction by switching than if you do not switch. This occurs when the straight line rate equals or exceeds the declining balance rate because when you switch the remaining adjusted basis is depreciated straight line over the remaining years of depreciation life.*

EXAMPLE 7-5 Declining Balance Switching to Straight Line Depreciation

Assume the $100,000 asset described in Example 7-4 is to be depreciated using 200% declining balance switching to straight line for a 5 year depreciation life, use the same half-year convention in the first year of depreciation. Calculate the annual depreciation.

Solution, All Values in Dollars:

In switching to straight line from declining balance depreciation, when you switch methods, the remaining adjusted basis is depreciated straight line over the remaining years of depreciation life. In this analysis it is desirable to switch in year four when two and a half depreciation years remain. The straight line rate of 1/2.5 (or 40%) for switching in year four equals the declining balance rate of 40%, so switching in year four is economically desirable (switching in year three, the straight line rate would be 1/3.5 which is less than the 200% DB rate of 40%).

Year	Method	Rate	x	Adjusted Basis	=	200% DB Depreciation
1	200% DB	0.40 x (1/2)		100,000		20,000
2	200% DB	0.40		80,000		32,000
3	200% DB	0.40		48,000		19,200
4	SL	0.40		*28,800		11,520
5	SL	0.40		28,800		11,520
6	SL	0.40 x (1/2)		28,800		5,760
Cumulative Depreciation After 6 Years						$100,000

200% Declining Balance (DB) Rate = 2/5 or 40%
Straight Line (SL) depreciation based on remaining life, 2.5 Yrs.
SL = 1/2.5 = 40% switch when DB Rate = SL Rate, Yr 4

Note that the straight line depreciation rate is applied in each of years four, five and six to the adjusted basis at the time of switching in year four and not to the new adjusted basis each year. Since a half-year deduction is taken in year one, the final half-year deduction occurs in year six. In general, with 200% declining balance switching to straight line, you always switch methods in the year after the mid-year of the depreciation life.

7.5d Units of Production Depreciation

Units of production depreciation deducts the asset cost over the estimated producing life of the asset (instead of over a given depreciation life) *by taking annual depreciation deductions equal to the product of the "asset cost," or other basis, times the ratio of the "units produced" in a depreciation year, divided by "expected asset lifetime units of production"*, such as initial mineral reserves. This method permits the asset to be depreciated for tax purposes in direct proportion to asset use. Units of production depreciation is allowed as an alternative to expensing mine development costs under U.S. tax law. Also, units of production depreciation is used by mining and petroleum public companies for calculating financial net income and cash flow for shareholder reporting purposes.

EXAMPLE 7-6 Units of Production Depreciation

Assume that the $100,000 cost to be depreciated in Example 7-3 is estimated to produce 50,000 product units over its useful life. If 14,000 product units are expected to be produced in year one, and 12,000 in year two, calculate the year one and two units of production depreciation.

Solution:

Year	Cost Basis	x	Depreciation Rate	=	Deduction
1	$100,000	x	(14,000/50,000)	=	$28,000
2	$100,000	x	(12,000/50,000)	=	$24,000

7.5e Modified Accelerated Cost Recovery System (MACRS) Depreciation

The cost of most tangible depreciable property is recovered for tax purposes using the modified accelerated cost recovery system methods. Cost and recovery methods are treated the same whether property is new or used. Salvage value is neglected in computing the appropriate depreciation deduction.

MACRS depreciation methods for personal property include 200% declining balance switching to straight line, and 150% declining balance switching to straight line. These rates are sometimes called "accelerated" depreciation rates because they give deductions faster than with straight line depreciation. Alternatively, you may irrevocably elect to use straight line depreciation over the regular depreciable life. The straight line method of depreciation is required for residential rental real property or non-residential real property purchased after 1986. Straight line depreciation often is called "straight line MACRS depreciation."

MACRS depreciable property is often called recovery property. All recovery property is depreciated over one of the following lives: 3 years, 5 years,

7 years, 10 years, 15 years, 20 years, 27.5 years or 39 years. Depreciation lives or recovery periods are determined based on Asset Depreciation Range (ADR) mid-point class lives that were in effect prior to the introduction of ACRS depreciation rates in 1981 (see Table 7-1). Recovery periods follow for some typical depreciable assets:

3 year property includes property with an ADR class life of four years or less. Under the ADR system, property with a midpoint life of four years or less includes: special tools and handling devices for manufacture of products such as food, beverages, rubber products, finished plastic products and fabricated metal products.

5 year property includes property with an ADR class life greater than four years and less than 10 years. Cars and light general vehicles are in this class which also includes chemical plant assets, research and experimentation equipment, qualified technological equipment, bio-mass properties that are small power production facilities, semi-conductor manufacturing equipment, and heavy, general purpose trucks including ore haulage trucks for use over the road.

7 year property includes property with an ADR class life of at least 10 years but less than 16 years. This class includes office furniture, fixtures, equipment such as mining machinery and oil and gas producing equipment and gathering pipelines, railroad track and equipment used to manufacture certain rubber products, metal products, steel mill and automotive products, food and beverage products, etc. Typical oil and gas equipment that would qualify for this depreciation class include:

Surface and well casing, tubing (including transportation)
Wellhead (christmas tree), pumping system
Downhole equipment including guide shoes, centralizers, etc.
Salt water disposal equipment.
Tank battery and separators including site preparation, and operation roads.
Installation of flow lines and other equipment.
Natural gas gathering lines placed in service after April 11, 2005.

Typical mining equipment that would qualify for this depreciation class includes:

Loaders, dozers, scrapers, drills, large compressors, haul trucks, conveyors and other equipment for quarrying metallic and non-metallic minerals (including sand, gravel, stone and clay) and the milling, beneficiation and other primary preparation for such material.

10 year property includes property with an ADR class life of at least 16 years but less than 20 years. This class includes equipment assets related to petroleum refining, manufacture of tobacco products, grain mill products, sugar and vegetable oil products, and synthetic natural gas from coal gasification.

15 year property includes property with an ADR class life of at least 20 years but less than 25 years. This includes electrical transmission lines placed in service after April 11, 2005, waste-water treatment plants, telephone distribution plants and comparable equipment, most liquefied natural gas plants and certain natural gas distribution lines related to property placed in service after April 11, 2005 or investments not subject to a binding contract prior to April 11, 2005. These natural gas distribution lines must be installed prior to Jan. 1, 2011. After such time, without further action from Congress, natural gas distribution lines will be re-assigned a 20-year recovery period and 35-year class life.

20 year property includes property with and ADR class life of at least 25 years or more, excluding real property with an ADR midpoint of 27.5 years or more. Municipal sewers, cable lines, electric utility steam power plants and water utility plants are included in this class.

27.5 year residential rental real property includes buildings or structures with respect to which 80 percent or more of the gross rental income is rental income from residential dwelling units. If any portion of the building or structure is occupied by the taxpayer, the gross rental income from the property includes the rental value of the unit occupied by the taxpayer.

39 year non-residential real property is real property that is not (1) residential rental property, or (2) property with a class life of less than 27.5 years. This class includes property that either has no ADR class life or whose class is 27.5 years or more.

Table 7-1 identifies the depreciation method, ADR class lives and recovery period (depreciation life) for each class of recovery property.

Table 7-1 Personal Property Depreciation Lives and Methods

Recovery Period	Depreciation Method*	Mid-Point ADR Class Lives**
3 Yr	200% DB Depreciation Switching to St. Line	4 yrs or less
5 Yr	200% DB Depreciation Switching to St. Line	4.5 to 9.5 yrs
7 Yr	200% DB Depreciation Switching to St. Line	10 to 15.5 yrs
10 Yr	200% DB Depreciation Switching to St. Line	16 to 19.5 yrs
15 Yr	150% DB Depreciation Switching to St. Line	20 to 24.5 yrs
20 Yr	150% DB Depreciation Switching to St. Line	25 or more yrs

* Depreciation deductions can also be computed using the straight line method over the applicable recovery period.
** Depreciation life (recovery period) is determined by the mid-point life of Asset Depreciation Range (ADR) lives for assets. The ADR lives applicable are for the ADR Class Life Depreciation System in effect before 1981. An investor must use mid-point ADR class lives for Alternative Minimum Tax depreciation. Those who elect to use the "Alternative Depreciation System" (ADS) which is also called "Alternative MACRS Depreciation" must use straight line depreciation over the mid-point ADR lives.

Table 7-2 Real Property Depreciation Lives and Methods

Recovery Period	Depreciation Method	ADR Class Life
27.5 Yr	Straight Line Depreciation	—
39 Yr	Straight Line Depreciation	—

As an alternative to computing the depreciation deductions each year for each class of depreciable personal property, the following Table 7-3 rates taken times depreciable cost give annual depreciation for three, five, seven and ten year life qualifying depreciable property that would qualify for the half-year convention in the first year. The rates in Table 7-3 are not valid for personal property subject to the mid-quarter convention or for real property. Under those circumstances, the reader will be required to make his or her own depreciation calculations or refer to year one mid-quarter convention rate tables published by the IRS and various accounting house companies.

Table 7-3 MACRS Depreciation Rates for Personal Property*

	Recovery Period is:					
Year	3 Year	5 Year	7 Year	10 Year	15 Year	20 Year
1	0.3333	0.2000	0.1429	0.1000	0.0500	0.03750
2	0.4445	0.3200	0.2449	0.1800	0.0950	0.07219
3	0.1481	0.1920	0.1749	0.1440	0.0855	0.06677
4	0.0741	0.1152	0.1249	0.1152	0.0770	0.06177
5		0.1152	0.0893	0.0922	0.0693	0.05713
6		0.0576	0.0892	0.0737	0.0623	0.05285
7			0.0893	0.0655	0.0590	0.04888
8			0.0446	0.0655	0.0590	0.04522
9				0.0656	0.0591	0.04462
10				0.0655	0.0590	0.04461
11				0.0328	0.0591	0.04462
12					0.0590	0.04461
13					0.0591	0.04462
14					0.0590	0.04461
15					0.0591	0.04462
16					0.0295	0.04461
17						0.04462
18						0.04461
19						0.04462
20						0.04461
21						0.02231
Cum.	1.0000	1.0000	1.0000	1.0000	1.0000	1.0000

** Above rates are applied to original cost basis each year. Year 1 and final year rates include ½-year convention. The 3, 5, 7 and 10 year life rates are based on 200% declining balance switching to the straight line method. The 15 and 20 year life rates are based on 150% declining balance switching to the straight line method. Separate tables exist if the mid-quarter convention is appropriate and for real property utilizing the mid-month convention. Additional information on this topic can be found in IRS Publication 946, How to Depreciate Property.*

EXAMPLE 7-7 Illustration of MACRS Depreciation

Machinery and equipment have been purchased and placed into service prior to the final quarter of the tax year for a cost of $100,000. The MACRS depreciation life is seven years which means the asset is depreciable by 200% declining balance switching to straight line when appropriate for a seven year life. Determine the annual allowable depreciation deductions assuming this is the only depreciable acquisition of the year so the half-year depreciation convention applies in year one. Then look at the effect on depreciation deductions of not getting the asset into service until the final quarter of the year, assuming this is the only depreciable acquisition of the year so the mid-quarter convention applies in year one.

Solution:

When depreciable assets in a given depreciation life category whose cost is 60% or more of total depreciable costs for a tax year are placed in service during the first three quarters of a tax year, the half-year convention applies in the first depreciation year to all depreciable costs in that depreciation life category that are placed in service in that year.

200% Declining Balance Switching to St. Line Depreciation With The Half Year Convention in Year 1.

200% declining balance 7-year depreciation life rate = 2/7 = 0.2857

Year	Method	Rate	x	Adjusted Basis	=	200% DB to St Line Depreciation
1	200% D.B.	2/7(.5)		$100,000		$14,285
2	200% D.B.	2/7		85,715		24,489
3	200% D.B.	2/7		61,226		17,493
4	200% D.B.	2/7		43,733		12,495
5	St. Line	1/3.5*		31,238		8,925
6	St. Line	1/3.5		31,238		8,925
7	St. Line	1/3.5		31,238		8,925
8	St. Line	1/3.5(.5)		31,238		4,463
Cumulative Depreciation						$100,000

*The straight line rate of 1/3.5 equals the declining balance rate of 2/7 or 0.2857, so switching to straight line is economically desirable.

Table 7-3, MACRS Rates for 7-year Life Depreciation

Year	7 Yr Life Rate	x	Initial Basis	=	200% DB to St Line Depreciation
1	0.1429		$100,000		$14,290
2	0.2449		100,000		24,490
3	0.1749		100,000		17,490
4	0.1249		100,000		12,490
5	0.0893		100,000		8,930
6	0.0892		100,000		8,920
7	0.0893		100,000		8,930
8	0.0446		100,000		4,460
Cumulative Depreciation					$100,000

Within round-off error accuracy, the Table 7-3 rates give the same depreciation deductions as the declining balance switching to straight line depreciation calculations.

The mid-quarter convention applies in the first depreciation year when assets in a given depreciation life category whose cost exceeds 40% of total depreciable costs for the year in that depreciation life category are placed in service during the final quarter of the tax year. Costs for each quarter, not just the final quarter, are affected by this convention. A half-quarter deduction is allowed in the quarter assets are placed in service.

200% Declining Balance Switching to St. Line Depreciation With the Mid-Quarter Convention in Year 1 and 8.

Year	Method	Rate	x	Adjusted Basis	=	200% DB to StLine Depreciation
1	200% D.B.	2/7(1.5/12)		$100,000		$ 3,571
2	200% D.B.	2/7		96,429		27,550
3	200% D.B.	2/7		68,879		19,679
4	200% D.B.	2/7		49,200		14,056
5	200% D.B.	2/7		35,144		10,041
6	St. Line	1/2.875*		25,103		8,731
7	St. Line	1/2.875		25,103		8,731
8	St. Line	1/2.875(10.5/12)		25,103		7,640
Cumulative Depreciation (Within Round off)						$100,000

*The straight line rate of 1/2.875 equals 0.3478.

7.6 Economic Stimulus Measures

Throughout history Congress has periodically incorporated measures into the tax code in attempts to stimulate the economy. Common measures used over the past decade including accelerating tax deductions and tax credits. United States tax law permits limited expensing of qualified depreciable property that would otherwise be treated as a depreciable cost. Some of the methods through which this may be accomplished are described below.

7.6a Code Section 179

Section 179 allows qualified small businesses to deduct all of the costs associated with new or used equipment as well as off-the-shelf software. Under 2013 law, up to $500,000 of qualified depreciable property placed in service through 2013 can be expensed. There is a limitation for companies that spend more than $2,000,000 on equipment with a dollar-for-dollar reduction to the $500,000 for every dollar you spend over $2,000,000. Therefore, if your company spends over $2,500,000 on equipment in 2013, Section 179 is not available.

Over the past decade, code Section 179 has been used to try to stimulate the economy. The following table relates to tax year, maximum deduction possible, and the phase out limit.

Tax Year	Maximum Deduction Possible	Phase out limit
2002	$24,000	$400,000
2003	$100,000	$400,000
2004	$102,000	$410,000
2005	$105,000	$420,000
2006	$108,000	$430,000
2007	$125,000	$500,000
2008	$250,000	$800,000
2009	$250,000	$800,000
2010	$500,000	$2,000,000
2011	$500,000	$2,000,000
2012	$139,000	$560,000
2013	$500,000	$2,000,000

There are other limitations on Section 179 beyond the phase out limitation. It is only available on "Qualified Property" which is defined as new or used equipment, that is tangible personal property, or any property that is attached to buildings that is not structural. Facts that would exclude the use of Section 179 include, but are not limited to, real property, property used outside the United States, and air conditioning/heating units in buildings.

Section 179 is more affectionately known as the "Hummer Deduction" because certain vehicles exceeding 6,000 pounds were not identified as automobiles and therefore were eligible for Section 179. In October of 2004, Congress limited the Section 179 deduction to vehicles in a weight class of 6,000 to 14,000 pounds at $25,000. For more current information see IRS Publication 946 or related documents at www.irs.gov. or, www.section179.org which is a free resource that stays very up to date.

7.6b Bonus Depreciation

Beyond Section 179, Congress has periodically allowed a broader range of investors to expense a portion of the cost of qualified depreciable property that would otherwise be depreciable. This provision known as "Bonus Depreciation" first appeared in the economic stimulus bill following September 11, 2001 and, for the 7th time most recently in The American Taxpayer Relief Act of 2012. The percentage allowed has changed dramatically over the years ranging from 30% to 100% as summarized below.

Bill Name	Rate	Years Allowed
Job Creation and Worked Assistance Act of 2002	30%	2001-2004
Jobs and Growth Tax Relief Reconciliation Act of 2003	50%	2002-2004
Economic Stimulus Act of 2008	50%	2008
American Recovery and Reinvestment Act of 2009	50%	2009
Small Business Jobs Act of 2010	50%	2010
The Tax Relief, Unemployment Insurance Reauthorization and Job Creation Act of 2010	100% & 50%	2010 - 2011 & 2012
American Taxpayer Relief Act of 2012	50%	2013

For qualified investors, bonus depreciation can be taken the same time you take Section 179 and regular MACRS depreciation. So, for an investment in 5-year depreciable personal property, in 2013, and investor could claim 50% of the cost plus 20% of the remaining 50% cost basis in the year the asset is placed in service, giving a total deduction of 60% of the asset cost. Bonus depreciation is limited to new equipment only, and the depreciable life under the MACRS system be less than or equal to 20 years. Bonus depreciation was scheduled to end with the 2013 calendar year.

7.6c Domestic Production Activities Deduction (Section 199)

The domestic production activities deduction, also known as D-PAD or the Production Deduction, is another economic stimulus that reduces the amount of income exposed to taxation and is intended to assure jobs related to production remain in the United States and are not sent overseas. In 2005, Section 199 of the tax code introduced a new deduction reducing the amount of taxable income to certain qualified producers. For eligible producers in the United States (excluding consultants, restaurants, and others), Section 199 reduces federal taxable income by a certain percentage. See the table below for percentages:

Tax Years	Allowable Percentage
2005-2008	3%
2007-2009	6%
2010 & beyond	9%*

*The allowable percentage rate for oil and gas production has been limited to 6%.

Corporation's face many limits in this deduction including 50% of all W2 wages paid in the USA, as reported to the IRS in a tax year. The Section 199 deduction is also allowed under Alternative Minimum Tax (AMT), which will be discussed in greater detail in Chapter 8.

Each of the deductions discussed herein could be treated differently for state income tax purposes. As with all tax issues, you should seek out additional information and tax guidance for your state with your qualified tax experts.

7.6d Tax Credits

Tax credits are another stimulus tool available to governments who want to encourage investments in a specific industry or sector of the economy. Credits are generally considered to be more valuable to investors than deductions because unlike deductions, which shelter dollars of income from income tax, tax credits represent a dollar for dollar reduction in tax liability. The subject of available tax credits is addressed separately in Chapter 8 of this textbook.

7.7 Depletion Methods

The owner of an economic interest in mineral deposits, oil and gas wells, or standing timber may recover his or her cost through federal tax deductions for depletion over the economic life of the property. You have an economic interest if through investment you have: (1) acquired any interest in minerals in place or standing timber, (2) received income by any form of legal relationship from extraction of the minerals or severance of the timber, to which you must look for a return of capital.

Oil, gas, and mineral depletion is computed by two methods: (1) cost depletion, and (2) percentage depletion. Only cost depletion applies to timber. For petroleum and mining both cost and percentage depletion must be computed each year. The result that gives the largest allowable tax deduction, accounting for the 50% or 100% percentage depletion limits applicable to mining and qualifying petroleum producers, is used as described later. You can switch methods from year to year with the exception that integrated oil and gas producers may only take cost depletion on oil and gas properties. For tax law definition purposes, an "integrated" oil and gas producer, as defined earlier in Chapter 7, Section 7-3, is an oil and gas producer that refines more than 75,000 barrels of crude oil per day (average daily production over a year) or has retail sales of oil and gas products exceeding $5,000,000 per year. An "independent" producer does not refine crude oil or sell oil and gas products in excess of the "integrated" producer limits. For percentage depletion calculation purposes, independent producers and royalty owners are subject to a "small producer limitation" which limits the production on which percentage depletion is applicable to 1,000 barrels per day of crude oil production or 6 million cubic feet of natural gas production, or the combined equivalent of both oil and gas production using 6,000 cubic feet of gas as equivalent to one barrel of crude oil. If independent producer production exceeds these limits, percentage depletion may be taken on the equivalent of 1,000 barrels per day of crude oil or 6,000,000 cubic feet of natural gas production prorated over total annual production.

7.7a Cost Depletion

The capitalized costs that generally go into the cost depletion basis for petroleum and mining projects are for mineral rights acquisition and or lease bonuses or their equivalent ascertained costs. Mining exploration costs and petroleum intangible drilling costs may be capitalized into the cost depletion basis but seldom are. Cost depletion is computed by dividing the total number of recoverable units in the deposit at the beginning of a year (tons, barrels, etc., determined in accordance with prevailing industry methods) into the adjusted basis of the mineral property for that year, and multiplying the resulting rate per unit either by the number of units for which payment is received during the tax year, if you use the cash receipts and disbursements method, or by the number of units sold if you use an accrual method of accounting. The adjusted basis is the original mineral rights acquisition or lease cost plus any additional costs capitalized into the cost depletion basis (such as mining exploration or petroleum drilling costs) for the mineral property, less the total depletion previously allowed or allowable over the life of the property. The depletion allowed or allowable each year is either percentage depletion or cost depletion as discussed in the following pages. The adjusted basis for cost depletion calculations can never be less than zero. *In equation form cost depletion equals:*

$$(\text{Adjusted Basis})\left(\frac{\text{Mineral Units Removed \& Sold During the Year}}{\text{Mineral Units Recoverable at Beginning of the Year}}\right)$$

where Adjusted Basis = Cost Basis ± Adjustments – Cumulative Depletion

Mineral rights acquisition, lease bonuses, and other equivalent ascertained costs, including mining geological and geophysical survey costs, and recording, legal and assessment costs, normally are the primary costs that go into the cost depletion adjusted basis.

Geological and geophysical (G&G) costs incurred in the oil and gas industry are now subject to straight line amortization with the half-year convention required in the first year. The half-year mandate is unique to amortization which typically employs a first year deduction that is proportional to the month the cost is incurred and placed on the tax books. Non-integrated producers amortize these costs over a 2-year period while current law requires integrated producers to amortize the same costs over a

7-year period of time. Eliminating this special provision in its entirety has been proposed by some members of Congress which presumably, would place all such costs back into the cost depletion basis as is currently done in mining. For all investor's in mining, G&G is often part of exploration expense, which for developed properties is recaptured, forming a portion of the cost depletion adjusted basis.

The IRS permits most other capital costs to be depreciated or amortized and companies generally do not put any costs in the cost depletion basis that are not required to be put there because percent depletion can be taken even if the cost depletion basis is zero. This means that you normally want to deduct every capital cost possible by a means other than cost depletion because you still get percentage depletion which is usually larger than cost depletion anyway. *Integrated and non-integrated producers with more than 1,000 barrels per day average daily production throughout the year do not qualify for percentage depletion deduction on net revenue from oil and gas production exceeding 1,000 barrels per day. Small oil and gas producers with less than 1,000 barrels per day of average daily production qualify for percentage depletion. All non-integrated producers may take percentage depletion on production up to 1,000 barrels per day, but not above this threshold.* However, all types of mining operations get the larger of allowed percentage or cost depletion on mining mineral revenue.

EXAMPLE 7-8 Cost Depletion

You paid $5,000,000 in a lease bonus payment to acquire 1,000,000 barrels of oil equivalent (BOE). The reserve estimate has been categorized as a proven reserve. 100,000 BOE were produced this year and sold for $79 per barrel. You expect to produce 50,000 BOE next year. Calculate the cost depletion for this year and next year assuming you do not qualify for percentage depletion. This assumes overall producer production currently exceeds 365,000 BOE per year or the investor is an integrated oil and gas producer.

Solution:

Price of product sold is not relevant in cost depletion calculations. Only the cost basis, (lease bonus payment in this example) and units produced and sold are considered.

Yr 1 = ($5,000,000)(100,000 / 1,000,000) = $500,000
Yr 2 = ($5,000,000-$500,000)(50,000 / 900,000) = $250,000

The $5,000,000 is adjusted by the actual depletion method taken in the preceding year. If percentage depletion were applicable and taken in year one, rather than cost depletion, the cost depletion basis for year two would be the initial cost basis reduced by the actual depletion deduction taken in year one. Under current law this is relevant in all mining scenarios and for non-integrated oil and gas producers with less than 1,000 barrels per day average daily production per year and is illustrated in Example 7-9.

7.7b Percentage Depletion

Percentage depletion is a specified percentage of gross income after royalties from the sale of minerals removed from the mineral property during the tax year. However, the deduction for depletion under this method cannot exceed 50% of mining taxable income or 100% of oil and gas taxable income from the property after all deductions except depletion and loss carry forward deductions. If percentage depletion exceeds 50% (or 100%) of taxable income, you are allowed to take 50% (or 100%) of the taxable income before depletion as your percentage depletion deduction. (There is no limitation on the maximum annual cost depletion that can be taken in a given year, except that the accrued cost depletion cannot exceed the cost basis of the property.) However, unlike depreciation and cost depletion, percentage depletion accruals are not limited to the cost basis of the property; percentage depletion may be taken after the cost basis in the property has been recovered. The amount of percentage depletion that an investor can take in a given year is affected only by the 50% or 100% limit on percentage depletion and possibly by a 65% of gross income limitation for oil and gas producers. In applying the 50% or 100% limit on percentage depletion when operating loss carry forwards from previous years are available, the depletion calculations and the 50% or 100% limit test are applied before loss carry forwards are deducted. This prevents loss carry forward deductions from affecting the 50% or 100% limit on percentage depletion.

In addition to the percentage depletion 100% limit on taxable income before depletion, *oil and gas producers eligible for percentage depletion also are subject to a 65% gross income limit which asserts that percentage depletion may not exceed 65% of the taxpayer's taxable income from all sources, not just the property being evaluated.* Since taxable income from all sources often is not known at the time of project economic analysis, the 65% gross income limitation often is neglected. This limitation can be especially important for smaller producers and royalty recipients. Depletion limits for small producers have been continually modified by Congress and are likely to continue to be in the future.

Table 7-4 Procedure to Determine Allowable Depletion

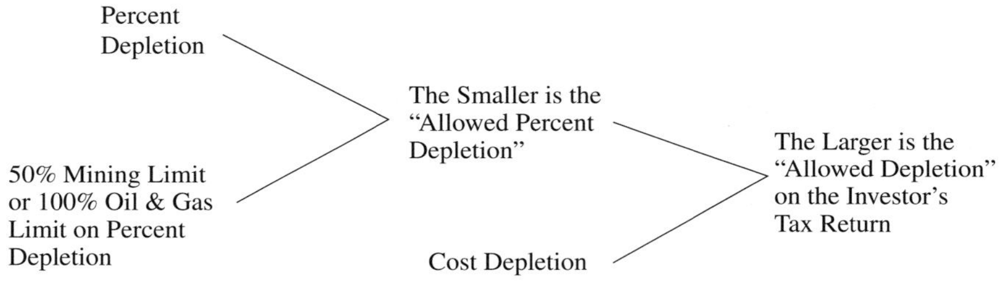

Gross income after royalties from a mining or petroleum property eligible for percentage depletion generally must be based on the amount for which the taxpayer sells the oil and gas or mineral product in the immediate vicinity of the well or mine. If the oil and gas or mineral product is processed or transported or both, the average market or field price before processing or transportation is the basis for percentage depletion calculations. Percentage depletion rates for oil and gas and various minerals are shown in Table 7-5.

Table 7-5 Applicable Percentage Depletion Rates

Mineral Deposits	Percentage Depletion,%
Oil and Gas*	15
Sulphur and uranium; and if from deposits in the U.S., asbestos, mica, lead, zinc, nickel, molybdenum, tin, tungsten, mercury, vanadium, and certain other ores and minerals including bauxite	22
If from deposits in the U.S., gold, silver, copper, iron ore**, oil shale, and geothermal liquids or vapor	15
Coal**, lignite and sodium chloride	10
Clay and shale used in making sewer pipe, bricks, or used as sintered or burned lightweight aggregates	7½
Gravel, sand, stone	5
Most other minerals and non-metallic ores	14

* 1) Integrated petroleum producers are not eligible for percentage depletion. 2) The fixed contract pre 2/1/75 natural gas percent depletion rate is 22%. 3) Stripper well (less than 15 barrels per day average production) depletion is increased 1% for each $1.00 per barrel that the average annual crude oil price is less than $20.00 per barrel, subject to a maximum 10% rate increase from 15% to 25%.

** The percentage depletion rates for coal and iron ore drop to 8% and 12% respectively after the cost depletion adjusted basis has been recovered by allowed percent or cost depletion deductions.

The percentage depletion rates from Table 7-5 are applied to the "gross income from the property after royalties," which is the gross income from mining or well head price for oil and gas. In addition to the extraction of minerals from the ground, "mining" includes treatment processes applied by the mine owner or operator to the minerals or the ore, and transportation that is not over 50 miles from the point of extraction to the plant or mill in which allowable treatment processes are applied. Treatment processes considered as mining depend upon the ore or mineral mined, and generally include those processes necessary to bring the mineral or ore to the stage at which it first becomes commercially marketable; this usually means to a shipping grade and form. However, in certain cases, additional processes are specified in the Internal Revenue Service regulations and are considered "mining." Net smelter return, or its equivalent, is the gross income on which mining percentage depletion commonly is based. Royalty owners get percentage depletion on royalty income so companies get percentage depletion on gross income after royalties. Small independent oil and gas producers are eligible to take percent depletion while integrated oil and gas producers are only eligible to take cost depletion.

Example 7-9 Allowable Depletion Deduction when Percentage and Cost Depletion are Applicable

Determine the allowable depletion deduction for years 1 and 2 and the impact on after-tax cash flow for the following parameters for a corporation in a gold mining scenario. A $10,000,000 mineral rights acquisition cost would be incurred at time zero to acquire an estimated 500,000 ounces of gold identified as a proven resource. Mine development costs will be charged at the end of year 1 and are estimated at $8,000,000. Expense 70% or $5,600,000 in year 1 with the remaining 30%, or $2,400,000 charged as capital in year 1 and amortized over 60 months, beginning in year 1 with a 12 month deduction as follows: (12/60)($2,400,000) = $480,000 per year. Mine Equipment costs of $25,000,000 will be charged as capital at time zero with depreciation beginning in year 1 and based on MACRS 7-year rates described in Table 7-3 including $3,573,000 in year 1 and $6,123,000 in year 2. Year 1 production is estimated at 32,000 ounces from reserves while year 2 production is estimated at 40,000 ounces. The price of gold is assumed to be $800 per ounce in years 1 and 2. The resulting gross revenue is $25,600,000 in year 1 and $32,000,000 in year 2. Royalties are estimated at 12.5% of gross revenue. Operating costs include all state and local severance and property taxes and are estimated to be $9,000,000 in year 1 and $12,000,000 in year 2. The applicable combined federal and state income tax rate is 40%.

Solution: All values Except Ounces in 000's of $

Year	0	1	2
Initial Reserves, 500,000 Ounces			
Production (Ounces)		32,000	40,000
Gold Price, $/Ounce		800	800
Gross Revenue		25,600	32,000
– Royalties 12.5%		-3,200	-4,000
Net Revenue*		22,400	28,000
– Operating Costs		-9,000	-12,000
– Mine Development (70%)		-5,600	-
– Depreciation		-3,573	-6,123
– Amortization		-480	-480
Taxable Income Before Depletion**		3,747	9,397
– 50% Limit in Mining***		-1,874	4,699
– Percentage Depletion (15%)***		3,360	-4,200
– Cost Depletion		640	695
Taxable Income		1,873	5,197
– Income Taxes (40%)		-749	-2,079
Net Income		1,124	3,118
+ Depreciation		3,573	6,123
+ Amortization		480	480
+ Depletion Taken		1,874	4,200
– Capital: Mine Equipment	-25,000		
– Capital: 30% of Mine Develop.		-2,400	
– Capital: Mine Acquisition	-10,000		
After-Tax Cash Flow	-35,000	4,651	13,921

* Net revenue is the basis for percentage depletion.

** The limit on annual percentage depletion is related to Taxable Income before Depletion, 50% in Mining, 100% for qualified oil and gas producers with less than 1,000 barrels per day average daily production.

*** Allowable depletion deduction indicated by "-" and determined by proper application of Table 7-4 each year.

Year 1 Depletion Calculations in 000's:

Yr 1 50% Limit on Percentage Depletion = $3,747(0.5) = $1,874
Yr 1 Percentage Depletion = $22,400(.15) = $3,360
Yr 1 Cost Depletion = $10,000 (32 / 500) = $640
*Yr 1 Depletion = 1,874 which is < 3,360 and > 640 per Table 7-4.

Year 2 Depletion Calculations in 000's:

Yr 2 50% Limit on Percentage Depletion = \$9,397(0.5) = \$4,699
Yr 2 Percentage Depletion = \$28,000(.15) = \$4,200
Yr 2 Cost Depletion = (\$10,000-\$1,874) (40 / (500-32)) = \$695
*Yr 2 Depletion = 4,200 which is < 4,699 and > 695 per Table 7-4.

EXAMPLE 7-10 Illustration of Depletion Calculations for Co-Product Ores

A mining operation yields annual sales revenue of \$1,500,000 from an ore containing the co-products lead, zinc and silver. \$1,000,000 of the revenue is from lead and zinc, and \$500,000 from silver. Operating costs are \$700,000 and allowable depreciation is \$100,000. Determine the taxable income assuming the cost depletion basis is zero and that operating costs and depreciation are proportional to revenue from different ores.

Solution:

Since silver is a 15% depletion rate mineral while lead and zinc are 22% depletion rate minerals, sales revenues must be prorated for percent depletion calculation purposes.

Sales Revenue	\$1,500,000	
– Operating Costs	–700,000	
– Depreciation	–100,000	
Taxable Before Depletion	700,000	
50% Limit on % Depletion	350,000	
Lead, Zinc % Depletion (.22)(1,000,000)	–220,000	select
Silver % Depletion (.15)(500,000)	–75,000	295,000
Taxable Income	\$ 405,000	

7.8 Amortization

It is permissible for a business to deduct each year as amortization a proportionate part of certain capital expenditures. Amortization permits the recovery of these expenditures in a manner similar to straight line depreciation over five years or a different specified life. As a general rule, amortization relates to intangible asset costs while depreciation relates to tangible asset costs. However, only certain specified expenditures may be amortized for federal income tax purposes.

Thirty percent of the cost associated with either mining development costs incurred by a corporation or intangible drilling costs incurred by an integrated oil and gas producer must be amortized over a 60 month period. Petroleum geological and geophysical costs are amortized over a 24 or 84 month period and are pro-rated based on the half-year convention beginning in the year the cost is incurred. Remaining amortization deductions may not be written off should the property be abandoned prior to conclusion of the scheduled deductions. A corporation's organization expenses under certain conditions may be amortized over 60 months. The cost of acquiring a lease for business purposes (other than a mineral lease) must be recovered by amortization deductions over the term of the lease. Research and experimental expenses may be amortized over a 60 month period or longer, or deducted currently as a business expense if connected with your trade or business. The cost of certified pollution control facilities may be amortized over a period of 60 months for installations in plants that were in existence prior to 1976. The cost of certified air pollution control facilities installed in connection with an electric generation plant which is primarily coal fired which was not in operation before January 1, 1976 is amortized over 84 months.

Limited start-up expenses incurred by a taxpayer in connection with setting up an active trade or business, or for investigating the possibility of creating or acquiring an active trade or business, may be amortized over 180 months. These start-up costs must meet two criteria: First, it must be a cost you could deduct if you paid or incurred it to operate an existing active trade or business. Second, it must be a cost paid before the day your trade or business begins. The cost of a patent developed through research is amortizable over 60-months or longer and maybe possibly be deducted when incurred. If the patent has a determinable life the patent may be amortized over that life or it may also be advantageous to elect a provision under code section 59(e) and amortize the patent over 10 years if you might be subject to AMT. Trademarks, goodwill, and franchises are considered code section 197 intangibles and may be amortized over 15 years. Amortization beginning in the month you acquire the 197 intangible, or the month the trade or business engages in the production of income. Companies cannot amortize any 197 intangible that was created rather than acquired, although certain exceptions apply.

The annual allowable amortization for qualifying expenditures is calculated in the same way that straight line depreciation is calculated for depreciable assets, with first year amortization proportioned to months of service.

EXAMPLE 7-11 Illustration of Amortization Calculations

A mineral investor is assumed to be involved in either mining or oil and gas development. A one million dollar mine development cost (or petroleum intangible drilling cost, IDC) is incurred in July of a calendar tax year (seventh month of year 0) for either mine development or oil and gas well drilling. Consider the investor is a corporation from a mining viewpoint and an integrated producer from an oil and gas viewpoint. Calculate the allowable tax deductions from this one million dollar year 0 cost.

Solution:

Only 70% of corporate mine development or integrated producer intangible drilling costs can be expensed in the year incurred, with the other 30% amortized over 60 months, beginning in the month the cost is incurred or placed on the tax books. Therefore, $700,000 of the year 0 cost can be expensed in year 0. thirty percent of the cost, $300,000, is deducted using straight line amortization over 60 months, with the first year amortization deduction (year 0 in this analysis) prorated from the month the cost was incurred. From the seventh to twelfth month of year 0 is 6 months so a 6/60 amortization deduction is taken in year 0. Alternatively, the year 0 deduction could be described as taking 6/12 of the straight line annual deduction of 1/5. This and subsequent years are summarized below.

Year	Amortization Deductions
0	(6/60)($300,000) = (6/12)(1/5)($300,000) = $30,000
1–4	(12/60)($300,000) = (12/12)(1/5)($300,000) = $60,000
5	(6/60)($300,000) = (6/12)(1/5)($300,000) = $30,000

7.9 Royalties, Production Payments, Severance and Property Taxes

Earlier in this chapter, discussion in Section 7.3 addressed the subject of costs that could be expensed. Under operating costs, it was pointed out that all royalties, severance taxes, ad valorem (property) taxes and some excise taxes are an allowed expense deduction in computing taxable income. As was also previously mentioned in Section 7.7b, royalty holders are generally entitled to the allowed percentage depletion deductions on royalty revenue or cost depletion on their mineral rights cost basis for a property. This is the same as for any producer, because they are considered to retain an "economic interest" in the property being depleted. An investor retains an economic interest in a property if the investor has acquired any interest in minerals in place or standing timber or receive income by any form of legal relationship from extraction of the minerals to which the investor must look for a return of capital.

In the mining and petroleum industry, the word "royalty" as applied to an existing mineral lease means compensation provided in the lease to the owner of the property for the privilege of developing and producing mining minerals or oil and gas from the leasehold, and consists of a share in the value of the minerals extracted. In the oil and gas industries, 'overriding royalties' and 'carried interests' are interests carved out of the lessee's share of the mineral value, also called the "working interest," or "net revenue interest" as distinguished from the owner's interest.

Royalties, whether overriding, carried or basic, are payments that extend to future production. In contrast, production payments generally terminate when they reach a total cumulative sum. A mineral production payment is treated for tax purposes as a loan by the owner of the production payment to the owner of the mineral property. The loan is to be repaid by an amount or fraction of annual production, analogous to the way mortgage payments pay off an initial loan amount. Therefore, as with a loan, the initial payment is not tax deductible by the lender nor is it taxable income to the borrower. All income from the property including the value of production payments, is taxable income to the owner of the property working interest and that owner is entitled to the applicable mineral depletion allowance. The owner of the production payment is not entitled to depletion on that amount.

In the process of calculating mineral project cash flow, the first items deducted from applicable mineral sale revenues are the royalty costs because in most instances, royalty owners are allowed to take depletion on royalty revenues. Therefore, the investors in mining or petroleum properties only get to take percentage depletion (when applicable for oil and gas) on the net revenue after royalties which in the oil industry is often referred to as the 'net revenue interest.' Landowner royalties vary with different mineral industries. In oil and gas, the standard royalty is 1/8 or 12.5% of the gross value of the product extracted from the property and may include an up front fee on a dollar per acre basis, this fee is sometimes referred to as a lease bonus or rental and generally goes into the cost depletion basis for a lease. An overriding royalty or carried interest is similar to a landowner's royalty and is subject to the same percentage depletion considerations. Participating interests also previously defined as net revenue interests and working interests may change over a project life, but they too represent an economic interest in the property and are subject to applicable percentage depletion considerations. On the other hand, percentage depletion is not allowed for lease bonuses, advanced royalty payments, or any other amount payable without regard to actual production of minerals. Only cost depletion is applicable in this situation.

A 'severance tax' is a state tax imposed on the severing of natural resources from the land and is based on the value or quantity of production. Severance taxes are also defined as mining taxes, excise tax or a net proceeds tax dependent upon each states unique wording. However, the tax is always based on actual production or output value of either oil and gas or mining minerals and timber. Severance taxes usually are calculated on a flat dollar per unit produced basis, or as a percentage of the value of the resource extracted.

A property tax (or ad valorem tax) is levied by the appropriate taxing authority on the value of a property. Property taxes can be levied by different cities, counties, states or school districts. Property taxes can be levied against either real or personal property. Real property is taxed in all states, but many states do not tax personal property. Royalty recipients are also subject to their portion of severance and ad valorem taxes. Such taxes are often paid in full by the producer who then allocates the taxes to the appropriate parties such as royalty recipients, thereby reducing the royalty income actually distributed.

Properly accounting for the detailed tax implications of all the various resource property taxes, royalties, and production payments goes well beyond the objectives of this textbook. In all evaluation situations, the investor's tax position must be carefully considered with appropriate tax personnel or material to determine the resulting tax benefits and liabilities or obligations of each investor.

7.10 Four Investor Financial Situations That Affect Cash Flow

All investors whether individual, corporate or government, fall into one of four financial situations for cash flow calculation purposes. The four financial situations are described as follows:

Expense An investor has other taxable income from existing salary, business or investment sources against which to use negative taxable income from new project operating expenses and deductions in any year. In this situation the new project is credited with tax savings from the operating expenses and deductions in the year incurred. This assumes the new project deductions are "deducted" against other income in the year deductions are incurred, so they are "expensed" against other income.

Stand Alone An investor is assumed to not have other taxable income against which to use negative taxable income generated by new project deductions in any year. Therefore, in analysis of a new project, negative taxable income must be carried forward to be used against project revenues when they are realized. This approach is often referred to as making project economics "stand alone."

Carry Forward An investor with sufficient corporate loss carry forward deductions from negative taxable income on existing projects would anticipate paying no regular federal income tax for a number of years into the foreseeable future. Such companies have significant exposure to Alternative Minimum Tax, (AMT), which is introduced in Chapter 8 of this textbook. This category of investor will utilize a different strategy of focusing on the minimization of Alternative Minimum Taxable Income and the resulting minimum tax since regular federal income tax liabilities have already been eliminated as previously mentioned.

Before-Tax An investor is a tax-free entity such as a government or charitable organization that is not required to pay any federal or state income taxes on revenues associated with investments. Therefore, before-tax analysis of project investment is appropriate.

If other income exists against which to use deductions from new projects, the investor realizes the tax benefits more quickly than when other income does not exist and negative taxable income must be carried forward. The economics of projects will always look better for investors who have other income against which to use deductions when incurred, compared to an investor that does not have other income. Tax savings are inflows of money, and the faster they are realized, the better project economics look. Therefore, it is very important to analyze the economic potential of projects from the viewpoint of the financial situation of the investor. This is true in all industries and countries. It is incorrect to carry negative taxable income forward in an analysis if other taxable income exists, and it also is incorrect to credit a project with tax savings from negative taxable income in any year if the investor is in a financial situation that requires carrying negative taxable income forward.

In this text, examples and problems in Chapter 7 are presented primarily from the viewpoint of investors who must carry negative taxable income forward using "stand alone" economics described earlier in this section. Chapter 8 illustrates analyses from both the viewpoints of "stand alone" and "expense" economics. Chapters 9 and 10 emphasize analyses from the viewpoint of investors that have other income against which to use deductions, so the "expense" economic analysis financial assumption is emphasized. The next example illustrates carrying negative taxable income forward using the "stand alone" financial assumption.

EXAMPLE 7-12 Illustration of the Stand Alone Financial Situation for Mineral Cash Flow Analysis

A corporate investor is considering acquiring and developing a mineral property believed to contain 1,000,000 units of mineral reserves (mineral units could be barrels of oil or ounces, tons, or pounds of another mineral). The mineral rights acquisition cost for the property would be $4,000,000 at time zero. Mineral development or intangible drilling costs of $5,500,000 and tangible equipment costs (mining equipment or oil/gas producting equipment and gathering lines) of $2,000,000 are projected to be incurred at time zero. MACRS depreciation of the $2,000,000 equipment cost will be based on seven year depreciation life assets, starting in year one, assuming the half year one convention is applicable (the half year convention is built into Table 7-3). Production is projected to be uniform for years one and two at 200,000 units per year. The product selling price is estimated to be $80.00 per unit in year one and $84.00 per unit in year two. Operating expenses are estimated to be $1,750,000 in year one, and $2,000,000 in year two. Royalty owners will receive 20% of revenues each year. When applicable, assume amortization of 30% of the mineral development or intangible drilling cost starts in time zero with a six month deduction and that the mineral is a 15% depletion rate mineral. The effective federal and state income tax rate is 40%. Determine project after-tax cash flow for years zero, one, and two assuming that the investor does not have other income against which to use negative taxable income in time zero, (so negative taxable income must be carried forward to make project economics "stand alone).

(A) The project is a mining venture being evaluated by a corporation.
(B) The project is a petroleum venture being evaluated by an integrated producer.
(C) The project is a petroleum venture being evaluated by an independent producer with more than 1,000 bbls/day of current production.
(D) The project is a petroleum venture being evaluated by an independent producer with less than 1,000 bbls/day of current production so all incremental production would qualify for the greater of percentage or cost depletion.

A) Corporate Mining, Stand Alone

Year	0	1	2
Revenue		16,000,000	16,800,000
-Royalties, 20%		-3,200,000	-3,360,000
Net Revenue		12,800,000	13,440,000
– Operating Costs		-1,750,000	-2,000,000
– Development, 70%	-3,850,000		
– Depreciation		-285,800	-489,800
– Amortization*	-165,000	-330,000	-330,000
Before Depletion	-4,015,000	10,434,200	10,620,200
– 50% Limit		5,217,100	5,310,100
– Percentage Depletion**		-1,920,000	-2,016,000
– Cost Depletion		800,000	520,000
– Loss Forward		-4,015,000	
Taxable Income	-4,015,000	4,499,200	8,604,200
– Tax @ 40%	0	-1,799,680	-3,441,680
Net Income	-4,015,000	2,699,520	5,162,520
+ Depreciation		285,800	489,800
+ Depletion		1,920,000	2,016,000
+ Amortization	165,000	330,000	330,000
+ Loss Forward		4,015,000	
– Mineral Rights	-4,000,000		
– Development 30%	-1,650,000		
– Equipment	-2,000,000		
ATCF	-11,500,000	9,250,320	7,998,320

* The $330,000 amortization deduction in years one and two is based on (12/60)(.3)($5,500,000) of the mine development cost. In time zero, with the application of the assumed six-month deduction, the amount is one half of the regular deduction or 6/60 of 30% of the mine development cost.

** The allowable depletion deduction has a minus (-) sign in front of it. Using Table 7-4, percentage depletion provides the largest allowable deduction.

Depreciation (7-year life MACRS):

Year 1 ($2,000,000)(0.1429) = $285,800
Year 2 ($2,000,000)(0.2449) = $489,800

Year 1 Cost Depletion:

$$\frac{\text{200,000 units produced}}{\text{1,000,000 units in reserve}} \text{ x \$4,000,000 Acq. Cost = \$800,000}$$

Year 2 Cost Depletion:

$$\frac{\text{200,000 units produced}}{\text{800,000 units in reserve}} \text{ x (\$4,000,000 – \$1,920,000) = \$520,000}$$

In year two cost depletion, the $1,920,000 adjustment is based on the projected year one percentage depletion actually taken by applying Table 7-4.

Calculating Cash Flows Using Equation 7-2:

Year 0 CF = –3,850,000 – 7,650,000 = –$11,500,000

Year 1 CF = 12,800,000 – 1,750,000 – 1,799,680 = $9,250,320

Year 2 CF = 13,440,000 – 2,000,000 – 3,441,680 = $7,998,320

B) Integrated Producer, Stand Alone

Year	0	1	2
Revenue		16,000,000	16,800,000
-Royalties		-3,200,000	-3,360,000
Net Revenue		12,800,000	13,440,000
– Operating Costs		-1,750,000	-2,000,000
– IDC, 70%	-3,850,000		
– Depreciation		-285,800	-489,800
– Amortization*	-165,000	-330,000	-330,000
– Cost Depletion		-800,000	-800,000
– Loss Forward		-4,015,000	
Taxable Income	-4,015,000	5,619,200	9,820,200
– Tax @ 40%	0	-2,247,680	-3,928,080
Net Income	-4,015,000	3,371,520	5,892,120
+ Depreciation		285,800	489,800
+ Depletion		800,000	800,000
+ Amortization	165,000	330,000	330,000
+ Loss Forward		4,015,000	
– Mineral Rights	-4,000,000		
– IDC 30%	-1,650,000		
– Equipment	-2,000,000		
ATCF	-11,500,000	8,802,320	7,511,920

* The $330,000 amortization deduction in years one and two is based on (12/60)(.3)($5,500,000) of the intangible drilling cost. In time zero, with the application of the six-month deduction, the amount is one half of the regular deduction or 6/60 of the applicable 30% of the IDC.

Depreciation (7-year life MACRS):

Year 1 ($2,000,000)(0.1429) = $285,800
Year 2 ($2,000,000)(0.2449) = $489,800

Year 1 Cost Depletion:

$$\frac{\text{200,000 units produced}}{\text{1,000,000 units in reserve}} \times \$4,000,000 \text{ Acq. Cost} = \$800,000$$

Year 2 Cost Depletion:

$$\frac{\text{200,000 units produced}}{\text{800,000 units in reserve}} \times (\$4{,}000{,}000 - \$800{,}000) = \$800{,}000$$

Calculating Cash Flows Using Equation 7-2:

Year 0 CF = –3,850,000 – 7,650,000 = –$11,500,000

Year 1 CF = 12,800,000 – 1,750,000 – 2,247,680 = $8,802,320

Year 2 CF = 13,440,000 – 2,000,000 – 3,928,080 = $7,511,920

C) Non-Integrated Producer > 1,000 Bbls/Day, Stand Alone

Year	0	1	2
Revenue		16,000,000	16,800,000
-Royalties		-3,200,000	-3,360,000
Net Revenue		12,800,000	13,440,000
– Operating Costs		-1,750,000	-2,000,000
– IDC, 100%	-5,500,000		
– Depreciation		-285,800	-489,800
– Cost Depletion		-800,000	-800,000
– Loss Forward		-5,500,000	
Taxable Income	-5,500,000	4,464,200	10,150,200
– Tax @ 40%	0	-1,785,680	-4,060,080
Net Income	-5,500,000	2,678,520	6,090,120
+ Depreciation		285,800	489,800
+ Depletion		800,000	800,000
+ Loss Forward		5,500,000	
– Mineral Rights	-4,000,000		
– Equipment	-2,000,000		
Cash Flow	-11,500,000	9,264,320	7,379,920

Depreciation (7-year life MACRS):

Year 1 ($2,000,000)(0.1429) = $285,800
Year 2 ($2,000,000)(0.2449) = $489,800

Year 1 Cost Depletion:

$$\frac{\text{200,000 units produced}}{\text{1,000,000 units in reserve}} \times \$4,000,000 \text{ Acq. Cost} = \$800,000$$

Year 2 Cost Depletion:

$$\frac{\text{200,000 units produced}}{\text{800,000 units in reserve}} \times (\$4,000,000 - \$800,000) = \$800,000$$

Calculating Cash Flows Using Equation 7-2:

Year 0 CF = –5,500,000 – 6,000,000 = –$11,500,000

Year 1 CF = 12,800,000 – 1,750,000 – 1,785,680 = $9,264,320

Year 2 CF = 13,440,000 – 2,000,000 – 4,060,080 = $7,379,920

D) Non-Integrated Producer < 1,000 Bbls/Day, Stand Alone

Year	0	1	2
Revenue		16,000,000	16,800,000
-Royalties		-3,200,000	-3,360,000
Net Revenue		12,800,000	13,440,000
– Operating Costs		-1,750,000	-2,000,000
– IDC, 100%	-5,500,000		
– Depreciation		-285,800	-489,800
Before Depletion	-5,500,000	10,764,200	10,950,200
– 100% Limit		10,764,200	10,950,200
– Percent Depletion*		-1,920,000	-2,016,000
– Cost Depletion		800,000	520,000
– Loss Forward		-5,500,000	
Taxable Income	-5,500,000	3,344,200	8,934,200
– Tax @ 40%	0	-1,337,680	-3,573,680
Net Income	-5,500,000	2,006,520	5,360,520
+ Depreciation		285,800	489,800
+ Depletion		1,920,000	2,016,000
+ Loss Forward		5,500,000	
– Mineral Rights	-4,000,000		
– Equipment	-2,000,000		
Cash Flow	-11,500,000	9,712,320	7,866,320

* The allowable depletion deduction has a minus (-) sign in front of it. Using Table 7-4, percentage depletion provides the largest allowable deduction.

Depreciation (7-year life MACRS):

Year 1 ($2,000,000)(0.1429) = $285,800
Year 2 ($2,000,000)(0.2449) = $489,800

Year 1 Cost Depletion:

$$\frac{\text{200,000 units produced}}{\text{1,000,000 units in reserve}} \times \text{\$4,000,000 Acq. Cost} = \text{\$800,000}$$

Year 2 Cost Depletion:

$$\frac{\text{200,000 units produced}}{\text{800,000 units in reserve}} \times (\text{\$4,000,000} - \text{\$1,920,000}) = \text{\$520,000}$$

In year two cost depletion, the $1,920,000 adjustment is based on the projected year one percentage depletion that is actually taken.

Calculating Cash Flows Using Equation 7-2:

Year 0 CF = –5,500,000 – 6,000,000 = –$11,500,000

Year 1 CF = 12,800,000 – 1,750,000 – 1,337,680 = $9,712,320

Year 2 CF = 13,440,000 – 2,000,000 – 3,573,680 = $7,866,320

Note that this solution for a non-integrated producer with production of less than 1,000 barrels per day may also be representative of economics for an individual mining scenario assuming that the effective income tax rate remains consistent. One difference between the two solutions would be that the individual mining scenario is subject to the 50% limit on percentage depletion while the non-integrated producer is subject to the 100% limit. However, in either scenario for this example, the project would be required to take the 15% depletion rate on net revenue resulting in no impact to after-tax cash flows. Note that depletion is always calculated b property or lease and not on a corporate basis.

7.11 Summary

The following is a summary of the various expenditures addressed in this Chapter and the most likely treatment for regular federal income tax purposes in economic evaluations.

Description	Method of Deduction
Operating Costs	All investors may expense 100%
Royalties	All investors may expense 100%
Severance Taxes	All investors may expense 100%
State Income Taxes	All investors may expense 100%
Research	All investors may expense 100%
Experimental Develop	All investors may expense 100%
Mine Development	Individuals may expense 100% Corporations may expense 70% and Amortize 30% over 60 months
Intangible Drilling Costs	Non-Integrated Producers may expense 100% Integrated Producers may expense 70% and Amortize 30% over 60 months
Buildings (Real Prop.)	For all investors, if the property is: Commercial Property (Non-Residential) Straight-line depreciation, 39 Yrs, Mid-Month Residential Rental Property Straight-line depreciation, 27.5 Yrs, Mid-Month
Equipment (Personal Prop.)	For all investors, depreciate over the applicable tax life (3 to 20 years) by the MACRS rates in Table 7-3, or by straight line, or by units of production using a measure such as proven units. Half year or mid-quarter convention may apply. Half-year convention is built into rates in Table 7-3.
Intangible Assets (goodwill, patents, copyrights, etc.)	For all investors, amortize over the appropriate life, which varies in accordance with the asset and tax code. For example, the acquisition of exclusive rights to a patent would be amortized over the remaining life of the patent. Goodwill is amortized over 15 years.

Description	Method of Deduction
Working Capital	It is common evaluation practice to treat working capital like land and simply charge the cost as a capital expenditure when incurred and write-off the cost basis when the property is sold. Section 8.10 in Chapter 8 offers more details concerning the "Cost of Goods Sold" calculation and the relationship to working capital.
Land (surface rights)	For all investors, write-off the original cost basis in the land when the property is sold. For individuals, gain or loss may be subject to long-term capital gain, see Chapter 8 for more details.
Common Stock	For all investors, write off the original cost basis against the sale of stock to determine the gain or loss. For individuals, gain or loss may be subject to long-term capital gain, see Chapter 8 for more details.
Mineral rights acquisition, lease bonus and recaptured exploration costs are the adjusted basis for Cost Depletion	For all mining investors, such expenditures form the basis for cost depletion deductions. Cost Depletion = $(\text{Adj Basis})\left(\frac{\text{Units Produced \& Sold}}{\text{Proven Reserves at Beginning of Yr}}\right)$
Petroleum geological and geophysical costs	Unlike mining, non-integrated producers may amortize said costs over a two year period while integrated producers must amortize the same over seven years. The half-year convention is used in the first year.
Percentage Depletion Basis	There is no cost basis for percentage depletion. When applicable, percentage depletion is based on a percentage of net revenue (Gross Revenue – Royalties) and may be subject to a 50% limit in mining or a 100% limit for oil and gas.

Other terms introduced in Chapter 7 include the following:

Amortization – is much like straight-line depreciation and is used to deduct the cost of intangible assets such as goodwill, copyrights, patent acquisitions, etc.

Depreciation – is related to the cost of tangible assets including both personal and real property. The most common methods include straight line, declining balance and units of production. In the United States, the fastest form of depreciation is declining balance switching to straight line when it is advantageous to do so.F

Straight Line: (Cost Basis)(1/n)

Declining Balance: (Adjusted Basis)(1/n) up to (Adjusted Basis)(2/n)
"Adjusted Basis" is cost basis less all depreciation previously taken.

Declining Balance Switching to Straight Line: Based on declining balance methodology, this approach switches back to the straight-line method when a taxpayer can achieve an equal or larger deduction by switching. This occurs when the fraction of (1/Remaining Life) is equal to or greater than the declining balance rate because with straight line, the rate is applied to the remaining cost basis. This is the approach utilized in the MACRS depreciation percentages in Table 7-3.

Units of Production:
(Cost Basis)(Units Produced)/(Units Available to be Produced)

In the resource industries, the units produced are based on proven units in reserves or hours of service.

MACRS – Modified Accelerated Cost Recovery System is that area of the U.S. tax code that identifies the details related to depreciation of personal and real property. This system replaced the Accelerated Cost Recovery System (ACRS), which replaced the older Asset Depreciation Range (ADR) method.

Write-offs may also be referred to as a book value, tax book value or written down value – it is a measure of the original cost of an asset that has not yet been deducted by the various methods available such as depreciation, amortization or depletion. In the case of land surface rights and common stock, the cost basis is only deductible when the property is sold.

PROBLEMS

Excel solutions at Stermole.com

7-1 Equipment (such as oil and gas producing equipment, mining machinery, or certain general industry equipment) has been purchased and put into service for a $2,000,000 cost. Calculate the MACRS depreciation (200% declining balance switching to straight line), and straight line depreciation per year, for a 7-year depreciation life, with the half year 1 convention applicable for both methods, assuming the equipment is put in service in year 1.

7-2 An owner may calculate depreciation using the "units of production" methods of depreciation. Consider a depreciable asset costing $100,000 that is expected to have a useful life of 120,000 units of production. Salvage value is estimated to be negligible. Estimated annual production for the next 7 years is 30,000, 30,000, 20,000 and 10,000 per year over the remaining 4 years. Use the "units of production" depreciation method and determine the depreciation each year.

7-3 A company has acquired a vehicle and light trucks costing $100,000 in the first quarter of the tax year and research equipment costing $500,000 in the fourth quarter of the tax year, so the mid-quarter convention is appropriate for depreciation calculations (more than 40% of depreciable cost is in the last quarter). The assets qualify as 5 year life depreciable property. Compute the MACRS depreciation and straight line depreciation for each year.

7-4 Depreciable residential rental real property has been purchased for $800,000 and put into service during the third month of the taxpayer's tax year. For the applicable 27.5 year depreciation life, determine the annual allowable straight line depreciation deductions. Remember that for real property, the first year depreciation is proportional to months of service and subject to the mid- month convention in the month real property is placed in service.

7-5 Mineral rights to a petroleum property have been acquired at time zero for a $5,000,000 lease bonus and mineral royalties amounting to 16%

of gross revenue. The reserve is estimated to contain 1,000,000 barrels and is categorized as a proven resource. Geological and geophysical expenses are expected to be $1,500,000 in time zero and amortized beginning in time zero with a half-year deduction. G&G is amortized over two years for independent producers and seven years for integrated producers. Further development of the lease would include time zero expenditures of $20,000,000 in intangible drilling costs and $10,000,000 of tangible completion costs. Expense the IDC accordingly for the producers described below. Start depreciation of the tangible equipment costs in year one using the 7-year MACRS depreciation with the half-year convention. Year one crude selling price is $88 per Bbl and production is 200,000 Bbls. Year one operating costs are estimated to be $5,500,000 and are inclusive of all severance and property taxes. Use a 40% effective state and federal income tax rate and assume the investor is in a stand-alone financial situation, so carry any losses forward and use against future project income.

A) Determine the time zero and year one cash flow assuming the property is acquired and developed at time zero by a small independent producer with less than 1,000 bbl/day crude related production. Expense 100% of the IDC in time zero. Amortize the G&G over two years with a half-year deduction beginning in time zero.

B) Determine the time zero and year one cash flow assuming the property is acquired and developed at time zero by an integrated petroleum company. Expense 70% of the IDC in time zero. Charge the remaining 30% as capital and amortize over 60 months. Take a 6-month deduction (6/60) beginning in time zero. Amortize the G&G over seven years beginning with a half year deduction in time zero.

7-6 Mineral rights to a gold/silver mineral property can be acquired by a company for a $500,000 bonus cost at time zero. A mineral development cost of $2,000,000 and mine equipment cost of $1,000,000 will be incurred at time zero. Year one production will be 200,000 tons of ore from initial reserves estimated to be 1,000,000 tons of ore, with net smelter return value of the ore estimated to be $18 dollars per ton. Royalties are 16% of gross income. Operating costs in year 1 are estimated to be $200,000. Assume 7-year life MACRS depreciation starts in year 1 using the half-year convention. Expense 70% of the mine development cost at time zero. Deduct the remaining 30% by amortization with a six month (6/60) deduction at time zero. Assume a 40% effective income tax rate and determine the estimated cash flow during time zero and year one for a corporation, assuming "stand alone" loss carry forward economic analysis.

7-7 A mineral reserve containing 100,000 tons of gold ore is to be developed and produced uniformly (20,000 tons per year) over years 1 through 5 by a corporate investor. The estimated net smelter return value of the ore is $120 per ton in year 1, and the net smelter return is expected to increase $15 per ton in each following year. Royalties are 5% of gross income. A one-time mineral development cost of $900,000 is to be incurred in time zero. Expense 70% of the mine development cost at time zero and capitalize the remaining 30% to be amortized over sixty months with a six month (6/60) amortization deduction at time zero. A mineral rights acquisition cost of $800,000 also will be incurred in time zero (the basis for cost depletion calculations), along with equipment cost of $1,000,000 to be depreciated using MACRS depreciation beginning at year one, for a 7-year life with the half year one convention. Write off the remaining book value from the depreciable asset at year 5. $1,000,000 will be invested in working capital at year 0 for in-process inventories, product inventories and accounts receivable. Assume all assets, including inventories, will be liquidated at the end of year 5 for a sale value of $1,000,000 and write off all remaining book values to determine the gain or loss. Treat the gain or loss as ordinary income. Operating costs are $900,000 in year one, escalating $100,000 per year in the following years. Other income and tax obligations do not exist against which to use negative taxable income, so losses must be carried forward to make the project economics stand alone. Determine the project cash flows for years 0 through 5, assuming a 40% effective income tax rate, and calculate the project after-tax DCFROR and NPV for i* = 12%.

7-8 You are considering investing in a new processing facility. The process patent rights will cost $2,000,000 in time zero, and must be amortized over 60 months (take 6 months of amortization in time zero). Research and development costs of $3,500,000 will be incurred during time zero and fully (100%) expensed in that year. Processing equipment costing $3,000,000 at time zero will go into service in year one and be depreciated using the 7-year life MACRS depreciation with the half-year convention (the half-year convention is included in Table 7-3 rates). Production is estimated to be 350,000 gallons of product per year, starting in year one. Product selling price is estimated to be $80 per gallon in year one, $82 in year two and $84 in year three. Patent royalties are 12.5% of gross revenues in each year. Operating costs are expected to be $30 per gallon of production in year one, $32 in year two, and $34 in year three. The effective federal and state income tax rate is 40.0%. No other income exists against which to use deductions, so all negative taxable income will be carried forward until used against project income (stand alone analysis). Determine the cash flows for years 0, 1, 2 and 3 without taking write-offs on remaining tax book values at year 3.

7-9 A mining project involves production from a 5,000,000 ton reserve. The time zero mineral rights acquisition cost of $2,000,000 is the basis for cost depletion. Development expenses of $3,500,000 will be incurred at time zero. Producing equipment costing $3,000,000 at time zero, will go into service in year one and be depreciated using the 7-year life MACRS depreciation with the half-year convention (the half-year convention is included in Table 7-3 rates). Production is estimated to be 350,000 tons per year, starting in year one. Product selling price is estimated to be $80 per ton in year one, $82 in year two, and $84 in year three. Royalties are 12.5% of gross revenues in each year. Operating costs are expected to be $30 per ton of production in year one, $32 in year two, and $34 in year three. The allowable percentage depletion rate is 15.0%. The effective federal and state income tax rate is 40.0%. No other income exists against which to use deductions so all negative taxable income will be carried forward until used against project income (stand alone analysis). Determine the cash flows for years 0, 1, 2 and 3 without taking writeoffs on remaining tax book values at year 3, assuming:

A) The investor is a corporation. Expense 70% of mineral development in time zero. Capitalize the other 30% and deduct by amortization over 60 months assuming a six month deduction (6/60) in time zero.

B) The investor is an individual. Expense 100% of mineral development cost in time zero.

7-10 A petroleum project involves production of crude oil from a 5,000,000 barrel reserve. Time zero mineral rights acquisition cost (lease bonus) of $2,000,000 is the basis for cost depletion. Intangible drilling expenses of $3,500,000 will be incurred in time zero. Tangible producting equipment costing $3,000,000 at time zero will go into service in year one and be depreciated using the 7-year MACRS depreciation with the half-year convention (the half-year convention is included in Table 7-3 rates). Production is estimated to be 350,000 barrels per year, starting in year one. Wellhead crude oil value before transportation costs is estimated to be $80 per barrel in year one, $82 in year two, and $84 in year three. Royalties are 12.5% of gross revenues (well-head value) each year. Operating costs are expected to be $30 per BOE of production in year one, $32 in year two, and $34 in year three. The allowable depletion rate is 15.0% when applicable. The effective federal and state income tax rate is 40.0%. No other income exists against which to use deductions, so all negative taxable income will be carried forward until used against project income (stand alone analysis). Determine the cash flows for years 0, 1, 2 and 3 without taking write-offs on remaining tax book values at year 3, assuming :

A) The investor is an integrated producer. Expense 70% of intangible drilling costs in time zero. Capitalize and deduct the other 30% by straight line amortization over 60 months assuming a six month deduction (6/60) in time zero. Only cost depletion may be taken by integrated producers.

B) The investor is an independent producer with less than 1,000 barrels per day average production. Expense 100% of intangible drilling costs in time zero. The larger of percentage depletion (subject to the 100% limit) and cost depletion is allowed on production up to 1,000 barrels per day. Use Table 7-4 to determine the applicable depletion deduction. To simplify the calculations, assume all production would qualify for percentage depletion.

C) The investor is an independent producer with more than 1,000 barrels per day. Expense 100% of intangible drilling costs in time zero; only cost depletion is allowed on incremental production above 1,000 barrels per day.

7-11 A new 5 megawatt hydroelectric plant would cost \$6 million dollars at time zero. It is expected that the plant would operate at its rated full capacity 6,000 hours per year. Power is expected to be sold for \$0.07 per kilowatt-hour (kwh) and operating costs are expected to be \$0.01 per kwh. Salvage is projected to be zero at the end of project life. Escalation of annual operating costs is projected to be offset by escalation of annual revenue, giving uniform profit of \$0.060 per kwh each year.

1) Calculate before-tax project ROR and NPV for i* = 10% and i* = 15% for evaluation life of A) 10 years, B) 20 years, C) 30 years, and D) 40 years. Assume end-of-year timing for all before-tax cash flows.

2) For a 30% effective income tax rate and assuming straight line 10 year life depreciation of the \$6 million plant cost starting in year one with a full year deduction, calculate the after-tax project ROR and NPV for i* = 10% for evaluation life of, A) 10 years, B) 20 years, C) 30 years, and, D) 40 years. Assume end-of-year timing for all after-tax cash flows.

CHAPTER 7 AUXILIARY PROBLEMS

A7-1 Your corporation is considering development of a gravel quarry. With all your new found expertise as an economic analyst, your boss has handed you the job to determine the after-tax cash flows for the following data in the project's first two years of operation including time zero.

Production and Capital Costs in 000's

Year	0	1	2
Production, (tons)		2,000	2,000
Initial Reserves, (tons)	20,000		
Average Selling Price, \$/ton		\$6.50	\$8.50
Royalty (% of Gross)		2.50%	2.50%
Average Operating Cost, \$/ton		\$2.50	\$2.50
Mine Development	\$8,000		
Mine Equipment	\$22,000		
Mineral Acquisition	\$10,000		
Working Capital	\$500		

This corporation does not have other income against which to utilize any negative taxable income realized in the early years of this project so carry any losses forward and utilize them against project revenues. Take a 6-month deduction starting in time zero when amortizing the appropriate portion of the mine development cost. Start 7-year equipment depreciation in year 1 based on applicable MACRS accelerated rates. The applicable percentage depletion rate is 5% on gravel. The effective state and federal tax rate is 40%.

A) Calculate the after-tax cash flows for evaluation periods 0, 1 and 2, neglect any write-offs that might otherwise be relevant at the end of year 2 assuming the project will continue beyond that point in time with similar cash flows.

B) Calculate the after-tax cash flows for evaluation periods 0, 1, 2 and a sale value at the end of year 2 of $40,000 (in 000's). The cost of closing the sale is estimated at $2,000, also expressed here in thousands, and will be treated as an additional operating expense against the sale value. Write-off all remaining tax book values to compute taxable income from the sale and the resulting after-tax cash flow from the sale at the end of year 2. Treat any taxable gain as ordinary income for income tax purposes. For a minimum rate of return of 12.0%, calculate the project NPV and determine the DCFROR.

A7-2 A project manager is evaluating whether it is economical to develop a project requiring expenditures at time 0 of $20,000 for land, $30,000 for inventory working capital, $80,000 for a steel building, $240,000 for equipment and $60,000 for vehicles. Starting in year 1 the manager estimates that production will generate annual end-of-year escalated revenue of $500,000 with escalated operating costs of $300,000. Operating costs and revenue will both escalate at a compound interest rate of 10% per year beginning in year 2. Use straight-line depreciation over 39 years for the building cost starting in year 1 assuming 12 months of service when computing your allowable deduction in year 1 under the mid-month convention. Use 7-Year MACRS depreciation rates for the qualifying equipment cost starting in year 1 with the half-year convention and the 5-Year MACRS rates for the vehicle cost, again, starting in year 1 with the half-year convention. The applicable combined federal and state income tax rate is 40%. No other income exists against which to utilize deductions so carry any losses forward.

A) Calculate the project cash flows for the first 4 years of this business. This problem involves practicing calculating cash flow in producing years of a project, neglect any sale value and applicable write-offs at the end of year 4 assuming the project would continue.

B) Calculate the project cash flows for the first 4 years of this business and also consider the after tax cash flow that would be realized if the business were to be sold at the end of year 4 for a sale value of $600,000. Write off all remaining tax book values at the end of year 4 to determine taxable gain (or loss) and treat the sale as ordinary income. For a minimum rate of return of 15%, calculate the overall project NPV, DCFROR and PVR based on the 4 years of ATCF including the sale value.

A7-3 A venture capitalist is considering investing in the following project. From an economic viewpoint, would you recommend it? This business would require expenditures at time 0 of $320,000 for land, $300,000 for inventory working capital, $1,800,000 for a business building, $3,000,000 for equipment and $360,000 for vehicles. Starting in year 1 it is estimated that production will generate annual end-of-year escalated revenue of $5,000,000 with escalated operating costs of $2,000,000. In the following years, it is estimated that revenues will escalate at 12% per year while operating costs will escalate 8% per year. At the end of year 4, it is expected that all the assets and working capital can be sold for an escalated terminal value of $6,000,000. Use straight-line depreciation over 39 years for the building cost starting in year 1, neglect the impact from the mid-month convention and take a full deduction in year 1. Also, use straight-line depreciation for a 7-year life for the equipment cost starting in year 1 and straight-line depreciation for a 5-year life for the vehicles also starting in year 1 (assume the half-year convention is relevant for both the 7 and 5 year property in year 1). Assume any sale value gain (or loss) would be accounted for as ordinary income. Write-off the remaining tax-book values against the sale value at the end of year 4 to compute the gain or loss from the sale.

Determine the investment DCFROR, assuming a 40% effective income tax rate. For an after-tax escalated dollar minimum DCFROR of 15%, determine the NPV and PVR.

A7-4 An oil lease was recently made available and you are considering the economics of acquiring and drilling on the lease. For each category of producer described below, expense the qualifying portion of intangible drilling costs in the year incurred. For Case C, assume a 6-month deduction beginning in time zero when amortizing the qualified IDC. Depreciate the tangible (equipment) completion cost beginning in year 1 using the 7-Year MACRS rates based on the half year convention. The lease bonus is the basis for cost depletion while the qualifying geological and geophysical costs will be amortized over two years. Take a six-month deduction on the G&G in time zero. Assume no other income exists against which to utilize deductions that might result from negative taxable income in the early years of the project, so you will have to carry losses forward (stand alone financial position). The effective state and federal income tax rate is 40%. Neglect the end-of-year 2 salvage and write-off considerations.

Year	0	1	2
Annual Production (Bbls)	—	87,500	60,000
Total Initial Reserves (Bbls)	500,000	—	—
Selling Price, $/Bbl	—	$40.00	$40.00
Oper Cost, $/Bbl	—	$8.00	$8.00
Intangible Drilling Costs	$1,200,000	—	—
Tangible Completion Costs	$800,000	—	—
Lease Bonus	$1,500,000	—	—
Geological and Geophysical	$600,000	—	—

Evaluate the year 0, 1 and 2 project cash flows from the viewpoint of:

A) Small Independent (non-integrated with < 1,000 bbls per day production)

B) Large Independent (non-integrated with > 1,000 bbls per day production)

C) Integrated Oil and Gas Producer

CHAPTER 8

INCOME TAX, WORKING CAPITAL, AND DISCOUNTED CASH FLOW ANALYSIS

8.1 Introduction

The objective of this chapter is to relate income tax effects, working capital and the concept of cash flow to discounted cash flow analysis as it relates to rate of return, net value analysis and ratio decision criteria applied after tax considerations. After-tax rate of return analysis commonly is referred to as Discounted Cash Flow Rate of Return or DCFROR analysis. Other names given to this method in the literature and textbooks are Profitability Index or P.I., Investor's Rate of Return, True Rate of Return and Internal Rate of Return. All of these names refer to the same method which easily is the most widely used economic analysis decision method in practice, even though Net Present Value and Ratios have advantages over DCFROR in certain analysis situations described in earlier chapters.

The effects of income tax considerations often vary widely from one investment alternative to another, so it generally is imperative to compare the relative economics of investment alternatives on an after-tax basis to have a valid economic analysis. Income taxes, both federal and state if applicable, are project costs, just as labor, materials, utilities, property taxes, borrowed money interest, insurance and so forth are project operating costs. It does not make sense to leave income taxes out of an analysis any more than it would make sense to omit labor, materials or any other operating cost from an analysis.

As described in Chapter 7, cash flow is what is left from sales revenue each year after paying all the out-of-pocket expenses for operating costs, capital costs and income taxes. All tax deductible expenses, except income taxes, are put into the operating cost category and capital costs, such as building and equipment costs, are deductible over a period of time greater than a year. In making proper after-tax analyses of investment alternatives, you must be careful to recognize that for economic analysis work the tax considerations that are relevant are what a company or individual does for tax purposes and not what a company does for "book" purposes, which means for financial accounting or shareholder reporting purposes. There sometimes is a tendency for evaluation personnel and accountants to get confused on this point. What a company does for annual report book purposes has no relevance to economic analysis of projects. What a company actually does in the way of taking tax deductions and credits on various capital and operating costs is what affects the amount of cash flow that new investments will generate at different points in time. To determine valid cash flow each evaluation period for economic analysis requires accounting for the proper costs, revenues and tax deductions at the points in time they will be incurred. It should be evident that this requires using actual tax considerations rather than "book" or "financial report" considerations which are different from actual tax considerations for literally all publicly owned companies.

8.2 Forms of Business Organizations and Tax Considerations

While there are a variety of ways to organize a business, common structures include a Regular C Corporation (C-Corp), Sub Chapter S Corporation (S-Corp), Partnership, Limited Liability Corporation (LLC), and a Sole Proprietorship. In this section, the Master Limited Partnership is also examined. Many reasons exist to organize a business under these umbrellas including limiting the liability of the individual owning the business, methods available to raise capital, taxes, and future growth to name a few. Although all of these reasons are important, limiting your personal liability is by far the greatest advantage of organizing your business under one umbrella and not another. An introduction to these entities follows, but as always, the reader should consult their legal and tax experts in forming any business entity.

8.2a Sole Proprietorship

A Sole Proprietorship is the simplest form of organization. In fact, individuals might be a sole proprietorship without even knowing it; examples include the youth who mows lawns or a local handyman fixing small items around your house. The key is that only one person can be the owner and therefore the owner keeps all the profits from the business and is responsible for its assets and liabilities. Of particular importance with this type of entity is that a sole proprietorship does not protect your personal assets from being used to pay accrued debts.

From a taxation perspective, a Sole Proprietorship is a flow through entity meaning that the entity itself does not pay taxes. Sole proprietorships report income and expenses on Schedule C of a personal 1040 and taxes are determined at the owner's applicable rate. The Sole Proprietor is still responsible for business taxes such as self-employment income (FICA) and when appropriate payments of estimated taxes at the federal and or state level.

8.2b Regular C-Corporation

C-Corporations are the most widely known form of business. The name C-Corp comes from Sub Chapter C of Chapter 1 of the Internal Revenue Code. Once you organize as a C-Corp you have formed a new entity, owned by the shareholders. This new entity is responsible for all liabilities and debt of the company, and protects the shareholders from personal loss. This protection is known as the Corporate Veil. To register as a Corporation you must file "Articles of Incorporation" as well as some other documents depending on state law. This process is time consuming and requires a professional in most circumstances.

C-Corporations file a tax return and pay federal income tax. Unlike Sole Proprietorships that pay 100% of Social Security and Medicare taxes, a C-Corp will pay half of these taxes with the employee paying the other half.

Double taxation of income is another aspect of C-Corporations. This is a common term used by investors and analysts alike. It refers to revenue that is taxed on the corporate tax return and then again, when after-tax earnings are distributed to shareholders in the form of a dividend, where it is subject to taxation on a shareholder's tax return. It's worth noting if a corporation does not pay a dividend there is no double taxation.

8.2c Sub Chapter S-Corporation

An S-Corp is under Subchapter S of Chapter 1 of the Internal Revenue Code. To start an S-Corp, the owner must first create a C-Corp and then convert it to an S-Corp by checking the box for S-Corp designation on Form 2553. By forming an S-Corp, owners have the same protection from liabilities as a normal C-Corp, but your business can be organized as either a LLC or C-Corp.

The tax advantage of an S-Corp is that all profits flow through to the shareholder personal income tax return (1040), eliminating the possibility of double taxation. Another advantage of forming an S-Corp is that the company only pays employment taxes on the wages paid to employees. These taxes are not paid on dividends distributed to the shareholders. Reasonable employee compensation is an important subject and S Corporations should seek guidance from tax professionals on all forms of compensation.

8.2d Partnerships

A partnership must have more than one member and each partner distributes money, property, or skills to the partnership for a portion of the partnership. Partnership ownership does not have to be equal and should be written down in a legal document called a Partnership Agreement. Although a partnership agreement is not legally required, it is good business practice.

Partnerships are flow through entities and the tax return filed for a partnership is simply an "informational return" on a Form 1065. All partners are issued a Schedule K-1, which represents a partner's share of all profits and deductions. Distributions of profits and deductions are usually made in accordance with ownership. Profits or deductions can be distributed in a manner that is not according to ownership, for one or two years, however distributions must be reconciled back to ownership percentage after that amount of time. Essentially, a company cannot allocate all deductions to one partner and all income to another partner with this distinction having been made to eliminate tax shelters. Unlike corporations, partnerships do not limit the liability of individual partners.

8.2e Limited Liability Company

A Limited Liability Company (LLC) is a hybrid type of organization that provides limited liability to its partners like a corporation, but is organized and taxed like a partnership. LLC's are a flow through entity and file the same type of informational return that a partnership files. You should contact a tax professional for guidance. To organize as a LLC you must file "Articles of Organization".

8.2f Master Limited Partnerships

Master Limited Partnerships or MLP's are partnerships that act like a corporation and whose shares are publicly traded. Most MLP's are in the oil and gas midstream sector, but today MLP's have been organized in all aspects of the industry, including exploration, storage, refining, proppant, and others. MLP's use complex tax accounting techniques that provide large dividends that are taxable, and tax deferred " return of capital" distributions. As an example, assume you invest \$10,000 in an MLP and that year the MLP sends you a dividend check for \$500. On your K-1 for that year, the company reports \$500 in profits, as well as depreciation on assets of \$500.

Your taxable income is $0 but you still receive a check for $500. Is that $500 taxable income? The quick answer is no, and this is typically why people buy MLP's. They get large dividend checks that are not taxable. So when are taxes paid? When the investment is sold.

Say you sell the above MLP units/shares for $10,000 more than a year later and you think you've broken even on the sale. However, the depreciation deduction you got reduced your basis in the underlying shares/units to $9,500, so when you sell for $10,000 you have ordinary income of $500. If you sold for a price of $10,250 you would have had $500 in ordinary income and $250 in long-term capital gain. MLP's are not tax shelters, or tax exempt, they are merely tax deferred.

8.3 Corporate and Individual Federal Income Tax Rates

Both corporate and individual federal income tax rates vary with the incremental level of taxable income after all allowable deductions have been taken. A positive consideration related to individual income taxation is that the levels of taxable income taxed at different rates are indexed (increased) for inflation each year. Yearly indexing of taxable income for inflation has the effect of eliminating income tax increases due to a cost of living percentage increase in salary or other taxable income equal to the inflation rate in a given year.

In the year 2014 there are six incremental corporate tax rates: 15.0%, 25.0%, 34.0%, 35.0%, 38.0%, and 39.0%. The 39.0% upper limit tax rate is due to a 5.0% surcharge that Congress built into corporate tax law in 1986 to phase out the tax benefits of the lower 15.0% and 25.0% tax rates for relatively high taxable income corporations. A corporation with taxable income over $100,000 must pay an additional tax equal to 5% of the amount in excess of $100,000, up to a maximum additional tax of $11,750. This extra tax operates to phase out the benefits of graduated rates for corporations with taxable incomes between $100,000 and $335,000 and causes the effective federal corporate tax rate to be 39% (34% + 5%) on the increment of taxable income between $100,000 and $335,000. A corporation having taxable income of $335,000 or more gets no benefit from the graduated rates and pays, in effect, a flat tax at a 34% rate on all levels of corporate taxable income up to $10,000,000. Since 1993, corporate taxable income in excess of $10,000,000 has been taxed at 35% instead of 34%. The old corporate surtax on taxable income above $100,000 up to $335,000 has been retained. In addition, a new 3% surtax was added to corporate taxable income above $15,000,000, up to a maximum of $100,000 in additional tax. The result of this surtax is to

Table 8-1, Individual Federal Income Tax Rates (2014 Data)

Un-married (Single) Individuals

If taxable income is	The Tax is:
Not over $9,075	10% of the taxable income
Over $9,075 but not over $36,900	$907.50 plus 15% of the excess over $9,075
Over $36,900 but not over $89,350	$5,081.25 plus 25% of the excess over $36,900
Over $89,350 but not over $186,350	$18,193.75 plus 28% of the excess over $89,350
Over $186,350 but not over $405,100	$45,353.75 plus 33% of the excess over $186,350
Over $405,100 but not over $406,750	$117,541.25 plus 35% of the excess over $405,100
Over $406,750	$118,188.75 plus 39.6% of the excess over $406,750

Married Individuals Filing A Joint Return

If taxable income is	The Tax is:
Not over $18,150	10% of the taxable income
Over $18,150 but not over $73,800	$1,815 plus 15% of the excess over $18,150
Over $73,800 but not over $148,850	$10,162.50 plus 25% of the excess over $73,800
Over $148,850 but not over $226,850	$28,925 plus 28% of the excess over $148,850
Over $226,850 but not over $405,100	$50,765 plus 33% of the excess over $226,850
Over $405,100 but not over $457,600	$109,587.50 plus 35% of the excess over $405,100
Over $457,600	$127,962.50 plus 39.6% of the excess over $457,600

assure a flat 35% corporate tax rate on all levels of corporate taxable income for corporations with more than $18,333,000 in taxable income.

Since both corporate and individual income tax rates vary at different levels of taxable income, it is necessary to use incremental analysis concepts to determine the proper tax rate for new project taxable income. However, for many large corporation evaluations, any new project income will be incremental income above the first $10,000,000 of corporate income from other sources. In this situation, the 35% federal corporate tax rate is relevant for all new project income and therefore is the rate that should be used in evaluating new investment projects. Remember that corporations and individuals also pay state tax in most states, so the overall effective federal plus state tax rate will be greater than 35% for corporations or the appropriate incremental federal rate for individuals. Usually the effective rate will be in the range of 35% to 40% for corporations, or 30% to 45% for individuals, as will be developed in Section 8.7.

As previously mentioned in Chapter 7, Section 199 of the tax code introduced a new deduction that may reduce certain qualified producers' taxable income. For eligible producers in the United States, (excludes consultants,

Table 8-2, Corporate Income Tax Rates (2014 Data)

*If corporate taxable income is:**

Over —	*but not over —*	*The tax is:*
$ 0	$ 50,000	15% of taxable income
$ 50,000	$ 75,000	$7,500 + 25% of excess over $50,000
$ 75,000	$ 100,000	$13,750 + 34% of excess over $75,000
$ 100,000	$ 335,000	$22,250 + 39% of excess over $100,000
$ 335,000	$10,000,000	$113,900 + 34% of excess over $335,000
$10,000,000	$15,000,000	$3,400,000 + 35% of excess over $10,000,000
$15,000,000	$18,333,000	$5,150,000 + 38% of excess over $15,000,000
$18,333,000	and up	$6,416,540 + 35% of excess over $18,333,000

*Corporate taxable income is not adjusted for inflation each year in the manner that individual taxable income brackets are adjusted.

restaurants, and others) 9% of Federal taxable income before this deduction may be claimed as an added reduction, but oil related production is capped at 6%. This deduction applies to federal taxable income but not all states recognize the deduction in computing state taxable income. This may require computing state and federal income taxes separately rather than utilizing an effective rate common to most textbook examples and problems. This deduction is limited annually by 50% of all W2 wages reported to the IRS. Finally, the deduction is also allowed for purposes of computing alternative minimum taxable income (discussed later in this chapter) where it is subject to the same limitation on wages paid.

8.4 Corporate and Individual Capital Gains Tax Treatment

Current tax law continues to make a distinction between capital and ordinary gains and losses. Corporations and individuals alike must compute the appropriate long-term and short-term gains and losses for tax purposes, however, all corporate net capital gains are treated as ordinary income subject to the appropriate corporate income tax rates described in Table 8-2. However, corporate capital losses can only be used against corporate capital gains and further can only be carried forward five years or back three years. Additional rules and limitations may apply for certain businesses. Individuals may deduct capital losses to the extent of capital gains plus an extra $3,000 per year in capital losses from ordinary income. Additional losses may be carried forward indefinitely.

In the sale of a capital asset, individuals and corporations have either capital long-term, or short-term gain or loss. If a capital asset is held for a period of less than one year and sold, the gain or loss resulting from the sale is considered a short-term gain or loss. Net short-term gains are treated like ordinary income and subject to the corresponding tax rates. While net short-term losses need to be carried forward to the next tax year. If the same asset is held longer than one year, the net gain or loss is considered long-term capital gain or loss and for individuals, taxed at lower rates of 20%, 15%, or 0%. In 2014, long term capital gains rates are 0% if your taxable income falls in the 10% or 15% income tax bracket and 15% if your taxable income falls in the 25%, 28%, 33%, or 35% income tax bracket. The rate is increased to 20% if your taxable income falls in the 39.6% income tax bracket. There is also a 28% bracket for "collectables" and a 25% tax bracket for gain due to depreciation.

Capital assets that you can depreciate, either Commercial buildings (39 years), or residential rental property (27.5 years) the gain needs to be separated into two categories. The total gain (sale value – adjusted basis) from the sale of the asset is separated into gain from the depreciation allowed and original gain from the sale of the asset (sale value - original basis). The gain from depreciation is taxed at 25%, while the long-term gain due to increase in the asset value is taxed at the the appropriate long-term capital gain rate.

Currently all qualified dividends are taxed at long-term capital gain rates and there is also a Medicare surtax that is added to investment income over a threshold. Based on Modified Adjusted Gross Income or MAGI, the threshold is set at $250,000 for married couples and $200,000 for single filers. Consult a tax professional for more information on the Medicare surtax and the threshold and limitations.

To calculate net short-term gain or loss, short-term capital gains and losses are calculated by adding the total gains and losses separately and then subtracting total losses from total gains. Similarly, long-term capital gains and losses are merged to determine the net long-term capital gain or loss. The total net short or long-term capital gain or loss is then determined by merging the net short-term gain or loss with the net long-term capital gain or loss in accordance with tax return procedures.

This is a brief summary of the current (2014) capital gains tax laws and not meant to be a holistic summary. There are a variety of rules and regulations that need to be followed to calculate capital gains under various terms and conditions. For all capital gains tax consequences consult a tax professional, or your companies tax experts.

EXAMPLE 8-1 Illustration of Individual Capital Gains Tax

An individual investor with $200,000 of annual taxable income purchased a parcel of land for $50,000 and now has an offer to sell it for $60,000. The individual is in the 33% federal ordinary income tax bracket and pays a 5.0% state tax rate on ordinary income. The applicable federal long-term capital gains tax rate is 15% but there is no corresponding reduction at the state level. State income taxes paid are deductible in computing federal taxable income.

A) Calculate the after-tax profit and the after-tax cash flow if the sale occurred 3 months after the date of purchase.

B) Calculate the after-tax profit and the after-tax cash flow if the sale occurred 12 months and one day after the date of purchase.

Solution, Case A:

If sold in three months, the gain on the sale would be taxed as ordinary income at both the state and federal level.

Sale Revenue	60,000
– Cost Basis in Land	–50,000
State Taxable Income	10,000
– State Income Tax (5%)	–500
Federal Taxable Income	9,500
– Federal Income Tax (33%)	–3,135
Net Income (Profit)	6,365
+ Cost Basis in Land	50,000
After-Tax Cash Flow	56,365

Or using Equation 8-1:

Effective Tax Rate = 0.05 + (0.33)(1 – 0.05) = 36.35%

Profit = 10,000 – 10,000(0.3635) = 6,365

After-Tax Cash Flow = 60,000 – 10,000(0.3635) = 56,365

Solution, Case B:

If sold in 12 months plus one day, the gain on the sale would qualify as long-term capital gain and a reduced federal tax rate of 15%, while the state tax rate is assumed to remain at 5.0%.

Sale Revenue	60,000
– Cost Basis in Land	–50,000
State Taxable Income	10,000
– State Income Tax (5%)	–500
Federal Taxable Income	9,500
– Federal Income Tax (15%)	–1,425
Net Income (Profit)	8,075
+ Cost Basis in Land	50,000
After-Tax Cash Flow	58,075

Or using Equation 8-1:

Effective Tax Rate = 0.05 + (0.15)(1 – 0.05) = 19.25%

Profit = 10,000 – 10,000(0.1925) = 8,075

After-Tax Cash Flow = 60,000 – 10,000(0.1925) = 58,075

8.5 Tax Treatment of Investment Terminal (Salvage) Value

Whenever an asset such as land, common stock, buildings or equipment is sold by individuals or corporations, the sale value (terminal value) is compared to original cost, or remaining tax book value of depreciable, depletable, amortizable or non-deductible asset costs to determine gain or loss. If the sale results in a gain, tax must be paid on the gain. If the sale results in a loss, the loss is deductible under the tax rules governing the handling of ordinary deductions and capital loss deductions. As we showed earlier, all long term capital gains are taxed at the ordinary income tax rates for corporations and at applicable long-term capital gains tax rate for individuals, so it is still necessary to compute whether ordinary gain or loss, or long term capital gain or loss is realized. If a loss results from the sale, the investor is eligible for either an ordinary income deduction write-off or a long term capital loss deduction write-off, again depending on the type of asset involved and the tax position of the investor. *Although corporations have capital gain income taxed as ordinary income, corporate capital losses can only be used against capital gains or carried forward.*

When either depreciable or non-depreciable property has been held for more than one year and sale value exceeds original cost, the increase in the value of property (difference in sale value and original cost) usually is treated as a long term capital gain. For individuals, any gain due to depreciation of personal property is treated as ordinary income. Accountants often refer to the tax on the gain due to depreciation as "recapturing depreciation." Since the deductions sheltered ordinary income, and were taken in an amount in excess of the current value of the asset, that component of a sale between the original purchase price and final book value is taxed at the same ordinary income tax rate. One exception is real property, where as mentioned in Section 8.4; for individuals, gain due to depreciation of real property (such as rental property) is currently taxed at a 25.0% capital gain tax rate when straight line depreciation is utilized.

EXAMPLE 8-2 Economics of Sale Value Tax Treatment

Assume an asset will be purchased in July of a calendar tax year for a cost of $100,000 and sold 2 years from that date for $180,000. The asset is being acquired by either 1) a corporation or, 2) an individual. Assume a 35% federal and 0% state income tax rate on all ordinary income. When appropriate, the individual long-term capital gains tax rate is assumed to be 15%. Calculate the after-tax cash flow and investment DCFROR on the sale for the following scenarios:

A) The asset is land, common stock or other non-depreciable property.

B) The asset is equipment, depreciable over 5-years using the MACRS rates.

C) The asset is commercial rental property and depreciated using the straight line method. Assume the building was placed into service in July of year one and the mid-month convention is appropriate.

Solutions:

A1 Corporate Analysis—Write off the land or common stock investment against the year 2 sale value. All corporate gain is taxed as ordinary income.

Year	0	1	2
Revenue		0	180,000
– Book Value		0	–100,000
Taxable Income		0	80,000
– Income Tax, 35%		0	–28,000
Net Income		0	52,000
+ Book Value		0	100,000
– Capital Cost	–100,000	0	0
After-Tax Cash Flow	–100,000	0	152,000

PW Eq: $0 = -100{,}000 + 152{,}000(P/F_{i,2})$

DCFROR, i = 23.3%

A2 Individual Analysis—Write off the land or common stock investment against the year 2 sale value. All individual gain is taxed as long-term capital gain.

Year	0	1	2
Revenue		0	180,000
– Book Value Write-off		0	–100,000
Taxable Income		0	80,000
– Income Tax, 15%		0	–12,000
Net Income		0	68,000
+ Book Value		0	100,000
– Capital Cost	–100,000	0	0
After-Tax Cash Flow	–100,000	0	168,000

PW Eq: $0 = -100{,}000 + 168{,}000(P/F_{i,2})$

DCFROR, i = 29.6%

B1 Corporate Analysis—The asset is personal property (equipment) depreciable over 5 years using the applicable MACRS rates. Other income exists against which to utilize deductions when taken.

Year	0	1	2
Revenue		0	180,000
– Depreciation		–20,000	0
– Book Value Write-off		0	–80,000
Taxable Income		–20,000	100,000
– Income Tax, 35%		7,000	–35,000
Net Income		–13,000	65,000
+ Depreciation		20,000	0
+ Book Value		0	80,000
– Capital Cost	–100,000	0	0
After-Tax Cash Flow	–100,000	7,000	145,000

PW Eq: $0 = -100{,}000 + 7{,}000(P/F_{i,1}) + 145{,}000(P/F_{i,2})$

DCFROR, i = 24.0%

B2 Individual Analysis—The asset is personal property (equipment) depreciable over 5 years using the applicable MACRS rates. Long-term capital gain tax rates applied to gain in increase of asset value. Gain due to depreciation is taxed as ordinary income. Other income exists against which to utilize deductions when taken.

Year	0	1	Ordinary Income, 2	Long-Term Cap. Gain 2
Revenue		0	100,000	180,000
– Depreciation		–20,000		0
– Book Value Write-off		0	–80,000	–100,000
Taxable Income		–20,000	20,000	80,000
– Income Tax, 35%		7,000	–7,000	0
– LT Gain Tax, 15%				–12,000
Net Income		–13,000	13,000	68,000
+ Depreciation		20,000		0
+ Book Value		0	80,000	0
– Capital Cost	–100,000	0		0
After-Tax Cash Flow	–100,000	7,000	93,000	68,000

161,000

Note: \$180,000 Sale Value Less Total Tax of \$19,000 = Sale ATCF of \$161,000

PW Eq: $0 = -100{,}000 + 7{,}000(P/F_{i,1}) + 161{,}000(P/F_{i,2})$

DCFROR, i = 30.4%

C1 Corporate Analysis—The asset is a commercial building, (real property) depreciable straight line over 39 years with the building placed into service in July of a calendar tax year. The mid-month convention is applied in the first year depreciation deduction. All gain is taxed as ordinary income. Other income exists against which to utilize deductions when taken.

Year 1 Depreciation: \$100,000(1/39)(5.5/12) = \$1,175

Year 2 Write-off: \$100,000 – \$1,175 = \$98,825

Year	0	1	2
Revenue		0	180,000
– Depreciation		–1,175	0
– Book Value Write-off		0	–98,825
Taxable Income		–1,175	81,175
– Income Tax, 35%		411	–28,411
Net Income		–764	52,764
+ Depreciation		1,175	0
+ Book Value		0	98,825
– Capital Cost	–100,000	0	0
After-Tax Cash Flow	–100,000	411	151,589

PW Eq: $0 = -100{,}000 + 411(P/F_{i,1}) + 151{,}589(P/F_{i,2})$

DCFROR, i = 23.3%

C2 Individual Analysis—The asset is a commercial building depreciable straight line over 39 years with the building placed into service in July of a calendar tax year. Mid-month convention applied in the first year depreciation deduction. Long-term capital gain tax rates applied to gain in increase of asset value. Gain due to depreciation is taxed at a 25% rate. Other income exists against which to utilize deductions when taken.

Year 1 Depreciation: $100,000(1/39)(5.5/12) = $1,175

Year 2 Write-off: $100,000 – $1,175 = $98,825

Year	0	1	Gain Due To Deprec 2	Long-Term Cap. Gain 2
Revenue		0	100,000	180,000
– Depreciation		–1,175		0
– Book Value Write-off		0	–98,825	–100,000
Taxable Income		–1,175	1,175	80,000
– Income Tax, 35%		411	0	0
– Gain DT Deprec, 25%		0	–294	0
– LT Gain Tax, 15%		0	0	–12,000
Net Income		–764	881	68,000
+ Depreciation		1,175	0	0
+ Book Value		0	98,825	0
– Capital Cost	–100,000	0	0	0
After-Tax Cash Flow	–100,000	411	99,706	68,000

167,706

Note: $180,000 Sale Value Less Total Tax of $12,294 = Sale ATCF of $167,706

PW Eq: $0 = -100{,}000 + 411(P/F_{i,1}) + 167{,}706(P/F_{i,2})$

DCFROR, i = 29.7%

8.6 State Tax Considerations

For individuals and corporations, state income tax calculations vary greatly with some states using fixed rates, while others impose incremental rates which may be based on the equivalent of federal taxable income before state income taxes or adjusted measures of value. For corporations, Colorado, Illinois, Indiana, Massachusetts, Michigan, and Pennsylvania employ a flat tax rate on applicable state taxable income while other states have no state income tax at all, including Alaska, Florida, Nevada, South Dakota, Texas, Washington, and Wyoming.

In states where no personal income tax is imposed, it is likely due to alternative taxes imposed on businesses that include mining, petroleum and perhaps timber severance, ad valorem, excise, and other taxes. Severance taxes are most typically imposed on investors who sever a natural resource from the state. Such taxes may be imposed on gross value of the resource, or a similar figure adjusted for transportation or processing necessary to realize a market value. These taxes may, or may not be offset by other local taxes such as property taxes. Just as the Federal government offers certain tax incentives on marginal properties of strategic importance (such as stripper production in oil and gas), more economically marginal properties may benefit from reduced severance tax rates, or no imposition of a tax at all. Some states offer tax holidays that initially, allow the producer to minimize risk by allowing them an opportunity to recover their investment before such taxes are imposed.

Ad valorem (according to the value) taxes may relate to the value of the resource and or the assets employed to sever the resource from the state or other taxing authority. Sometimes included under the heading of property taxes, the value may be established in a variety of calculations related to the resource. This might include a percentage of remaining reserves or more complex discounted cash flow calculations.

Excise taxes may be imposed at the Federal, State or local level but generally exist today at the Federal level. Such taxes act more like a sales tax and are often based on the units produced rather than the value of each unit.

As mentioned in Chapter 7, all severance taxes, ad valorem taxes, excise and other taxes paid or incurred in a tax year are deductible as an operating expense in computing Federal taxable income. Therefore, most models would treat all taxes other than income taxes as part of the operating expense associated with a project. In most text examples, a single effective tax rate is then employed to simplify the overall income tax liability calculations. Under current law, state corporate or individual tax paid is deductible for purposes of calculating federal taxable income, but federal tax is usually not an allowable deduction when computing state taxable income. The following effective income tax rate reflects this situation:

$$\text{Effective Income Tax Rate} = s + f(1 - s) \qquad \text{Eq. 8-1}$$

Where: "s" is the incremental state income tax rate in decimal form
"f" is the incremental federal income tax rate in decimal form

EXAMPLE 8-3 Calculation of Corporate Effective Tax Rates

Consider a $12,000,000 increment of corporate income subject to the incremental federal corporate tax rate of 35% and a 7% state corporate tax rate. Calculate the effective federal plus state tax rate and the tax to be paid on the income for this corporation.

Solution:

Using Equation 8-1:

Effective Corporate Tax Rate = 0.07 + 0.35(1-.07)
= 0.3955 or 39.55%

Total Tax Due = $12,000,000(0.3955) = $4,746,000

The same result could be obtained without the use of the effective tax rate as follows:

State Tax	= $12,000,000(0.07)	= $ 840,000
Federal Tax	= ($12,000,000 – 840,000)(0.35)	= $3,906,000
Total Tax		$4,746,000

8.7 Tax Credits

There are many forms of tax credits but the two most common are Investment Tax Credits and Business Tax Credits, both of which are described in this section. Typically, credits are thought to be more valuable then deductions because a tax credit is a dollar for dollar reduction in your tax liability, making them the primary stimulus tool that Congress has available at its disposal. However, it is important to understand many states do not recognize federal tax credits, therefore it is necessary to compute state taxable income separately when addressing this much tax detail. Furthermore, the tax credits described in this section are subject to restrictions and time limits and a tax accountant should be consulted before making investment decisions.

Investment tax credits are a specific form of tax credit aimed at increasing a certain type of investment opportunity and are typically included in the tax code in addition to the normal allowance for depletion, depreciation, and amortization (DD&A). Originally, investment tax credits were created to protect domestic companies from foreign competition, but today these tax credits are applied toward supporting research, pollution control, and energy sustainability.

A business tax credit is not a specific credit at all, instead it's a compilation of different credits all found on Form 3800. Any credit found on Form 3800 can be called a business tax credit. These credits include research, enhanced oil recovery or EOR, pension plans, and many others.

Energy Credits. In general, the following credits are available for eligible systems placed in service on or before December 31, 2016:

> **Solar:** The credit is equal to 30% of expenditures, with no maximum credit. Eligible solar energy property includes equipment that uses solar energy to generate electricity, heating or cooling, and hybrid solar lighting systems.
>
> **Fuel Cells:** The credit is equal to 30% of expenditures, with no maxi mum credit. However, the credit for fuel cells is limited to $1,500 per 0.5 kilowatt(kW) of capacity.
>
> **Small Wind Turbines:** The credit is equal to 30% of expenditures, with no maximum credit for small wind turbines (up to 100 kW) started before December 31, 2013.
>
> **Geothermal Systems:** The credit is equal to 10% of expenditures, with no maximum credit limit stated. Eligible geothermal energy property includes geothermal heat pumps and related equipment.
>
> **Microturbines:** The credit is equal to 10% of expenditures, with no maximum credit limit stated. The credit for microturbines is capped at $200 per kW of capacity.
>
> **Combined Heat and Power (CHP):** The credit is equal to 10% of expenditures, with no maximum limit stated. Eligible CHP property generally includes systems up to 50 MW in capacity that exceed 60% energy efficiency. The energy property must be operational in the year in which the credit is first taken.

Enhanced Oil Recovery. The EOR credit may be claimed on up to 15% of the eligible costs attributable to a qualified domestic EOR project for increasing the production of crude oil or to production of Alaskan natural gas for tax years beginning after 2004. The amount of this credit is phased out when the market price of crude oil exceeds an indexed figure using the GDP Price Deflator. For 2013, the indexed price of crude oil is determined based on the base price times the deflator (the index is actually used as an inflator here) or, $28.00(1.5901) = $44.50. Hence, this credit remains completely phased out as the market prices exceed the limit. Current information regarding the GDP Price Deflator can be found at www.IRS.gov.

Research & Experimentation Credit. A credit may be claimed on up to 14% of incremental research expenses incurred in the U.S above the base level of spending. The incremental expenditures include; 1) qualified research expenditures in the U.S. incurred in a year in excess of the base amount, 2) research payments made to a qualified organization and 3) research payments made to an energy research consortium. The base period is established over a 4-year period of spending. Several approaches may be utilized to establish the applicable credit. This credit has been subject to annual renewal by Congress but is currently applicable through 2013.

Bio Diesel Fuels Credit. This credit is based on the sum of three separate credits including the biodiesel mixture credit, the biodiesel credit and the small agri-biodiesel producers' credit. These credits can amount to $0.50 per gallon for the bio-diesel mixture and the biodiesel credits and $0.10 per gallon for qualified agri-biodiesel fuels producers. Agri-biodiesel credits are limited to 15 million gallons per year. These credits will expire at the end of 2013 unless modified by Congress.

Various other credits include but are not limited to work opportunity credits, alcohol fuels credit, low income housing credits, disabled access credits, renewable electricity, empowerment zones, Indian employment, employer social security credits and new market credits. The list goes on for production of a variety of energy efficient products, economic stimulus, etc.

Tax credits from all sources are credits against your regular tax bill and not deductions from taxable income such as depreciation. A dollar of tax credit saves a dollar of tax cost, while a dollar of deduction saves the investor's tax rate times a dollar of income. General business tax credits are limited to the net income tax liability less the greater of the taxpayer's tentative minimum tax liability or 25% of the regular tax liability in excess of

$25,000. Variations to this limit exist in certain circumstances. Unused business tax credits may be carried back five years or forward for up to 20 years. If not used in 20 years the credit becomes a deduction in the following year.

EXAMPLE 8-4 Tax Credit Effects on Cash Flow Compared to Depreciation Effects

Consider a project evaluation year in which annual revenue is $500,000 and operating expenses are $150,000. Assume an investor 40% effective income tax rate and calculate the annual revenue cash flow for the year assuming: Case 1) no depreciation deduction or tax credits are applicable; Case 2) annual depreciation is $100,000 with no tax credits applicable; Case 3) annual depreciation is zero with a $100,000 tax credit applicable. Also calculate the maximum tax credit that could be utilized in the Case 3 project evaluation year.

Solution: All Values in Thousands of Dollars

	Case 1 No Deprec. or Tax Credit	Case 2 $100 Deprec. No Tax Credit	Case 3 $100 Tax Credit and No Deprec.
Revenue	500	500	500
–Op. Expenses	–150	–150	–150
–Depreciation	—	–100	—
Taxable Income	350	250	350
–Tax @40%	–140	–100	–140
+Tax Credit	—	—	+100
Net Income	210	150	310
+Depreciation	—	+100	—
Cash Flow	210	250	310

Note that in Case 2 the $100,000 depreciation deduction reduced taxable income by $100,000 compared to Case 1 with no depreciation or tax credit, which reduced the income tax by $40,000 and increased the cash flow by $40,000 to $250,000 from $210,000. However, in Case 3 the $100,000 tax credit with no depreciation saved

\$100,000 in tax compared to Case 1 with no depreciation or tax credit, which increased cash flow \$100,000 to \$310,000 from \$210,000. In this analysis, based on a 40% effective income tax rate, one dollar of tax credit saves the investor one dollar while one dollar of depreciation saves the investor \$0.40. Obviously, a dollar of tax credit is more important to an investor than a dollar of tax deductions.

The maximum tax credit that can be utilized in a year is the lessor of the income tax liability or \$25,000 plus 75% of federal income tax liability in excess of \$25,000. If the entire \$140,000 income tax liability for Case 3 is assumed to be federal tax liability, \$25,000 + 0.75(\$140,000 – \$25,000) = \$111,250 would be the maximum usable tax credit in the year. Any unused credits in a year can be carried forward to subsequent years. If part of the 40% effective income tax rate is due to state tax, the maximum tax credit calculation would be based on the federal tax obligation.

EXAMPLE 8-5 Tax Credits and Energy Savings

An investor is considering the purchase of energy-saving equipment that would cost \$200,000 at time 0 and qualify for a 30% investment tax credit. The equipment would be depreciable using MACRS 5-year depreciation starting in year 1 when the equipment is put into service. Assume a 30% tax credit would also be taken in year 1. When the tax credit is taken, depreciation is based on the difference between equipment cost and the credit or 70% of the cost basis. The equipment is projected to generate annual savings from reduced energy costs amounting to \$70,000 per year in years 1 through 5. At the end of year 5 the equipment is thought to be obsolete and no longer serviceable so consider a zero salvage value and write off the remaining tax book value at the end of year 5. Assuming no other income exists against which to use deductions when incurred, and that the appropriate combined federal and state income tax rate is 40%, calculate the project DCFROR and NPV for $i^* = 15\%$ if:

A) The tax credit is considered to not be applicable.
B) The tax credit is applicable.
C) Other income exists to claim the full tax credit value in year 1.

Solution in Thousands of Dollars:

A) ATCF where tax credit is not considered to be applicable:

Year	0	1	2	3	4	5
Savings		70.0	70.0	70.0	70.0	70.0
- Depreciation		-40.0	-64.0	-38.4	-23.0	-34.6
Taxable Income		30.0	6.0	31.6	47.0	35.4
- Income Tax		-12.0	-2.4	-12.6	-18.8	-14.2
+ Tax Credit						
Net Income		18.0	3.6	19.0	28.2	21.2
+ Depreciation		40.0	64.0	38.4	23.0	34.6
- Capital, Equip.	-200.0					
ATCF	-200.0	58.0	67.6	57.4	51.2	55.8

PW Eq: $0 = -200.0 + 58.0(P/F_{i,1}) + 67.6(P/F_{i,2}) + 57.4(P/F_{i,3})$

$+ 51.2(P/F_{i,4}) + 55.8(P/F_{i,5})$

DCFROR = 14.2 % < i* = 15%, reject investment
NPV @ 15% = $-3.7 < 0, reject investment

Without the tax credit, this project is economically unsatisfactory. In Case B the tax credit is shown to convert this scenario into an economically satisfactory investment opportunity for the parameters as described.

B) ATCF where 30% tax credit is applicable, stand alone model:

Tax credit = $200,000(30%) = $60,000 or 60 in 000's
Cost basis for depreciation = 200,000 – 60,000 = 140,000

Year	0	1	2	3	4	5
Savings		70.0	70.0	70.0	70.0	70.0
- Depreciation		-28.0	-44.8	-26.9	-16.1	-24.2
Taxable Income		42.0	25.2	43.1	53.9	45.8
- Income Tax		-16.8	-10.1	-17.2	-21.6	-18.3
+ Tax Credit		16.8	10.1	17.2	15.9	0.0
Net Income		42.0	25.2	43.1	48.2	27.5
+ Depreciation		28.0	44.8	26.9	16.1	24.2
- Capital, Equip.	-200.0					
ATCF	-200.0	70.0	70.0	70.0	64.3	51.7

PW Eq: $0 = -200.0 + 70.0(P/A_{i,3}) + 64.3(P/F_{i,4}) + 51.7(P/F_{i,5})$

DCFROR = 19.8% > i* = 15%, accept investment
NPV @ 15% = $22.9 > 0, accept investment

The economic impact of the tax credit was to convert an economically unsatisfactory scenario in an economically acceptable project. This is further enhanced by the financial ability of an investor to utilize deductions when other income exists that might have its tax liability reduced immediately as opposed to a credit being carried forward and used against future project income tax. Consider Case C to illustrate this point.

C) ATCF where 30% tax credit is applicable, other income and income tax exists against which to utilize the available tax credit:

Tax credit = \$200,000 (30%) = \$60,000 or 60 in 000's
Cost basis for depreciation = 200,000 – 60,000 = 140,000

Year	0	1	2	3	4	5
Savings		70.0	70.0	70.0	70.0	70.0
- Depreciation		-28.0	-44.8	-26.9	-16.1	-24.2
Taxable Income		42.0	25.2	43.1	53.9	45.8
- Income Tax		-16.8	-10.1	-17.2	-21.6	-18.3
+ Tax Credit		60.0	0.0	0.0	0.0	0.0
Net Income		85.2	15.1	25.9	32.3	27.5
+ Depreciation		28.0	44.8	26.9	16.1	24.2
- Capital, Equip.	-200.0					
ATCF	-200.0	113.2	59.1	52.8	48.4	51.7

PW Eq: $0 = -200.0 + 113.2(P/F_{i,1}) + 59.1(P/F_{i,2}) + 52.8(P/F_{i,3})$

$+ 48.4(P/F_{i,4}) + 51.7(P/F_{i,5})$

DCFROR = 22.7 % > i* = 15%, accept investment
NPV @ 15% = \$31.2 > 0, accept investment

This analysis assumes claimed tax credit was not in excess of the annual limitations previously described. Timing of deductions and tax credits and the investor's ability to utilize those items can significantly impact economic performance of an investment as demonstrated here.

8.8 Alternative Minimum Tax (AMT)

Alternative Minimum Tax (AMT) is a separate tax that is applicable to both individuals and businesses. In certain circumstances, this confusing aspect of the tax code may diminish economic benefits offered by Congress through various stimulus measures that are not applicable to both federal tax and AMT. Certain deductions and credits designed to encourage investment may be claimed for regular Federal income tax but may not be allowed in computing AMT. In certain circumstances, the deductions and credits are allowed for both regular Federal taxes and AMT.

AMT was firmly established by the Revenue Reconciliation Act of 1989 to prevent corporations and individuals from using deductions, exemptions, and credits to completely avoid their regular federal income tax liability. AMT is computed by determining the taxpayer's alternative minimum taxable income (AMTI) and the tentative minimum tax (TMT) related to that income. If TMT is greater than the regular federal tax liability, investors must pay the difference as their alternative minimum tax. The difference occurs because AMTI is generally based on slower methods of deducting costs than what is allowed for regular Federal income tax purposes. Therefore, more income is initially exposed to tax. As a result, many corporate and individual taxpayers must pay AMT in addition to their regular Federal income tax liability.

AMT was introduced in the late 1960's and was intended to stop a small number of millionaires from eliminating their Federal income tax through various deductions and credits. In 2013, the Tax Policy Center estimated that 33% of Americans with income between $200,000 and $500,000 would be subject to AMT. Only 2% of people with income between $100,000 and $200,000 would pay AMT, and less than 1% of those Americans making less than $100,000. People making over $1,000,000 have a smaller percentage of people paying AMT than those making less than $500,000.

A simplistic breakdown of this tax follows:

Regular Tax Calculation

Revenue
– Operating Costs
– Depreciation
– Depletion
– Amortization
– State Income Tax

Federal Taxable Income

35% of Federal Taxable Income = Regular Federal Income Tax on Corporate Taxable Income Above $10 Million.

Alternative Minimum Tax Calculation

Federal Taxable Income
+ Net Operating Loss (Loss Forward)
± Adjustments
+ Tax Preference Items (TPIs)
± Adjusted Current Earnings Adjustment
± Other AMT Items
– AMT Net Operating Loss

Alternative Minimum Taxable Income

20% of AMTI (Corporate Rate)
= Tentative Minimum Tax

Alternative Minimum Tax Based On:

Tentative Minimum Tax (TMT)
– Regular Federal Income Tax

= Alternative Minimum Tax (AMT)

The starting basis for AMT is regular federal taxable income from all sources. A number of "adjustments" and "preferences" are taken to regular federal taxable income to determine alternative minimum taxable income (AMTI), which is then taxed at 20.0% for corporations. In 2014, the AMT rates for joint returns and unmarried individuals are 26% on AMTI up to \$182,500 and 28% on AMTI in excess of that amount. AMTI taken times the appropriate AMT tax rate gives tentative minimum tax (TMT). Finally, the difference between the TMT and the regular federal tax liability is the taxpayer AMT for a given year, which if positive, is paid in addition to the regular tax, if any.

Prior to 2013, Congress had to pass legislation establishing inflation adjustments to determine AMT. A portion of the American Taxpayer Relief Act of 2012 made permanent the standard deductions for individuals and families and indexed the AMT system for the effects of inflation. It is estimated by the Tax Policy Center that 3.9 million Americans will pay AMT totaling \$25.6 billion dollars, on average increasing each persons tax bill by just over \$6,600.

A partial list of corporate "AMT Adjustments" includes; depreciation, mine exploration and development costs, long-term contracts (percentage of completion accounting methodology must be used), amortization of pollution control facilities, certain installment sales, and the alcohol fuels credits.

An "AMT adjustment" is defined as the yearly difference between the regular tax deduction for a given expenditure and its allowed deduction under AMT rules. As an example, for real property placed into service in 1999 and beyond, MACRS depreciation guidelines may be used in computing both regular federal and alternative minimum taxable income resulting in no depreciation adjustment. However, for depreciable personal property, the MACRS recovery periods are applicable for AMT purposes, but you must use a slower 150% declining balance switching to straight line methodology.

So, for a \$1,000,000 investment in 7-year MACRS depreciable personal property, the first year deduction for regular federal income tax would be:

$$\$1{,}000{,}000(2/7)(1/2) = \$1{,}000{,}000(0.1429) = \$142{,}900$$

For AMT purposes, the first year deduction would be:

$$\$1{,}000{,}000(1.5/7)(1/2) = \$1{,}000{,}000(0.1071) = \$107{,}100$$

The difference of $35,800 would represent additional income exposed to Alternative Minimum Tax that year, or it might be described as an adjustment for purposes of computing Alternative Minimum Taxable Income (AMTI).

Table 8-3, 150% Declining Balance for AMT Depreciation

Year	3 Years	5 Years	7 Years	10 Years
1	25.00%	15.00%	10.71%	7.50%
2	37.50%	25.50%	19.13%	13.88%
3	25.00%	17.85%	15.03%	11.79%
4	12.50%	16.66%	12.25%	10.02%
5		16.66%	12.25%	8.74%
6		8.33%	12.25%	8.74%
7			12.25%	8.74%
8			6.13%	8.74%
9				8.74%
10				8.74%
11				4.37%

Mining development costs are 70% expensed and 30% amortized over 60 months for regular tax purposes, but these costs must be deducted straight line over 10 years for AMT purposes. Therefore, in the first year of such expenditures, AMTI will increase, but in later years, the adjustment will reduce the AMTI exposure for that expenditure. The AMT adjustment on mining development costs can be avoided by using straight-line, 10 year life amortization deductions for regular tax purposes.

Unlike adjustments, "AMT Preferences" (also known as Tax Preference Items (TPIs) always increase the amount of AMTI. Corporate Tax Preference Items include but are not limited to; mining percentage depletion that exceeds the cost depletion adjusted basis for a property, integrated petroleum producer intangible drilling costs (IDCs), tax exempt interest on certain bonds and reserves for losses on bad debts of financial institutions.

An integrated oil and gas company can avoid the Tax Preference Item for IDCs by amortizing all IDCs over 60 months for regular federal income tax purposes.

The "Adjusted Current Earnings Adjustment" (also known as the ACE Adjustment) attempts to align publicly traded companies taxable income as reported to the shareholders (measured by the ACE) with the company

AMTI. A corporation's AMTI must be increased by 75% of the amount by which its ACE exceeds its AMTI, computed without the adjustments for either the ACE preference or AMT Loss Forward deduction. Enough said!

For married persons filing jointly, the AMT exemption or patch is $82,100 and indexed annually for inflation. For individuals, the exemption amount is $52,800 and also indexed for inflation. For corporations, the exemption is $40,000 but not indexed for inflation.

The AMT Loss forward deduction is known in the tax code as an Alternative Net Operating Loss (or, Alternative NOL) and is calculated in a manner similar to other loss forward deductions, except that the Alternative NOL is reduced by all tax preference items and tax items that must be adjusted for AMTI. This deduction may not offset more than 90% of AMTI computed without the Alternative NOL.

A taxpayer may recover any paid AMT in subsequent years that AMT is not paid, through the "Minimum Tax Credit" (MTC). A corporation is entitled to a credit against regular tax that equals its full AMT liability from previous years, but not exceeding its regular tax payment. Individuals however, must exclude certain adjustments and preferences when calculating their MTC. The MTC is a benefit to the taxpayer if it can be used quickly (due to time value of money). Depending on a taxpayers financial position, if year to year the company is moving in and out of an AMT liability, generally the effects of the tax are neglected due to the limited time value of money issues and the difficulty of trying to estimate the tax. However, for corporations with a longstanding tradition of exposure to AMT, minimization of this tax becomes the objective within the context of economic modeling.

Oil and gas producers may not use certain tax credits against regular federal income tax when they are under AMT. The alternative fuels credits related to coalbed methane and tight gas sands and the enhanced oil recovery credit cannot reduce regular federal income tax below TMT. This means that in any year a firm owes AMT, it may not use the above tax credits. For eligible producers that expect they will pay AMT for several years, the loss of the tax credits can be a serious economic detriment.

Another onerous aspect of AMT is its regressive nature. When product prices are low, profits are squeezed which generates losses regarding regular federal taxable income. However, this may create more exposure to AMTI, as the generated deductions may not be fully deductible for AMTI. So, investors are hit with higher AMT when they can least afford to pay higher taxes.

AMT is expensive not only in terms of the additional tax burden it presents, but also because of the effort required to calculate the tax each year. Corporations must now maintain several sets of books to account for the regular federal income tax, shareholder financial reporting, adjusted current earnings, AMT and other business transactions. For some investors, the cost of monitoring the AMT calculations may exceed the resulting tentative minimum tax payment.

Subchapter S corporations, partnerships, real estate mortgage investment conduits (REMICs) and foreign corporations (excluding their income from U.S. business) are exempt from AMT. However, income from these entities is transferred to individuals or shareholders who must then calculate regular federal income tax and AMT. All other corporations and individuals with income must also compute AMT yearly. Therefore, it is necessary to consider the impact of AMT on investments and project evaluations but given the complexity, usually this tax is neglected unless the investor is assured of a long-term exposure to AMT. As previously mentioned, in such cases the tax rates reflect applicable AMT rates and deductions are modified to reduce the exposure to AMT. On a long run basis, due to the Minimum Tax Credit, AMT should not result in additional tax being paid, it simply is a timing issue that each investor must address individually as to its significance in the projects being evaluated.

8.9 Discounted Cash Flow Rate of Return (DCFROR), Net Present Value (NPV) and Ratio Analysis

DCFROR is defined commonly as the rate of return that makes the present worth of positive and negative after-tax cash flow for an investment equal to zero. This is another way of saying DCFROR is the rate of return that makes after-tax NPV equal to zero. Discounting means to "present worth" and the name "discounted cash flow rate of return" comes from the fact that classically, present worth or discounting equations most often have been used to obtain the DCFROR. It already has been shown many times earlier in this text that the same rate of return results from writing an annual or future worth equation or in general by comparing costs and incomes (or negative and positive cash flow) at any point in time, as long as all cash flows are brought to the same point in time. It was mentioned earlier in this chapter that other names commonly used for DCFROR are Profitability Index (P.I.), Investor's ROR, True ROR, and Internal ROR or IRR. Polls of industry presently indicate that DCFROR is the number one economic evaluation decision method used by about two thirds of industrial companies that use a formal economic evaluation procedure to evaluate the economic potential of investments. In this regard it is relevant to note that most major industrial companies use formal discounted cash flow investment evaluation procedures of the type described, discussed, and illustrated in this text.

Net present value (NPV) on an after-tax basis equals the present worth of positive and negative cash flow calculated at the after-tax minimum rate of return. NPV greater than zero indicates a satisfactory investment. Project DCFROR is compared to the after-tax minimum rate of return, "i^*", to determine if a particular project is satisfactory compared to other alternative uses that exist for the investment capital. *For after-tax analysis using any valid analysis technique, the minimum rate of return, "i^*", must be expressed on an after-tax basis. Comparing an after-tax DCFROR for a project with other investment opportunities expressed on a before-tax basis would be meaningless.* With proper handling of inflation and escalation in analyses it was emphasized earlier that all alternatives must be compared on the same basis, either using escalated dollar analysis or constant dollar analysis. Similarly, with after-tax analysis, all alternatives must be on an after-tax basis including other opportunities represented by the minimum rate of return, "i^*".

After-tax present value ratio, (PVR), or benefit/cost ratio, (B/C Ratio), is calculated using after-tax positive and negative cash flow similar to the NPV and DCFROR calculations. Correct ratio denominators are the present worth of project negative cash flow not covered by positive cash flow in the year negative cash flow is incurred or in earlier years. PVR greater than zero is satisfactory while B/C Ratio greater than one is satisfactory.

To calculate DCFROR, NPV or ratios, the first thing that must be done is to calculate after-tax cash flow for each year of the evaluation life. This includes converting all capital costs and salvage values to after-tax values by accounting properly for all appropriate tax considerations. It is desirable to place the after-tax negative and positive cash flows on a time diagram to insure that the subsequent evaluation handles them at the correct point in time. After-tax evaluation calculation procedures are illustrated in Examples 8-6, 8-7, 8-8 and 8-9 for relatively straightforward evaluation cases. In Chapters 9, 10 and 11, DCFROR, NPV and ratios are applied to a wide variety of evaluation situations that will familiarize the reader with the handling of these and other evaluation methods in a diversity of investment situations. The DCFROR, NPV, and ratio calculations are very straightforward once the after-tax cash flows are determined. The key to correct, successful economic evaluation work rests heavily on experience with proper methods for the following evaluation points: (1) correct handling of all allowable income tax deductions, especially depreciation, amortization, depletion and deferred deductions to determine correct taxable income; (2) adding back to net income the proper non-cash deductions to obtain cash flow (deferred deductions, amortized research and development expenses, and special tax write-offs are add-back items frequently mishandled); (3) proper handling of tax considerations for costs that may be written off for tax purposes in the year in which they are incurred against other income rather than being capitalized and deducted over a period of time greater than one year; (4) correct accounting for tax effects on salvage value, either tax to be paid or tax write-offs to be taken (in some investment situations such as land investment, salvage value may be the major project income so it is imperative that salvage tax considerations be handled correctly to get valid analysis results); (5) proper handling of incremental tax credit considerations when looking at differences between alternatives, such as in mutually exclusive income alternative analysis of projects for which tax credits are applicable.

The next example illustrates the sensitivity of DCFROR analysis for different methods of handling the tax deductions for a given cost. Some costs such as equipment and buildings are depreciable by either the MACRS rates or by straight line depreciation. Other costs such as operating expenses, research, development, intangible drilling costs and mineral exploration or development may, at least in part, be expensed in the year incurred. Expensing is the fastest method of deducting costs for tax purposes and depending on the investor financial situation, may require either, (1) carrying losses forward, if other taxable income does not exist against which to use negative taxable income in any year, (making the project "stand alone"); (2) crediting the project with tax savings in the year negative taxable income is incurred by assuming other taxable income will exist against which to use deductions. Economic results are affected significantly by the method that costs may be deducted for tax purposes and by the financial assumption concerning whether income will or will not exist against which to use negative taxable income in the year incurred.

EXAMPLE 8-6 The Effect of Tax Deduction Timing and the Investor Financial Situation on DCFROR Results

A $100,000 investment cost has been incurred by a corporation to generate a project with a 5 year life and estimated zero salvage value. Project escalated dollar income is estimated to be $80,000 in year 1, $84,000 in year 2, $88,000 in year 3, $92,000 in year 4, and $96,000 in year 5. Operating expenses are estimated to be $30,000 in year 1, $32,000 in year 2, $34,000 in year 3, $36,000 in year 4, and $38,000 in year 5. The effective income tax rate is 40.0%. Write-off remaining book values at the end of project year 5. For a minimum rate of return of 10%, calculate the project NPV and DCFROR if the initial $100,000 investment goes into service in year 1 and is handled in four different ways for after-tax analysis purposes. Consider the $100,000 investment is:

A) Depreciable straight line for a 5 year life assuming the half-year 1 convention.

B) Depreciable by MACRS for a 5 year life assuming the half-year 1 convention.

C) Expensed as a research cost in time 0 with negative taxable income carried forward to be used against project income (stand alone economics).

D) Expensed as research cost in time 0 assuming other taxable income exists against which to use the deduction.

Solution: All Values in Thousands of Dollars

Note that the cumulative amount of tax deductions is $100,000 by all four methods of analysis. Only the timing of the tax deductions differs between methods. Since all methods of analysis involve the same cumulative revenues and tax deductions, they also involve the same cumulative tax and cash flow. However, as you go from A) straight line depreciation, to, B) MACRS depreciation, to, C) expensing and carrying forward, to, D) expensing against other income, the timing of tax deductions, and therefore tax savings, is affected significantly causing notable differences to occur in the DCFROR results.

In reviewing the four solutions, note that in each case, the cumulative net income will equal the cumulative cash flow generated by the project. In all cases, the cumulative value is $102 but to obtain this value for the Case C) net income, combine the cumulative income with the loss forward deductions.

This equality between cumulative net income and cumulative cash flow is not by chance. In calculating the after-tax cash flow, capital costs are charged to the project while depreciation is deducted to determine taxable income and then added back to net income. Therefore, the depreciation deduction is cancelled out, except for the tax effects. In focusing on net income, depreciation and write-offs represent an allocation of the capital costs, rather than a tax deduction. The timing difference in the two series is what's critical to the economic evaluation process.

A) Straight Line Depreciation

The half-year 1 deduction causes book value amounting to a half year depreciation deduction to exist at the end of year 5. This book value is deducted (written-off) at year 5. Note that cumulative depreciation over the 5 year project life plus the write-off equals the $100 capital cost.

Note that the cumulative income tax paid over the five-year life is $68 and the cumulative cash flow is $102. You will observe that these cumulative numbers are the same for Cases B, C and D. This is not a coincidence! Only the timing of the deductions varies which affects the timing of the income tax and cash flow from Cases A to D.

Year	0	1	2	3	4	5	Cumulative
Revenue		80.0	84.0	88.0	92.0	96.0	440.0
–Oper. Costs		–30.0	–32.0	–34.0	–36.0	–38.0	–170.0
–Depreciation		–10.0	–20.0	–20.0	–20.0	–20.0	–90.0
–Write-off						–10.0	–10.0
Taxable Income		40.0	32.0	34.0	36.0	28.0	170.0
–Tax @ 40%		–16.0	–12.8	–13.6	–14.4	–11.2	–68.0
Net Income		24.0	19.2	20.4	21.6	16.8	102.0
+Depreciation		10.0	20.0	20.0	20.0	20.0	90.0
+Write-off						10.0	10.0
–Capital Costs	–100.0						–100.0
Cash Flow	–100.0	34.0	39.2	40.4	41.6	46.8	102.0

PW Eq: $0 = -100 + 34.0(P/F_{i,1}) + 39.2(P/F_{i,2}) + 40.4(P/F_{i,3})$
$+ 41.6(P/F_{i,4}) + 46.8(P/F_{i,5})$

i = DCFROR = 27.45%

NPV @ 10% = $51.1

B) MACRS 5-Year Depreciation

Note that cumulative depreciation over the 5 year project life plus the write-off equals the $100 capital cost as with straight line depreciation. However, the timing is different and the faster deductions (bigger deductions in early years) with MACRS depreciation relative to straight line give faster tax benefits and better economics as shown by the 29.0% DCFROR with MACRS depreciation compared to 27.45% with straight line depreciation.

Year	0	1	2	3	4	5	Cumulative
Revenue		80.0	84.0	88.0	92.0	96.0	440.0
–Oper Costs		–30.0	–32.0	–34.0	–36.0	–38.0	–170.0
–Depreciation		–20.0	–32.0	–19.2	–11.5	–11.5	–94.2
–Write-off						–5.8	–5.8
Taxable Income		30.0	20.0	34.8	44.5	40.7	170.00
–Tax @ 40%		–12.0	–8.0	–13.9	–17.8	–16.3	–68.0
Net Income		18.0	12.0	20.9	26.7	24.4	102.0
+Depreciation		20.0	32.0	19.2	11.5	11.5	94.2
+Write-off						5.8	5.8
–Capital Costs	–100.0						–100.0
Cash Flow	–100.0	38.0	44.0	40.1	38.2	41.7	102.0

PW Eq: $0 = -100 + 38.0(P/F_{i,1}) + 44.0(P/F_{i,2}) + 40.1(P/F_{i,3})$

$+ 38.2(P/F_{i,4}) + 41.7(P/F_{i,5})$

i = DCFROR = 29.02%

NPV @ 10% = $53.0

C) Expense Research and Carry Loss Forward (Stand Alone)

Remember, a "stand alone" financial scenario assumes the project being evaluated is the only source of income available for the investor. Therefore, any negative taxable income (a loss in that year) must be carried forward and used against positive taxable income in later years.

Note again, the cumulative deduction realized equals the $100 cost but the deduction and tax benefits from the deduction are realized more quickly than for either depreciation case. Therefore, expensing the $100 cost gives a better economic result, as the 32.65% DCFROR compared to the smaller depreciation case results illustrates.

Year	0	1	2	3	4	5	Cumulative
Revenue		80.0	84.0	88.0	92.0	96.0	440.0
–Oper Costs		–30.0	–32.0	–34.0	–36.0	–38.0	–170.0
–Research	–100.0						–100.0
–Loss Forward		–100.0	–50.0				–150.0
Taxable Inc.	–100.0	–50.0	2.0	54.0	56.0	58.0	20.0
–Tax @ 40%			–0.8	–21.6	–22.4	–23.2	–68.0
Net Income	–100.0	–50.0	1.2	32.4	33.6	34.8	–48.0
+Loss Forward		100.0	50.0				150.0
–Capital Costs							
Cash Flow	–100.0	50.0	51.2	32.4	33.6	34.8	102.0

PW Eq: $0 = -100 + 50(P/F_{i,1}) + 51.2(P/F_{i,2}) + 32.4(P/F_{i,3}) + 33.6(P/F_{i,4}) + 34.8(P/F_{i,5})$

i = DCFROR = 32.65%

NPV @ 10% = $56.7

D) Expense Research Against Other Income

Again, the cumulative deduction equals the $100 cost, but having other income on the investor tax return in year 0 against which to use the negative taxable income (-$100) gives the investor the tax benefit of inflow of money immediately in year 0. This gives a better economic result than any of the other cases. In the U.S., where quarterly estimated tax payments must be made by all business investors, tax savings from tax deductions generally are realized within three months of incurring tax deductible costs.

Year	0	1	2	3	4	5	Cumulative
Revenue		80.0	84.0	88.0	92.0	96.0	440.0
–Oper Costs		–30.0	–32.0	–34.0	–36.0	–38.0	–170.0
–Research	–100.0						–100.0
Taxable Inc.	–100.0	50.0	52.0	54.0	56.0	58.0	170.0
–Tax @ 40%	40.0	–20.0	–20.8	–21.6	–22.4	–23.2	–68.0
Net Income	–60.0	30.0	31.2	32.4	33.6	34.8	102.0
–Capital Costs							
Cash Flow	–60.0	30.0	31.2	32.4	33.6	34.8	102.0

$$\text{PW Eq: } 0 = -60.0 + 30.0(P/F_{i,1}) + 31.2(P/F_{i,2}) + 32.4(P/F_{i,3}) + 33.6(P/F_{i,4}) + 34.8(P/F_{i,5})$$

$$i = \text{DCFROR} = 44.16\%$$

$$\text{NPV @ } 10\% = \$62.0$$

The reader should observe from these analysis results that the faster an investor realizes tax deductions and the tax benefits from the tax deductions, the better the economics of projects become. Expensing the $100,000 cost against other income gives a 60% increase in the DCFROR that is obtained by straight line depreciation of the cost. If you have to carry negative taxable income forward to make the project economics "stand alone" as in part "C," the project economics do not look as good as when other income is assumed to exist against which to use deductions in the year incurred, as in part "D."

Finally, as an alternative to treating the research cost in part "D" as a tax expense item, consider it to be depreciable with a rate of 1.0 in year 0. This is an approach sometimes used in industry practice, so the reader should be aware of the equivalence of either approach as the following year 0 cash flow calculations for part "D" illustrate.

An Alternative to "D"

	Year 0 Research as an Expensed Cost	Year 0 Research as a Depreciable Cost
Revenue		
–Oper Costs		
–Research	–100.0	
–Research as Depreciation		–100.0
Taxable Income	–100.0	–100.0
–Tax @40%	40.0	40.0
Net Income	–60.0	–60.0
+Depreciation		100.0
–Capital Costs		–100.0
Cash Flow	–60.0	–60.0

Example 8-6 involved a single investment cost that was either depreciated or expensed for tax deduction purposes. Most businesses also require inventory costs, commonly called working capital, which are not depreciable as discussed in the following section.

8.10 Working Capital

Working capital is the money necessary to operate a business on a day-to-day basis. It normally is comprised of money required for raw material inventory, in-process materials inventory, product inventory, accounts receivable, and ready cash. For evaluation purposes, working capital generally is considered to be put into a project at the start of a business or production operation and to be fully recovered at the end of the project life when inventories are liquidated.

Working capital is not allowable as a tax deduction in the year it is incurred so it often has a very negative effect on project economics. Working capital cost may not be expensed, depreciated, amortized or depleted until inventory assets are actually used or put into service. One way to explain working capital and why it is not deductible for tax purposes in the year it is incurred, is to consider the determination of the "Cost of Goods Sold" as it is handled on corporate or individual business tax returns. Table 8-3 illustrates the steps necessary to calculate the annual cost of goods sold for a business operated either by an individual, partnership or corporation. In this cost of goods sold calculation, value of inventories at the year end is working capital and is not tax deductible.

Beginning of Year Inventory
+ Raw Material Costs from Purchases During the Year
+ Labor Costs to Convert Raw Material or Parts Into Products
+ Materials, Parts & Supply Costs Incurred During the Year
+ Other Costs Related to Production of Products

= Cost of Materials, Supplies and Goods Available for Sale
– Inventory Value at Year End Based on Lesser of Cost or Value
(This is money tied up in Working Capital)

= Cost of Goods Sold (Deductible as Annual Operating Cost)

Table 8-3 Calculation of Cost of Goods Sold Related to Working Capital

Working capital represents the capital cost required to generate raw material inventories, in-process inventories, product inventories and parts and supplies inventories. As inventories are used and product sold, working capital cost items become allowable tax deductions as operating costs through the cost of goods sold calculation. However, as inventory items are used they typically are replaced so inventories are maintained at a similar level over the project life. If significant increases or decreases in working capital are projected to occur from year to year, positive or negative working capital costs can be accounted for from year to year in project analyses.

Now it should occur to you that raw material and parts in inventory often are acquired at different costs during a year. How do you determine the value of items left in inventory at the end of a tax year when items were acquired for different costs during the year with some used and some left in inventory? FIFO, LIFO and average inventory accounting are the three basic inventory accounting systems that determine the costs of items used during a tax year to be deducted as operating expenses and the costs of items left in inventory and treated as working capital. FIFO is the acronym that stands for "First-In-First-Out." Using FIFO inventory accounting, the first items to go into inventory are considered to be the first items to come out and be used and deducted as operating expenses. Therefore, under FIFO inventory accounting, the last items purchased during a tax year are the cost basis for inventory assets tied up in working capital.

LIFO is the acronym for "Last-In-First-Out." Using LIFO inventory accounting, the last items to go into inventory are considered to be the first items to come out to meet sales in that period. Under LIFO, if inventories increase at the end of the period, the first items that were acquired or produced form the cost basis for the inventory and represent money tied up in working capital. In an inflationary environment, LIFO gives tax deductions for the larger cost items acquired or produced later in that period. In a period of deflation, the opposite is true.

The current administration has proposed to eliminate LIFO as a viable method of valuing inventories in the United States. In the 2014 Budget they proposed, "the repeal of the LIFO method would eliminate a tax deferral opportunity available to tax payers that hold inventories, the costs of which increase over time. In addition, LIFO repeal would simplify the Code by removing a complex and burdensome accounting method that has been the source of controversy between taxpayers and the Internal Revenue Service."

They go on to suggest, " International Financial Reporting Standards do not permit the use of LIFO method, and their adoption by the Securities and Exchange Commission would cause violations of the current LIFO book/tax conformity requirement. Repealing LIFO would remove this possible impediment to the implementation of these standards in the United States." From General Explanations of the Administration's Fiscal Year 2014 Revenue Proposals, Department of the Treasury, April, 2013.

Changes in inventory methods may only be made once every five years and that requires the approval of the IRS. Companies choose LIFO because inherently, this country tends to realize inflation in cost of product produced and sold, rather than deflation. Therefore, using LIFO results in a realistic summary of costs incurred for product produced and sold in a given accounting period. From an economic perspective, value is added to the shareholder under this methodology, not taken away, as the administration seems to be suggesting.

Most examples and problems in this textbook that include working capital are based on a basic LIFO format, assuming that when inventories build up, a cost is incurred that is not deductible at that time. When inventories are drawn down, the value of these less expensive units is recognized as a deduction in the cost of goods sold. However, this non-cash deduction is usually listed separately, so as not to be confused with the cash component of costs in that period. Since what is done for tax purposes is also used in financial reporting, Net Income may be smaller under this method but cash flow is improved and it's the later that represents value added to an investor.

Ultimately, the SEC and the IRS will have to reach reconciliation on this change in inventory options assuming the country does move fully towards the International Financial Reporting Standards, which are further discussed in Chapter 9.

Average inventory accounting is based on using annual weighted average prices or values of assets in inventory for the cost of goods sold and working capital calculations. In most western world countries other than the U.S., LIFO inventory accounting is not permitted. Therefore, FIFO and average inventory accounting are emphasized in countries other than the U.S.

In accounting terminology working capital is defined as the difference between current assets and current liabilities. This definition is consistent with our "Cost of Goods Sold" calculation explanation of working capital. When a new business or production facility is started-up, it often generates and produces product for three or four months before product is sold and income is received for product sold. Assuming the business pays cash for raw materials, parts and supplies during the start-up period, the cost of these items increases the "current assets" of the business. If all items have been paid for with cash (no time payments), no current liabilities are accrued, so current assets minus current liabilities equals the working capital which is the value of items in inventory including product inventory.

EXAMPLE 8-7 Project Analysis with Annual Changes in Working Capital: FIFO, LIFO, and Average Inventory Accounting

A project is being analyzed that has product selling price, production costs, annual production and annual sales summarized as follows:

Product Price and Production Cost Information

Year	0	1	2	3
Selling Price, $/Unit	$21	$21	$21	$21
Production Cost, $/Unit	$10	$13	$15	$17

Production/Inventory Information

Year	0	1	2	3
Units Produced	500,000	1,000,000	1,000,000	500,000
Units Sold	0	800,000	1,000,000	1,200,000
Change in Inventory	500,000	200,000	0	-700,000
Cumulative Inventory	500,000	700,000	700,000	0
Cost of Units Produced	$5,000,000	$13,000,000	$15,000,000	$8,500,000

To generate this production, a year 0 capital cost of $10,000,000 is projected to be incurred with 7-year life MACRS depreciation applicable starting in year 1. The project will terminate at the end of year 3, with zero salvage value and a write-off on remaining depreciable book value. The effective income tax rate is 40%. Calculate project DCFROR assuming the cost of goods sold (COGS) operating cost and working capital valuations are based on:

A) First-In-First-Out (FIFO) inventory accounting
B) Last-In-First-Out (LIFO) inventory accounting
C) Average inventory accounting

Solution:

In comparing the FIFO, LIFO, and average inventory accounting economic results for the analysis, note that LIFO gives the largest cost of goods sold operating cost deductions and the smallest working capital costs in early project years relative to FIFO and average inventory accounting results. Therefore, the best economic results occur with LIFO. With escalating production costs from year to year, LIFO always gives faster tax deductions relative to FIFO and average inventory accounting, which is why virtually all large U.S. companies use LIFO inventory accounting for all major raw material and product inventory items. For this analysis, and in general for all analysis situations, average inventory accounting gives project results that are in between FIFO and LIFO results.

A) FIFO Inventory Accounting

Cost of Goods Sold—FIFO

Year	0	1	2	3
Beginning Inventory, $	0	5,000,000	9,100,000	10,500,000
+ Cost of Product Produced	5,000,000	13,000,000	15,000,000	8,500,000
Cost of Available Goods	5,000,000	18,000,000	24,100,000	19,000,000
– Inventory Value at Yr End	5,000,000	9,100,000	10,500,000	0
Cost of Goods Sold	0	8,900,000	13,600,000	19,000,000

Year 1 Year End Inventory Value = 700,000 * $13 = $9,100,000
Year 1 COGS = (500,000 * $10) + (300,000 * $13) = $8,900,000
Year 2 Year End Inventory Value = 700,000 * $15 = $10,500,000
Year 2 COGS = (700,000 * $13) + (300,000 * $15) = $13,600,000
Year 3 Year End Inventory Value = 0 * $17 = $0
Year 3 COGS = (700,000 * $15) + (500,000 * $17) = $19,000,000

After-Tax Cash Flows Using FIFO

Year	0	1	2	3
Revenue	0	16,800,000	21,000,000	25,200,000
– Cost of Goods Sold	0	–8,900,000	–13,600,000	–19,000,000
– Deprec. Equipment	0	–1,429,000	–2,449,000	–1,749,000
– Deprec Writeoff	0	0	0	–4,373,000
Taxable Income	0	6,471,000	4,951,000	78,000
– Income Tax @ 40%	0	–2,588,400	–1,980,400	–31,200
Net Income	0	3,882,600	2,970,600	46,800
+ Deprec. Equipment	0	1,429,000	2,449,000	1,749,000
+ Deprec. Writeoff	0	0	0	4,373,000
– Equipment	–10,000,000	0	0	0
+/– Working Capital	–5,000,000	–4,100,000	–1,400,000	10,500,000
ATCF	–15,000,000	1,211,600	4,019,600	16,668,800
Economic Measures:	NPV @ 12%	$1,150,709	DCFROR	= 15.15%

The calculated inventory values reflect the total value of the working capital investment. The change in the value of the working capital is reflected in the yearly working capital charges and credits in the after-tax cash flows.

B) LIFO Inventory Accounting

Cost of Goods Sold—LIFO

Year	0	1	2	3
Beginning Inventory, $	0	5,000,000	7,600,000	7,600,000
+ Cost of Product Produced	5,000,000	13,000,000	15,000,000	8,500,000
Cost of Available Goods	5,000,000	18,000,000	22,600,000	16,100,000
– Inventory Value at Yr End	5,000,000	7,600,000	7,600,000	0
Cost of Goods Sold	0	10,400,000	15,000,000	16,100,000

Year 1 End of Year Inventory Value
= (500,000 * $10) + (200,000 * $13) = $7,600,000
Year 1 COGS = (800,000 * $13) = $10,400,000
Year 2 End of Year Inventory Value
= (500,000 * $10) + (200,000 * $13) = $7,600,000
Year 2 COGS = (1,000,000 * $15) = $15,000,000
Year 3 End of Year Inventory Value = (0 * $17) = $0
Year 3 COGS
= (500,000 * $10) + (200,000 * $13) + (500,000 * $17) = $16,100,000

After-Tax Cash Flows Using LIFO

Year	0	1	2	3
Revenue	0	16,800,000	21,000,000	25,200,000
– Cost of Goods Sold	0	–10,400,000	–15,000,000	–16,100,000
– Deprec. Equipment	0	–1,429,000	–2,449,000	–1,749,000
– Deprec Writeoff	0	0	0	–4,373,000
Taxable Income	0	4,971,000	3,551,000	2,978,000
– Income Tax @ 40%	0	–1,988,400	–1,420,400	–1,191,200
Net Income	0	2,982,600	2,130,600	1,786,800
+ Deprec. Equipment	0	1,429,000	2,449,000	1,749,000
+ Deprec. Writeoff	0	0	0	4,373,000
– Equipment	–10,000,000	0	0	0
+/– Working Capital	–5,000,000	–2,600,000	0	7,600,000
ATCF	–15,000,000	1,811,600	4,579,600	15,508,800
Economic Measures:	NPV @ 12%	$1,307,187	DCFROR	= 15.70%

Note again that the calculated inventory values reflect the total value of the working capital investment. The change in the value of the working capital is reflected in the yearly working capital charges and credits in the after-tax cash flows.

C) Average Inventory Accounting

Cost of Goods Sold—Average Inventory Value

Year	0	1	2	3
Beginning Inventory, $	0	5,000,000	8,400,000	9,635,294
+ Cost of Product Produced	5,000,000	13,000,000	15,000,000	8,500,000
Cost of Available Goods	5,000,000	18,000,000	23,400,000	18,135,294
– Inventory Value at Yr End	5,000,000	8,400,000	9,635,294	0
Cost of Goods Sold	0	9,600,000	13,764,706	18,135,294

Year 1 Average Value Per Unit
= ($18,000,000 / 1,500,000) = $12 per unit
Year 1 End of Year Inventory Value = (700,000 * $12) = $8,400,000
Year 1 COGS = (800,000 * $12) = $9,600,000
Year 2 Average Value Per Unit
= ($23,400,000 / 1,700,000) = $13.76 per unit (rounded)
Year 2 End of Year Inventory Value = (700,000 * $13.76) = $9,635,294
Year 2 COGS = (1,000,000 * $13.76) = $13,764,706
Year 3 Average Value Per Unit
= ($18,135,294 / 1,200,000) = $15.11 per unit (rounded)
Year 3 End of Year Inventory Value = 0 * $15.11 = $0 (all units sold)
Year 3 COGS = (1,200,000 * $15.11) = $18,135,294

After-Tax Cash Flows Using Average Inventory Value

Year	0	1	2	3
Revenue	0	16,800,000	21,000,000	25,200,000
– Cost of Goods Sold	0	–9,600,000	–13,764,706	–18,135,294
– Deprec. Equipment	0	–1,429,000	–2,449,000	–1,749,000
– Deprec Writeoff	0	0	0	–4,373,000
Taxable Income	0	5,771,000	4,786,294	942,706
– Income Tax @ 40%	0	–2,308,400	–1,914,518	–377,082
Net Income	0	3,462,600	2,871,776	565,624
+ Deprec. Equipment	0	1,429,000	2,449,000	1,749,000
+ Deprec. Writeoff	0	0	0	4,373,000
– Equipment	–10,000,000	0	0	0
+/– Working Capital	–5,000,000	–3,400,000	–1,235,294	9,635,294
ATCF	–15,000,000	1,491,600	4,085,482	16,322,918
Economic Measures:	NPV @ 12%	$1,207,038	DCFROR	= 15.35%

Note again that the calculated inventory values reflect the total value of the working capital investment. The change in the value of the working capital is reflected in the yearly working capital charges and credits in the after-tax cash flows.

EXAMPLE 8-8 Relative Sensitivity of DCFROR and NPV to Project Life and Start of Production

A new project is being considered that would require the investment of $200,000 for processing equipment and $60,000 for working capital at year 0. The equipment would be depreciated using 5 year life straight line depreciation starting with the half-year convention in year 1 when the equipment is expected to go into service. Annual revenues are projected to be $300,000 and annual operating costs are projected to be $200,000 with a wash-out of escalation of operating costs and revenue each year. Salvage value and working capital return are expected to total $100,000 at the end of the project. The effective income tax rate is 40% and minimum DCFROR is 12%. Calculate DCFROR and NPV for:

Case A) A 10 year project evaluation life

Case B) A 20 year project evaluation life.

Case C) Assume technical difficulties or environmental permitting delays cause the Case A cash flows in years 1 through 10 to be realized in years 2 through 11 with zero cash flow in year 1.

Solution: All Values in Thousands of Dollars

Case A) 10 Year Evaluation Life

Year	0	1	2–5	6	7–9	10
Revenue	—	300	300	300	300	400*
–Operating Costs	—	–200	–200	–200	–200	–200
–Depreciation	—	–20	–40	–20	—	—
–Write-off	—	—	—	—	—	–60**
Taxable Income	—	80	60	80	100	140
–Tax @ 40%	—	–32	–24	–32	–40	–56
Net Income	—	48	36	48	60	84
+Depreciation	—	+20	+40	+20	—	—
+Write-off	—	—	—	—	—	+60
–Capital Costs	–260	—	—	—	—	—
Cash Flow	–260	+68	+76	+68	+60	+144

* Revenue includes $100 salvage and working capital return.
** Original working capital investment tax deduction write-off.

NPV Eq: $0 = -260 + 68(P/F_{i,1}) + 76(P/A_{i,4})(P/F_{i,1}) + 68(P/F_{i,6}) + 60(P/A_{i,3})(P/F_{i,6}) + 144(P/F_{i,10})$

DCFROR = 25.24%, NPV @ 12% = +$160.6

Case B) 20 Year Evaluation Life

Year	0	1	2–5	6	7–19	20
Revenue	—	300	300	300	300	400*
–Operating Costs	—	–200	–200	–200	–200	–200
–Depreciation	—	–20	–40	–20	—	—
–Write-off	—	—	—	—	—	–60**
Taxable Income	—	80	60	80	100	140
–Tax @ 40%	—	–32	–24	–32	–40	–56
Net Income	—	48	36	48	60	84
+Depreciation	—	+20	+40	+20	—	—
+Write-off	—	—	—	—	—	+60
–Capital Costs	–260	—	—	—	—	—
Cash Flow	–260	+68	+76	+68	+60	+144

* Revenue includes $100 salvage and working capital return.
** Original working capital investment tax deduction write-off.

NPV Eq: $0 = -260 + 68(P/F_{i,1}) + 76(P/A_{i,4})(P/F_{i,1}) + 68(P/F_{i,6}) + 60(P/A_{i,13})(P/F_{i,6}) + 144(P/F_{i,20})$

DCFROR = 26.77%, NPV @ 12% = +$251.5

Although before-tax profit literally doubles for the 20 year life project as compared to the 10 year life project, DCFROR only increases 1.5% (from 25.2% to 26.7%, a 6% change). The change in NPV due to doubling the project life, however, is much more significant. The 20 year life NPV of +$251.5 is $90.4 greater than the 10 year life project NPV of $160.6 (a 56% increase). Discount rate magnitude is the reason NPV results, in this case and in general, are more sensitive than DCFROR results to changes in cash flow beyond 10 years in the future. The NPV discount rate of 12% is smaller than the DCFROR results of 25.2% and 26.7%. As a result of the mathematical definition of the single payment present worth factor, $(1/(1+i)^n)$, larger values of "i" cause the present worth factors to be much smaller than for smaller discount rates when the evaluation period, n, is 10 or greater. In this analysis, since the 12% NPV discount rate is much smaller than the DCFROR rates, this causes the years 11 through 20 cash flows to have a much greater impact on the NPV result than on DCFROR result.

Case C) Rework Case A for 1 Year Startup Delay

Year	0	1	2	3-6	7	8-10	11
Cash Flow	–260	0	+68	+76	+68	+60	+144

$$\text{NPV Eq: } 0 = -260 + 68(P/F_{i,2}) + 76(P/A_{i,4})(P/F_{i,2}) + 68(P/F_{i,7}) + 60(P/A_{i,3})(P/F_{i,7}) + 144(P/F_{i,11})$$

DCFROR = 19.78%, NPV @ 12.0% = +$115.6

This is a 21.6% reduction in DCFROR to 19.78% from the base Case A result of 25.24% and a 28.0% reduction in NPV to +$115.6 from the base Case A result of +$160.6. These discounted cash flow criteria changes are significant enough to emphasize the importance of the timing as well as the magnitude of costs and revenues that go into analyses.

8.11 International Project Evaluations

Companies, individuals, and governments invest and sell product outside their own countries for many different reasons. Reduction of operating costs (labor and the overhead on labor), penetration of international markets, hedging against currency exchange rate swings, and improvement of product delivery and technical service to international customers are some of the reasons.

Investors in the resource industries do not have the luxury of picking a country, they have to go where the resources occur and are determined to be economically viable.

International economic analyses are made more complex due to all the possible financial aspects of projects and where money related to these projects is actually moving. This segment of the textbook offers a brief discussion of some of the many facets of these evaluations that often are neglected in domestic evaluations. Because of the added complexity, international considerations are often addressed by corporate finance individuals that are familiar with the current financial and tax status, rather than having project engineers address them.

Because commodity prices are often reflected in US dollars, forecasting exchange rates and in some cases, the cost of hedging strategies related to those forecasts is an added parameter to be considered. While revenues may be in U.S. dollars or pounds, the operating costs may be in the host country currency or a combination of currencies due to labor costs, overhead on labor, energy costs and the cost of materials parts and supplies. For some U.S. companies, outsourcing labor and its overhead in the form of medical and retirement related benefits has been a common approach to reduction of operating expenses. These savings may be further expanded or diminished by the exchange rate between the U.S. dollar and the local currency in which wages are paid. The reduction in operating expense not only exposes more revenue to taxation, but also reduces the magnitude of the W2 wage limit applied to the allowable deduction in computing federal taxable income, (50% of labor expense reported to the IRS on W2 wages paid.) This is just one example of why international project analyses are made in a comprehensive after-tax environment.

Many countries enter into income tax treaties to avoid the full double taxation of income from a project and help to maintain economically viable investment options. The U.S currently has income tax treaties with at least 59 countries. The details of these treaties are varied from country to country. In general, these treaties provide that income tax paid in a foreign country may be used as a tax credit to reduce the tax paid if the foreign income (cash flow) is brought back to the home country of the producer. Without such treaties, the double taxation of income would make many foreign projects uneconomic. Foreign income brought back to the producer's home country may be subject to a different income tax rate and different deductions. In some cases, if tax treaties do not exist, or other project investment opportunities exist in the foreign region, cash may never leave that country, or may be moved to a location offshore. This may help to avoid not only additional income tax liability, but also the incurrence of withholding taxes imposed when currency is removed from a country. These are common to most countries, including the United States.

When foreign revenue is recognized in the United States, producers are generally entitled to tax deductions on capital expenditures related to that revenue that are smaller as a result of slower methodologies often applied to longer lives. For example, for projects located in the U.S., mine development or integrated petroleum intangible drilling costs are 70% expensed and 30% amortized over 60 months. Similar investments in foreign projects may be deducted using the straight line methodology over a 10 year life. This exposes more of the revenue to taxation. In Canada, foreign revenue is not entitled to recognize a 10 percentage point rate deduction when computing federal income taxes due.

In addition to income tax, foreign projects must incorporate any withholding tax related to cash flow leaving the country, interest paid on debt and in some cases principal paid on debt as well. Other taxes include import taxes, excise taxes, value added taxes, etc., that may or may not be deductible in computing taxable income in that country. Royalties are in effect a tax that may be imposed on a measure of insitu gross value, produced gross value, produced refined value or some measure of operating profit. While all of these taxes paid are true costs they usually do not qualify as relevant expenditures subject to income tax treaties, but instead may be allowable as deductions only. This reduces the economic benefit in terms of the overall combined tax liability.

EXAMPLE 8-8a Exchange Rate Variation for DCFROR and NPV Sensitivity

To illustrate how exchange rate projections relate to an international project analysis, consider the Example 8-8, Case A project to be a U.S. project so all revenues, salvage value, capital costs, operating costs, tax deductions and cash flows are in U.S. dollars. However, assume the revenues have been generated by selling 1,000 product units per year in Australia at a fixed contract price of $400 Australian per unit for a base case exchange rate of $0.75 U.S. per $1.00 Australian. This gives $400,000 Australian revenue per year which converts to $300,000 U.S. per year for the $0.75 U.S. per Australian dollar base exchange rate. This yields the Example 8-8, Case A base case analysis results of DCFROR = 25.24% and NPV @ 12.0% = $160,600. Analyze the sensitivity of these base case economic results to changing the $0.75 base case exchange rate to:

1) $0.65 U.S. per $1.00 Australian due to a strengthened U.S. dollar.

2) $0.85 U.S. per $1.00 Australian due to a weakened U.S. dollar. (Note that requiring $0.85 U.S. to buy $1.00 Australian versus $0.75 means the domestic currency (U.S. dollar) has weakened relative to the Australian dollar.

Solution: All Values in Thousands of U.S. Dollars

Case 1) Exchange Rate = $0.65 U.S. / $1.00 A

Annual Revenue = $400 A ($0.65 U.S./$1.00 A) = $260 U.S.

Year	0	1	2-5	6	7-9	10
Revenue		260	260	260	260	*360
– Operating Costs		–200	–200	–200	–200	–200
– Depreciation		–20	–40	–20	0	0
– Write-off						**–60
Taxable Income	0	40	20	40	60	100
– Tax @ 40%	0	–16	–8	–16	–24	–40
Net Income	0	24	12	24	36	60
+ Depreciation	0	20	40	20	0	0
+ Write-off	0	0	0	0	0	60
– Capital Costs	–260					
Cash Flow	–260	44	52	44	36	120

* Revenue includes $100 U.S. salvage and working capital return.

** Original working capital investment tax deduction write-off.

$$\text{NPV Eq: } 0 = -260 + 44(P/F_{i,1}) + 52(P/A_{i,4})(P/F_{i,1}) + 44(P/F_{i,6}) + 36(P/A_{i,3})(P/F_{i,6}) + 120(P/F_{i,10})$$

DCFROR = 14.19%, NPV @ 12.0% = +$25.0

Projecting exchange rates is difficult and involves great uncertainty. It is necessary, however, in multiple currency analyses due to the sensitive impact that exchange rates have on analysis results. Strengthening of the U.S. dollar to $0.65 U.S. per $1.00 A from $0.75 U.S. per $1.00 A has weakened the economics of this hypothetical project significantly as measured by either DCFROR dropping to 14.19% from 25.24% or, NPV dropping to $25,000 from $160,000. *Anywhere in the world, strengthening of a domestic currency makes the economics of export projects less desirable.* On the other hand, as Case 2 shows, *weakening of a domestic currency makes export project economics much better.*

Case 2) Exchange Rate = $0.85 U.S. / $1.00 A

Annual Revenue = $400 A ($0.85 U.S. / $1.00 A) = $340 U.S.

(Note the U.S. dollar has weakened relatively to the $0.75 U.S. per $1.00 A exchange rate since more U.S. dollars are required to purchase an Australian dollar)

Year	0	1	2-5	6	7-9	10
Revenue		340	340	340	340	*440
– Operating Costs		–200	–200	–200	–200	–200
– Depreciation		–20	–40	–20	0	0
– Write-off						**–60
Taxable Income	0	120	100	120	140	180
– Tax @ 40%	0	–48	–40	–48	–56	–72
Net Income	0	72	60	72	84	108
+ Depreciation	0	20	40	20	0	0
+ Write-off	0	0	0	0	0	60
– Capital Costs	–260					
Cash Flow	–260	92	100	92	84	168

* Revenue includes $100 U.S, salvage and working capital return.
** Original working capital investment tax deduction write-off.

$$\text{NPV Eq: } 0 = -260 + 92(P/F_{i,1}) + 100(P/A_{i,4})(P/F_{i,1}) + 92(P/F_{i,6}) + 84(P/A_{i,3})(P/F_{i,6}) + 168(P/F_{i,10})$$

DCFROR = 35.48%, NPV @ 12.0% = +$296.2

This weakened U.S. domestic currency analysis shows that export project economics are improved by weakening the value of a domestic exchange rate. The price paid for this benefit is higher prices for imports. Import project economics are hurt by a weaker domestic exchange rate and import project economics are enhanced by strengthening domestic exchange rates. Governments try to establish and execute exchange rate policies that keep exchange rates in a range that is acceptable to both import and export businesses. Obviously, that is a difficult objective to achieve consistently in this age of interactive international finance.

8.12 Mining and Petroleum Project After-Tax Analysis

Mining and petroleum project discounted cash flow analyses are similar to non-mineral analyses in terms of general procedure. In any discounted cash flow type analysis you first convert all project revenues and costs to positive and negative cash flows. You do this by accounting for the tax deductibility of costs and the tax to be paid, or tax savings to be realized, on resulting positive or negative taxable income each year.

The unique feature about discounted cash flow analysis of mining or petroleum projects, compared to non-mineral projects, is the handling of certain tax deductions. Chapter 7 addressed the tax handling of *mining exploration and development costs and petroleum intangible drilling costs* and pointed out that 100% of these costs *may be expensed by "individual" mineral project operators, or "independent" petroleum producers. "Corporate mining operators," or "integrated petroleum producers," may only expense 70% of these costs. The other 30% of the intangible drilling or mining development costs are amortized over 60 months,* with the first year deduction proportional to the months the cost was incurred. Mineral rights acquisition, or lease bonus costs are unique to mining and petroleum projects and generally represent the adjusted basis for cost depletion deduction calculations. One exception is that geological and geophysical costs related to oil and gas projects in the U.S. are now amortized over a 2 year period of time. Percentage depletion deductions also are unique to mining and petroleum projects. *All mining producers and independent petroleum producers get to take the greater of allowed percentage depletion and cost depletion, while integrated petroleum producers are only allowed to take cost depletion on oil and gas production. For non-integrated producers, percentage depletion is limited each year to 1,000 bbls/day of oil or gas equivalent. The annual deduction for percentage depletion cannot exceed 100% of project taxable income or 65% of income from all sources. For mining, there is an annual limit on percentage depletion set at 50% of project taxable income before the depletion deduction.*

There are some unique severance and excise tax considerations related to mineral and petroleum projects. Most non-mineral, petroleum and mining projects alike involve depreciable costs, so there is nothing unique to mining and petroleum project evaluations in this regard. A typical mining/petroleum project discounted cash flow analysis is illustrated in the following example.

To summarize some of the distinct aspects of petroleum and mining taxation, consider the following summation of selected deductions applicable to computing taxable income for regular federal income tax purposes:

Mine Development

Corporations: Expense 70%, Amortize 30% Over 60 Months
Individuals: Expense 100%

Mine Exploration

Corporations: Expense 70%, Amortize 30% Over 60 Months
Individuals: Expense 100%

Both investors are subject to a recapture provision in the event property is deemed to be economically viable and developed.

Petroleum Intangible Drilling Costs, (IDC's)

Integrated Producers: Expense 70%, Amortize 30% Over 60 Months
Non-Integrated Producers: Expense 100%

Dry hole costs may be expensed in the year incurred by all investors.

Capitalization of Costs—To charge a cost to a project and deduct over time.

Depreciation—Related to Tangible Property

Personal Property (generally equipment)
Methods include; MACRS, Straight Line, Units of Production

Real Property (generally buildings)
Methods include; Straight Line

Amortization—Related to Intangible Property

Oil and Gas Geological and Geophysical Costs
Non-Integrated, 24 months
Integrated, 84 months
Half-year deduction in first year for all producers
No write-off if the asset is sold or abandoned prior to the end of the prescribed amortization period.
30% Corp. Mine Development, 60 months
30% Integrated IDC's, 60 months

First year amortization deduction is generally proportional to month the asset goes into service. For qualifying oil and gas G&G, "the first year deduction is based on the mid-point of the tax year the expenses were paid or incurred"—Tax Code Section 167(h)(1) and (h)(2). Therefore, a half-year deduction is to be considered for this class of expenditures.

Depletion—Deduction unique to the resource industries

Cost Depletion—Mining

The cost of acquiring and delineating the extent and quality of a resource (including recaptured exploration) form the basis for this deduction.

Cost Depletion—Oil and Gas

Generally the costs of acquiring an oil and gas lease (lease bonus, surveying, legal) are deducted by cost depletion. Geological and geophysical costs related to the property are deducted separately by amortization over a 24-month period for non-integrated producers and 84 months for integrated companies.

Percentage Depletion—Based on an applicable percentage (Table 7-5) of the net revenue (gross revenue less royalties and in some cases, certain transportation charges.)

Limits may apply on the amount of percentage depletion that may be taken in any one year. These limits include a 50% limit in mining and possibly, a 100% limit in oil and gas. With regards to oil and gas, only non-integrated producers may consider percentage depletion on the first 1,000 barrels of oil or equivalent produced each day throughout the year. A 65% limit may also impact the amount of this deduction for certain small producers or royalty recipients.

Only one method of depletion may be taken each year, use Table 7-4 to determine your allowable deduction, subject to the 65% limit.

Costs that may be expensed—Deducted when incurred

For all producers, the costs associated with product produced and sold in a tax year are generally deductible in full. These costs include labor, overhead on labor, materials parts and supplies for product produced and sold and most excise taxes, sales taxes, ad valorem (property) taxes and related expenditures.

Cash flows should be computed on a "cash basis" as opposed to an "accrual basis" so that cash flows reflect the true timing of receipts and disbursements related to the project. Often times this detail is neglected, especially in evaluation models that are tied to the company's accounting system.

EXAMPLE 8-9 A Mining or Petroleum Project Evaluation Using DCFROR, NPV and PVR

An investor is considering acquiring and developing a mineral property believed to contain 500,000 units of mineral reserves (mineral units could be barrels of oil or tons, pounds or ounces of another mineral). Mineral production is projected to be 100,000 mineral units per year over the 5 year project life with mineral reserves depleted at the end of year five. The mineral rights acquisition cost for the property would be $1,500,000 at time zero. A mineral development cost (or intangible drilling cost) of $7,500,000 is anticipated at time zero along with tangible equipment costs (mining equipment or oil and gas producing equipment, gathering lines, and tangible well completion costs) of $3,000,000 and working capital costs of $1,000,000, all projected to be incurred at time zero. Equipment depreciation will be based on MACRS 7-year life depreciation starting in year one when the assets are placed into service. Write off the remaining equipment book value at year five. The product selling price is estimated to be $70.00 per unit in year one, escalating 10% per year in succeeding years. Operating expenses are estimated to be $800,000 in year one, escalating 8% per year in succeeding years. Royalties are 15% of revenues each year. Assume that the sale value and abandonment costs will be offsetting, so write off all remaining book values at the end of year five. Use an effective income tax rate of 38%. Expense all deductions against other income. When applicable, assume the mineral produced is a 15% depletion rate mineral and begin amortizing development or IDC costs with a full 12 month deduction in year zero. Calculate the project DCFROR, NPV and PVR for a minimum after-tax rate of return of 20%, assuming:

A) The project is a mining venture being evaluated by a corporation.
B) The project is a petroleum venture being evaluated by an integrated producer.
C) The project is a petroleum venture being evaluated by an independent producer with mor ethan 1,000 bbls/day of current production.

D) The project is a petroleum venture being evaluated by an independent producer with less than 1,000 bbls/day of current production so all incremental production would qualify for the greater of percentage or cost depletion.

Solution: All Values in Thousands of Dollars

A) Corporate Mining, Expense Scenario

Year	0	1	2	3	4	5
Revenue		7,000	7,700	8,470	9,317	10,249
–Royalties		–1,050	–1,155	–1,271	–1,398	–1,537
Net Revenue		5,950	6,545	7,200	7,919	8,711
–Oper Costs		–800	–864	–933	–1,008	–1,088
–Dev 70%	–5,250					
–Depreciation*		–429	–735	–525	–375	–268
–Amortization**	–450	–450	–450	–450	–450	
Before Deplt	–5,700	4,271	4,496	5,292	6,087	7,355
–50% Limit		2,136	2,248	2,646	3,043	3,678
–Percent Depl***		–893	–982	–1,080	–1,188	–1,307
–Cost Depl		300	152			
Taxable Inc	–5,700	3,379	3,515	4,212	4,899	6,048
–Tax @ 38%	2,166	–1,284	–1,336	–1,600	–1,862	–2,298
Net Income	–3,534	2,095	2,179	2,611	3,037	3,750
+Depreciation		429	735	525	375	268
+Depletion		893	982	1,080	1,188	1,307
+Amortization	450	450	450	450	450	
+Mineral Rights	–1,500					
+Dev 30%	–2,250					
–Equipment	–3,000					
+/–Working Cap	–1,000					
ATCF	–10,834	3,866	4,345	4,666	5,050	5,959****

* The write-off of remaining book value of the equipment is combined with year-5 depreciation.

** The $450 amortization deduction in years 0 through 4 is (12/60)(.3)($7,500 Mine Development Cost).

*** The *allowable depletion* deduction has a minus (–) sign in front.

**** Write-offs for depreciation and working capital totaled $1,669 and generate $634 in tax savings ($1,669*0.38 tax rate) reflected in the Year 5 ATCF. Therefore, $5,325 + $634 in tax savings from write-offs equals $5,959.

DCFROR Calculation

$$0 = -10{,}834 + 3{,}866(P/F_{i,1}) + 4{,}345(P/F_{i,2}) + 4{,}666(P/F_{i,3}) + 5{,}050(P/F_{i,4}) + 5{,}959(P/F_{i,5})$$

i = DCFROR = 30.9%

NPV Calculation for $i^* = 20\%$

$$NPV = -10{,}834 + 3{,}866(P/F_{20,1}) + 4{,}345(P/F_{20,2}) + 4{,}666(P/F_{20,3}) + 5{,}050(P/F_{20,4}) + 5{,}959(P/F_{20,5}) = \$2{,}936$$

PVR Calculation

2,936 / 10,834 = 0.39

B) Integrated Producer, Expense Scenario

Year	0	1	2	3	4	5
Revenue		7,000	7,700	8,470	9,317	10,249
–Royalties		–1,050	–1,155	–1,271	–1,398	–1,537
Net Revenue		5,950	6,545	7,200	7,919	8,711
–Oper Costs		–800	–864	–933	–1,008	–1,088
–IDC 70%	–5,250					
–Depreciation*		–429	–735	–525	–375	–937
–Amortization**	–450	–450	–450	–450	–450	
–WC Write-off						–1,000
–Cost Depl.		–300	–300	–300	–300	–300
Taxable Inc	–5,700	3,971	4,196	4,992	5,787	5,386
–Tax @ 38%	2,166	–1,509	–1,595	–1,897	–2,199	–2,047
Net Income	–3,534	2,462	2,602	3,095	3,588	3,339
+Depreciation		429	735	525	375	937
+Depletion		300	300	300	300	300
+Amortization	450	450	450	450	450	
–Lease Bonus	–1,500					
–IDC 30%	–2,250					
–Equipment	–3,000					
+/–Working Cap	–1,000					1,000
ATCF	–10,834	3,641	4,086	4,370	4,713	5,576

* The write-off of remaining book value of the equipment is combined with year 5 depreciation.

** The $450 amortization deduction in years 0 through 4 is (12/60)(.3)($7,500 Intangible Drilling Cost).

DCFROR Calculation

$$0 = -10{,}834 + 3{,}641(P/F_{i,1}) + 4{,}086(P/F_{i,2}) + 4{,}370(P/F_{i,3}) + 4{,}713(P/F_{i,4}) + 5{,}576(P/F_{i,5})$$

i = DCFROR = 27.9%

NPV Calculation for $i^* = 20\%$

$$NPV = -10{,}834 + 3{,}641(P/F_{20,1}) + 4{,}086(P/F_{20,2}) + 4{,}370(P/F_{20,3}) + 4{,}713(P/F_{20,4}) + 5{,}576(P/F_{20,5}) = \$2{,}080$$

PVR Calculation

2,080 / 10,834 = 0.19

C) Non-Integrated Producer > 1,000 Bbls/Day, Expense Scenario

Year	0	1	2	3	4	5
Revenue		7,000	7,700	8,470	9,317	10,249
–Royalties		–1,050	–1,155	–1,271	–1,398	–1,537
Net Revenue		5,950	6,545	7,200	7,919	8,711
–Oper Costs		–800	–864	–933	–1,008	–1,088
–IDC	–7,500					
–Depreciation*		–429	–735	–525	–375	–937
–WC Write-off						–1,000
–Cost Depl.		–300	–300	–300	–300	–300
Taxable Inc	–7,500	4,421	4,646	5,442	6,237	6,386
–Tax @ 38%	2,850	–1,680	–1,766	–2,068	–2,370	–2,427
Net Income	–4,650	2,741	2,881	3,374	3,867	3,959
+Depreciation		429	735	525	375	937
+Depletion		300	300	300	300	300
–Lease Bonus	–1,500					
–Equipment	–3,000					
+/–Working Cap	–1,000					1,000
Cash Flow	–10,150	3,470	3,915	4,199	4,542	6,196

* The write-off of remaining book value of the equipment is combined with year 5 depreciation.

DCFROR Calculation

$$0 = -10{,}150 + 3{,}470(P/F_{i,1}) + 3{,}915(P/F_{i,2}) + 4{,}199(P/F_{i,3}) + 4{,}542(P/F_{i,4}) + 6{,}196(P/F_{i,5})$$

i = DCFROR = 30%

NPV Calculation for $i^* = 20\%$

$$NPV = -10{,}150 + 3{,}470(P/F_{20,1}) + 3{,}915(P/F_{20,2}) + 4{,}199(P/F_{20,3}) + 4{,}542(P/F_{20,4}) + 6{,}196(P/F_{20,5}) = \$2{,}571$$

PVR Calculation

2,571 / 10,150 = 0.25

D) Non-Integrated Producer < 1,000 Bbls/Day, Expense Scenario

Year	0	1	2	3	4	5
Revenue		7,000	7,700	8,470	9,317	10,249
–Royalties		–1,050	–1,155	–1,271	–1,398	–1,537
Net Revenue		5,950	6,545	7,200	7,919	8,711
–Oper Costs		–800	–864	–933	–1,008	–1,088
–IDC	–7,500					
–Depreciation		–429	–735	–525	–375	–268
Before Depl.	–7,500	4,721	4,946	5,742	6,537	7,355
–100% Limit		4,721	4,946	5,742	6,537	7,355
–Percent Depl.*		–893	–982	–1,080	–1,188	–1,307
–Cost Depl.		300	152			
Taxable Inc	–7,500	3,829	3,965	4,662	5,349	6,048
–Tax @ 38%	2,850	–1,455	–1,507	–1,771	–2,033	–2,298
Net Income	–4,650	2,374	2,458	2,890	3,316	3,750
+Depreciation		429	735	525	375	268
+Depletion		893	982	1,080	1,188	1,307
–Lease Bonus	–1,500					
–Equipment	–3,000					
+/–Working Cap	–1,000					
Cash Flow	–10,150	3,695	4,174	4,495	4,879	5,959**

* The *allowable depletion* deduction has a minus (–) sign in front.

** Write-offs for depreciation and working capital totaled $1,669 and generate $634 in tax savings ($1,669*0.38 tax rate) reflected in the Year 5 ATCF. Therefore, $5,325 + $634 in tax savings from write-offs equals $5,959.

DCFROR Calculation

$$0 = -10{,}150 + 3{,}695(P/F_{i,1}) + 4{,}174(P/F_{i,2}) + 4{,}495(P/F_{i,3}) + 4{,}879(P/F_{i,4}) + 5{,}959(P/F_{i,5})$$

i = DCFROR = 32.5%

NPV Calculation for $i^* = 20\%$

$$NPV = -10{,}150 + 3{,}695(P/F_{20,1}) + 4{,}174(P/F_{20,2}) + 4{,}495(P/F_{20,3}) + 4{,}879(P/F_{20,4}) + 5{,}959(P/F_{20,5}) = 3{,}177$$

PVR Calculation

3,177 / 10,150 = 0.31

Note that this solution for a non-integrated producer with production of less than 1,000 barrels per day may also be representative of economics for an individual mining scenario assuming that the effective income tax rate remains consistent. One difference between the two solution would be that the individual mining scenario is subject to the 50% limit on percentage depletion while the non-integrated producer is subject to the 100% limit. However, in either scenario for this example, the project would be required to take the 15% depletion rate on net revenue resulting in no impact to after-tax cash flows. Note that depletion is always calculated by property or lease and not on a corporate basis.

PROBLEMS

Excel solutions at Stermole.com

8-1 A corporation wants you to evaluate the economic potential of a project with time zero cost of $1,000,000 for research, a $400,000 cost for land, $1,400,000 for a building, $300,000 inventory cost for raw materials and spare parts and $2,000,000 for equipment. For income taxes, the research cost will be expensed at time zero; the equipment will be depreciated over five years using the MACRS rates from Table 7-3 (start depreciation in year 1). The building will be depreciated straight line over 39 years with a full year deduction beginning in year one. The land, inventory costs, equipment and building book value will all be written off against the escalated dollar sale value of $4,000,000 at the end of year 3. The project is estimated to generate end of year 1 revenue of $3,000,000 and operating costs of $1,000,000. Both will escalate 8.0% per year in years 2 and 3. The effective corporate ordinary income tax rate is 40.0% with any gain on the year 3 sale treated as ordinary income. Determine the DCFROR, NPV and PVR for an after-tax escalated dollar minimum rate of return of 15.0%

A) Assume a "stand alone" financial situation and carry losses forward to be used against project income.

B) Assume an "expense" financial situation assuming other corporate income exists against which to use losses (negative taxable income) in the year incurred. This means there is no loss forward deduction.

8-2

Working Capital		Working Capital
Cost = $50,000		Return = $70,000
Res & Experiment	Sales=$500,000.	Sales=$500,000
Cost = $100,000	OC=$400,000	OC=$400,000
0	1.	5

As shown on the time diagram, time 0 working capital cost of $50,000 and research and experimentation expenses of $100,000 on a project are expected to generate increased sales of $500,000 per year from existing process equipment for increased annual operating costs of $400,000. A washout of annual escalation of operating costs and revenues is assumed. Working capital return (inventory liquidation value) of $70,000 is expected to be realized at year 5. The effective income tax rate is 40%. Determine the DCFROR on investment capital if:

A) Research and experimental costs are deducted for tax purposes as operating expenses at time 0. Other income is assumed to exist against which to use the time 0 negative taxable income.

B) Research and experimental costs are expensed at time zero with negative taxable income carried forward to be used against project revenues (stand alone analysis).

C) Research and experimental costs are capitalized and deducted for tax purposes by amortization over years 1 to 5.

D) Assume this project involves production of product in the U.S. with all costs incurred in U.S. dollars. Further, none of the project costs will be affected by exchange rate changes over time. Assume the Case A annual revenue of $500,000 US is realized from product sales of €500,000 and an exchange rate of $1.00/€1.00. Therefore, if 1,000 units were sold at €500.00 per unit, converting the euros back to dollars would result in €500,000($1.00/€1.00) = $500,000. As a sensitivity, consider the economic impact on this project from uniform variations in the exchange rates over the next 5 years as follows.

Case D1: assume a weakening of the U.S. dollar using $1.15 per €1.00.
Case D2: assume a strengthening U.S. currency using $0.85 per €1.00.

8-3 Development of a coal property which a corporation may purchase for a mineral rights acquisition cost of $10 million is being considered. Mineral development capital of $10 million will be needed in evaluation time 0 for overburden stripping with the cost considered to be incurred in the first month of time 0. Mine equipment costs of $15 million also will be incurred in time 0 along with $2 million cost for working capital. The mine life is estimated to be 5 years. Mine equipment will be depreciated over 7 years using modified ACRS rates, starting in time 0 with the half-year convention. Salvage value and working capital return will be $5 million at the end of year 5 with any taxable gain taxed as ordinary income. The effective tax rate is 40%. Coal reserves are estimated to be 5 million tons and production for years 1 through 5 is projected to be 1 million tons per year. Coal selling price is estimated to be $30 per ton in year 1, escalating 10% per year in years 2 through 5. Royalties are 8% of revenue. Mining operating costs are estimated to be $12 per ton in year 1, also escalating by 10% per year in following years. Calculate the project DCFROR and NPV for a minimum DCFROR of 20% to determine if the mine development economics are satisfactory for:

A) No other income exists against which to use tax deductions, so carry negative taxable income forward and use against project income and tax. This makes the project "stand alone."

B) Other taxable income does exist so realize tax benefits from negative taxable income in the year incurred.

8-4 Annual cash flow from a new investment is projected to be:

Cash Flow	–$150,000	$60,000	$70,000	$80,000	$90,000
Year	0	1	2	3	4

As the year 1 through 4 positive cash flows are realized it is anticipated that they will be invested in treasury bonds paying 12% annual interest and maturing at year 4. Calculate the DCFROR and the Growth DCFROR on the investment, assuming a 40% income tax rate is relevant and that after-tax treasury bond interest will be reinvested each year in identical bonds.

8-5 A manufacturing plant can be purchased for $180,000. An additional $20,000 must be invested in working capital for raw material and spare parts inventory and accounts receivable money tied up in operating costs. The $180,000 plant cost will be depreciated straight line over 7 years using the half-year depreciation convention in year 1. Actual salvage value is estimated to be $170,000 for used machinery and equipment and working capital return at year 15. Annual sales revenue is estimated to be $100,000 in year 1 with operating costs of $40,000. In years 2 to 15, escalation of operating costs and sales revenue are projected to be a washout. The effective income tax rate is 40%. The minimum ROR is 15% after taxes. Calculate the project DCFROR and NPV.

8-6 A mining investor operating as a corporation is considering buying the mineral rights to a small mineral property. The mineral rights acquisition cost will be $1,000,000 at time 0 and depreciable mining equipment costs will be $1,000,000 at year 1 in escalated dollars. MACRS depreciation will be used for a 7-year depreciation life starting in year 2 with the half-year convention. Mineral development cost of $500,000 will also be incurred at year 1. Production rates will be 100,000 units per year in years 2 and 3 and 150,000 units per year in years 4 and 5 which will deplete the reserves. Salvage value of all assets at year 5 is considered to be nil. The mineral product will be sold for $20 per unit while production operating costs are estimated to be $8 per unit. Assume a washout of escalation of operating costs and sales revenue each year and neglect the effect of escalating sales revenue on percent depletion. The mineral produced is in the 22% percentage depletion category. Assume an effective tax rate of 40%. Determine the project cash flow for each year and calculate DCFROR and NPV for a minimum DCFROR of 15%.

8-7 XYZ Corp. is evaluating the purchase and development of a petroleum property that can be acquired for $100,000 now (time 0). The purchase would be followed immediately by intangible drilling costs of $750,000 at month 7 of year 0 and $250,000 at month 7 of year 1. Tangible well completion and producing equipment costs of $1,000,000 would be required at year 1. Anticipated production is 200 barrels of oil per day (BPD) in year 2, decreasing each year by 40 BPD in years 3 through 6. Assume oil will sell for $22 per barrel (before royalties of 14% of sales) in the first producing year, with oil price escalating by 8% annually thereafter. Assume 350 operating days per year. Operating costs are estimated to be $175,000 in the first producing year and escalating 10% annually until production is suspended at the beginning of year 7. XYZ Corp. has an effective tax rate of 38%. The company has other oil income against which to expense pre-tax losses, however all oil production by the company is less than 1000 BPD now and in the foreseeable future. The well completion and producing equipment costs will be depreciated by MACRS depreciation for a 7-year depreciation life starting in evaluation year 2 with the half-year convention. Use DCFROR and NPV (for i =15%) to evaluate this investment for the 6 year project life if the company is an independent and:

A) Risk of failure is neglected, i.e. the probability of successful well completion and production through evaluation year 6 is 100%.
B) The probability of success between year 0 and year 1 is 40% and after year 1 is 100%. If drilling at year 0 results in failure, the company will take a write-off of the acquisition cost at the end of year 1 when the property mineral rights will be abandoned for a $50,000 cost.
C) The part "A" and "B" analyses are for an integrated producer.
D) The part "A" analysis is for "stand alone" loss carry forward economic analysis.

8-8 Consideration is being given to the investment of $420,000 at time zero for machinery and equipment to be depreciated using 7-year straight line depreciation starting in year 1 with the half-year convention. Annual sales are projected to be $400,000 less annual operating costs of $200,000. Escalation of operating costs and sales revenue is expected to be a washout from year to year. $100,000 for working capital investment is also needed at time zero and working capital return is expected to equal the initial working capital investment at the end of the project. Salvage value of the machinery and equipment is expected to be zero. The minimum DCFROR is 15% and the effective income tax rate is 35%. Calculate DCFROR and NPV for:

A) A 9 year evaluation life.
B) An 18 year evaluation life.

8-9 The following data relates to a processing facility.

Costs and production are in thousands. Production is in gallons and declining due to substitution of a new product in the market.

Year	0	1	2	3	4	5
Production, (Gal.)		175	100	75	55	35
Research & Develop.	7,500	2,500				
Equipment		6,700				
Patent Rights	1,000					
Operating Costs		1,750	1,000	750	500	250
Selling Price, $/Gal.		80.00	80.00	80.00	80.00	80.00

Royalties are 12.5% of gross revenue.
Effective State and Federal tax rate is 40%.
Liquidation value in Year 5 is $0.
Equipment is depreciated using 7-year MACRS rates starting in year 1 with the half-year convention.
Patent cost is for exclusive rights to the process so amortize straight line over the remaining patent life of 5 years. Take a full 12 month deduction starting in time zero when the cost is incurred.

1) Calculate the after-tax escalated dollar dollar cash flows and the DCFROR, NPV and PVR for a minimum rate of return after taxes of 15% assuming:

A) Other income exists against which to use deductions (expense scenario).

B) No income exists; carry losses forward (stand alone).

2) Risk adjust Part 1a. assuming a 70% probability the year 0 costs are successful and lead to the year 1 thru 5 after-tax cash flows. There is a 30% probability of failure in year 1 which would result in a one time abandonment cost of $100,000. If failure occurs at year 1 there will be no completion of the project so write off all remaining book values in year 1 when the abandonment cost is expensed against other income.

8-10 The following data relates to an oil and gas lease.

Costs and Production are in thousands.
Production is in barrels of oil equivalent (BOE).

Year	0	1	2	3	4	5
Production, (BOE)		175	100	75	55	35
Intangibles (IDC's)	7,500	2,500				
Tangible Equipment		6,700				
Lease Bonus	1,000					
Operating Cost/Yr.		1,750	1,000	750	500	250
Selling Price, $/BOE		80.00	80.00	80.00	80.00	80.00

Royalties are 12.5% of gross revenue.
Effective State and Federal tax rate is 40%.
Liquidation value in Year 5 is $0.
Tangible equipment is depreciated using 7-year MACRS rates starting in year 1 with the half-year convention.
For integrated producers assume 30% of intangible drilling costs are amortized using a full 12 month deduction beginning in the year the costs are incurred in both years 0 and 1. The uniform amortization schedules are for simplicity in amortization calculations.
Lease bonus is recovered through cost depletion. Assume initial proven reserves equal cumulative production in years 1 through 5 (440 BOE).
No geological or geophysical costs are allocated to this lease.
Crude oil is a 15% percentage depletion mineral when applicable.

1) Calculate the after-tax escalated dollar cash flows and the DCFROR, NPV and PVR for a minimum rate of return after taxes of 15% assuming:
   A) Integrated producer with other income exists against which to use deductions in the year incurred (expense scenario).
   B) Integrated producer with no other income so carry any project losses forward and use against future project revenues (stand alone).

2) Risk adjust Part 1a. assuming a 70% probability the year 0 costs are successful and lead to the year 1 thru 5 after-tax cash flows. There is a 30% probability of failure in year 1 which would result in a one time abandonment cost of $100,000. If failure occurs, write off all remaining book values in year 1 when the abandonment cost is expensed.

3) Make the analyses in Parts 1 and 2 for an independent producer with daily production in excess of the 1,000 bbl/day limitation.

4) Make the analyses in Parts 1 and 2 for an independent producer with daily production less than the 1,000 bbl/day small producer limitation. Assume the incremental production in this model will not allow total daily production to exceed this threshold.

8-11 The following data relates to a mining operation.

Costs and production are in thousands.
Production in tons.

Year	0	1	2	3	4	5
Production, (Tons)		175	100	75	55	35
Mine Development	7,500	2,500				
Mining Equipment		6,700				
Mineral Acquisition	1,000					
Operating Cost/Yr.		1,750	1,000	750	500	250
Selling Price, $/Ton		80.00	80.00	80.00	80.00	80.00

Royalties are 12.5% of gross revenue.
Effective State and Federal tax rate is 40%.
Liquidation value in Year 5 is $0.
Mine equipment is depreciated using 7-year MACRS rates starting in year 1 with the half-year convention.

For corporations assume 30% of mine development costs are amortized using a full 12 month deduction beginning in the year the costs are incurred. The uniform amortization schedules are for simplicity only.

The Mineral Acquisition cost is recovered through cost depletion. Assume initial proven reserves equal cumulative production in years 1 through 5.

The mineral produced is assumed to be a 15% percentage depletion mineral when applicable.

1) Calculate the after-tax escalated dollar cash flows and the DCFROR, NPV and PVR for a minimum rate of return after taxes of 15% assuming:
   A) Corporate producer with other income exists against which to use deductions in the year incurred (expense scenario).
   B) Corporate producer with no other income so carry any project losses forward and use against future project revenues (stand alone).

2) Risk adjust Part 1a. assuming a 70% probability the year 0 costs are successful and lead to the year 1 thru 5 after-tax cash flows. There is a 30% probability of failure in year 1 which would result in a one time abandonment cost of $100,000. If failure occurs, write off all remaining book values in year 1 when the abandonment cost is expensed.

3) Make the analysis in Parts 1a. and 1b. for an individual producer. For individual investors mine development may be 100% expensed when incurred rather than being subject to the 70/30 split. Assume all other tax considerations remain as described above.

CHAPTER 8 AUXILIARY PROBLEMS

A8-1 Your company invests $1,500,000 in a parcel of land it expects to develop in two years time. After the 2nd year, a buyer makes an offer to purchase the land for $2,500,000. Property taxes and lot security fees were $75,000 in year 1 and $80,000 in year 2. Closing costs are estimated at 3.5% of the sale price. The investor is a corporation with a 35.0% federal income tax rate and a 5.0% state income tax rate on ordinary income. All corporate long-term capital gain is taxed as ordinary income. Other income exists against which to utilize all negative taxable income in the year incurred (expense scenario). Compute the after tax cash flows in time zero, year 1 and year 2 from the investment, holding and subsequent sale of this land (sale occurs at the end of year two) and the corresponding investment DCFROR.

A8-2 Assume the investor is an individual with a 28.0% federal tax rate on ordinary income, a 4.0% state income tax rate and that all long-term capital gain qualifies for a 15.0% federal tax rate and the same 4.0% state tax rate. You purchase 100 shares of common stock for $44.00 per share and a commission of $20 and sell the stock three years later for $110 per share and pay another $20 commission on the sale. Compute after tax cash flows from this investment and the corresponding DCFROR.

A8-3 You purchase a rental property for $425,000 cash and expect to realize revenues of $25,000 per year in years 1 and 2 after management fees with additional expenses of $20,000 per year for property taxes, maintenance, association fees, etc. Assume the investor is an individual with a 28.0% federal tax rate on ordinary income, a 4.0% state income tax rate and that long-term capital gain on appreciation of real estate qualifies for a 15.0% federal tax rate. Gain due to depreciation on real estate rental property would qualify for a 25% tax rate by law. If you sold the property for $480,000 after two years net commissions, determine the after-tax cash flows in time zero, year 1 and year 2 and corresponding after-tax DCFROR on this investment.

A8-4 A project manager is evaluating whether it is economical to develop a project requiring expenditures at time 0 of $200,000 for land, $50,000 for product inventory working capital, $580,000 for a business building, $440,000 for equipment and $75,000 for vehicles. The working capital investment is based on 5,000 units being produced in time zero at a cost of $10.00 per unit with no units sold at that time. Starting in year 1 the manager estimates that production will ramp up to 23,000 units before full production of 25,000 units per year is realized in years 2, 3 and 4. The year 1 product selling price is targeted at $25.00 per unit with this amount escalating 10% per year thereafter. Sales in years 1 through 4 are estimated to be uniform at 25,000 units per year. Year 1 production costs per unit are expected to be $11.00. In the following years, it is estimated that operating costs per unit produced will escalate at 10% per year beginning in year 2. The company uses the annualized FIFO accounting methodology to value inventory. At the end of year 4, it is expected that the business (including all assets and working capital product inventory of 3,000 units) can be sold for an escalated terminal value of $2,000,000. Use straight-line depreciation over 39 years for the building cost starting in year 1, assuming 7 months of service in year 1. Use MACRS depreciation for a 7-year life for the equipment cost starting in year 1 with the half-year convention. Similarly, for the vehicle cost start depreciation in year 1 using the MACRS rates based on the half-year convention as well. Assume any gain from the sale of this business at the end of year 4 is taxed as ordinary income. Write-off the remaining tax book values at the end of year 4.

Assuming a 40% effective federal and state income tax rate, determine project after-tax cash flows for time zero and years 1 thru 4 (including the sale of the business at the end of year 4) and calculate the DCFROR, NPV and PVR for the project. The investor has an escalated dollar minimum ROR of 15%. From an economic perspective, should this project be accepted?

A8-5 A project manager is evaluating whether it is economical to develop a project requiring expenditures at time 0 of $200,000 for land, $50,000 for product inventory working capital, $580,000 for a business building, $440,000 for equipment and $75,000 for vehicles. The working capital investment is based on 5,000 units being produced in time zero at a cost of $10.00 per unit with no units sold at that time. Starting in year 1 the manager estimates that production will ramp up to 23,000 units before full production of 25,000 units per year is realized in years 2, 3 and 4. The year 1 product selling price is targeted at $25.00 per unit with this amount escalating 10% per year thereafter. Sales in years 1 through 4 are estimated to be uniform at 25,000 units per year. Year 1 production costs per unit are expected to be $11.00. In the following years, it is estimated that operating costs per unit produced will escalate at 10% per year beginning in year 2. The company uses the annualized LIFO accounting methodology to value inventory. At the end of year 4, it is expected that the business (including all assets and working capital product inventory of 3,000 units) can be sold for an escalated terminal value of $2,000,000. Use straight-line depreciation over 39 years for the building cost starting in year 1, assuming 7 months of service in year 1. Use MACRS depreciation for a 7-year life for the equipment cost starting in year 1 with the half-year convention. Similarly, for the vehicle cost start depreciation in year 1 using the MACRS rates based on the half-year convention as well. Assume any gain from the sale of this business at the end of year 4 is taxed as ordinary income. Write-off the remaining tax book values at the end of year 4.

A) Assume a 35% federal income tax rate and a 5.0% state income tax rate. Determine project after-tax cash flows for time zero and years 1 thru 4 (including the sale of the business at the end of year 4) and calculate the DCFROR, NPV and PVR for the project. The investor's escalated dollar minimum ROR is 15%. Should this project be accepted from an economic viewpoint?

B) Assume this project is a qualified U.S. production activity. Demonstrate the impact on after-tax cash flows and economics by considering an allowable 6% deduction on taxable income in years 1, 2 and 3 of the project and a 9% deduction in year 4 on taxable income from the sale of product each year. Assume the 50% limit related to wages paid each year is not a factor.

A8-6 An oil lease containing an estimated 2,000,000 barrels of oil may be obtained at time zero for a lease bonus cost of $7,000,000. Additional time zero geological and geophysical costs are estimated to total $700,000. These acquisition and g&g costs would be followed by development of the lease and would involve an end of year 1 investment of $5,000,000 in intangible drilling costs and $4,000,000 in tangible completion costs and equipment. When appropriate, assume a six-month deduction in the year costs are incurred for all amortizable costs. Depreciation of tangible equipment will begin in year 1 assuming all such costs may be treated as 7-year MACRS depreciable property. Production in the latter half of year 1 is estimated at 150,000 barrels of oil equivalent (BOE). Year 2 production is estimated at 350,000 BOE with 275,000 in year 3 and 200,000 in year 4. It is expected that the property would be sold for $8,000,000 at the end of year 4. Assume a uniform selling price of $75.00 per barrel of oil equivalent each year over the 4-year producing period. Operating costs are estimated to be $15.00 per BOE and also forecasted to remain constant. Royalties are estimated at 12.5% of gross revenue. Assume all remaining book values will be written off against the sale value and assume any gain will be taxed as ordinary income. Other income exists against which to use all deductions in the year incurred. Assume a 35% Federal income tax rate and a 5.0% State income tax rate. The property is in the United States and the investor's escalated dollar after-tax minimum rate of return is 15%.

A) Calculate the ATCF's for the project if the investor is:
   1) Integrated Oil and Gas Producer
   2) Non-Integrated Producer with > 1,000 BOE per day
   3) Non-Integrated Producer with < 1,000 BOE per day
   For Case 3, assume all production is < 1,000 total BOE per day.

B) Using the Case A models, make the following risk assessments of the project for the described investors. If after acquiring the lease and incurring the time zero g&g, the project had an 80% probability of success, what would be the expected NPV in this project? Assume failure would result in an end of year 1 abandonment cost of $50,000 and that all book values in the property would be written off as well at the end of year 1.

A8-7 A mining company has already located an economically viable copper deposit and is re-assessing the after-tax cash flows and economics as they enter development. The project involves the costs and production characteristics summarized in the table below. Calculate the after-tax cash flow (ATCF) for this venture. Assume a 6-month deduction for all amortizable costs begins in the year such costs are incurred. Assume all equipment and infrastructure costs will be depreciated based on the MACRS 7-year schedule assuming the half-year convention. Start all depreciation at the end of year 1 when all assets are assumed to be in a condition or state of readiness and available for service. Assume a 3.0% royalty (tax) on the gross revenue from the mine each year. To simplify this analysis, write off all remaining book values against the assumed sale value of $2 billion at the end of year 4 and assume any gain will be taxed as ordinary income. Other income exists against which to use all deductions in the year incurred. Assume a 35% Federal income tax rate and a 5.0% state income tax that is deductible for computing Federal taxable income. This project is in the United States and the investor is seeking a 15% after-tax minimum rate of return.

Note: Annual revenue is calculated on the net pounds of refined copper each year which is based on (annual tonnage) x (pounds per tonne) x (average grade) x (solvent extraction recovery rate). "M" represents millions and tonnes are metric measures with equivalent pounds per tonne summarized below.

Variation on Auxiliary Problem 8-7A, M = 1,000,000, t = Metric Tonne

Year	0	1	2	3	4
Production,					
Tonnes of Ore in M		10.00	17.00	17.00	17.00
Reserves @ Beginning					
of Year in M	200.00	190.00	173.00	156.00	139.00
Pounds per Tonne		2,204.62	2,204.62	2,204.62	2,204.62
Average Grade		0.015	0.015	0.015	0.015
Solvent Extraction					
Recovery		0.990	0.990	0.990	0.990
Cu Price $ per Pound		$2.00	$2.00	$2.00	$2.00
Operating Costs,					
$ per Tonne of Ore		$16.00	$16.00	$16.00	$16.00
Project Sale Value in M$					2,000.00
Capital Investment in M$					
Mine Acquisition	50				
Mine Development	250				
Mine Equipment	900	400			
Infrastructure	25	40			
Working Capital	20	30			

A) Calculate the after-tax cash flows (ATCF's) for the project and corresponding DCFROR, NPV and PVR.

A8-8 An investor has requested that you evaluate the economic potential of purchasing a gold property now (at time zero) for a $5,000,000 mineral rights acquisition cost. Mine development costs are estimated to be $15,000,000 at time zero with an additional $5,000,000 charged at year 1 for pre-production stripping. Mining equipment costs will total $25,000,000 and should be charged to the project at time zero. Production is projected to start at year one with the mining of 350,000 tons of ore. Production in years 2, 3 and 4 is projected to be uniform at 450,000 tons per year. It is assumed that reserves will be depleted at the end of year 4. Average grade is 0.1 ounces of gold per ton with metallurgical recovery estimated to be 93%. The price of gold is estimated to be $850.00 per ounce in year 1 with that amount escalating 15% in year 2 and held constant thereafter for evaluation purposes. Royalties are estimated at 10% of gross revenue. Operating costs include all state and local severance and property taxes and are estimated to be $270 per ounce produced and sold in year 1 with this amount escalating by 8.0% per year over the mine life. Working capital for product inventory, accounts receivables less payables and spare parts is estimated at $2,500,000 and should be charged to the project at time zero. Reclamation costs are estimated at $15,000,000 and are expected to be expensed at the end of year 5. Salvage for residual value of mining equipment and working capital return is placed at $12,000,000 and would also be realized at the end of year 5.

A) Determine the ATCF's for a corporation assuming the property is in the United States. The mineral acquisition cost is the basis for cost depletion. Mine development is subject to the 70/30 rule with 70% expensed when incurred and 30% amortized straight line over a 60 month life. Take a six-month amortization deduction (6/60) in the year amortizable costs are incurred (years 0 and 1). Use 7-year MACRS depreciation of the $25,000,000 mining equipment cost starting in year 1. Royalties and operating costs are expensed when incurred for tax deduction purposes. Reclamation is expensed as an operating cost when incurred at year 5 while salvage value is treated as ordinary income at the end of year 5. Salvage is not subject to royalty or percentage depletion. Other income exists against which to utilize all deductions when incurred. Assume an effective state and federal combined income tax rate for the investors at 40%. Write off all remaining book values in year 5. Calculate the project after-tax cash flows and for an after-tax escalated dollar minimum rate of return of 10%, determine the project rate of return, net present value and present value ratio.

B) Determine the after-tax cash flow's for a corporation developing this property in a country with the following mining tax law assumptions: Mine development costs will be amortized straight line over a 3-year period. Assume uniform deductions start the year after such costs are incurred. Depreciation of the mining equipment cost starts in year 1 with the straight line method over 4 years and a full year deduction beginning in year 1. You should also amortize the mineral acquisition cost in the property over the 4-year producing life with four equal deductions in years 1-4. Royalties and operating costs are expensed when incurred for tax deduction purposes. Reclamation is expensed as an operating cost when incurred at year 5. Salvage value is treated as ordinary income at the end of year 5 but not subject to royalties. Other income exists against which to utilize all deductions when incurred. Assume a federal government income tax rate of 30%. A dividend withholding tax of 10% would be paid on all positive after-tax cash flow from the preceding year. The withholding tax is 100% deductible against income in the year incurred including the salvage year. Write off any remaining book values in year 5 when assets are sold. Calculate the project after-tax cash flows and for an after-tax escalated dollar minimum rate of return of 10%, determine the project rate of return, net present value and present value ratio.

CHAPTER 9

AFTER-TAX DECISION METHODS AND APPLICATIONS

9.1 Introduction

DCFROR is used more widely as an after-tax investment economic decision method than all other economic decision methods. NPV is the second most used economic decision method and ratios are the third most used evaluation technique. These discounted cash flow investment analysis techniques are the best approaches known today for evaluating the economic potential of alternative investments. It is important to remember that all of the discounted cash flow techniques are systematic, quantitative approaches to evaluating investments based on given sets of assumptions and input data. If you put garbage in, you will get garbage out of any analysis calculation using any technique of analysis. There is nothing magical about discounted cash flow results. They are based on the evaluation assumptions concerning: (1) tax considerations, (2) handling inflation and escalation, (3) risk adjusting or not risk adjusting results when finite probability of failure exists, (4) the financial situation of the individual or organization for which the analysis is being made, (5) significance of terminal value magnitude, timing and tax considerations, (6) cash investment analysis versus leveraged analysis with borrowed money, (7) correct handling of the discounted cash flow analysis calculations whether it involves DCFROR, NPV, PVR or another technique, and finally, (8) correct application of the discounted cash flow analysis results to analyze mutually exclusive or non-mutually exclusive income or service producing alternatives.

Proper use of the discounted cash flow analysis techniques gives investors a better chance of correctly analyzing the potential of alternative investments than can be achieved using any other evaluation technique. The key to successful application of the discounted cash flow techniques is consistency. If you analyze a project in escalated dollars you must compare it with results of other projects analyzed in escalated dollars. As discussed in Chapter 11, if you leverage a project investment with borrowed money, you should compare it to other projects analyzed with similar borrowed money leverage.

Similarly, when considering an investor's minimum rate of return, it is important to recognize that if the financial cost of capital approach is to be utilized, the cost of debt and the risk free bond rate of return used in the capital asset model must be expressed on an after-tax basis. This requires recognition that the cost of financing is generally deductible (except for construction loans – see Chapter 11 for more details). Further, interest received from an investment in bonds would be treated as ordinary income upon which taxes must be paid. These adjustments are easily achieved by multiplying each parameter times the quantity (1-tax rate). The resulting product(s) represent the after-tax cost of borrowed money interest and the after-tax rate of return from a bond investment. If an investor is utilizing a true opportunity cost of capital based upon perceived returns to be realized in the future, such measures of economic return should be based on after-tax performance using after-tax cash flow in the methodology presented in Chapters 7 and 8 of this text.

Broad acceptance and utilization of discounted cash flow analysis occurred in most industries around the world in the 1960's and 1970's. Prior to that time, techniques of analysis such as payback period, which is described in the next section, and several different average and/or accounting rate of return calculations which are defined and illustrated in Section 9.10 of this chapter were utilized by investors to evaluate the economic potential of investments. It will be shown that the older techniques do not properly account for the timing and tax effects related to project costs and revenues. Therefore, the older techniques are inconsistent in their usefulness for evaluating economic differences in project investments. This is the primary reason investors have shifted in recent decades from using these older analysis techniques to using the discounted cash flow analysis criteria.

9.2 Payback Period Analysis

Payback period (or payout period) is the time required for positive project cash flow to recover negative project cash flow from the acquisition and/or development years. Payback can be calculated either from the start of a project or from the start of production. For the calculation of payback period, positive cash flow is generally considered to flow uniformly during a year rather than at end, middle or beginning of a year. Sometimes payback period calculations are based on discounted cash flow at a specified discount rate such as 10%, 12% or some other rate that often represents the minimum DCFROR.

The basic economic analysis philosophy behind the use of payback period as an evaluation technique is that the faster you get investment dollars back from project cash flow, the better the economics of an investment. However, this often is not the case. Payback can be very misleading as an indicator of economic differences in investment projects because it neglects what happens after payback. For example, a project with a 2 year payback period and a 3 year life may be economically inferior to a project with a 4 year payback period and a 20 year life.

As a measure of risk, or financial analysis rather than economic analysis reasons, payback period calculations can be useful. If an investor is considering a foreign investment in an underdeveloped country associated with high political instability and the investor cannot recover initial investments within a year or two, he may elect to forego investing even though long-term investment calculation results look very good. Similarly, a company in a tight financial situation and needing money to meet current obligations such as for operating expenses and debt repayment may elect to invest in projects with short payback periods to help meet short-term cash flow needs, even though these projects have much poorer economic potential than other potential investments with longer payback periods.

Another application of payback relates to the writing of joint venture contracts. Working interests, carried interests and related reversionary interests often change after payback. Because different joint venture partners often are in different financial and tax situations, before-tax payback is almost always the basis for payback used in legal contracts. Tax holidays for state or provincial mineral severence or excise taxes often involve a before-tax payback calculation.

The following two examples illustrate the mechanics of calculating payback in four different ways and show how the project with the shortest payback may not be the best economic choice.

EXAMPLE 9-1A Payback Calculations

To illustrate the mechanics of the different methods for determining payback, calculate the undiscounted and discounted payback for a 12.0% minimum rate of return from both the start of the project (time zero), and from the start of production (beginning of year 2, or the end of year 1) for the following project with all after-tax cash flow (ATCF) dollar values in thousands:

Year	0	1	2	3	4
ATCF	–100	–200	150	200	250

Solution:

This project has a DCFROR of 32.85% and an NPV @ 12.0% of $142.24, both of which indicate acceptable economics. For Payback, assume the time zero cash flow is a discrete sum at that point and that the subsequent cash flows in periods 1 through 4 flow continuously during each corresponding year.

Payback From the Start of the Project, (Time Zero):

Year	0	1	2	3	4
ATCF	–100	–200	150	200	250
CUM ATCF	–100	–300	–150	50	300

2 Years + (150 / 200) = 2.75 Years

The year 2 cumulative after-tax cash flow of –150 represents the cumulative cost yet to be recovered from the positive cash flow. Its absolute value forms the basis for the numerator in the payback calculation. Rounding up, this could be described as a 3 year payback. If an investor considers time zero as a full year, rather than a discrete point, the payback could be described as either 3.75 or 4 years.

Payback from the Start of Production (Year One):

Year	0	1	2	3	4
ATCF	–100	–200	150	200	250
CUM ATCF	–100	–300	–150	50	300

1 Year + (150 / 200) = 1.75 Years

While the point in time where payback occurs does not change, the starting reference point does. So looking back from the payback point to the start of production is 1.75 years.

Discounted Payback from the Start of the Project (Time Zero):

Discounted payback involves making the same calculations, but utilizing the discounted after-tax cash flows, (DATCF) for each year as illustrated:

Year	0	1	2	3	4
ATCF	–100	–200	150	200	250
DATCF	–100	–179	120	142	159
CUM DATCF	–100	–279	–159	–17	142

Where: $-200(P/F_{12\%,1}) = -179$
$150(P/F_{12\%,2}) = 120$, etc...

3 Years + (17 / 159) = 3.1 Years

Discounted Payback was illustrated graphically earlier in the development of the Cumulative NPV Diagram in Chapter 3. The point where cumulative NPV equals zero is the graphical approach to discounted payback as illustrated:

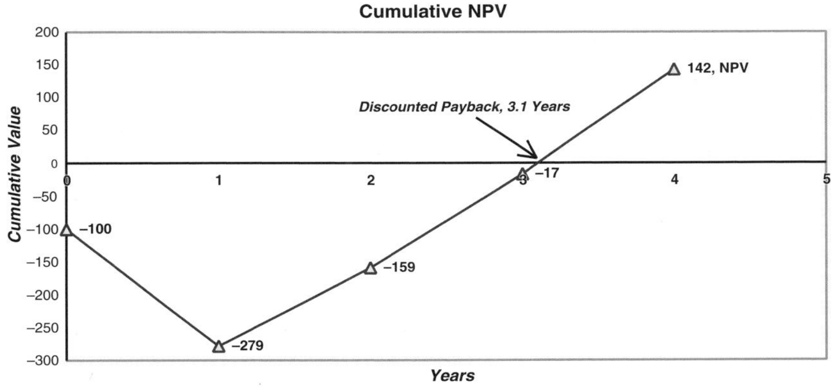

Figure 9-1 Cumulative NPV Illustrating Discounted Payback

Discounted Payback from the Start of Production (Year One):

Year	0	1	2	3	4
ATCF	–100	–200	150	200	250
DATCF	–100	–179	120	142	159
CUM DATCF	–100	–279	–159	–17	142

2 Years + (17 / 159) = 2.1 Years

EXAMPLE 9-1B Payback Calculations and Results Compared to Discounted Cash Flow Analysis Results

If projects "A" and "B" are mutually exclusive investments, which is indicated to be preferable using undiscounted payback period, discounted payback period, NPV, PVR and DCFROR. The minimum rate of return is 12%.

Cash Flow =	–$100	—	—	—	$285.6
Project A)	0	1	2	3	4 years
Cash Flow =	–$100	$46.2	$46.2	$46.2	$46.2
Project B)	0	1	2	3	4 years

Solution:

Assuming revenue is realized uniformly over year 4:

Project "A", Undiscounted Payback = 3 + (100/285.6) = 3.35 years

If the project "A" revenue is assumed to be a lump sum revenue such as from the sale of real estate or common stock, then the Project "A", Undiscounted Payback is 4 years.

Project "B", Undiscounted Payback = 2 + (100-92.4)/46.2 = 2.16 years

Undiscounted Payback indicates select Project "B" with the smaller payback.

Diagrams for Discounted Cash Flow at 12%

Discounted Cash Flow =	–$100	—	—	—	$285.6($P/F_{12,4}$)=$181.5
A)	0	1	2	3	4 year

Project A Discounted Payback = 3 + (100/181.5) = 3.55 years
If the project A revenue is assumed to be lump sum revenue, then Discounted Payback = 4 years.

Discounted Cash Flow =	–$100	$41.25	$36.83	$32.88	$29.36
B)	0	1	2	3	4 years

Where year 1 discounted cash flow equals 46.2($P/F_{12,1}$) and so forth for years 2, 3 and 4.

Project B Discounted Payback = 2 + (100-78.08)/32.88 = 2.67 years

Discounted Payback Indicates Select Project "B", the smaller payback.

Net Present Value Analysis (Mutually Exclusive Investments)

$NPV_A = 285.6(P/F_{12,4}) - 100 = +\$81.5$ Select Largest NPV, "A"

$NPV_B = 46.2(P/A_{12,4}) - 100 = +\$40.3$

Present Value Ratio Analysis

$PVR_A = 81.5 / 100 = +0.815$

$PVR_B = 40.3 / 100 = +0.403$

Since both ratios relate to the same investment dollars, select "A", whether the alternatives are mutually exclusive or non-mutually exclusive.

Discounted Cash Flow Rate of Return

Trial and error analysis gives $DCFROR_A$ = 30% and $DCFROR_B$ = 30%. Because of differences in the distribution of positive cash flow on the project "A" and "B" diagrams, these 30% DCFROR results have very different meaning after the first year. Incremental analysis must be made for a valid economic decision with DCFROR. Make the incremental analysis so that incremental cost (negative cash flow) is followed by revenue (positive cash flow).

Incremental Cash Flow	0	–$46.2	–$46.2	–$46.2	+$239.4
For Project A–B)	0	1	2	3	4 years

PW Eq: $0 = -46.2(P/A_{i,3}) + 239.4(P/F_{i,4})$

Trial and Error, i = Incremental "A-B" DCFROR = 29.9% > $i^* = 12\%$

Select Project "A"

All discounted cash flow analysis techniques indicate "Select A". Payback period on either a discounted or undiscounted basis indicates "Select B," showing the inconsistency in 'payback' as a method for selecting investments that will maximize profitability from available investment dollars.

9.3 Savings are Analogous to Income

In economic evaluation work we very frequently find ourselves confronted with analysis of determining the most economic way to provide a service. This is the most common type of evaluation problem of all and in Chapter 3 we discussed the five basic economic analysis approaches to analyze this type of problem. The five basic approaches are (1) comparison of present worth costs, (2) comparison of annual worth costs, (3) comparison of future worth costs, (4) incremental ROR or Net Value Analysis or (5) break-even analysis such as service life break-even analysis. Of these five methods incremental ROR and Net Value analysis are very popular because of the large number of companies and individuals that use ROR and Net Value analysis as the primary decision making criterion for all types of project analyses. Incremental analysis of alternatives that provide a service always generates incremental costs and savings, and dollars saved are just like dollars earned!

For after-tax DCFROR, Net Value, or Ratio analysis of alternatives involving savings you must convert savings to after-tax cash flow exactly the same as incremental income must be converted to cash flow. If an incremental investment generates savings by reducing operating costs below a former level, the lower operating costs will result in lower tax deductions for operating costs which means you have more taxable income in the same amount as if the savings were incremental revenue.

The following example illustrates DCFROR and NPV analysis of an investment that generates savings.

EXAMPLE 9-2 DCFROR and NPV Analysis Involving Savings

A natural gas distribution company is evaluating the economic potential of installing a new compressor that costs $420,000 to satisfy gas compression requirements and save 80,000 MCF per year of natural gas (where MCF equals thousand cubic feet) compared to the present operating costs. The gas saved could be sold to industrial customers for $3.00 per MCF and compressor life is estimated to be 10 years with zero salvage value. The new compressor would be depreciated straight line over a 7-year life starting at year 0 with the half year convention. Assume compressor maintenance costs will be exactly offset by increased sales revenues due to increased gas selling prices. The effective income tax rate is 40% and the minimum DCFROR is 12%. Use DCFROR and NPV analysis to determine if it is economical to buy the new compressor. Assume other income exists against which to use deductions in any year.

Solution: All Values in Thousands, Except Selling Price
C=Capital Cost, OC = Operating Cost, S = Savings

To illustrate the concept of incremental analysis that is required to make a proper economic evaluation of the example problem, consider the following. Let X equal the "new" compressor natural gas usage in thousands of MCF per year so X + 80 MCF per year represents "present" compressor natural gas use in thousands of MCF per year. The savings of \$240 (80 MCF times \$3.00) per year from going to the new compressor must be converted to cash flow the same as incremental income would be converted to cash flow.

Old	–	OC = (X+80)MCF(\$3.00/MCF)	OC = (X+80)MCF(\$3.00/MCF)
	0	1	.10
New	C=\$420	OC = X MCF(\$3.00/MCF)	OC = X MCF(\$3.00/MCF)
	0	1	.10
New	C=\$420	S = \$240	S = \$240
–Old	0	1	.10

Year	0	1–6	7	8–10
Revenue	–	240	240	240
–Depreciation	–30	–60	–30	–
Taxable Inc.	–30	180	210	240
–Tax @ 40%	12	–72	–84	–96
Net Income	–18	108	126	144
+Depreciation	30	60	30	–
–Capital Costs	–420	–	–	–
Cash Flow	–408	168	156	144

$$\text{PW Eq: } 0 = -408 + 168(P/A_{i,6}) + 156(P/F_{i,7}) + 144(P/A_{i,3})(P/F_{i,7})$$

$$i = \text{DCFROR} = 39.2\% > i^* = 12\%,$$
new compressor is satisfactory

$$\text{NPV @ } i^* \ 12\% = -408 + 168\overset{4.111}{(P/A_{12,6})} + 156\overset{0.4523}{(P/F_{12,7})}$$

$$+ 144\overset{2.402}{(P/A_{12,3})}\overset{0.4523}{(P/F_{12,7})} = +\$510 > 0,$$
satisfactory

The DCFROR of 39.2%, which is more than three times the minimum DCFROR of 12%, indicates very satisfactory economics for the new compressor, consistent with positive NPV of $510,000 that is greater than the cost of $420,000 that generated the NPV. *Whenever NPV is positive and similar in magnitude to the cost that generated it, project economics are very good and typically relate to a project with a DCFROR three or four times the minimum DCFROR.*

9.4 Sunk Costs and Opportunity Costs in Evaluations

Sunk costs are costs that have already been incurred in the past and that nothing we do now or in the future can affect. Economic analysis studies for investment decision making purposes deal with project costs and revenues and tax effects yet to be incurred now or in the future. *Sunk costs are not relevant to the analysis of either income or service producing investment alternatives except for remaining sale value and tax effects, which are opportunity cost considerations* discussed in the next paragraph. Past commitments to expend money as well as past expenditures are sunk revenues and costs. Revenues realized in the past from a project are sunk revenues the same as past costs are sunk costs. Classic examples of sunk costs include the costs of equipment acquired several years ago and now being considered for replacement, the costs for research or exploration work incurred in earlier years, and the cost of common stock or land several years ago for a personal investment. In all of these situations the cost is in the past and, except for remaining sale value and tax effects, is not relevant to our analysis of whether to develop, keep or replace the asset or investment.

Opportunity cost is hidden or implied cost that is incurred when a person or organization forgoes the opportunity to realize positive cash flow from an investment in order to take a different investment course of action. For example, if you elect not to sell your personal automobile for its second-hand value of $8,000 in order to keep it and use it, you are incurring an opportunity cost of $8,000. In analyzing whether to replace the vehicle (or any other existing asset) with a new vehicle or asset the opportunity cost of $8,000 must be accounted for as illustrated in Chapter 10, Examples 10-3 and 10-4 related to replacement analysis.

Another opportunity cost situation involves analysis of whether to sell a project or property or whether to keep and develop the project or property. If an investor forgoes realizing a sale value positive cash flow in order to keep and develop a property, an opportunity cost equal to the positive cash flow that could be realized from selling must be included in the analysis of development economics. *Proper incremental analysis of mutually exclusive develop versus sell or joint venture alternatives automatically accounts for the proper sunk cost and opportunity cost considerations in that analysis, as illustrated in Example 9-3.*

A personal investment situation involving important opportunity cost considerations concerns analysis of whether to keep or sell common stock purchased in the past. Assume you purchased stock three months ago for $20 per share and the price has dropped to $8 per share. The original $20 per share cost is sunk but the tax effects are not. If you sell for $8 per share you also get a $20 per share tax deduction which is $12 per share in excess of what is needed to eliminate any gain from the sale. The $12 per share excess tax deduction would be short term capital loss that could be used against other short term capital gains assuming other gains exist. For a 30% effective income tax rate, the $12 per share deduction would save $3.60 per share in taxes from using the deduction against other short term capital gain income, giving total cash flow from selling of $11.60 per share ($8 sale value plus $3.60 tax savings). An investor who forgoes selling for $8 per share is actually incurring an opportunity cost of $11.60 per share to keep the stock. This rationale relates to common stock sales that stock brokers often refer to as "tax selling."

Finally, the minimum rate of return (or opportunity cost of capital or hurdle rate) is the classic example of the most widely used opportunity cost in economic analysis. As discussed in several places earlier in the text, the minimum rate of return is not the cost of borrowed funds, (an investor may not even be using borrowed funds), but minimum rate of return represents other opportunities thought to exist for the investment of capital both now and in the future over the life of a project. An investor incurs an opportunity cost equal to the rate of return that could be realized by investing elsewhere in other projects if he elects to invest in a new project being analyzed. Thus the term minimum rate of return is interchangeable with opportunity cost of capital.

Example 9-3 illustrates sunk cost and opportunity cost handling in a develop versus sell income-producing analysis situation while Example 9-5 illustrates sunk costs and opportunity costs in a break-even analysis related to service-producing assets. In Chapter 10 sunk cost and opportunity cost considerations are applied to the evaluation of service-producing alternatives in Examples 10-3 and 10-4.

EXAMPLE 9-3 Sunk Costs and Opportunity Costs in The Analysis of Develop versus Sell

The time diagram shows costs and revenues for a 6 year project life with research costs in years -1 and 0 (year 0 represents the start of production with negative numbering of pre-production years). To simplify the cash flow analysis, consider the project to be non-mineral or petroleum, so depletion is not applicable. Assume the year 0 equipment cost is placed into service at year 0 with straight line, 5 year life depreciation starting at year 0 with the half-year convention. Escalation of year 1 through 5 sales and operating costs is projected to be a washout. Project salvage value is zero. Other taxable income and tax obligations are assumed to exist against which to use tax deductions in any year. The effective tax rate is 40%. All values are in thousands of dollars.

Research or Exploration Cost = 150	Research or Exploration Cost = 100 Eq.Cost = 200	Annual Sales = 250 250 Annual OC = 90 90	L = 0
–1	0	1 5	

Assume the escalated dollar minimum DCFROR is 15% and make the following four analyses:

A) Calculate project DCFROR assuming the evaluation is being made prior to year -1, so none of the project dollar values shown on the diagram are sunk.

B) Make DCFROR analysis to determine if project development should continue, assuming the evaluation is being made after the year -1 costs have already been incurred (so they are sunk) but prior to incurring the year 0 costs. Assume the year -1 research or exploration costs have generated no assets of value for sale to outside interests, therefore, no opportunity cost will be incurred from keeping the property for continued development.

C) Make the "B" analysis assuming the year -1 research costs have generated patents for which a $200 cash sale value offer at year 0 has been received.

D) Re-analyze the "C" analysis assuming the year -1 research cost was instead a surface land cost that could not be expensed at year -1, but would be deducted as a write-off either against the $200 sale value at time zero, or, against other income at the end of year 5 if the project is kept.

Solution: All Values in Thousands of Dollars

Case A) Year –1 Cost Is Not Sunk

Year	–1	0	1–4	5
Revenue			250	250
–Oper. Costs			–90	–90
–Development	–150	–100		
–Depreciation		–20	–40	–20
Taxable Income	–150	–120	120	140
–Tax @ 40%	60	48	–48	–56
Net Income	–90	–72	72	84
+Depreciation		20	40	20
–Capital Costs		–200		
Cash Flow	–90	–252	112	104

PW Eq @ Yr –1:

$$0 = -90 - 252(P/F_{i,1}) + 112(P/A_{i,4})(P/F_{i,1}) + 104(P/F_{i,6})$$

$i = \text{DCFROR} = 16.7\% > i^{*} = 15\%$, so satisfactory

Case B) Year –1 Cost Is Sunk

The year -1 costs and tax effects are sunk and not relevant to the analysis. No opportunity cost exists from not selling the property because no year 0 sale value exists. Year 0 through 5 cash flows are the same as for part "A".

Year	–1	0	1–4	5
Develop Cash Flow	–90 (Sunk)	–252	112	104
Abandon Cash Flow	–90 (Sunk)	0	0	0
Develop – Abandon	0	–252	112	104

PW Eq @ Yr 0:

$$0 = -252 + 112(P/A_{i,4}) + 104(P/F_{i,5})$$

$i = \text{DCFROR} = 33.85\% > i^* = 15\%$, so satisfactory

Case C) Year -1 Cost Is Sunk and an Opportunity Cost Exists

The year -1 cost and tax effects are still sunk. However, the year 0 sale value of $200 minus tax of 0.40($200) or $80 would yield sale cash flow of $120. An investor who passes up the opportunity to realize positive cash flow from selling in order to retain or develop, incurs an opportunity cost equal to the positive sale cash flow. This opportunity cost occurs naturally from proper incremental analysis of the mutually exclusive develop versus sell alternatives as follows:

Year	–1	0	1–4	5
Develop Cash Flow	–90 (Sunk)	–252	112	104
Sell Cash Flow	–90 (Sunk)	+120	0	0
Develop – Sell	0	–372	112	104

PW Eq @ Yr 0:

$$0 = -372 + 112(P/A_{i,4}) + 104(P/F_{i,5})$$

$i = \text{DCFROR} = 14.94\% < i^* = 15\%$, so slightly unsatisfactory

From an economic viewpoint, development is slightly less desirable than selling. Note that the Develop minus Sell incremental analysis converts the sale positive cash flow of $120 to a negative incremental $120 cash flow. This is effectively a $120 opportunity cost that the investor incurs in addition to the year 0 development cost if development is accepted. Even though development alone looks satisfactory as shown in the "B" analysis, proper accounting for the opportunity cost from keeping the property instead of selling makes selling a slightly better or break-even alternative compared to developing.

Case D) Year -1 Cost is Sunk but Tax Effects are not Sunk.

The time zero sale cash flow is the $200 sale value minus the tax on the sale taxable income of $200 - $150 land book value which yields tax of $50(0.4) = $20. This gives after-tax sale cash flow of $200 - $20 tax = $180. Although the land cost of $150 is sunk, the remaining sale value and tax effects are not sunk and give sale value cash flow of $180 instead of the $120 cash flow in the "C" analysis when the year -1 cost and all tax effects were sunk.

If the project is developed instead of being sold, the land book value of $150 will be written off at the end of year five against other income, saving $150(0.4 tax rate) = $60 in tax at year five. This makes the year 5 develop cash flow $104 plus $60, or $164.

Year	–1	0	1–4	5
Develop Cash Flow	–150 (sunk)	–252	+112	+164
Sell Cash Flow	–150 (sunk)	+180	0	0
Develop – Sell	0	–432	+112	+164

PW Eq @ Time Zero:

$$0 = -432 + 112(P/A_{i,4}) + 164(P/F_{i,5})$$

i = DCFROR = 12.1% < i* = 15.0% so reject development and sell.

The different tax situation with regard to the year -1 sunk cost has changed the economics from break-even in "C" to an advantage for selling in Case D.

9.5 Break-even Analyses

Break-even analysis involves specifying all project parameters except one and calculating what that parameter needs to be to give a project a specified DCFROR, or in other words, an NPV equal to zero at the desired discount rate. On an after-tax basis, it is necessary to be very specific about the parameter to be calculated and its relative impact on taxes and cash flow. If an investor wants to determine the revenues for a project that are required to give an after-tax rate of return of 15%, he or she must recognize that those revenues are before-tax values, subject to taxation. More specifically the investor is wanting to determine the before-tax revenues that would generate sufficient after-tax cash flows to give the investor the desired after-tax return on investment.

Break-even analyses may include calculating break-even parameters such as annual revenues, product selling prices, project selling prices (or minimum project selling price) and break-even acquisition costs (also referred to as maximum project purchase price). There are several different methods that can be used to make the break-even calculations. When using a computer, an iterative process similar to solving for rate of return is usually employed. However, for hand calculations, the use of an explicit relationship for the parameter and the overall project cash flow is developed by letting the parameter be defined as a variable such as "X," and letting the project cash flows be expressed in terms of the parameter. This results in one present, annual or future worth equation expressed in terms of one unknown break-even parameter, which can be determined by solving the equation for that parameter.

The following examples in this section address break-even revenue and product selling price considerations while incorporating other material considered earlier in the text, including the proper handling of escalation and inflation, risk analysis and sunk cost / opportunity cost issues. In each example it is important to consider not only the project assumptions, but the meaning of the parameter being determined. If you want break-even revenues for a before-tax return on investment, you only need to calculate the before-tax net annual value. However, if you are looking for the before-tax revenues required to give a specified after-tax rate of return on investment, then the calculation becomes a little more laborious.

While each of these parameters relates directly to a dollar amount, other relevant break-even parameters include, but are not limited to, ore grades or wash yields in mining, decline curve parameters in oil and gas, or break-even service lives in replacement analyses such as in refining or other industry applications.

EXAMPLE 9-4 Escalated Dollar and Constant Dollar Break-even Revenue Analysis

If an investor spends $100,000 on equipment and $50,000 on development at time 0 to generate revenues for a 5 year period and zero salvage value, what uniform and equal annual net revenues after operating costs for years 1 through 5 are required to give:

A) 20% before-tax escalated dollar ROR.

B) 20% before-tax constant dollar ROR assuming 10% inflation per year.

C) 20% after-tax escalated dollar DCFROR for expensing the $50,000 development cost against other income at year 0 and depreciating the $100,000 equipment cost straight line over years 1 through 5 starting in year 1 with a full year deduction to simplify the analysis. Use a 40% effective tax rate.

D) 20% after-tax constant dollar DCFROR assuming 10% per year inflation for the tax considerations of part "C".

Solution:

A) Before-Tax, Escalated Dollar Break-even Analysis

$$\text{Net Revenue Per Year} = \$150{,}000(\overset{0.33438}{A/P_{20,5}}) = \$50{,}157$$

B) Before-Tax, Constant Dollar Break-even Analysis

$1 + i = (1 + f)(1 + i')$ where $f = 0.10$ and $i' = 0.20$,

so the equivalent escalated dollar ROR, $i = 0.320$ or 32.0%

$$\text{Net Revenue Per Year} = \$150{,}000(\overset{0.4264}{A/P_{32,5}}) = \$63{,}960$$

Alternate Solution to Case "B"

Convert all escalated dollar break-even revenues, "X," to equivalent constant dollar results by discounting "X" at the 10% inflation rate to express all revenue in terms of year 0 purchasing power. Then handle the time value of money by discounting again at the constant dollar minimum ROR of 20%.

$$150{,}000 = X(P/F_{10,1})(P/F_{20,1}) + X(P/F_{10,2})(P/F_{20,2}) + X(P/F_{10,3})(P/F_{20,3}) + X(P/F_{10,4})(P/F_{20,4}) + X(P/F_{10,5})(P/F_{20,5})$$

X = Net Revenue Per Year = $63,960

C) After-Tax, Escalated Dollar Break-even Analysis

For after-tax analysis, first convert costs and revenues to cash flows expressed in terms of the unknown parameter, "X."

Year	0	1–5
Revenue		X
–Development	–50,000	
–Depreciation		–20,000
Taxable Inc.	–50,000	X–20,000
–Tax @ 40%	20,000	–.4X+ 8,000
Net Income	–30,000	.6X–12,000
+Depreciation		20,000
–Capital Costs	–100,000	
Cash Flow	–130,000	.6X+8,000

PW Eq: $0 = -130{,}000 + (.6X + 8{,}000)\overset{2.991}{(P/A_{20,5})}$

$0 = -130{,}000 + 1.7946X + 23{,}928$

X = $59,106 net revenue per year to give a 20% escalated dollar DCFROR.

D) After-Tax Constant Dollar Break-even Analysis

The easiest analysis is to work in escalated dollars and use the escalated dollar minimum DCFROR of 32% that is equivalent to the 20% constant dollar DCFROR, as calculated in part "B."

PW Eq: $0 = -130{,}000 + (.6X + 8{,}000)\overset{2.3452}{(P/A_{32,5})}$

$0 = -130{,}000 + 1.4071X + 18{,}762$

X = $79,055 net revenue per year to give a 20% constant dollar DCFROR.

Note the four break-even results are all different. *It is very important to explicitly understand the assumptions related to all economic analysis calculations to properly interpret and apply the results for investment decision making. Break-even calculations are no exception. Whether results relate to before-tax or after-tax calculations, done in escalated or constant dollars, with or without risk adjustment, and on a cash investment or leveraged basis are key assumptions that have a significant effect on any proper economic analysis.* There is no substitute for understanding the calculation mechanics and the meaning of relevant discounted cash flow analysis assumptions in order to be able to apply evaluation results properly for economic decision making.

Example 9-5 Opportunity Cost in Breakeven Analysis

Consider that you have been asked to determine the three equal end-of-year before-tax breakeven revenues that would cover overhaul and operating costs to provide service for the next three years with an existing machine. A 20% after-tax escalated dollar DCFROR on investment dollars is desired. The existing machine has a present secondhand market value of $7,000,000 now (at time 0), and a current tax book value of zero. If the existing machine is kept, a $10,000,000 overhaul cost must be incurred now (time 0) to retrofit the machine to handle new product quality standards. The overhaul cost would be depreciable (since it is assumed to change the use or life of the asset) starting in time 0 using MACRS 7-year life depreciation with the half-year convention. Annual escalated dollar operating costs are projected to be $3,000,000 in time 0, $6,000,000 in year 1, $7,000,000 in year 2 and $4,000,000 in year 3. The $3,000,000 time 0 operating cost represents an accrual of costs in months 0 through 6 which are closer to time zero than year 1. The $6,000,000 year 1 operating cost is an accrual of costs to be incurred in months 7 through 18 and so forth. End of year 3 equipment salvage value is estimated to be $2,000,000. Assume any taxable gain on salvage is taxed as ordinary income. Other taxable income is assumed to exist against which to use tax deductions in the year they are realized. The effective income tax rate is 40%.

Solution: All values in cash flows in 000's

If the investor forgoes selling the equipment for $7,000,000 to keep and retrofit it for continued use, the after-tax cash flow from the foregone sale value must be accounted for as an opportunity cost and the cost of continuing to own the equipment. Alternatively stated, the required revenue from continued operating of the machine must generate an NPV equal the NPV of selling. First, consider the after-tax cash flow if the asset was sold and the gain is fully taxable since the tax book value was stated to be zero:

Foregone ATCF if not Selling the Equipment Today:

Revenue	7,000
- Bk Value	0
Taxable Inc	7,000
- Tax @ 40%	-2,800
Net Income	4,200
Bk. Value	0
ATCF	4,200

If the investor passes up selling the equipment, an NPV of $4,200,000 will be foregone, and this opportunity cost must be recovered along with repair and operating expenditures from the breakeven before-tax revenues in years 1 through 3. Opportunity costs are always properly reflected in incremental calculations. This may also be achieved by simply inserting the opportunity cost into the cash flows of keeping the machine which creates an incremental analysis where the economic objective is to cause the incremental NPV to equal zero.

Summarizing the relevant parameters in 000's:

Year	0	1	2	3
Breakeven Revenue		X	X	X
Salvage Value				$2,000
Operating Cost	$ 3,000	$6,000	$7,000	$4,000
Repair Cost	$10,000			
Opportunity Cost	$ 4,200			

MACRS Depreciation Using Table 7-3, Base on 7-Year Life

Time 0	(0.1429)($10,000) = $1,429
Year 1	(0.2449)($10,000) = $2,449
Year 2	(0.1749)($10,000) = $1,749
Year 3*	(0.4373)($10,000) = $4,373

* Includes write-off taken against year 3 sale value

Year	0	1	2	3
Revenue		X	X	X+2,000
–Oper. Costs	–3,000	–6,000	–7,000	–4,000
–Depreciation	–1,429	–2,449	–1,749	–4,373
Taxable Income	–4,429	X–8,449	X–8,749	X–6,373
–Income Tax, 40%	1,772	–.4X+3,380	–.4X+3,500	–.4X+2,549
Net Income	–2,657	.6X–5,069	.6X–5,249	.6X–3,824
+Depreciation	1,429	2,449	1,749	4,373
–Repair Cost	–10,000			
–Opportunity Cost	–4,200			
ΔATCF	–15,428	.6X–2,620	.6X–3,500	.6X+ 549

Economically, the objective is to find a value of X that provides the desired incremental minimum rate of return of 20%. Stated another way, the investor is seeking to determine the necessary before-tax revenue that would cause the incremental NPV (ΔNPV) at 20% to equal zero as follows:

$$\Delta NPV\ 0 = -15{,}428 + (.6X-2{,}620)\overset{0.8333}{(P/F_{20\%,1})} + (.6X - 3{,}500)\overset{0.6944}{(P/F_{20\%,2})}$$

$$+ (.6X + 549)\overset{0.5787}{(P/F_{20\%,3})}$$

$$0 = 1.2638X - 19{,}725$$

Note that simplifying the parameters in the incremental NPV equation two terms result. These terms include the incremental present worth after-tax revenue (1.2638X) and the incremental present worth after-tax cost of $19,725. Solving for the before-tax revenue in the expression gives X = $15,608 in 000's.

Alternatively you could also evaluate each option individually as summarized below:

Keep and Repair

Year	0	1	2	3
Revenue		X	X	X+2,000
–Oper. Costs	–3,000	–6,000	–7,000	–4,000
–Depreciation	–1,429	–2,449	–1,749	–4,373
Taxable Income	–4,429	X–8,449	X–8,749	X–6,373
–Income Tax, 40%	1,772	–.4X+3,380	–.4X+3,500	–.4X+2,549
Net Income	–2,657	.6X–5,069	.6X–5,249	.6X–3,824
+Depreciation	1,429	2,449	1,749	4,373
–Repair Cost	–10,000			
Keep ATCF	–11,228	.6X–2,620	.6X–3,500	.6X+549

Sell

Year	0	1	2	3
Revenue	7,000			
–Oper. Costs				
–Depreciation				
Taxable Income	7,000			
–Income Tax, 40%	(2,800)			
Net Income	4,200			
+Depreciation				
–Repair Cost				
Sell ATCF	4,200			

Incremental Keep–Sell

Year	0	1	2	3
Keep ATCF	(11,228)	.6X–2,620	.6X–3,500	.6X+549
–Sell ATCF	4,200			
Keep–Sell ΔATCF	(15,428)	.6X–2,620	.6X–3,500	.6X+549

The incremental ATCF's are identical from each approach.

As an additional calculation (not asked for the in the example statement): Assume the described machine produced 1,000 units in each of years 1, 2 and 3. What before-tax uniform escalated dollar selling price per unit in years 1, 2 and 3 would provide the investor with a 20% after-tax escalated dollar DCFROR from this asset?

In the previous solution to this problem, the breakeven before tax revenue required was $15,608,000 per year in years 1, 2 and 3. If we had 1,000 units produced and sold each year, taking the production times a price "X" provides $15,608,000 in revenue each year. Or, the breakeven price would be $15,608,000 / 1,000 units = $15,608 per unit.

Every problem is a little different and may require you to think about a slightly different setup to solve these breakeven questions. The key issue remains one of consistency in the approach.

It may be of interest to observe that if the investor desired to achieve a 12.2% constant dollar DCFROR for assumed annual inflation of 7% per year over the project life, the break-even analysis would give the same result. A 12.2% constant dollar DCFROR is equivalent to a 20% escalated dollar DCFROR for 7% inflation per year using Equation 5-1:

$$1 + i = (1 + f)(1 + i')$$

Constant dollar break-even calculations and escalated dollar break-even calculations are equivalent if the appropriate rates are used.

EXAMPLE 9-6 Expected Value Break-even Analysis

An investor has paid $100,000 to develop a facility that is estimated to have a 70% probability of successfully producing 5,000 product units per year for each of the next 2 years, after which the facility is expected to be obsolete with a zero salvage value. The 30% probability of failure is associated with an escalated dollar facility salvage value of $50,000 at year 1. Today's dollar operating costs are $40,000 per year and are estimated to escalate 15% in year 1, and 10% in year 2. Product selling price is estimated to escalate 25% in year 1, and 15% in year 2. Determine the required escalated dollar selling price per unit in each of years 1 and 2 to give the investor a 12% constant dollar expected DCFROR. Assume inflation will be 6% in year 1, and 10% in year 2. The $100,000 cost will be depreciated using Modified ACRS depreciation for a 5 year life starting in year 1 with a half-year deduction. Other income exists against which to use deductions in any year. The effective income tax rate is 40% and all salvage considerations are treated as ordinary income.

Solution: All Values in Dollars

Let X = Today's Dollar Selling Price Per Unit

This analysis is presented in escalated dollar values, but for either escalated or constant dollar analysis, escalated dollar costs and revenues must be projected.

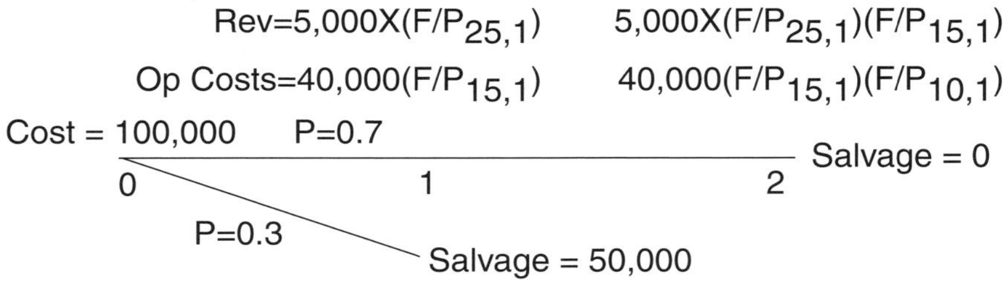

To work in escalated dollars, which are the dollars shown on the diagram, we must calculate the escalated dollar minimum DCFROR for years 1 and 2 that are equivalent to the 12% constant dollar DCFROR for the inflation rates of 6% in year 1 and 10% in year 2.

$1 + i^{*} = (1 + f)(1 + i^{*\prime})$

Year 1: $f = 0.06$, $i^{*\prime} = 0.12$, so $i^{*} = 0.187$ or 18.7%

Year 2: $f = 0.10$, $i^{*\prime} = 0.12$, so $i^{*} = 0.232$ or 23.2%

Year	0	1(Failure)	1(Success)	2(Success)
Revenue		50,000	6,250X	7,187X
–Oper Costs			–46,000	–50,600
–Depreciation		–20,000	–20,000	–32,000
–Write-off		–80,000		–48,000
Taxable		–50,000	6,250X–66,000	7,187X–130,600
–Tax @ 40%		20,000	–2,500X+26,400	–2,875X+52,240
Net Income		–30,000	3,750X–39,600	4,312X–78,360
+Depreciation		20,000	20,000	32,000
+Write-off		80,000		48,000
–Capital Costs	–100,000			
Cash Flow	–100,000	70,000	3,750X–19,600	4,312X+1,640

Expected PW Eq:

$$0 = -100{,}000 + 70{,}000\overset{0.8425}{(P/F_{18.7,1})}(.3) + (3{,}750X - 19{,}600)\overset{0.8425}{(P/F_{18.7,1})}(.7)$$

$$+ (4{,}312X + 1{,}640)\overset{0.8117}{(P/F_{23.2,1})}\overset{0.8425}{(P/F_{18.7,1})}(.7)$$

X = \$21.77 per unit is the today's dollar selling price.
Year 1 Escalated Dollar Price is \$21.77(1.25) = \$27.21

Year 2 Escalated Dollar Price is \$27.21(1.15) = \$31.29

Example 9-7 Breakeven Acquisition Cost Valuation of a Petroleum Joint Venture

An independent petroleum producer with less than 1,000 barrels per day of oil equivalent production has the opportunity to participate in the joint venture development of an oil well. The well has several potentially productive zones and the operator feels the well has a 100% probability of successfully generating minimum oil equivalent production of 36,000 barrels in year 1, 24,000 barrels in year 2, and 12,000 barrels in year 3. However, the potential production zones differ significantly in depth so drilling, fracturing and well completion costs could vary over a wide range, depending on the zone or zones completed. You have been asked to calculate the maximum breakeven tangible and intangible well costs that the independent producer could incur and realize a 15% escalated dollar DCFROR on invested dollars for the following assumptions. Well development costs will be incurred at year 0 and 70% of the well costs will be intangible while 30% will be tangible. The investor did not acquire the mineral rights and as a result, has zero dollars invested in the minerals in place. The investor would have a 50% working interest and a 36% net revenue interest in the stated production over the well life. Crude oil prices are estimated at \$75 per barrel each year over the 3-year project life and operating costs are estimated at \$180,000 per year despite declining production in years 2 and 3. Other income is considered to exist against which to use any negative taxable income from this project (expense scenario). The investor's combined state and federal income tax rate is 40%. Neglect any salvage and do not write off remaining book values assuming a wash of salvage, closure costs and write-offs having zero impact on cash flow.

Solution: All Values except the Selling Price in 000's of Dollars

Total well drilling and completion costs will be equal to X so the investor's 50% working interest is represented as 0.5X.

Tangible Completion Cost = (0.30)(0.5)X = 0.15X
Intangible Drilling Cost = (0.70)(0.50)X = 0.35X

Use Table 7-3 MACRS 7-year depreciation rates on 0.15X to determine annual depreciation deductions. Start depreciation in year 1.

Non-integrated producers may expense 100% of qualified IDC's in the year incurred.

After-Tax Cash Flow Calculations Based on Net Revenue and Working Interest %'s, Production and Cash Flows in 000's

Year	0	1	2	3
Production		36	24	12
Selling Price, $/Bbl		75	75	75
Revenue (100%)		2,700	1,800	900
Net Revenue (36%)		972	648	324
–Net Oper Cost (50%)		–90	–90	–90
–Intangible Drilling	-.35X			
–Depreciation		–.0214X	–.0367X	–.0262X
Taxable Before Depl.	–.35X	882–.0214X	558–.0367X	234–.0262X
Percentage Depletion		–146	–97	–49
100% Limit Test*				
Taxable Income	–.35X	736–.0214X	461–.0367X	185–.0262X
– Income Taxes, 40%	.14X	–294+.0086X	–184+.0147X	–74+.0105X
Net Income	–.21X	442–.0128X	277–.0220X	111–.0157X
+ Depreciation		.0214X	.0367X	.0262X
+ Depletion		146	97	49
- Tangible Equip.	–.15X			
After-Tax Cash Flow	–.36X	588+.0086X	374+.0147X	160+.0105X

* The 100% limit test is discussed following the solution.

The economic objective is to determine how much can be spent on drilling this well and still achieve a 15% DCFROR, or an NPV of zero at 15%.

$$\text{PW Eq: } 0 = -0.36X + (588+.0086X)\overset{0.8696}{(P/F_{15\%,1})}$$

$$+ (374+0.0147X)\overset{0.7561}{(P/F_{15\%,2})} + (160+.0105X)\overset{0.6575}{(P/F_{15\%,3})}$$

PW Eq: 0 = –0.3345X + 899 X = 2,688

Based on the Investor's working interest 50%:

Tangible Completion Cost = (0.30)(0.50)2,688 = 403
Intangible Drilling Cost = (0.70)(0.50)2,688 = 941

Calculating Taxable Income before Depletion Based on Breakeven Costs to Test 100% Limit on Percentage Depletion

Year	0	1	2	3
Production		36	24	12
Selling Price, $/Bbl		75	75	75
Revenue (100%)		2,700	1,800	900
Net Revenue (36%)		972	648	324
–Net Operating Cost		-90	-90	-90
–Intangible Drilling	-941			
–Depreciation		-58	-99	-70
Taxable Before Depl.	-941	824	459	164
Percentage Depletion		-146	-97	-49
100% Limit Test*		824	459	164

The check shows that there is sufficient Taxable Income before Depletion each year to claim the percentage depletion deductions reflected in the analysis. The percentage depletion deductions do not exceed the 100% limit, therefore no adjustments are necessary.

9.6 Three Methods of Investment Valuation

Placing correct value on investment property and projects is extremely important to investors, bankers and sellers alike. Frequently, how much a property is worth at a given time under a given set of market conditions must be determined. Sometimes, financial considerations such as the maximum mortgage loan that can be obtained on an investment and the loan terms will affect determination of the value of a property. However, projected future earnings usually comprise the primary factor that determines the market value of business assets. Lending institutions are just as anxious as buyers and sellers to know the answers to valuation problems. Often they depend upon a professional class of 'rule-of-thumb' appraiser rules to develop the guidelines on which to base their commitments. Investment bankers perform the same appraisal service in relation to putting value on companies, projects and investment situations.

To determine how much you should pay for property that you may be considering acquiring, how much you should be willing to accept as sale value on a property you own, or how much you can take as an income tax deduction on business property that you contribute to a charity, you must determine the property "fair market value" on the date of the transaction. As defined by the U.S. Internal Revenue Service in Publication 334, *fair market value is the price that property would sell for on the open market. It is the price that would be agreed on between a willing buyer and a willing seller, with neither being required to act, and both having reasonable knowledge of the relevant facts.* The term "market value" often is used interchangeably with "fair market value."

There are three basic approaches that appraisers, investment bankers and investors take in determining the market value of investment property. These approaches are 1) replacement cost, 2) market valuation based on comparable sales, and 3) discounted cash flow analysis valuation of projected future positive and negative cash flows.

The replacement cost approach to valuation is based on analyzing cost for land, mineral rights, buildings and equipment, roads, development, and other costs to replace an existing facility, production operation, real estate investment or general investment project. You need to be very careful to include all costs that are relevant for this type of analysis and that can be a difficult task sometimes. Different projects that on the surface seem similar or identical may have significantly different development or operating costs for subtle reasons that an inexperienced evaluator might overlook.

The comparable sales approach to valuation is based on looking at recent sale prices for properties or investments similar to the one being valued. This approach works very well in housing real estate where many transactions occur regularly for similar properties over any given period of time in given locations. To a lesser degree this approach is applicable to apartment house, office building and land real estate investments. The consideration that you must be very careful about in making comparable sales analysis is the comparable equivalence of properties being analyzed. When you get into the analysis of income producing projects, business and general investments, subtle differences in location, property taxes, operating costs such as energy costs, development or needed improvement costs, size of operation (which may affect efficiency of operation), existing product sale contracts and many other factors can cause significant differences in investment valuations. *Comparable sales often is a poor approach to valuation of natural resource properties.* The value of mineral, petroleum and timber rights varies significantly with size of reserves, projected timing for development of reserves, expected rate of production of reserves, expected cost for development and production of reserves, projected product price at different future points in time related to production, and, future salvage value of the assets to name some of the significant parameters to be considered. Usually at least several of these parameters differ significantly for different properties, making comparable sales a very poor approach to valuation of natural resource properties. *Different size and quality of natural resource reserves affects the timing and cost of production, which generally makes it imperative to go to discounted cash flow valuation of natural resource investments rather than trying to utilize the comparable sales approach.*

Discounted cash flow analysis, for valuation purposes, relates directly to after-tax net present value analysis of the investments to be assessed. This requires projecting the magnitude and timing of project capital investment costs and operating costs to produce product at a given rate with projected future product selling prices. All expected inflows and outflows of money, including salvage values or abandonment costs, need to be taken into account. Proper tax effects and any risk of failure need to be accounted for properly in a valid discounted cash flow valuation. These calculations and concepts have been the subject of emphasis in the previous eight chapters of this text, so we will conclude this discussion by emphasizing the importance of the magnitude and timing of input cost and revenue data and the income tax and evaluation assumptions applied to these data to obtain valid discounted cash flow valuation results. Section 9.7 further emphasizes that *after-tax NPV of a project, in general, does not represent the maximum price that an investor can pay to receive the DCFROR discount rate on invested dollars.* Since acquisition costs of various types are tax deductible through depreciation, amortization, depletion or write-offs upon sale or abandonment of a project, the value of an investment usually is bigger than its NPV. Example 9-8 illustrates these considerations in detail.

9.7 NPV Use For Break-even Acquisition Cost Valuation

Net Present Value (NPV) represents the additional after-tax cost that can be incurred at the point in time NPV is calculated and still give the investor the minimum after-tax rate of return on invested dollars. The words "additional after-tax costs" means "additional negative after-tax cash flow." Acquisition, or other additional costs being considered, are before-tax expenditures. Investors must account for the tax deductibility of all costs to determine the tax savings from those expenditures and the impact on cash flow and after-tax NPV. Netting the present worth of these tax savings against the acquisition cost gives the "after-tax acquisition cost," which equals the after-tax project NPV. Re-phrasing the last sentence, what an investor is looking for with this calculation is the additional before-tax cost that will make his or her after-tax NPV equal zero. In general, if an acquisition or other additional cost is tax deductible, an investor can pay more than the after-tax NPV for the project and still get the desired minimum after-tax rate of return on the total investment. Whether acquisition or other costs are for assets that are depreciable, amortizable, depletable or non-depreciable until sold (such as land) is very important, necessary input information for valid break-even cost analyses. The following example illustrates these concepts.

EXAMPLE 9-8 NPV Related to Break-even Acquisition Cost

Consider a project with an equipment cost of $15 million and an experimental research and development cost of $10 million at time 0. Uniformly equal escalated dollar revenues of $20 million per year for years 1 through 5 are expected to be generated with escalated dollar operating costs of $5 million per year. Salvage value at year 5 is expected to be 0. Expense the full experimental development cost in year 0 and assume other taxable income exists against which to use the deduction. Depreciate the equipment straight line over 5 years starting in time 0 with the half-year convention. Use a 40% effective income tax rate. For a minimum escalated dollar DCFROR of 20%, calculate project NPV. Then make the following acquisition cost analyses.

Case 1: Prior to starting this project, what could an investor pay at time zero to acquire the right to develop the project if a 20% DCFROR is satisfactory? Assume the acquisition cost would be treated as a patent or business agreement cost for tax purposes and amortized straight line over 5 years (years 1 through 5).

Case 2: After developing the project and realizing the year 1 revenue and operating cost, what could an investor pay to acquire the project at the beginning of year 2 to get a 20% DCFROR on invested dollars? Assume this acquisition cost would be specified so that 60% of the cost is considered to be for depreciable assets and 40% of the cost is for 5 year life amortizable business agreement or patent costs.

Solution: All Values in Thousands of Dollars

Case 1: After-tax NPV Acquisition Analysis

Year	0	1–4	5
Revenue		20,000	20,000
–Oper Costs		–5,000	–5,000
–Development	–10,000		
–Depreciation	–1,500	–3,000	–1,500
Taxable Inc.	–11,500	12,000	13,500
–Tax @ 40%	4,600	–4,800	–5,400
Net Income	–6,900	7,200	8,100
+Depreciation	1,500	3,000	1,500
–Equip. Costs	–15,000		
Cash Flow	–20,400	10,200	9,600

$NPV = 10{,}200(P/A_{20,4}) + 9{,}600(P/F_{20,5}) - 20{,}400 = +\$9{,}860$

If you pay $9.86 million to acquire the property and the acquisition cost is tax deductible as a patent cost, as in Case 1, NPV will still be positive. You can afford to pay more than the NPV of $9.86 million and still get a 20% DCFROR on invested dollars. This is illustrated now for an assumed $10 million acquisition cost considered amortizable over five years.

Year	0	1–4	5
Revenue		20,000	20,000
–Oper Costs		–5,000	–5,000
–Development	–10,000		
–Depreciation	–1,500	–3,000	–1,500
–Amortization		–2,000	–2,000
Taxable	–11,500	10,000	11,500
–Tax @ 40%	4,600	–4,000	–4,600
Net Income	–6,900	6,000	6,900
+Deprec./Amort.	1,500	5,000	3,500
–Equip. Cost	–15,000		
–Amort. Cost	–10,000		
Cash Flow	–30,400	11,000	10,400

$$NPV = -30{,}400 + 11{,}000(P/A_{20,4}) + 10{,}400(P/F_{20,5}) = +\$2{,}250$$

Although the NPV of the initial project was $9.86 million, spending $10 million to acquire the patent rights has still left the project with positive NPV because of the patent tax deduction effects. The amount that can be paid for the patent to make project NPV zero is calculated by expressing cash flow in terms of the before-tax acquisition cost, X. This is achieved by charging the project with a before-tax capital cost, X, at year 0 that is assumed to be amortizable straight-line over five years (1 through 5) in this specific analysis. This gives taxable income, income tax, net income, and after-tax cash flows that are functions of the break-even acquisition cost, X.

Year	0	1-4	5
Revenue		20,000	20,000
–Oper Cost		–5,000	–5,000
–Development	–10,000		
–Depreciation	–1,500	–3,000	–1,500
–Amortization		–0.2X	–0.2X
Taxable	–11,500	12,000 – 0.2X	13,500 – 0.2X
–Tax @ 40%	4,600	–4,800 + 0.08X	–5,400 + 0.08X
Net Income	–6,900	7,200 – 0.12X	8,100 – 0.12X
+Deprec./Amort.	1,500	3,000 + 0.2X	1,500 + 0.2X
–Capital Equipment	–15,000		
–Capital Acquisition	–X		
Cash Flow	–20,400 – X	10,200 + 0.08X	9,600 + 0.08X

$$NPV = 0 = -20{,}400 - X + (10{,}200 + 0.08X)(P/A_{20,4}) + (9{,}600 + 0.08X)(P/F_{20,5})$$

$$0 = 9{,}860 - X + 0.08X(P/A_{20,5})$$

We want the value of the acquisition cost, X, that will make the net present value equal zero since that is the value of X that gives the investor the minimum rate of return (20% in this case) on invested dollars, therefore:

$$X = 9{,}860 + 0.08X(P/A_{20,5})$$

From the initial analysis we know $9,860 is the project NPV without any additional acquisition cost. From our own cash flow analysis we can see that 0.08X is the annual tax savings from the annual amortization deductions of 0.2X used to reduce taxable income that would be taxed at a 40% tax rate. In general, acquisition or additional cost breakeven analyses may simplify to the following:

Breakeven Additional Cost X = NPV + PW Tax Savings Generated From Tax Deductions on X +/– PW After-Tax Terminal Value Resulting From the Additional Cost(s) 9-1

Remember, the break-even acquisition cost is a before-tax value, NPV is after-tax net present value, and the tax savings on X are a function of the allowable deductions generated from the acquisition cost itself. Equation 9-1 is a general equation that always works to determine break-even before-tax additional costs of any kind, not just for acquisition cost valuation analysis. For this analysis, applying Equation 9-1, X = $12,970 or approximately $13,000. Now we can verify that a $13,000 acquisition cost, that is amortizable over five years, makes NPV equal to zero.

Year	0	1–4	5
Revenue		20,000	20,000
–Oper Costs		–5,000	–5,000
–Development	–10,000		
–Depreciation	–1,500	–3,000	–1,500
–Amortization		–2,600	–2,600
Taxable	–11,500	9,400	10,900
–Tax @ 40%	4,600	–3,700	–4,300
Net Income	–6,900	5,700	6,600
+Deprec./Amort.	1,500	5,600	4,100
–Equip. Cost	–15,000		
–Amort. Cost	–13,000		
Cash Flow	–33,400	11,300	10,700

$$NPV = -33{,}400 + 11{,}300(P/A_{20,4}) + 10{,}700(P/F_{20,5}) = 0$$

The project DCFROR is 20% for the $13 million acquisition cost.

Case 2: After-Tax NPV Acquisition Analysis at the End of Year One All Values in Millions of Dollars

After the year 0 costs and year 1 revenues and operating cost have been incurred they are sunk. Even the cash flows calculated for the initial project are not relevant to our analysis because the investor cash flow will be based on tax deductions related to acquisition cost paid for the project assets.

To make the Case 2 analysis, calculate the years 2 through 5 revenue cash flow after-tax without accounting for any capital costs or tax deductions other than operating expenses. Using these cash flow results, calculate year 1 NPV and equate it to the year 1 after-tax acquisition cost, similar to the Case 1 analysis.

Years 2 through 5 revenue cash flow, without accounting for depreciation or amortization tax, deductions is: 20 – 5 – 0.4($15) tax, or +$9.0. Year 1 NPV from this cash flow is $9.0(P/A_{20,4})$ or +$23.30. To calculate the before-tax acquisition cost that is 60% depreciable and 40% amortizable that would give an after-tax acquisition cost equal to the NPV of 23.30 at year 1,

Let X = Acquisition Cost, 60% Depreciable, 40% Amortizable

Year 2 Depreciation = 0.6X(1/5)(1/2) = 0.06X
Year 2 Amortization = 0.4X(1/5)= 0.08X

Years 3, 4 & 5 Depreciation = 0.6X(1/5) = 0.12X
Years 3, 4 & 5 Amortization = 0.4X(1/5) = 0.08X

Year 5 Write-off = 0.18X for Depreciation and 0.08X for Amortization

Year 2 Tax Savings = 0.14X(0.4 tax rate) = 0.056X
Years 3, 4 Tax Savings = 0.20X(0.4 tax rate) = 0.08X
Year 5 Tax Savings = 0.46X(0.4 tax rate) = 0.184X

Year 1 PW Tax Savings

$$= 0.056X((\overset{0.8333}{P/F_{20,1}}) + 0.08X(\overset{0.6944}{P/F_{20,2}}) + 0.08X(\overset{0.5787}{P/F_{20,3}}) + 0.184X(\overset{0.4823}{P/F_{20,4}})$$

$$= 0.2373X$$

X – 0.2373X = After-Tax Acquisition Cost = NPV = $23.30

X = $30.55 is the acquisition cost that, 60% depreciable, 40% amortizable makes NPV = 0 for a minimum DCFROR of 20%.

This example was designed to illustrate the importance that the type of asset being acquired has on acquisition cost analysis results. Whether assets being acquired are depreciable, amortizable, depletable, expensable or not deductible except as a write-off against terminal value (land and inventory asset costs), all such benefits must be taken into account in a proper valuation analysis.

9.7a NPV Use for Break-even Sale Value Analysis

Many people without thinking about valuation analysis details intuitively assume break-even property value is the same for a potential buyer or seller. *Break-even acquisition cost and break-even sale value are not equal unless the tax effects for buyer and seller are offsetting.* Since sale value is always taxable income in the year of the sale, the acquisition cost would have to be fully expensed in the year incurred for break-even acquisition cost and sale value to be equal. Since acquisition cost is almost always capitalized and deducted over a period of time greater than one year, break-even acquisition cost and break-even sale value are seldom equal. In general, this is a major reason that serious negotiations are often needed for buyers and sellers to agree on a property sale value. Example 9-8a illustrates break-even sale value analysis.

EXAMPLE 9-8a NPV Related to Break-even Sale Value

What sale value at year 0 for the project described in Example 9-8, Case 1, with after-tax NPV of $9,860,000 would be economically a break-even with keeping and developing the project? Assume the effective tax rate of 40% is applicable for the seller as it was for the buyer.

Solution: All Values in Thousands of Dollars

Sell versus keep and develop analysis involves evaluation of mutually exclusive alternatives. Mutually exclusive alternatives with equal NPV's are economically equivalent or break-even choices. Since the Develop NPV equals $9,860, we must calculate the break-even sale value that will make the after-tax sale NPV equal $9,860. Since all costs prior to year 0 are sunk, and no remaining book values were given in the analysis of Example 9-8, the sale value must be assumed to be fully taxable in year 0.

Let Y = Break-even Project Sale Value

Therefore, Y equals taxable income and 0.40Y is the income tax due on the sale value. Sale cash flow is Y – 0.40Y = 0.60Y = NPV for selling. We want the NPV for selling to equal the NPV for developing of $9,860. Setting the two NPV's equal to each other and solving for Y:

0.6Y = $9,860, Y = $16,433

This result is greater than the $13,000 break-even acquisition cost calculated in Example 9-8 for this project. However, if the break-even acquisition cost, X, could be fully expensed in year 0 instead of being amortized over 5 years the break-even acquisition cost would equal the $16,433 break-even sale value. To illustrate, assume X equals the acquisition cost that can be 100% expensed. Tax savings in year 0 from X being deducted against other income equals 0.40X. Using Eq 9-1 gives:

X = $9,860 + 0.4X

0.6X = $9,860, therefore, X = $16,433, identical with the break-even sale value.

9.8 Valuation of Public Projects and Investments

Valuation of public and governmental investment projects and properties requires the same sound valuation approaches that are necessary for private companies and individuals. The big difference between public and private valuation is lack of taxation of public investments so before-tax analysis is appropriate. The profit motive should exist in public investments the same as it does in private investments except the profits usually are received as benefits to the public rather than dividends or profit distribution. Good use of public investment funds minimizes our tax costs and maximizes the public benefits we receive per public dollar invested.

In public investment evaluations it is just as important as in private evaluations to (1) clearly define investment alternatives, (2) convert intangible considerations to tangible dollar values when possible and (3) use an investment decision method based upon proper handling of the time value of money at a satisfactory minimum rate of return to compare alternative investments. In general, the same methods of analysis used in the evaluation of mutually exclusive and non-mutually exclusive private investment alternatives are valid and necessary for the correct evaluation of public projects.

Public projects, whether funded at the local, state or national government level, inevitably are funded by an agency that has limited resources because citizens make far more requests and demands for service than monetary resources permit carrying out. Therefore, it is very important that the best possible use is made of available funds, so it is necessary to use an opportunity cost of capital minimum rate of return in evaluating public projects the same as in evaluating private investment projects.

Determination of benefits that will accrue to the public from investment in various government projects such as roads, bridges, airports, dams and recreation areas is necessary to establish the relative desirability of projects under consideration. It is, of course, difficult to determine all the public benefits that may be derived from a given investment situation. However, as in evaluating private investments, someone must take the responsibility to attempt to reduce intangible considerations to tangible values that can be handled in an orderly fashion using a given evaluation method to compare various alternatives. Comparing benefits to costs and accounting for the time value of money is the correct basis for valid economic analysis of public or private investments. This means that a suitable minimum rate of return must be selected. As in private enterprise, the minimum rate of return should reflect the other opportunities which are available for investment of existing capital. Determination of a suitable minimum rate of return is difficult because it is hard to know for sure what ROR other opportunities might yield unless putting money in the bank is the other alternative. This is seldom the case in public projects. Certainly the minimum rate of return should be greater than the cost of public money or the projects should not be undertaken. If it will cost the public a ten percent interest rate on bonds for a project the minimum rate of return must be at least ten percent. How much greater than ten percent it really should be depends on what alternative projects would yield that may have to be passed over if a particular project is carried out. This opportunity cost of capital for public project analysis is directly analogous to private investment opportunity cost of capital.

9.9 Tax Calculations and Cash Flow versus Shareholder Reporting and Net Income

Mark Twain once wrote;

OCTOBER: This is one of the peculiarly dangerous months to speculate in stocks. The other are July, January, September, April, November, May, March, June, December, August, and February.

— *Pudd'nhead Wilson's Calendar*

Some 19 years after Twain's death, when the stock market crashed in October 1929, public confidence in the markets plummeted. Investors and the banks who were lending money lost considerable sums of cash in the Great Depression that followed. Congress recognized that for the economy to recover, the investing public needed a restoration of faith in the markets and related financial information. After a series of hearings, Congress passed the Securities Act of 1933. This law, together with the Securities Exchange Act of 1934, which created the Securities and Exchange Commission (SEC), was designed to restore investor confidence in the financial markets by providing investors and the markets with more reliable information and a clear set of rules. This should all sound rather familiar in light of recent turmoil in the financial markets.

Congress established the SEC in 1934 to enforce the newly-passed securities laws, to promote stability in the markets and, most importantly, to protect investors. President Franklin Delano Roosevelt appointed Joseph P. Kennedy, (President John F. Kennedy's father), to serve as the first Chairman of the SEC.

The mission of the SEC is to protect investors, maintain fair, orderly, and efficient markets, and facilitate capital formation. To accomplish this mission, the SEC has relied in part on the Financial Accounting Standards Board (FASB) to recommend accounting rules and regulations in different sectors. Over the years, the combined rules and regulations form what is known as Generally Accepted Accounting Principals, (GAAP). These rules and regulations are intended to provide all investors certain elements of information from; 1) the prospectus that may describe the nature of the business and potential risk and, 2) the periodic measures of profitability reflected in quarterly, semi-annual and annual reports. If all providers follow the same rules in reporting profits, investors would have a solid platform from which to decide, how to invest. The intended result of this standardized information flow is a more efficient and transparent capital market that facilitates the capital formation or the potential for growth in the economy.

The near collapse of portions of the financial markets in 2008 sent the SEC scurrying again to shore up investor confidence. But in this regard, the SEC has not acted alone. The Chairman of the SEC, together with the Chairman of the Federal Reserve, the Secretary of the Treasury, and the Chairman of the Commodities Futures Trading Commission, serves as a member of the President's Working Group on Financial Markets and work together with Congress towards this important objective by various means of legislation.

In this textbook, emphasis has been placed on after-tax cash flow derived from appropriate tax deductions for various expenditures. It is important to recognize that publically traded companies have multiple sets of books that are developed to meet tax return requirements established by Congress and implemented by the IRS, as well as financial requirements outlined by the SEC. There are other sets of books for computing the federal Alternative Minimum Tax and state severance and income taxes as well as tracking internal performance measures.

While we have established that value is actually derived by measuring changes in cash in the bank or After-Tax Cash Flow (ATCF), financial data is generally centered on intermediate measures such as Net Income, or certain industry measures of Operating Profit such as Earnings before Interest, Taxes, Depreciation, and Amortization (EBITDA). Other financial statements such as the Balance Sheet play a critical role in reflecting the position of assets and liabilities in the firm, but the general interest in the context of this text is how financial net income compares with the project ATCF emphasized in after-tax economic evaluations. Under GAAP, the Consolidated Statement of Cash Flows reconciles the differences in Net Income and Cash flow but there are many different definitions of cash flow that will be introduced following Example 9-9.

It is worth noting that Net Income and ATCF serve two very different economic and financial objectives. The key issue here is proper and consistent application of each. On a cumulative basis over the life of a project, we know that cumulative net income derived from tax deductions and cumulative after-tax cash flow will always be the same. Certain reconciliations for percentage depletion and loss forward deductions may be necessary for certain investors to maintain the equality. This said, the problem with either a tax derived or financial measure of net income from year to year is that it does not portray the actual cash position of the investor as it relates to the project and therefore, is not useful in discounted cash flow analysis to measure the overall value of an investment opportunity. In this regard, another disadvantage of financial data is an inability to properly account for economic sunk cost and opportunity cost considerations although some of these issues are addressed later in the context of value added calculations.

In past years, the Securities and Exchange Commission had proposed that the U.S. transition towards adaptation of IFRS but the poor performance of the economy lead to a revision in the thinking. Today, the U.S. remains under GAAP but at some point, this subject seems certain to return.

In their August 28th, 2008 announcement, the SEC noted that

> "The increasing integration of the world's capital markets, which has resulted in two-thirds of U.S. investors owning securities issued by foreign companies that report their financial information using IFRS, has made the establishment of a single set of high quality accounting standards a matter of growing importance. A

common accounting language around the world could give investors greater comparability and greater confidence in the transparency of financial reporting worldwide.

An international language of disclosure and transparency is a goal worth pursuing on behalf of investors who seek comparable financial information to make well-informed investment decisions. The increasing worldwide acceptance of financial reporting using IFRS, and U.S. investors' increasing ownership of securities issued by foreign companies that report financial information using IFRS, have led the Commission to propose this cautious and careful plan. Clearly setting out the SEC's direction well in advance, as well as the conditions that must be met, will help fulfill our mission of protecting investors and facilitating capital formation."

According to the SEC, more than 100 countries around the world, including all of Europe, currently require or permit IFRS reporting. Approximately 85 of those countries require IFRS reporting for all domestic, listed companies. In a general sense, IFRS reporting is not as specific in regard to the treatment of costs in different industries which may give management more room to improve the appearance of net income. One example is the treatment of development costs which generally are expensed under GAAP but may be capitalized under IFRS procedures if the expenditures are related to a viable ongoing project.

To summarize in a general sense, some of the major differences in current U.S. tax law and GAAP; *financial reporting for non-mineral companies often involves straight line depreciation based on lives of 5 to 40 years for personal and real property. Generally these methods of depreciation are based on the cost basis less anticipated salvage with no adjustment to the salvage value for time value of money and no consideration for the half-year convention in the first or last year. Mineral companies (including oil and gas companies) use units of production depreciation over the estimated producing life of a property for financial shareholder reporting. For tax purposes the full cost of personal property is depreciated over 3 to 20 years using 200% or 150% declining balance switching to straight when advantageous to the investor. The first year depreciation deduction is subject to the half-year or mid-quarter limitations for tax purposes. Research and development, mineral development and petroleum intangible drilling costs are expensed in the full or maximum amount for tax purposes. Research and Development may be expensed in financial reporting, while mine development and intangible drilling costs are deducted by units of production depreciation over the estimated producing life of a property for financial shareholder reporting with no first year limitation. Petroleum costs may be further subject to the use of successful efforts or full cost accounting measures described later.* Example 9-9 is a hypothetical illustration of some of the described differences.

EXAMPLE 9-9 Comparison of Tax Related ATCF and Financial Reporting Net Income

A new publicly traded company invested $440,000 last year in tax based MACRS 5-year life property. The estimated salvage value of these assets is $80,000 at the end of year 5. The assets were put into service this year and an additional $100,000 was spent on the development of software product estimated to be saleable for the next 10 years. Sales revenue of $500,000 and cost of goods sold of $300,000 were realized this year. Assume the effective company income tax rate is 40% and determine the tax and shareholder reporting net income and after-tax cash flow for the year. Assume the $100,000 development cost will be expensed as experimental development for tax, but amortized straight line over 10 years for financial reporting. Claim a full-year amortization deduction in this first year. For tax purposes, depreciate the equipment using the accelerated MACRS 5-year schedule based on the half-year convention but for financial reporting, use the straight line method over 10 years and apply the rate to the cost basis adjusted for anticipated salvage with no adjustment for time value of money or inflation and neglect the half-year convention. Compute the ATCF based on the described accelerated tax deductions and relate to hypothetical shareholder reporting Net Income and Cash Flow from operations for the described treatment of costs.

Solution: All Values in 000's of Dollars

Tax Depreciation: $440(0.2000) = $88
Financial Depreciation: ($440-$80)(1/10) = $36
Financial Amortization: $100(1/10) = $10

	Accelerated Tax Model	Slower Tax Model	Shareholder Net Income & ATCF
Revenue	500	500	500
–Cost of Goods Sold	–300	–300	–300
–Tax Depreciation	–88		
–Financial Depreciation		–36	–36
–Development	–100		
–Financial Amortization		–10	–10
Taxable Income	12	154	154
–Income Tax	–5	–62	–5
–Deferred Tax*			–57
Net Income	7	92	92
+Depreciation	88	36	36
+Amortization		10	10
+Deferred Tax			57
Cash Flow from Operations	95	138	195
–Development Capital		–100	–100
After-Tax Cash Flow	95	38	95

* Deferred tax is the difference in actual tax paid and the tax that would have been paid if slower methods of depreciation and amortization were utilized in computing taxable income. This may not actually appear in financial statements as a separate line item.

Note that although after-tax cash flow is the same from both the accelerated tax and shareholder report calculations, the net income results are very different. Investors looking at net income (earnings) as a measure of financial success are likely to be more impressed with the $92,000 shareholder based figure versus the $7,000 from tax data. It is worth noting that financial net income measures use all non-cash deductions such as depreciation and amortization as a charge against revenue rather than as a tax deduction. These charges are in lieu of any capital costs that are never observed in net income figures. The accounting argument for this procedure is simple; the capital assets acquired are in part responsible for generating income for years to come, and therefore should be ratably charged against those future revenues as the asset is utilized and used up over time.

Financial reporting continues to evolve. For example one major area of change has been the reformation of the old Sources and Uses of Funds Statement to the Consolidated Statement of Cash Flows. It seems inevitable that greater emphasis will continue to be placed on cash flow information being reported to shareholders. However, even as this occurs the SEC will need to define the appropriate measure of expected after-tax cash flow to work with in defining "cash flow per share" much as "net income per share" is emphasized today. To illustrate variations in the definition of cash flow consider the following:

Operating Cash Flow = Financial Net Income + Depreciation + Depletion + Amortization ± Changes in Working Capital ± Deferred Taxes

Operating cash flow is the first of several cash flow numbers contained in the shareholder report Consolidated Statement of Cash Flows. When a shift to greater emphasis on cash flow reporting from net income reporting occurs, it is likely that "operating cash flow" will be the cash flow that is emphasized.

Project Cash Flow = Financial Net Income + Depreciation + Depletion + Amortization ± Changes in Working Capital ± Deferred Taxes – Capital Expenditures for Project Being Analyzed

Or = Operating CF – Project Capital Costs

This is the basic project cash flow definition that we have dealt with throughout the text to this point.

Free Cash Flow = Financial Net Income + Depreciation + Depletion + Amortization ± Changes in Working Capital ± Deferred Taxes – Capital Expenditures for Existing Plant Facilities – Dividends

Or = Operating CF – Existing Project Capital Costs – Dividends

In the free cash flow calculation, by subtracting capital expenditures necessary to maintain plant and equipment (but not optional ones for new plants or headquarters) and also subtracting dividends, you get a measure of truly discretionary funds that could be pocketed without harming the business. Companies with free cash flow can use it to boost dividends, to buy back shares, pay down debt, acquire other businesses, or develop new projects. Free cash flow is considered to be very desirable by both common stock shareholders and potential company purchasers.

Under current GAAP, petroleum companies utilize two different accounting methods known as "successful-efforts" and "full-cost" accounting that amongst a number of issues are used for handling certain acquisition and exploration related expenditures. For shareholder earnings reporting purposes under successful-efforts accounting, dry hole costs are expensed but successful well development and completion costs are capitalized and deducted over the producing life of the lease. This is generally achieved by use of units of production depreciation. However, under full-cost accounting, dry hole, development and completion costs are all capitalized and deducted by units of production deprecation. The rational behind full-cost accounting is that dry hole expenditures are part of delineating the extent of the resource and therefore should be ratably charged rather than expensed when incurred. To the author's knowledge, the distinctions in full-cost and successful efforts as defined in GAAP do not currently exist in IFRS procedures. This is one example of why any transition or adoption of the international financial reporting standards in the United States will involve an extended period of time as the conversion is sure to be a costly process of education and application for both internal accounting in public companies and for investors comparing and interpreting results.

Given the same level of exploration activity, successes, and production a company using successful-efforts accounting will report lower earnings to shareholders in the early years of projects than a full-cost company will report since a larger portion of drilling cost is written off earlier. But the same company will report higher earnings to shareholders in later years from using successful-efforts accounting in comparison to full-cost accounting which spreads the earnings more uniformly over the production life. Full-cost accounting is attractive to young exploration companies because earnings look better in the early years than they would with successful efforts accounting which helps in raising drilling venture capital. The following example illustrates these tax deduction versus shareholder book deduction concepts.

EXAMPLE 9-10 Petroleum Company Shareholder Earnings With Successful Efforts Versus Full Cost Accounting

A new petroleum exploration corporation has raised $2 million with a 1 million share common stock equity offering at a net $2 per share. The company has acquired the mineral rights to a property for $100,000 (for analysis simplicity assume percentage depletion may not be taken on either oil or gas production) and has drilled two wells in its first year of operation. One well was a dry hole costing $100,000, the other was a producing oil well with intangible drilling costs of $120,000, tangible well and pipeline costs of $70,000, crude oil revenues of $700,000 and operating expenses of $70,000 including severance taxes. 14,000 barrels of crude oil were produced in the first year with initial producible reserves estimated to be 70,000 barrels over 10 years. Royalty owners get 15% of all crude oil revenues. Assume a 40% income tax rate and calculate the net income and cash flow this year (total and per common stock share) for: A) Normal accelerated tax deductions for an independent petroleum producer. B) Capitalize all intangible drilling costs and deduct them straight line (instead of units of production for simplicity) over the 10 year estimated producing well life. Depreciate tangible costs straight line over the estimated 10 year producing well life assuming a full first year straight line deduction. C) Use accelerated deductions from part "A" for tax purposes and straight line deductions from part "B" for shareholder reporting purposes. This is full-cost accounting (all drilling costs are capitalized for shareholder earnings reporting purposes) in accordance with Financial Accounting Standards Board procedures. D) Use accelerated deductions for tax purposes and straight line deductions based on successful-efforts accounting for shareholder earnings reporting purposes (expense dry hole cost but capitalize successful well drilling cost).

Solution: All Values in Thousands of Dollars

	Tax (Accel.)	Tax (St.Line)	Shareholder (Full-Cost)	Shareholder (Success-Ef.)
Revenue	700	700	700	700
–Royalties	–105	–105	–105	–105
–Op. Costs	–70	–70	–70	–70
–IDC	–220	–22	–22	–112
–Depreciation	–10	–7	–7	–7
–Cost Depletion	–20	–20	–20	–20
Taxable Income	275	476	476	386
–Tax @ 40%	–110	–190	–110	–110
–Deferred Tax			–80	–44
Net Income	165	286	286	232
+Depreciation	10	7	7	7
+Cost Deplet.	20	20	20	20
+Deferred Tax			80	44
+IDC	220	22	22	112
–IDC	–220	–220	–220	–220
–Tangible Costs	–70	–70	–70	–70
–Mineral Rts Cost	–100	–100	–100	–100
Net Cash Flow	25	–55	25	25
Net Income/Share	\$0.165	\$0.286	\$0.286	\$0.232
Cash Flow/Share	\$0.025	–\$0.055	\$0.025	\$0.025

The accelerated tax deductions give smaller taxable income than straight line deductions and this yields a smaller tax obligation and bigger cash flow. Cash flow represents the net inflow or outflow of money each year so cash flow is what management wants to maximize, which is why accelerated deductions are taken for tax purposes. However, when brokers and common stock shareholders around the world talk about earnings per share of common stock they usually refer to net income earnings per share of common stock rather than cash flow earnings. When you look at net income earnings to evaluate a company you are treating deductions for depreciation, depletion and amortization as out of pocket costs in the amount deducted each year. This makes the method chosen to deduct various costs critically important to the net income earnings results that will be obtained. Taking the straight line deductions shown in the second column of the previous cash flow calculation table and using them for shareholder report earnings calculation purposes with full-cost accounting of drilling costs gives bigger net income earnings than with successful efforts accounting. *Dry hole drilling costs must be expensed for shareholder reporting under successful efforts accounting while such costs are capitalized and deducted by units of production depreciation under full cost accounting.* Comparing the full-cost accounting net income earnings of $286,000 with the successful-efforts accounting net income earnings of $232,000 illustrates the difference for this example. Note that the net cash flow is identically $25,000 for both approaches and this is the same net cash flow obtained with accelerated deductions for tax purposes. Most companies now evaluate projects (or other companies for acquisition purposes) using annual cash flow projections over the life of projects. Unless general investors adopt this cash flow analysis approach instead of looking at point value net income earnings, it will continue to be necessary to deal with shareholder reporting calculation procedures that are different from normal tax deduction procedures. However, remember that it is what is done for tax purposes that really determines when companies or individuals realize tax savings or incur tax costs, so proper project analysis must be based on tax deduction considerations and not shareholder earnings report deduction considerations.

9.10 Net Income Analysis Compared to Cash Flow Analysis

Before discounted cash flow analysis received industry acceptance around the world as the standard basis for economic analysis of investments, net income, rather than cash flow, was the basis for rate of return analysis of investments. There are several old rate of return analysis techniques and all are based on looking at various ratios of annual or average net income divided by either cumulative initial investment cost, average investment cost, or remaining book value of investment costs. Using net income as the basis for investment analysis implicitly treats depreciation, amortization and depletion like all other tax deductions, that is, as out of pocket costs. Of course depreciation, amortization and depletion are not out of pocket annual costs and it can be very misleading to treat them as such for evaluation purposes. The following simple example introduces and illustrates two net income based rate of return definitions and calculations in comparison with DCFROR. More than thirty years ago, these two net income based ROR techniques were probably the most widely used economic evaluation techniques.

EXAMPLE 9-11 Net Income vs Cash Flow and Related Criteria

A depreciable investment expected to cost $10,000 is projected to generate revenues of $9,400, $8,400, $7,400, $6,400 and $5,400 at the end of each of years 1 through 5 respectively with a zero salvage value at the end of year 5. Operating costs are expected to be $3,500 each year. The $10,000 investment goes into service in year 1 and is depreciated straight line over a five-year life for financial purposes. For tax purposes, use the 5-year MACRS rates from table 7-3. The effective income tax rate is 40% and other income exists against which to use all deductions. The after-tax, escalated dollar opportunity cost of capital is 12%.

A) Calculate the DCFROR and NPV on this investment based on the MACRS tax depreciation.

B) Define and calculate Return on Capital Employed, (ROCE) based on both MACRS and straight-line depreciation.

C) Define and calculate Average Rate of Return based on straight-line depreciation.

Solution: All Values in Thousands of Dollars

A) After-Tax Cash Flow and DCFROR, MACRS Depreciation

Year	0	1	2	3	4	5
Revenue	–	9.40	8.40	7.40	6.40	5.40
– Oper. Costs	–	–3.50	–3.50	–3.50	–3.50	–3.50
– Depreciation		–2.00	–3.20	–1.92	–1.15	–1.73
Taxable Income		3.90	1.70	1.98	1.75	0.17
– Inc Tax @ 40%		–1.56	–0.68	–0.79	–0.70	–0.07
Net Income		2.34	1.02	1.19	1.05	0.10
+ Depreciation		2.00	3.20	1.92	1.15	1.73
– Capital Cost	–10.0					
Cash Flow	–10.0	4.34	4.22	3.11	2.20	1.83

PW Eq: $0 = -10.0 + 4.34(P/F_{i,1}) + 4.22(P/F_{i,2}) + 3.11(P/F_{i,3})$

$+ 2.20(P/F_{i,4}) + 1.83(P/F_{i,5})$

DCFROR, i = 20.76% > 12.0%, acceptable project

DCFROR is a relative measure of value for the total project expressed as a compound interest rate. It is compared with investing capital elsewhere at the minimum rate of return. As previously described, it can be thought of as the year to year after-tax return on the unpaid portion of our investment over the project life.

NPV @ 12% = +1.889

NPV *is the value added by investing in this project and not investing the limited capital in other opportunities at 12.0% where the resulting NPV would equal zero.*

B) Net Income Based "Return on Capital Employed" (ROCE)

Whereas tax reporting usually involves accelerated MACRS depreciation deductions, as mentioned in this section; financial reporting usually involves more uniform and slower deduction methods like units of production over the life of a property or straight line as illustrated below assuming the half year convention is relevant in the first year:

Year	0	1	2	3	4	5
Revenue	–	9.40	8.40	7.40	6.40	5.40
– Oper. Costs	–	–3.50	–3.50	–3.50	–3.50	–3.50
– Depreciation	–	–1.00	–2.00	–2.00	–2.00	–3.00
Taxable Income	–	4.90	2.90	1.90	0.90	–1.10
– Income Tax 40%	–	–1.96	–1.16	–0.76	–0.36	0.44
Net Income	–	2.94	1.74	1.14	0.54	–0.66
+ Depreciation	–	1.00	2.00	2.00	2.00	3.00
– Capital	–10.0	–	–	–	–	–
ATCF	–10.0	3.94	3.74	3.14	2.54	2.34

DCFROR = 19.3%, NPV @ 12% = 1.676

Before looking at the ROCE calculation (based on the annual net incomes), consider the fifth year net income and cash flow for the project. The net income is negative but cash flow is still positive, which indicates that value is still being added. Managers are constantly faced with the decision of when to terminate or shut down an operation, but a focus on cash flow will help determine when value ceases to occur. In reality however, such periods in time do occur and can create conflict in the overall decision-making process.

In the older literature, R*eturn on Capital Employed (ROCE), often is referred to as "Accounting Rate of Return, Return on Assets and Return on Net Assets." Definitions may vary slightly among financial analysts but in this text it is defined as:*

$$\text{ROCE} = \frac{\text{Annual Net Income}}{\text{Book Value of Assets Employed}}$$

Using net income rather than cash flow, you can see deductions like depreciation, depletion and amortization (along with all write-offs) are treated as a cash cost to the project, rather than as non-cash deductions which is what they truly are. Net income never includes the capital expenditures but instead, uses depreciation, depletion, amortization and write-offs to allocate such costs, in this case, over the revenue producing life of the property.

To determine ROCE, the book value of the assets generating net income must be determined. Often, average book value is used in the denominator rather than beginning or end of year book value. The average approach is utilized here. For example; average year 1 MACRS tax depreciation book value is (10+8)/2 = 9 while straight line financial depreciation is (10+9)/2 = 9.5.

Net Income & Average Book Value, MACRS

Year	0	1	2	3	4	5
MACRS Net Income	–	2.34	1.02	1.19	1.05	0.10
Avg Book Value	–	9.00	6.40	3.84	2.30	0.86
ROCE		26.00%	15.94%	30.99%	45.65%	11.63%

Net Income & Average Book Value, St Line

Year	0	1	2	3	4	5
SL Net Income	–	2.94	1.74	1.14	0.54	–0.66
Avg Book Value	–	9.50	8.00	6.00	4.00	1.50
ROCE		30.95%	21.75%	19.00%	13.50%	–44.0%

In this example, and in general, the ROCE results are different each year for both tax and financial deductions. This randomness can make it physically impossible to use this evaluation technique to fairly and consistently compare the economic potential of investment alternatives. Over the years, some have advocated using the third year ROCE value as representing an overall average, but this is rather arbitrary at best.

Another application of ROCE is to calculate allowed return on regulated investments. Around the world, regulated utility investment return is based on this type of calculation as discussed in Section 9.11 of this chapter. For regulated return analysis, allowed regulatory deductions instead of tax deductions are the basis for analysis of revenue and costs that may be received and incurred.

C) Average Rate of Return

This technique is known as the "operator method," "engineers method," and "Dupont method" in older literature.

$$\text{Average ROR} = \frac{\text{Average Project Net Income}}{\text{Cumulative Capital Invested}}$$

This technique was probably developed because investors recognized the futility of trying to utilize ROCE calculations in economic decision-making. The application of this definition follows using straight-line deductions:

$$\text{Average ROR} = \frac{[(2.94+1.74+1.14+0.54-0.66)/5](100)}{10.0} = 11.4\%$$

Since the calculation is based on the initial investment, the 11.4% Average ROR is analogous to a flat interest rate of return. Note further that this result is significantly different from the 20.76% DCFROR calculated in part A to this example.

As a sensitivity analysis to the various criteria presented, consider what the impact would be if the $10,000 initial investment were spread out over a four-year period of time beginning in time 0. Revenues, operating costs and depreciation would begin four years from the start of project development when the assets are placed into service.

The resulting after-tax cash flows are incorporated into the following present worth equation:

$$\text{PW Eq: } 0 = -2.5 - 2.5(P/A_{i,3}) + 4.3(P/F_{i,4}) + 4.2(P/F_{i,5}) + 3.1(P/F_{i,6}) + 2.2(P/F_{i,7}) + 1.8(P/F_{i,8})$$

DCFROR, i = 11.7%

Incurring the capital investment over an extended period for the same annual after-tax cash flows has lowered the DCFROR significantly to 11.7% from 20.76%. However, the ROCE and Average ROR results are unchanged because they do not account for the time value of money. Whether costs are incurred over several years, or as a lump sum, has no effect on the old analysis technique results. This is indicative of the reason most investors in all industries have shifted from the net income methodologies to discounted cash flow for economic analysis of alternative investments.

However, publicly traded companies still emphasize net income (or earnings) per share rather than cash flow per share to shareholders. The reason for focus on net income has more to do with the financial corporate comparisons of performance on a year-to-year basis. While useful in this context, it's a proven poor way to evaluate individual investment opportunities. Cumulatively, projects drive value for a business and it's our belief that a focus on financial criteria based on cash flow would eliminate some of the economic conflict that exists today as managers try to decide whether they should maximize net income or cash flow in the coming year.

9.10a Value Added

Value Added or VA, is a net income based analysis variation of Return on Capital Employed, or ROCE. In industry practice, the term "Value Added" may be referred to as "Shareholder Value Added" or SVA, or "Economic Value Added," or EVA™. However, the later term, as indicated is a trademark of G. Bennett Stewart III. In many ways, the concept of measuring VA is a throwback to net income analysis techniques that were utilized twenty-five or more years ago. Fortune magazine stated that many major corporations such as Coca Cola, AT&T and Quaker Oats to name a few are utilizing VA to evaluate the year to year performance of business units. Does this mean that discounted cash flow analysis is being replaced by the net income analysis techniques that most investor's scrapped twenty five or more years ago in evaluating the economic potential of projects? The answer is a definite no. To explain, VA will be defined, and then several different applications will be explored. Some of these have the potential of being very useful, and some of them may be misleading and therefore, not useful.

The concept of value added is defined as annual after-tax operating profit (net income or earnings) minus the total annual cost of capital. The relevant definition of net income may vary among consultants. Some prefer one accounting methodology vs another, capitalizing certain costs versus expensing, etc. Such issues are neglected in this discussion. The annual cost of capital may be calculated by taking the cost of business assets times the opportunity cost of capital. For most investors, after the first year, the annual cost of capital is based on the remaining non-depreciated asset value, similar to the denominator of ROCE. Again, the magnitude of the capital asset basis will vary among consultants. The concept of "total annual cost of capital" is really just an opportunity cost incurred when investors keep a project, business venture or company and pass up selling the assets and investing the after-tax cash flow at i*. This topic has long been addressed in this textbook many years before the evolution of Value Added concepts in the 1990's.

If VA is positive, it generally is stated that the project or business unit is creating value or wealth for the company shareholders. Note that a business unit with a positive VA is always directly analogous to a project with ROCE greater than the financial cost of capital.

To illustrate how closely related ROCE and VA are, consider the following:

$$\text{ROCE} = \frac{\text{Net Income}}{\text{Asset Book Value}}\text{, if} > i^*\text{, ROCE is satisfactory}$$

"Asset book value" refers to the book value of all assets at the beginning of a period (for either tax or financial shareholder reporting purposes) for a corporation, but again; this definition can vary slightly for each consultant.

Rearranging the above inequality by multiplying each side times the "asset book value" gives:

$$\text{Net Income} > i^*(\text{Asset Book Value})\text{, is satisfactory}$$

This tells management and investors alike that successful corporations need to generate net income in excess of the interest that could have been earned had the company liquidated the assets and invested the cash in other perceived opportunities (a measure of an opportunity foregone). Note that this assumes the asset book value is representative of the cash value (market value) of assets from liquidation of the assets, which may be a significant assumption!

Rearranging the inequality once again by subtracting the product of i*(Asset Book Value) from both sides results in the following:

$$\text{Value is Added When;}\quad \text{Net Income} - i^*(\text{Asset Book Value}) > 0$$

This is the basic definition of value added provided earlier in this section. Note the direct relationship of this approach to the ROCE calculation introduced earlier. Further, you can see that successful investors must generate net income in quantities greater than the product of the asset book value times the opportunity cost of capital if value is to be added to the portfolio.

While many companies may base these calculations on financial treatment of expenditures – in his book, "The Quest for Value," G. Bennett Stewart recommends several modifications to the financial reporting procedures in order to make value added results more meaningful in relationship to cash flow. Some of the adjustments would include the adoption of LIFO inventory procedures, adjusting for deferred taxes, capitalizing of all R&D and utilizing full cost accounting so all R&D, development and exploration charges are reflected in the capital base – not just successful expenditures. Such adjustments are intended to allow operating costs to reflect actual expenditures for goods sold during the year. As was illustrated in Chapter 8, in inflationary times, the LIFO methodology will lower taxable income and tax, which increases cash flow and value when compared to the FIFO approach. Stewart argues that by making his recommended adjustments, the asset book value will more clearly represent actual value of expenditures incurred and hence, the true investment required to generate the revenues realized for the year. Such adjustments would be welcome, but may still not provide a balance sheet or net income statement that reflects the true market value, which is what true opportunity cost is based on.

If VA or ROCE are to be used for economic decision-making, three considerations should be addressed in attempting to capture the true measure of value being added. (1) tax deductions, rather than shareholder report financial deductions, must be the basis of the analysis so that net income is based on actual tax paid, not an accrual based on straight line, project life depreciation. This can also be accomplished by adjusting the financial net income for deferred tax considerations. (2) the opportunity cost of capital, rather than the financial cost of capital must be utilized. Opportunity cost of capital represents the rate of return potential for those other opportunities that exist for investment of funds. Investors don't want to accept investments that simply achieve the financial cost of capital, so why should the value added opportunity cost calculation be any different? As discussed in Chapter 3, Section 3.7, use of financial cost of capital as a minimum rate of return will show investors the projects that will make money for them, but it is necessary to use opportunity cost of capital to determine the investments that generate maximum value possible from available investment capital and assets. If a company has a financial cost of capital of 12.0% and rationed or limited available capital, and other investment opportunities to invest all available capital at 20.0% or higher, accepting a 15.0% rate of return would be making sub-optimal use of funds and not add maximum value. (3) For VA or ROCE use in economic analysis of existing projects or business units, the actual "marked to the market" opportunity cost value of business assets being analyzed (best represented by the after-tax cash flow realized if all assets were liquidated) should be the basis rather than either tax or shareholder book value. To illustrate, assume a company owns an office building that is almost fully depreciated for tax and or shareholder reporting purposes. The company wants to analyze whether it is better to sell the building and invest the after-tax cash flow at their opportunity cost of capital or to keep and operate the building. The remaining tax book value is only relevant in determining the gain or loss from the sale while the financial book value really has no economic impact. The market determines the building value at any time based on the future cash flow that assets might be expected to generate and the investor must project the actual market value to make a valid analysis.

Four situations where value added calculations may usefully augment discounted cash flow economic analysis of projects are discussed:

1) VA forces managers to think about the balance sheet and the assets that are under their control and to what extent those assets are being utilized. However, this is the basic axiom of opportunity cost as advocated by these authors for years. So while certainly not new in concept, VA may provide a different approach to understanding this important evaluation consideration. There is a cost to holding idle plant facilities, working capital or other non-performing assets.

2) VA or ROCE analysis gives investors a post analysis procedure for checking whether a given project or business unit is meeting its economic objectives at any current point in time. Looking at a one-year picture of performance using VA or ROCE is much easier than looking at discounted cash flow analysis for the life of a project. However, VA and ROCE can only be used as short-term indicators.

3) VA and ROCE provide a short term indicator of the economic performance of business units involving many combined projects that would involve much effort to analyze for the life of a project with discounted cash flow. However, if VA or ROCE results indicate change is needed,

discounted cash flow analysis should be done for the business unit to evaluate the economic impact on future cash flow generation due to proposed current changes and how those results compare with selling or shutting down. This analysis should be based on market value opportunity costs and an opportunity cost of capital discount rate, not financial reporting book values and financial cost of capital.

4) Companies sometimes like to use VA or ROCE analysis techniques as a basis to evaluate managerial performance. Discounted cash flow analysis isn't very useful for this purpose since it typically covers a longer period. Generally, the basis for rewarding improvements should not be associated with the absolute value added in any given period, but on whether value added can be consistently increased over a period of time. This can help avoid short run management decisions to sell now or defer capital expenditures for the big bonus this year, then worry about the future later. Often it's not easy to compare managers fairly using the VA for a given period. To illustrate, suppose two managers work for the same company, one operates a 30-year-old fully depreciated plant while the other manages a recently upgraded facility. The opportunity costs charged against net income will most likely be higher for the newer plant given the recent capital expenditures. However, that doesn't necessarily mean the new plant manager is under-performing compared to the old plant manager. By comparing the relative change in value added over time, each manager will be evaluated on a more level playing field.

A simplistic illustration of value added is presented in Example 9-12 and 9-12a.

Example 9-12 Value Added (VA)

To illustrate the concept of VA calculations, determine the after-tax value added each year from Example 9-11 and compute the corresponding present value for the annual figures. Compare the present value of VA to the project after-tax NPV. In making the Value Added calculation, adjust the financial net income for deferred taxes and base the opportunity cost on the beginning of period financial book value (from straight line depreciation) each year. The financial net income data from Example 9-11 Part B is summarized below. The corporate after-tax opportunity cost of capital remains at 12%.

Year	0	1	2	3	4	5
Revenue	–	9.40	8.40	7.40	6.40	5.40
– Oper. Costs	–	–3.50	–3.50	–3.50	–3.50	–3.50
– Depreciation	–	–1.00	–2.00	–2.00	–2.00	–3.00
Taxable Income	–	4.90	2.90	1.90	0.90	–1.10
– Income Tax 40%	–	–1.96	–1.16	–0.76	–0.36	0.44
Net Income	–	2.94	1.74	1.14	0.54	–0.66

The book value necessary for calculating the annual cost of capital, or annual opportunity cost, is based on the book value of the assets at the "beginning" of each year which is summarized below per the use of straight-line depreciation:

Year	0	1	2	3	4	5
Beg Book Value	–	10.00	9.00	7.00	5.00	3.00
Cost of Capital *(Book Value)(i*=12%)*	–	–1.20	–1.08	–0.84	–0.60	–0.36

Deferred tax is based on the difference between the actual tax paid in each of years 1–5 and the tax reported to the shareholders in the financial report for each of those years. So, using the tax paid in Example 9-10 parts A and the financial tax reported to shareholders in Part B, the deferred tax is calculated as follows:

Year	0	1	2	3	4	5
Actual Tax Pd (A)	–	–1.56	–0.68	–0.79	–0.70	–0.07
–Financial Tax (B)	–	–1.96	–1.16	–0.76	–0.36	0.44
Deferred Tax	–	0.40	0.48	–0.03	–0.34	–0.51

Adjusting the Financial Net Income (based on SL depreciation) for the deferred taxes and the cost of capital, gives the project "Value Added" each year:

Year	0	1	2	3	4	5
Net Income	–	2.94	1.74	1.14	0.54	–0.66
±Deferred Tax	–	0.40	0.48	–0.03	–0.34	–0.51
–Cost of Capital	–	–1.20	–1.08	–0.84	–0.60	–0.36
Value Added	–	2.14	1.14	0.27	–0.40	–1.53

$$\text{PV @ } 12\% = 2.14(P/F_{12\%,1}) + 1.14(P/F_{12\%,2}) + 0.27(P/F_{12\%,3}) - 0.40(P/F_{12\%,4}) - 1.53(P/F_{12\%,5})$$

$= 1.889$ *equivalent to the After-tax NPV using the MACRS tax deductions.*

For all the extra effort, the resulting present value of the value added each year is the same measure of performance that is utilized by most corporations and individual investors alike, NPV! But a downside of this concept is the focus on a net income based criteria which may force the early closure of this project at the end of year 3 or 4 depending on whether the focus is value added oriented or cash flow oriented. This project continues to generate positive cash flow, which is adding value and generating the NPV of 1.889, yet VA or ROCE would demand suspension of the project before its full value may be obtained!

EXAMPLE 9-12a Value Added Using Tax (MACRS Depreciation) Rather Than Financial Shareholder Deductions

Re-calculate the VA from Example 9-12 based on the MACRS depreciation used for regular tax, which eliminates the deferred tax adjustment. All other assumptions remain the same. The previous calculations for MACRS depreciation that were presented in Example 9-11a down to net income are summarized as follows:

Year	0	1	2	3	4	5
Revenue	–	9.40	8.40	7.40	6.40	5.40
– Oper. Costs	–	–3.50	–3.50	–3.50	–3.50	–3.50
– Depreciation	–	–2.00	–3.20	–1.92	–1.15	–1.73
Taxable Income	–	3.90	1.70	1.98	1.75	0.17
– Inc Tax @ 40%	–	–1.56	–0.68	–0.79	–0.70	–0.07
Net Income	–	2.34	1.02	1.19	1.05	0.10
Beg Bk Value	–	10.00	8.00	4.80	2.88	1.73
Cost of Cap @ 12%	–	–1.20	–0.96	–0.58	–0.35	–0.21
Net Income	–	2.34	1.02	1.19	1.05	0.10
– Cost of Capital	–	–1.20	–0.96	–0.58	–0.35	–0.21
Value Added	–	1.14	0.06	0.61	0.70	–0.11

Due to limited space, VA is rounded above, but more detail is provided below in the present worth equation:

$$\text{PW EQ: } 1.14(P/F_{12\%,1}) + 0.06(P/F_{12\%,2}) + 0.612(P/F_{12\%,3}) + 0.7044(P/F_{12\%,4}) - 0.1056(P/F_{12\%,5})$$

$$= 1.889 \text{ which is identical to the after-tax NPV!}$$

9.11 "Regulated" Company Investment Analysis

The maximum return on investment allowed for regulated company investments is limited by federal and state law in accordance with rules governed by federal and state regulatory commissions. Typical regulated investments include the telephone communications industry, electric utility power generation, transmission and distribution companies, interstate pipeline natural gas transmission companies and intrastate natural gas pipeline distribution companies. The various federal and state regulatory commissions are required by law to establish investment return rates that are "just and reasonable" for regulated investments from the viewpoints of both the public purchasing a product and the investor producing or transporting the product. The regulatory commissions must walk a narrow line to determine regulated investment rates that are adequate to permit a company to stay in business and provide the needed service, but not permit rates that would give excessive return on investment from the public viewpoint. In other words, the regulatory commission strives to set regulated rates that do not cause "undue discrimination" nor give "unjust preference" to the consumer, to the investor, and to the general public interest.

The terms "revenue requirement" and "cost of service" often are used interchangeably in referring to the revenue that is required to cover all costs for providing a service and to give the investor an adequate return on investment. In equation form:

Revenue Requirement Per Year =

Allowed Regulated Return on Equity Rate Base — Eq. 9-2
+ Operating and Maintenance Expenses
+ Income Taxes
+ Regulated Depreciation
+ Interest on Debt if Applicable

In the simplest of analysis situations the annual revenue requirement is divided by the total units of service to be provided per year to obtain the revenue requirement per unit of service. However, in most real world situations, annual revenue requirements differ from year to year as do units of service to be produced. This requires determination of "equivalent annual revenue requirements" to be divided by "equivalent annual production" to obtain a time value of money weighted average revenue requirement per unit of service produced. Calculations get more complicated rapidly when different customers have different volume of service requirements that merit different incremental pricing scenarios. However, the basic analysis principles are relatively straight forward and that is what we endeavor to introduce here.

To determine the allowed regulated return on investment each year, it is necessary to determine the allowed regulated rate base each year that is taken times the allowed regulatory rate of return. Specific details of the rate base calculation may differ with different regulatory agencies, but the general rate base calculation is as follows for a given year:

Total Equity Plus Debt Investment Rate Base =

Original Investment Cost Including Working Capital — Eq. 9-3
– Arithmetic Average Cumulative Regulated Depreciation
– Arithmetic Average Cumulative Deferred Tax
± Working Capital Investment Changes*

*Working Capital may include average annual value of materials and supplies inventory, average annual value of natural gas stored underground and average annual cash and bank balances to name some of the common components.

Equity Investment Rate Base =

Total Investment Rate Base – Debt Financial Investment — Eq. 9-4

Allowed Regulated Return on Equity Investment =

Equity Rate Base x Allowed Regulated Rate of Return — Eq. 9-5

The "Allowed Regulated Return on Equity Rate Base" is equivalent to Net Income calculated using regulated depreciation as the following illustrates for a restatement of Equation 9-2:

Revenue Required Per Year
– Operating and Maintenance Expenses
– Regulated Depreciation
– Interest on Debt if Applicable

= Taxable Income
– Federal & State Income Taxes

= Regulated Return (Net Income) on Equity Rate Base

Regulated depreciation is generally straight line over allowed regulatory depreciation lives except for producing equipment and gathering pipelines which are deducted by units of production depreciation. Some typical capital assets with tax and typical regulatory depreciation lives follow:

	Modified ACRS Tax Deprec. Life	Regulated Deprec. Life
Computer / Electronic Equipment	5 yr	10 yr
Producing Equipment / Gathering Lines	7 yr	Units of Prod.
Transmission Pipelines / Storage Fac.	15 yr	29 yr

For economic analysis purposes, expenditures that can be expensed for tax deduction purposes (whether considered to be capital costs or operating costs) generally are treated as operating expenses for regulatory analysis purposes and added to revenue requirements in the year incurred.

While the "revenue requirement" (cost of service) calculation generally is considered the most important economic measure of regulated investments, many other economic and non-economic factors also receive consideration by the regulatory commissions. Value of service to the customer, quality of service, comparative rates for similar service, competitive service from alternate sources and general economic conditions including price inflation are factors that can affect a regulatory commission judgement concerning reasonableness of a regulated investment rate and the associated revenue requirement calculations.

After determining the regulated revenue requirements for each year in the evaluation life of a regulated project, discounted cash flow analysis with either ROR, NPV or PVR analysis is done by converting the actual project costs and regulated revenue requirements to after-tax cash flow using tax depreciation deductions (not regulated) and actual income tax (not regulated). These calculations are the same as for any unregulated evaluation once the regulated required revenues are determined.

PROBLEMS

Excel solutions at Stermole.com

9-1 At the present time a company is purchasing a raw material required for its production operation for \$0.259 per pound. Projected annual usage for the next 3 years is 525,000 pounds, 470,000 pounds and 460,000 pounds respectively at years 1, 2 and 3. The company is considering the economic desirability of installing equipment now, at year 0, for a cost of \$39,000 that will enable them to use a cheaper raw material costing \$0.143 per pound. However, using the cheaper raw material will increase operating costs by an estimated \$0.04 per pound. Development costs to change over to the new process are estimated to be \$8,000 during the first year (to be expensed for tax purposes at the end of year 1). Equipment will be placed into service at year 1 and depreciated straight line over 5 years with a half-year deduction starting in year 1. The effective federal plus state tax rate is 40% and the escalated dollar after-tax minimum rate of return is 12%.

A) Calculate the escalated dollar DCFROR and NPV that can be expected on the equipment and development cost investments to change to the cheaper raw material if a 3 year evaluation life is used with a zero salvage value, and a tax write-off is taken on the book value of the equipment at the end of year 3 due to scrapping it at that time?

B) What is the undiscounted payback period?

C) What is the constant dollar DCFROR assuming 10% inflation per year?

9-2 An integrated petroleum company acquired the mineral rights to a property in the United States 2 years ago for a lease bonus of \$400,000. The property was drilled this month (year 0) for intangible drilling costs of \$600,000. The geological evaluation of well logs indicates that completion of the well is associated with a 60% probability of producing 40 barrels of crude per day with a price of \$30 per barrel during the first year (350 producing days) of production (assume to be year 1) with a 40% probability of producing nothing and realizing a net abandonment cost and producing equipment salvage of \$100,000 income at year 1. The new well producing equipment and tangible completion cost would be \$200,000 at year 0 with a \$100,000 intangible completion cost for fracturing also incurred at year 0 if the well is completed. This $100,000 cost is treated as an intangible drilling cost for tax deduction purposes. If the well produces the revenue of 40 barrels per day during the first year (which is estimated to be 25% of reserves) the royalty owners have offered to sign a contract giving the company the option to sell the well to the royalty owners for $350,000 cash at year 1 including all producing equipment and mineral rights. Modified ACRS depreciation over 7 years will start in year 1 with the half-year convention on tangible costs. Other income and tax obligations exist against which to use the year 0 intangible drilling cost (IDC) deductions. The effective tax rate is 40% and any gain or loss on the sale is taxed or deducted as ordinary gain or loss. Royalties are 18% of crude oil revenue and production operating costs are estimated to be $60,000 in year 1. Neglect any windfall tax. For a minimum escalated dollar DCFROR of 20%, use Expected NPV Analysis to evaluate if the well should be completed or abandoned at year 0, assuming the well will be sold at year 1 if completed.

√ 9-3 A petroleum company wants you to evaluate the economics of abandoning a stripper oil well versus selling the well to an interested investor. If the well is abandoned, a $20,000 abandonment cost must be incurred now (year 0) and a salvage value of $30,000 will be realized on the used producing equipment. $5,000 of book value remains on the producing equipment and will be written-off against the salvage value or other income at year 0 if the well is sold or abandoned. Assume other income exists against which to use deductions. The effective ordinary income tax rate is assumed to be 40%.Calculate the stripper well selling price that will make the economics of selling at year 0 a break-even with abandonment at year 0. If the projected abandonment cost is increased to $50,000 from $20,000, how is the break-even selling price affected?

?? 9-4 A real estate broker, who makes his living by buying and selling properties, is evaluating the purchase of 10 acres of land for $60,000 cash now to be sold in the future for a profit. What escalated dollar sale value must the land have in 2 years to give a constant dollar investment DCFROR of 20% per year if annual inflation is projected to be 10%? Assume that the capital gain from the land sale will be taxed as ordinary income at an effective tax rate of 30%.

9-5 A company incurred a cost of $500,000 2 years ago to acquire the development rights to a property for which an offer of $1 million cash has been received now at time 0. The $500,000 acquisition cost incurred at year -2 will be written-off against the sale value if sold at time 0, or assume it has been amortized over the production years 1 through 5 in calculating the after-tax cash flows given. Any gain from the sale would be taxed as ordinary income at the effective tax rate of 40%. Development of the property would generate escalated dollar after-tax cash flow in millions of dollars of -1.5 in year 0, and +1.0, +1.8, +1.2, +0.8 and +0.4 in years 1 through 5 respectively. If the minimum escalated dollar DCFROR is 20%, should the company keep and develop the property or sell if there is considered to be a 60% probability of development generating the year 1 through 5 positive cash flow, and 40% probability of failure generating zero cash flow in years 1 through 5? What development probability of success will make the economics of development a break-even with selling?

9-6 A corporation has an investment opportunity that will involve a time zero $100,000 depreciable cost for machinery and equipment. It will be depreciated starting in year 1 with an additional machinery and equipment expenditure of $50,000 at the end of year 1. Use 7-year life modified ACRS depreciation for all equipment with the half year convention in the first year. Working capital investment of $25,000 is required at time zero. Income attributed to these investment is $200,000 in year 1 and $280,000 per year in years 2 and 3. Operating costs are estimated to be $140,000 the first year and $190,000 per year in years 2 and 3. The effective tax rate is 40%. It is estimated that the business developed by this investment could be sold at the end of year 3 for $250,000 (including equipment and working capital). What discounted cash flow rate of return would be earned by this investment opportunity? What additional development cost could be incurred and expensed for tax purposes against other income at year 0 and still obtain a 15% DCFROR on invested dollars?

9-7 An individual investor is evaluating the purchase of 100 acres of land today for $100,000. The investor expects to be able to sell the land 3 years from now for $250,000. The investor wants to know the escalated dollar DCFROR on invested dollars that she can expect to receive on this investment. Gain from the sale should be assumed to be individual long term capital gain, taxed at the effective ordinary income tax rate, assumed to be 30%. Property tax costs of $2,500 in each of years 1, 2 and 3 are assumed to be expensed against other ordinary income each year including year 3. After determining the escalated dollar DCFROR on invested dollars, determine the equivalent constant dollar DCFROR if inflation is assumed to be 8% per year over the 3 year investment life.

9-8 An individual has $100,000 to invest and is considering two ways of investing it. Using a 10 year economic evaluation life, you are asked to analyze the investments and select the best investment alternative using after-tax year 10 future value analysis. Assume the individual has a 30% effective federal plus state tax rate. The investment alternatives are as follows: (1) Buy common stock projected to grow at an average before-tax rate of 10% per year over the next 10 years. Ordinary income tax applies to the sale value 10 years from now. The stock is assumed to pay no annual dividends. (2) Buy a new 10 year life corporate bond with a 10% annual dividend rate and reinvest dividends as received in a bond fund account, projected to pay an average annual before-tax interest rate of 10% per year. Account for the payment of tax on bond dividend income annually. After making the analysis requested, determine the common stock before-tax rate of growth that would make the two investments economically equivalent.

9-9 The investment of $500,000 at time zero for depreciable machinery and equipment will generate sales revenues for 5 years that increase by a constant arithmetic gradient of $10,000 each year to exactly offset escalation of operating costs each year which start at $50,000 per year in year 1 and increase $10,000 per year. The initial investment will be depreciated over 7 years using Modified ACRS depreciation, starting in year 0 with the half-year convention. Assume a zero salvage value. The effective income tax rate is 40%. What break-even sales revenue is needed each year to yield a 25% DCFROR on investment dollars?

9-10 Project costs, sales and terminal value for a 6 year life project are shown on the time diagram in thousands of dollars. Assume all costs and revenues are in escalated dollars and assume a wash-out of escalation of operating costs and sales revenue in each of revenue-producing years 2 through 6.

	$C_{Work\ Cap}=\$200$		
	$C_{Equip}=\$500$	Sales/Year=\$900 . . . . \$900	W.C. Return
$C_{Res}=\$100$	$C_{Develop}=\$300$	O.C./Year=\$200 . . . . \$200	& Salvage
0	1	2 6	= \$400

The salvage value is for working capital return and depreciable asset salvage. Expense research and experimental development costs at years 0 and 1. Assume other income exists against which to use negative taxable income in any year. Depreciate capital equipment straight line over 5 years starting in year 1 with a half-year deduction. The effective income tax rate is 40%. Use an escalated dollar minimum DCFROR of 15% and:

A) Determine whether project economics are favorable using NPV analysis.

B) Determine the before-tax additional research cost in year 0 that would cause the project to have a 15% after-tax DCFROR.

C) Determine if it is economically desirable to accept an offer of \$900,000 at year 1 to sell the patent rights from the year 0 research compared to keeping the rights and developing them. Assume sale gain would be taxed as ordinary income and that none of the year 1 costs have been incurred. Also, assume the time 0 research cost and tax effect are sunk.

D) What patent selling price at year 1 makes selling a break-even with development before having incurred any year 1 costs?

E) For the Case "A" development scenario that generated an NPV of \$663, what additional time 0 cost could be incurred to allow the investor to achieve a minimum rate of return of 15%? Assume this cost would be depreciated beginning in year 1 using straight line, 5 year life depreciation with the half-year convention. Assume no additional salvage income would be realized, so salvage income and dismantlement costs offset each other.

9-11 Using the net income generated in Problem 9-10, Case A, calculate the annual "value added" in years 2 through 6 and then determine the overall present value of the value added. Use the same after-tax opportunity cost of capital of 15% and neglect deferred taxes assuming the investor has used the slower straight-line deductions for tax as well as financial reporting so there is no difference.

9-12 Evaluate the economic potential of the project described in problem 9-10 if the research at time zero has a 40% probability of success, and if success leads to the end of year 1 development, equipment and working capital costs which yield a process with a 70% probability of success that results in the year 2 through 6 sales and salvage value given. If failure occurs after the year 1 investments, assume the working capital will be liquidated for $200,000 and the related book value of working capital and depreciable costs wil be written off at the end of year 2 and used against other income. Assume that if the time zero research fails no salvage is realized.

9-13 Work problem 9-10A for the situation where sales per year are unknown instead of $900,000 per year and determine the selling price per unit for sales of 10,000 units per year to give a 15% project DCFROR. Assume that escalation of the selling price per unit after year 2 will be sufficient for sales revenue increases to washout any operating cost increases, that is, you will be calculating the year 2 break-even selling price per unit and it will escalate in following years to cover cost increases.

PW units = ~~[illegible]~~ 21,587.74

9-14 It is proposed to invest $200,000 now at year zero in a facility depreciable by 7-year life Modified ACRS depreciation starting in year zero with the half-year convention. An additional $100,000 will be spent on research and development at year zero (expensed for tax purposes at year zero) to produce a new product. It is estimated that this facility and research work have a 60% probability of successfully producing 1000 product units per year in each of years 1, 2 and 3. At year 3 thefacility is projected to become outdated and to be sold for an escalated $50,000 salvage value. The product units would sell for $280 per unit today and selling price is projected to escalate 12% in year 1, 10% in year 2 and 8% in year 3. Operating costs are to be incurred in years 1, 2 and 3 and are estimated to be $40 per unit today in year 0 and to escalate 10% per year. If the project fails, assume the facility will be sold at year 1 for an escalated $100,000 salvage value with a write-off taken on the remaining book value at year 1. Assume that other income and tax obligations do not exist against which to use tax deductions and tax credits in year 0, but that other income will exist in year 1 against which to use possible failure write-off deductions. Assume the effective tax rate is 40%. For a constant dollar minimum DCFROR of 10% and inflation rates of 6% in year 1, 8% in year 2 and 10% in year 3, calculate the constant dollar expected NPV for the project. Verify that escalated dollar expected NPV equals constant dollar expected NPV by calculating the escalated dollar expected NPV.

9-15 A natural gas pipeline to transport gas from a new gas well would cost our company $220,000 with operating costs of $5,000 per year projected over the 6 year project life. The XYZ Pipeline Company has a gathering line nearby and has offered to transport our gas for $0.10 per MCF (thousand cubic feet of gas) by spending $50,000 to build a gathering line to connect our well to their existing line. To determine whether $0.10 per MCF is a reasonable transport charge, calculate the break-even price per MCF transported that would give our company a 12% DCFROR on the $220,000 pipeline investment for the following production schedule and modified ACRS depreciation for a 7-year life starting in year 1 with the half-year convention on the pipeline cost. Use mid-year average production and time value of money factors. Assume a 40% income tax rate. Neglect any opportunity cost from the forgone sale cash flow in this break-even development cost analysis.

Year	0	0.5	1.5	2.5	3.5	4.5	5.5
Annual Prod. MMCF		1,900	1,440	1,030	730	440	150

9-16 Development of a coal property which our corporation purchased two years ago for a mineral rights acquisition cost of $10 million is being reconsidered. Our company has other income and tax obligations against which to use tax deductions in any year. Mineral development capital of $10 million will be needed in evaluation year 0 for overburden stripping. Mine equipment costs of $15 million also will be incurred in year 0 along with $2 million cost for working capital. The mine life is estimated to be 5 years. Mine equipment will be depreciated over 7 years using Modified ACRS rates, starting in year 0 with the half-year convention. Salvage value and working capital return will be $5 million at the end of year 5 with any taxable gain taxed as ordinary income. The effective tax rate is 40%. Coal reserves are estimated to be 5 million tons and production for years 1 through 5 is projected to be 1 million tons per year. Coal selling price is estimated to be $30 per ton in year 1, escalating 10% per year in years 2 through 5. Royalties are 8% of revenues. Mining operating costs are estimated to be $12 per ton in year 1, also escalating by 10% per year in following years. 1) Calculate the project DCFROR and NPV for a minimum DCFROR of 20% to determine if the mine development economics are preferable to selling assuming that we have an offer to sell the coal property at year 0 for $20 million cash with any gain taxed as ordinary income. 2) Calculate the sale price that will make selling a break-even with development. 3) Finally, calculate the year 0 mineral development cost incrementally in addition to the $10 million dollar cost in the analysis that would just give the investor a 20% DCFROR on invested dollars.

9-17 Your integrated oil and gas company owns a 100% working interest in a lease. To develop the lease, two alternatives are considered:

Case A. Develop the lease for your current 87.5% net revenue interest.

Case B. "Farm-out" the property and take an carried interest until the project pays out. Under the farm-out, you would receive a 5.0% carried interest (5.0% of revenues, carved out of the working interest) until payout occurs. Payout is based on undiscounted 'net revenues less operating costs', to recover before-tax capital costs of $350,000. Because of the carried interest, the producer has an 82.5% net revenue interest to payout. Upon payout, your company would back in for a 25.0% working interest and a 21.875% net revenue interest (25% of the 87.5% net revenue interest).

Year zero intangible drilling costs are estimated at $250,000 while tangible completion costs in the same period are estimated to be

$100,000. Start amortizing 30% of the IDC in year 0 with a 6 month deduction. Also, begin depreciating the tangible equipment in year 1 using seven year life MACRS with the half-year convention. Write-off all remaining book values in year 4 when the lease is assumed to be abandoned. For this example, neglect any potential sale value or abandonment costs in year 4. Operating costs are estimated to remain constant at $4.00 per barrel (includes production costs, severance and ad valorem taxes). Oil prices are forecasted to be $20.00 per barrel in year 1 and 2 and then escalate 5.0% per year in each of years 3 and 4. Production is in barrels, and is estimated to be as follows:

Production	—	17,500	9,000	6,500	3,000
Year	0	1	2	3	4

The escalated dollar minimum rate of return is 12.0%. The effective tax rate is 38.0% and other income exists against which to use all deductions in the year they are realized. Use net present value, present value ratio, and rate of return analysis to determine which of these two mutually exclusive alternatives is the economic choice.

9-18 An integrated oil and gas producer has an existing gas well with cumulative production to date of 2.0 Bcf (billion cubic feet) with an ultimate recovery of approximately 2.6 Bcf. An in-fill well is being considered that will both accelerate production and increase reserves. The total cost of the new in-fill well is estimated to be $168,000 at year 0. 75% of the well cost will be treated as an intangible drilling cost (IDC) with the remaining 25% considered to be tangible completion costs, depreciated by MACRS over seven years, with the half-year convention beginning in year 0. Take 6 months amortization in year 0 on the applicable portion of the IDC. The producer has a 100% working interest in the field and an 87.5% net revenue interest. The mineral rights cost basis has already been recovered so no cost depletion is allowed on the incremental production. Production is in Mcf (thousands of cubic feet of gas), operating costs are in actual dollars and production and operating costs in the first 6 months are treated as year 0 values. If the in-fill well is drilled, production will come from both the "modified existing" and the "new in-fill" wells as shown below.

Year	Existing Gas Well Prod (Mcf)	New Gas Well Production	Modified Existing Prod (Mcf)	Selling Price, $/Mcf	Existing Well Annual Oper Costs	New Well Annual Oper Costs	Infill-Exist. Incremental Production	Infill-Exist. Incremental Oper Costs
0	80,000	100,000	70,000	$1.25	$2,000	$1,000	90,000	$1,000
1	140,000	160,000	120,000	$1.25	$4,000	$2,000	140,000	$2,000
2	125,000	100,000	70,000	$1.50	$4,000	$2,000	45,000	$2,000
3	100,000	50,000	40,000	$1.75	$4,000	$2,000	–10,000	$2,000
4	75,000	30,000	20,000	$2.00	$4,000	$2,000	–25,000	$2,000
5	50,000	10,000	10,000	$2.25	$4,000	$2,000	–30,000	$2,000
6	25,000	0	0	$2.50	*$4,000	$0	–25,000	–$4,000

* The operating cost in year 6 only applies to the "existing" gas well since no cost exists with the acceleration alternative due to no production.

The after-tax escalated dollar minimum rate of return is 12.0% and the net of salvage and abandonment cost is estimated to be zero. The effective state and federal tax rate is 38.0%. Assume other income exists against which to use all deductions in the year they are incurred. Determine whether the "in-fill" well should be drilled using ROR, NPV and PVR analyses.

9-19 Two years ago, a chemical company acquired patent rights to a new product manufacturing process for a cost of $2.5 million dollars. The total cost is still on the books but will be amortized uniformly over a 5 year life beginning in year 1 if the project is developed. Today, (time zero) the company is trying to determine whether to keep the patent rights and develop the process or to sell it to another firm for a cash offer they have received of $4.5 million. If the company should elect to develop the process, experimental development costs of $12 million (to be expensed for tax purposes) and equipment costs of $15 million will be required today, time zero. The year 0 equipment cost will be depreciated by MACRS over a 7 year recovery period with the half year convention beginning in year 1. Write-off the remaining book values at the end of year four when the project is terminated due to declining market demand for the product. The capital expenditures are expected to have an 80.0% probability of generating revenues of $25.0 million and operating costs of $10.0 million in each of the next four years. Escalation of revenues and operating costs is assumed to be a washout so assume the same profit margin is maintained each year. If the project fails (Probability = 20.0%), the equipment can be sold net of abandonment costs for $10 million in year 1 and the patent and equipment costs written off at that time. Assume other income exists against which to use all deductions in the year incurred. The effective tax rate is 38.0%.

Develop:

Cost of Patent = \$2.5	Dev. = \$12.0 Equip. = \$15.0	P = 0.80	Rev. = \$25.0 OC = \$10.0	Rev. = \$25.0 OC = \$10.0
–2	0		1	4
		P = 0.20	Yr. 1 Net Salvage = \$10.0	

Sell:

Cost of Patent = \$2.5	Sell = \$4.5		
–2	0	1	4

A) For an escalated dollar minimum rate of return of 15%, determine whether the process should be developed or sold.

B) For a constant dollar minimum rate of return of 15% and 8.7% inflation per year, determine whether the project should be developed or sold.

9-20 A gas pipeline manager has determined that he will need a compressor to satisfy gas compression requirements over the next five years or 60 months. The unit can be acquired for a year zero investment of \$1,000,000. The compressor would be depreciated over 7 years, using MACRS rates and the half-year convention, beginning in year 0. The cost of installation at time zero is \$75,000 and a major repair cost of \$225,000 is estimated at the end of year 3. Both the installation cost and the repair cost will be expensed in the evaluation year they are incurred. The compressor would be sold at the end of year five for \$300,000 so write off the remaining book value at that time. The alternative to purchasing is to lease the machine for a year 0 payment of \$75,000 to cover installation costs and beginning of month lease payments of \$24,000 per month for 60 months. Lease payments include all major repair and maintenance charges over the term of the lease. A balloon payment to purchase the compressor after the fifth year is not being considered since the compressor is not expected to be needed after the specified service life. This is an operating lease so expense all lease costs like operating costs. The after-tax, escalated dollar, nominal (or annual) discount rate is 12% compounded monthly. Other income exists against which to use all deductions in the year incurred. The combined state and federal effective tax rate is 40.0%. Use incremental rate of return, net present value, and present value ratio analysis techniques to determine whether leasing or purchasing is the economic choice.

9-21 A new $10,000, 10 year life U.S. Treasury Bond pays annual dividends of $800 based on the before-tax 8.0% annual yield to maturity. For an investor with a 38.0% effective state and federal tax rate, compute the after-tax rate of return on the bond investment. Then consider the following: (A) After purchasing the bond, if market interest rates instantly increased to 10.0%, or decreased to 6.0%, how would the bond value be affected? (B) If the bond has a 30 year life instead of a 10 year life, how do market interest rate changes to 10.0% or 6.0% affect the value? (C) If the 30 year 8.0% bond is a new $10,000 face value (year 30 maturity value) zero coupon bond instead of a conventional bond, how is value affected by the interest rate changes?

CHAPTER 9 AUXILIARY PROBLEMS

A9-1 Your company is considering investing $350,000 in surface land rights and $600,000 in a steel warehouse building with both costs incurred at time zero. Manufacturing equipment costing $400,000 would be installed at time zero to generate carwash units to be delivered across the country. Spare parts and product inventory are estimated at $500,000 also at time zero. Depreciate the building starting in year 1 by the straight line method over 39 years assuming depreciation begins in July of a calendar tax year. The equipment is depreciated using 5-year MACRS rates starting in year 1, while the land and working capital expenditures will be written off with all other remaining book values against the sale of the business at the end of year 5. Product sales in each of years 1–5 are estimated to be $4,500,000 per year with cost of goods sold estimated at $2,500,000 per year. Sales and operating expenses are forecasted to remain uniform over the project life. Your company would hope to sell the business at the end of year 5 for $15,000,000 net of all closing costs. The company uses an after-tax minimum rate of return of 15%. The effective state and federal income tax rate is 40% and other income is thought to exist against which to use all deductions.

1) Use NPV analysis to determine if this business venture should be undertaken.

2) When does the project achieve payback?

3) Based on car wash equipment sales of 2 units per week for 50 weeks per year, what price per complete car wash unit would allow the business to generate an after-tax escalated dollar return of 15% on the invested capital?

4) How much more could be spent today (time zero) on 5-year MACRS depreciable equipment and still earn a 15% after-tax return? Use the 5-year business model for this calculation.

A9-2 Suppose you just finished the 2nd year of operations in the wholesale carwash business described in problem A9-1. A commercial business broker just called with an offer to buy the business and all the related assets for $12 million.

1) Would you recommend selling or continuing to own the business for the next three years and then selling as originally planned for the same $15 million?

2) What selling price for all the assets related to the business would make you economically indifferent between continuing with operations and selling?

A9-3 An investor paid $100,000 for a machine today (time 0) that is estimated to have a 70% probability of successfully producing 5,000 product units per year for each of the next 3 years, at which time the machine is estimated to be obsolete with a salvage value of 0. Product price (the unknown, X, yet to be calculated) is estimated to be $X per unit in year 1 escalated dollars and to increase 10% per year in year 2 and 6% in year 3. Total operating costs are estimated at $8,000 in year 1 escalated dollars and to increase by 15% in year 2 and 8% in year 3. The annual inflation rate is estimated at 7%. Determine the year 1, 2, and 3 escalated dollar product selling price necessary for the investor to receive a 12% annually compounded constant dollar expected DCFROR on invested dollars. Use MACRS depreciation rates for a 5-year life, starting depreciation at time 0 with the half-year convention. Write-off the remaining book value at the end of year 3. Assume other taxable income exists to use time 0 negative taxable income against. Assume a 40% income tax rate. If the project fails, assume a zero net after-tax cash flow is realized in year 1 (30% of the time). This assumes that after-tax equipment dismantlement costs will exactly offset tax write-off and salvage value benefits and simplifies the problem.

A9-4 A gathering line to transport natural gas from a new gas well to an existing trunk line is estimated to cost $200,000 at time 0 with escalated dollar operating costs estimated at $9,000 per year at each of production years 1 through 4. The gas well is expected to be shut-in at the end of year 4 and that the pipeline's salvage value will be 0. The projected natural gas production to be handled by the pipeline is as follows where "Bcf" = billion cubic feet:

Year	0	1	2	3	4
Annual Production	—	2.0Bcf	1.5Bcf	1.0Bcf	0.5Bcf

The pipeline cost of $200,000 is to be depreciated over a 7-year life using MACRS depreciation, starting in year 1 with the half-year convention. A write-off on remaining book value would be taken at year 4. Assume an effective income tax rate of 40%. Calculate the uniform transportation price per Mcf (thousand cubic feet) of natural gas transported that would give the pipeline investor:

A) A 15% escalated dollar DCFROR on invested capital.

B) A 15% constant dollar DCFROR on invested capital for inflation of 8% per year over the project life.

A9-5 A conveyor to transport coal (or mineral concentrate) from a loading point to a shipping facility is estimated to cost $200,000 at time 0 with escalated dollar operating costs estimated at $9,000 per year at each of production years 1 through 4. The use of the conveyor is expected to terminate at the end of year 4 and that the conveyor's salvage value will be 0. The projected coal (or mineral concentrate) production to be handled by the conveyor is as follows where "M tons" = thousand tons:

Year	0	1	2	3	4
Average Annual Conveyed Tons	—	2,000	1,500	1,000	500 (M tons)

The conveyor cost of $200,000 is to be depreciated over a 7-year life using MACRS depreciation, starting in year 1 with the half-year convention. A write-off on remaining book value would be taken at year 4. Assume an effective income tax rate of 40%. Calculate the uniform transportation price per ton of coal (or mineral concentrate) transported that would give the investor:

A) A 15% escalated dollar DCFROR on invested capital.

B) A 15% constant dollar DCFROR on invested capital for inflation of 8% per year over the project life.

A9-6 Your company is considering the following project and wants to examine the economic and financial implications. Other income exists against which to utilize all deductions in the year incurred. All values in thousand of dollars.

Year	0	1	2	3	4	5
Revenue		1,300	1,300	1,300	1,300	1,300
Operating Costs		–500	–600	–700	–800	–900
Equipment Costs	–500					
Working Capital	–100					

The equipment cost should be depreciated using the 5-year MACRS rates for tax with straight line depreciation over 10 years (no half year convention) used for financial reporting. Start all depreciation in year 1. The company uses the LIFO inventory methodology so write off the initial working capital investment in the final year for both the tax and financial net income models. The effective tax rate is 40%. Write off all remaining book values at the end of year 5. The investor's minimum rate of return is an escalated dollar, after-tax measure of 15% per year.

1) Calculate the after-tax cash flow for tax purposes and corresponding NPV and DCFROR. The minimum rate of return is an escalated dollar after-tax value of 12% per year.

2) Calculate the financial net income from this project based on the described deductions and determine the annual return on capital employed in years 1 through 5.

3) After accounting for deferred tax and opportunity cost considerations, determine the annual value added in years 1 through 5 from this investment opportunity and the corresponding present value of those amounts.

CHAPTER 10

AFTER-TAX SERVICE ANALYSIS

10.1 General Replacement Philosophy

Replacement of existing assets with new and usually more capital intensive assets is the most common service analysis situation. Replacement of physical assets usually is considered for one of three general reasons (1) the present asset is inadequate for the job, for instance, more capacity may be needed; (2) the present asset is worn out or physically impaired causing excessive maintenance or declining efficiency and; (3) the present asset is obsolete, that is, improved assets are available that do the job more efficiently.

In engineering economy literature related to replacement, the present asset sometimes is described as the "defender" and the proposed new asset is called the "challenger". This appropriately describes the alternatives in replacement studies, but whatever the alternatives are called the most important aspect concerning replacement is that it should be based on asset performance economy and not on physical deterioration. There frequently is a reluctance on the part of managers to replace physically satisfactory equipment even though economic savings will result from the replacement. Financial and intangible considerations often get entangled with the economics of the replacement of equipment. Sometimes managers state that it is not economical to replace equipment at this time when they mean that from an economic viewpoint the replacement should be made now, but because of financial and intangible considerations the replacement will be deferred. It is quite important to separate economic, financial, and intangible considerations to get the final replacement decision in proper perspective. This generally will result in more decisions based on the economic viewpoint.

Intangible replacement considerations may include the relative risks and uncertainties involved between alternatives. Economic analysis of replacement alternatives usually is based upon the assumption that risk and uncertainty are similar for the different alternatives under consideration. This may not be the case. Old assets when compared to new assets have relatively lower capital cost, shorter life and higher operating cost and, therefore, relatively lower projection risk and uncertainty. If the projected annual costs for an old and new machine that will perform the same service are equal the intangible difference in the risk between the two alternatives may sway the decision to the old asset, although that is a relative judgement on the part of the evaluator and managers involved with the decision.

Replacement analysis does not require any new engineering economy decision methods techniques. The techniques of ROR, NPV, PVR, annual worth, present worth, future worth and break-even analysis applied after tax considerations are the decision methods used for a large majority of industrial replacement analyses. *From a practical viewpoint, you can think of all investment decisions as being replacement decisions concerning whether to replace a present asset or investment opportunity yielding some minimum rate of return with another investment that promises to give a higher return on investment* (or lower annual cost, present cost or future cost if the same service is performed). In most replacement situations such as comparing an old and a new asset the tax deduction advantages differ greatly between alternatives. In almost all cases replacement analyses should be made after tax to obtain valid decision-making results. Before-tax analysis can lead to incorrect economic decisions because tax considerations often are very different between replacement alternatives being evaluated. Example 10-1 illustrates the after-tax application of five primary analysis methods utilized in industry practice for comparing alternatives that provide a common service.

EXAMPLE 10-1 Service Producing Analysis Using Annual Cost, Present Worth Cost, Incremental DCFROR and NPV Methods and Break-even Cost Per Unit of Service

The installation of automated equipment costing $60,000 is proposed to reduce labor and material costs for an operation over the next four years. The equipment would be scrapped at the end of four years. Labor and maintenance operating costs with the new equipment are expected to be $10,000 in year one, $12,000 in year two, $14,000 in year three and $16,000 in year four in escalated dollars. The operating costs per year under the existing labor intensive mode of operation are projected to be $40,000 in year one, $42,000 in year two, $44,000 in year three and $46,000 in year four in escalated dollars. New equipment depreciation will be based on the modified ACRS seven year rates beginning in year 0 with the half year convention. The effective income tax rate is 40% and minimum DCFROR is 20%. It is assumed that other income exists against which to use all deductions in the year incurred, and that the alternatives will provide the same service of producing 1000 units of product per year for each of years 1 through 4. Evaluate the alternatives using a four year evaluation life with:

A) Incremental DCFROR Analysis
B) Incremental NPV Analysis
C) Equivalent Annual Cost Analysis
D) Present Worth Cost Analysis
E) Break-even Cost Per Unit of Service

Solution:

A and B) For incremental DCFROR and NPV analysis, the easiest solution approach is to examine the incremental differences between the alternatives before-tax, then account for the tax considerations on the incremental costs and savings to get after-tax costs and cash flow. This analysis approach follows:

Before-Tax Diagrams, C=Cost, OC=Operating Cost, S=Savings

New	C=$60,000	OC=$10,000	OC=$12,000	OC=$14,000	OC=$16,000
	0	1	2	3	4
Old	—	OC=$40,000	OC=$42,000	OC=$44,000	OC=$46,000
	0	1	2	3	4
New	C=$60,000	S=$30,000	S=$30,000	S=$30,000	S=$30,000
–Old	0	1	2	3	4

It was shown in Chapter 3 that negative incremental operating costs are the same as positive savings. The savings of $30,000 yearly are converted to cash flow, accounting for depreciation of the $60,000 investment with a write-off of remaining book value at year 4 included in year 4 depreciation.

Incremental Cash Flows in Dollars

Year	0	1	2	3	4
Savings		30,000	30,000	30,000	30,000
–Depreciation	–8,571	–14,694	–10,496	–7,497	–18,742*
Taxable Income	–8,571	15,306	19,504	22,503	11,258
–Tax @ 40%	3,429	–6,122	–7,802	–9,001	–4,503
Net Income	–5,143	9,184	11,703	13,502	6,755
+Depreciation	8,571	14,694	10,496	7,497	18,742
–Capital Cost	–60,000				
Cash Flow	–56,571	23,878	22,198	20,999	25,497

* Remaining book value write-off is combined with year 4 depreciation.

$$\text{PW Eq: } 0 = -56{,}571 + 23{,}878(P/F_{i,1}) + 22{,}198(P/F_{i,2}) + 20{,}999(P/F_{i,3}) + 25{,}497(P/F_{i,4})$$

$$i = \text{Incremental Investment DCFROR} = 22.9\%$$

Compared to $i^* = 20\%$ in escalated dollars, this is a slightly satisfactory incremental investment, indicating accept the new equipment. Getting 22.9% DCFROR is slightly better than getting a 20% DCFROR in other projects. (Note that if you make a before-tax analysis, the \$30,000 savings per year give a 34.9% before-tax ROR on the \$60,000 initial investment which possibly could lead to a different economic conclusion, depending on the before-tax minimum ROR used. Analyses must always be done after-tax to be valid.) NPV analysis verifies the DCFROR results:

$$\text{NPV @ } i^* = 20\% = -56{,}571 + 23{,}878\overset{0.8333}{(P/F_{20\%,1})} + 22{,}198\overset{0.6944}{(P/F_{20\%,2})}$$

$$+ 20{,}999\overset{0.5787}{(P/F_{20\%,3})} + 25{,}497\overset{0.4823}{(P/F_{20\%,4})}$$

$$= +\$3{,}190$$

The incremental investment NPV result of + \$3,190 is greater than zero and satisfactory, again indicating slight economic advantage to accepting the new equipment. The + \$3,190 NPV is only about 5% of the \$60,000 equipment cost that generated it, therefore, the NPV is only slightly greater than zero. This indicates a slight advantage to accepting the incremental investment.

C and D) For cost analysis on a present, annual or future basis, we must convert the operating costs and depreciation deductions to after-tax cash flow, which accounts for the tax savings from using these items as tax deductions. Then we can calculate the after-tax present worth and annual worth costs for each alternative. Remember, it is assumed other income exists against which to use all deductions.

New Machine Cash Flows and Cost Analysis

Year	0	1	2	3	4
Revenue					
–Op. Costs		–10,000	–12,000	–14,000	–16,000
–Depreciation	–8,571	–14,694	–10,496	–7,497	–18,742*
Taxable Income	–8,571	–24,694	–22,496	–21,497	–34,742
–Tax @ 40%	3,429	9,878	8,998	8,599	13,897
Net Income	–5,143	–14,816	–13,497	–12,898	–20,845
+Depreciation	8,571	14,694	10,496	7,497	18,742
–Capital Cost	–60,000				
Cash Flow	–56,571	–122	–3,002	–5,401	–2,103

* Remaining book value write-off is combined with year 4 depreciation.

$$PW\ Cost_{NEW} = 56{,}571 + 122\overset{0.8333}{(P/F_{20\%,1})} + 3{,}002\overset{0.6944}{(P/F_{20\%,2})}$$

$$+ 5{,}401\overset{0.5787}{(P/F_{20\%,3})} + 2{,}103\overset{0.4823}{(P/F_{20\%,4})}$$

$$= \$62{,}898$$

$$AC_{NEW} = 62{,}898\overset{0.3863}{(A/P_{20\%,4})} = \$24{,}297$$

The sign convention used in both the present worth cost and annual cost calculations is that negative cash flow is equivalent to a positive cost and positive cash flow is equivalent to a negative cost.

Old Machine Cash Flows and Cost Analysis

Year	0	1	2	3	4
Revenue					
–Op. Costs		–40,000	–42,000	–44,000	–46,000
Taxable Income		–40,000	–42,000	–44,000	–46,000
–Tax @ 40%		16,000	16,800	17,600	18,400
Net Income		–24,000	–25,200	–26,400	–27,600
–Capital Costs					
Cash Flow	0	–24,000	–25,200	–26,400	–27,600

$$\text{PW Cost}_{\text{OLD}} = 24{,}000\overset{0.8333}{(P/F_{20\%,1})} + 25{,}200\overset{0.6944}{(P/F_{20\%,2})}$$

$$+\ 26{,}400\overset{0.5787}{(P/F_{20\%,3})} + 27{,}600\overset{0.4823}{(P/F_{20\%,4})} = \$66{,}088$$

$$\text{AC}_{\text{OLD}} = 66{,}088\overset{0.3863}{(A/P_{20\%,4})} = \$25{,}530$$

Since annual cost results are obtained by taking present worth cost results for both alternatives times the same capital recovery factor, clearly the results of either cost analysis must give the same economic conclusion. Comparison of the new and old equivalent annual costs or present worth costs gives the same economic decision reached with incremental DCFROR and NPV analysis. The results for all four methods show slight economic advantage to the new alternative. Notice that the difference between the present worth cost results gives the identical $3,190 incremental difference that we got with incremental NPV analysis, giving further indication and proof of the relationship between the different methods of analysis and why they all consistently give the same economic conclusion.

E) Break-even Cost Per Unit of Service Analysis

Instead of using incremental DCFROR, incremental NPV, present worth cost or equivalent annual cost analysis to evaluate economic difference between service-producing alternatives, it is possible to calculate the break-even price per unit of service produced by each service alternative to cover all costs at a specified after-tax DCFROR. The service alternative with the smallest cost per unit of service is the economic choice. To make this break-even price or cost per unit of service analysis, we build revenues into the cost analysis cash flow calculations. These revenues equal the annual service production multiplied by an unknown variable, x, that represents price per unit of service to give the investor the specified DCFROR on invested dollars. In the following cash flow calculations for the New and Old machines, notice the deductions and numerically known cash flow terms are identical to the cost analysis cash flow results. Only the revenue terms which are a function of the break-even cost per unit of service variable, x, are new and in addition to the cost analysis cash flow terms.

New Machine Break-even Price Per Unit of Service Cash Flows

Year	0	1	2	3	4
Revenue		1,000x	1,000x	1,000x	1,000x
–Op. Costs		–10,000	–12,000	–14,000	–16,000
–Depreciation	–8,571	–14,694	–10,496	–7,497	–18,742*
Taxable Income	–8,571	1,000x	1,000x	1,000x	1,000x
		–24,694	–22,496	–21,497	–34,742
–Tax @40%	+3,429	–400x	–400x	–400x	–400x
		+9,878	+8,998	+8,599	+13,897
Net Income	–5,143	600x	600x	600x	600x
		–14,816	–13,497	–12,898	–20,845
+Depreciation	+8,571	+14,694	+10,496	+7,497	+18,742
–Capital Cost	–60,000	—	—	—	—
Cash Flow	–56,571	600x	600x	600x	600x
		–122	–3,002	–5,401	–2,103

* Remaining book value write-off is combined with year 4 depreciation.

$$\text{PW Eq: } 0 = -56{,}571 + (600x - 122)\overset{0.8333}{(P/F_{20,1})} + (600x - 3{,}002)\overset{0.6944}{(P/F_{20,2})}$$

$$+ (600x - 5{,}401)\overset{0.5787}{(P/F_{20,3})} + (600x - 2{,}103)\overset{0.4823}{(P/F_{20,4})}$$

62,898 = 1,553.2x, so x = $40.50 per unit for new asset.

Observe that the $40.50 per unit break-even price can also be obtained more easily by taking the new machine present worth cost of \$62,898 and dividing it by present worth production multiplied by the quantity one minus the tax rate. This gives the new asset break-even price per unit of service:

$$\$62{,}898/[(1{,}000 \text{ units/yr})(\overset{2.5887}{P/A_{20,4}})(1 - 0.4)] = \$40.50 \text{ per unit.}$$

Once we have obtained present worth cost of service, it is much easier to divide it by present worth production multiplied by one minus the tax rate (which effectively may be thought of as after-tax present worth production) than it is to start from scratch and develop the year to year cash flow as a function of break-even price, x, as we presented.

For the old alternative with a present worth cost of service of \$66,088, the break-even price per unit of service:

$$\$66{,}088/[(1{,}000 \text{ units/yr})(\overset{2.5887}{P/A_{20,4}})(1 - 0.4)] = \$42.54 \text{ per unit.}$$

The ratio of break-even cost per unit of service for new compared to old is the same as the ratio of present worth cost of service for new compared to old or the ratio of annual cost of service for new compared to old, so the same economic conclusions must be reached with all of these criteria. In this case the conclusion is to select the new alternative.

An analysis situation that sometimes makes it advantageous to use cost per unit of service analysis instead of present worth cost, annual cost or incremental NPV or ROR analysis is when estimated service to be received from year to year changes with different assets due to considerations such as different maintenance and major overhaul schedules on equipment. Assuming the full service that can be provided by different alternatives is needed and can be utilized even though it is not the same from year to year for different alternatives, break-even price per unit of service produced is a convenient method of fairly comparing the alternatives without having to lay out the time diagrams for each alternative to give the same service per month or year as well as for the same common study period (evaluation life). When service differs from period to period with different alternatives, but the full service of any alternative can be utilized, it can be very difficult or physically impossible to make projections to compare fairly present worth cost or annual cost for providing the same service per period and cumulatively over the evaluation life with each alternative. In this situation, break-even cost per unit of service analysis gives a valid analysis technique that avoids the necessity of developing time diagrams for each alternative to give the same service each period as well as cumulatively over the evaluation life. However, *it is very important to note that break-even cost per unit of service analysis implicitly assumes that the full service of each alternative can be utilized each period (such as a year) even though service may be different with each alternative from period to period.*

10.2 Leasing Compared to Purchasing

Leasing represents yet another type of investment decision. Leasing allows an investor to obtain the use of an asset for a period of time without necessarily taking ownership of that asset. In the traditional sense of the word, leasing may be thought of as a rental agreement providing for the use of equipment, buildings, land, or virtually any type of asset over a specified period of time. Leasing has become a very popular alternative for a variety of reasons. Many individuals prefer leasing to purchasing a vehicle because it may free up cash to invest elsewhere or, allow them to drive a more expensive car when compared with purchasing. Leasing also allows people to drive a relatively new vehicle.

From the business side, its important to recognize that the issue of whether leasing is preferred to some form of purchasing is a secondary economic evaluation. In other words, whether or not leasing is preferred to purchasing does not create an economic justification for the use or need for the new asset in question. A leasing versus purchasing analysis simply suggests which alternative method of financing would be preferred to minimize the cost of acquiring the necessary asset for which service is required. The first analysis must be to justify the economic need for the asset. This need can be based on replacement of existing equipment, expansion of operations, new plant design or performance improvements. Once the decision justifying the new equipment is made then the economics of purchase versus leasing can be addressed.

From an evaluation viewpoint, there are several issues causing investors to evaluate the economics of leasing versus purchasing. These issues include economic, financial, and tax considerations similar to most service analyses. For investors with limited borrowing capacity, leasing may represent an opportunity to utilize an additional source of funds. As in the individual case previously mentioned, leasing may free up existing cash for home improvements, common stock or real estate investments, vacations, a college education, or simply eliminate the need to borrow money to purchase. From a corporate viewpoint, it might mean other corporate cash could be invested elsewhere in the company where it can generate income or create savings and provide at least the opportunity cost of capital return on investment. Or, it might mean the corporation does not need to borrow money to purchase. Besides the balance sheet, there are further implications related to tax and the impact on cash flow, as well as net income.

When assets are purchased, the investor gets to depreciate the assets over specified MACRS recovery periods. These depreciation deductions shelter income from taxation which lowers the investor's tax liability and improves cash flow. Further, any interest paid on borrowed money is often fully deductible, sheltering other income from tax. Under an operating lease, the lease payments can be deductible as an operating expense by the lessee. The lessor is the asset owner and gets the depreciation deduction. Another important consideration includes the impact on net income earnings for shareholder reporting purposes. For publicly traded companies, leasing may have either a positive or negative impact on shareholder earnings depending on the magnitude of the operating lease payments to be expensed and the corresponding depreciation and interest deductions for a given year if the same asset were purchased. Since shareholder reporting deductions are usually based on slower depreciation methods over longer lives than the equivalent tax deductions, this gives a much smaller deduction, or allocation of the cost, resulting in enhanced net income figures. Also, the type of lease you have is important in determining the relevant tax implications. Some of these differences are outlined in the following paragraphs. The economics will vary depending on several factors including the investor's ability to utilize deductions, the required service life of the lease and the equipment depreciation life.

Operating Versus Capital Leases

Leases are referred to as either an "operating lease" or "capital lease." A third category is often referred to as a "leveraged lease," which commonly involves a third party in the contractual arrangement. FASB Statement 13 outlines four conditions that, if at the inception of a lease, it meets one or more of these, the lease shall be classified as a capital lease by the lessee. Otherwise, it shall be treated as an operating lease. These conditions include the following:

1) Transference of ownership occurs by the end of the lease term.
2) Lease contains a bargain purchase option at its conclusion.
3) The lease term is 75% or more of the estimated economic life of the leased property. This criterion is waved if the asset lease begins in the final 25% of the estimated economic life of the asset.
4) The present value at the beginning of the lease term of the minimum lease payments (without regard to taxes, transaction fees, etc.) is equal to or exceeds 90% of the price for which the asset might be sold in an arms length transaction between unrelated parties. The lessee's discount rate used to compute present value is that rate representing their incremental cost of borrowing money. This option may be waved if the property is in the final 25% of its economic life at the beginning of the lease.

If one of the above conditions is recognized, the lessee must recognize both the asset (present value of payments) and the liability in the balance sheet. If the present value of the payments to be made exceeds the current fair market value of the asset, the market value is to be recognized as the current asset value. FASB Statement 13 offers much more detail with regard to the proper treatment of various lease terms and conditions. Operating lease payments are generally expensed by the lessee.

An ***"operating lease"*** *is a form of a rental agreement that provides for the use of an asset by the lessee (user) for a period of time specified in the lease agreement.* In this situation, the lessor (owner) retains the ownership of the equipment and may provide necessary maintenance and repairs on the leased asset, although this later condition is not essential and varies with each lease. Further, an operating lease may be canceled at any time by the lessee subject to the specific terms of the lease itself which may include penalty clauses for such action. *Operating lease payments are deductible in the full amount for tax purposes when these costs are incurred by the lessee. The lessor retains ownership and is therefore entitled to depreciate the asset over the MACRS specified life.* Since nothing is owned by the lessee, usually, any anticipated salvage value would not be relevant to the economic evaluation. However, there are exceptions here depending on the service period needed for the equipment and other considerations. For example, often times, from an individual viewpoint, if you are looking at leasing an automobile, there is a mileage penalty (say $0.10 per mile) imposed should you drive the vehicle more than say, 15,000 miles per year. The maximum mileage and the penalty per mile can vary with each manufacturer. This penalty is usually paid to the manufacturer, rather than the dealer. Often though, the penalty and other excess wear charges can be avoided if you were to exercise your option to purchase the vehicle at the end of the lease and then immediately sell the vehicle. Some dealers offer consignment programs to help avoid this penalty and in doing so, you might actually make or lose a little on the sale, depending on your vehicle, the used car market, etc.

*A **"capital lease"** (sometimes called a financial lease), differs from an operating lease in that it represents an alternative method of acquiring an asset, or effectively, it represents an installment loan to purchase the asset.* A capital lease cannot be canceled at will by the lessee since this form of lease is really an agreement to purchase the asset. Maintenance usually becomes the responsibility of the lessee who is taking title to the equipment. Under a capital lease, the lessee is no longer entitled to deduct the full lease payments when they are incurred. Instead, the lessee most often will depreciate the asset cost basis and is also allowed to deduct the imputed interest included in the lease payments since the lease payments are considered to be analogous to a financing or a loan mortgage payment. It is important to note that the depreciable cost basis in a capital lease is not necessarily the cash purchase price of the asset. Instead, the basis is determined by discounting the future capital lease payments to the present at a period interest rate that reflects the cost of borrowed funds over the period of time commensurate with the lease. This discounted depreciable cost basis may be greater or less than the cash purchase price. *The discount rate used to establish the depreciable cost basis is not the opportunity cost of capital. Instead, the applicable discount rate is specified to be reflective of current or prevailing equivalent borrowed money interest rates available in the marketplace. The IRS publishes a schedule of applicable rates each month for use in these calculations. These are semi-annually compounded nominal rates referred to as the "Applicable Federal Rate" (AFR).* There are short, medium and long term AFR's so you must select the one that best matches the lease term. If you are using annual evaluation periods you should convert the semi-annual period AFR to the equivalent effective annual rate using text Equation 2-9 developed in Section 2.3 in Chapter 2. If you can prove your cost of borrowing is less, the lower rate may be allowed. Remember, a lower interest rate will result in a larger cost basis and bigger depreciation deductions, sheltering more income from taxation. However, the imputed interest component of the capital lease payment is deductible in the period as well, so a smaller interest rate will reduce the allowable interest deduction.

"Leveraged leases" vary from operating and capital leases in that a third party becomes involved in the arrangement. Assume a company has a need for equipment in an ongoing operation. However, the lease terms offered by the equipment dealer are too expensive. Instead of negotiating directly with the equipment dealer, the company might go to a third party and negotiate a lease. The third party would then acquire the equipment and lease it back to the company. This acquisition may involve the third party going out and soliciting funds from other banks or lending institutions, often on a non-recourse basis, to finance 60% to 80% of the purchase price. The third party would put up the balance. The lending agencies recourse in the event of default would be through various liens, etc., on the actual equipment. Leveraged leases are used for equipment in all industries including aircraft, buildings and electric generating plants. These lease arrangements could be structured as either capital or operating leases.

Remember, lease payments, interest and depreciation only qualify as tax deductions when the asset is held or used for generating income. If a business application does not exist, the costs are certainly still relevant, but in most circumstances, no tax deductions are available. This means from an individual viewpoint, such analyses are often made on a before tax basis. IRS Publications 17 and 917 may be helpful in identifying specific tax questions if the asset in question is used for both personal and business applications.

Summary of the Economic Evaluation Differences Between an Operating Lease and a Capital Lease

Operating Lease (Rental Agreement)

- Lease payments may be expensed in their full amount when incurred.
- Ownership is usually optional and subject to a buyout option upon completion of the lease period. Therefore, salvage value may or may not be relevant depending on the service period being considered and other issues such as penalties regarding excessive use.
- No depreciation is taken by the lessee.

Capital Lease, (Installment Loan Purchase)

- Lease payments are not deductible in the full amount, when incurred.
- The imputed interest component of the lease payment is an allowable deduction. (The imputed interest rate is based on rates for prevailing borrowed funds published by the IRS at the time the lease is initiated.)

- The present value of the capital lease payments (discounted at the same imputed interest rate previously described) may be depreciated over the specified MACRS recovery period.
- Salvage value at the end of the service period is always relevant since the investor will own the asset at the end of the capital lease.

Some authors have advocated that the economic evaluation of whether to lease or purchase an asset is really a "financial" decision. As a financial evaluation, it is then argued that instead of using the opportunity cost of capital to reflect time value of money (the discount rate), an investor should use a discount rate reflecting the true cost of borrowed funds. This approach deviates from the basic premise of time value of money calculations where the appropriate compound interest rate, or discount rate, is representative of the lost return potential from investing available capital elsewhere (opportunity cost of capital). For example, suppose an individual had his or her wealth invested in various opportunities that yielded an average before-tax rate of return of 12.0%. The 12.0% might be from a combination of stocks, mutual funds, bonds, CD's, and real estate investments. Further, the investor is considering liquidating some of these investments and using the cash to purchase a new car, in comparison to leasing the same vehicle. If that person chooses to invest his or her own funds in purchasing the vehicle, the opportunity of earning 12.0% on that capital will be lost. The investor's opportunity cost of capital is what is relevant to the discounted cash flow economic evaluation. Even though the car could be purchased with, lets assume, 9.0% annual interest rate on borrowed money, in theory that same borrowed money could also be invested in those other 12.0% opportunities (neglecting risk and tax effects to simplify the analysis). It is opportunity cost of capital that is relevant here, not the financial cost of capital. For any business or corporation, the same consideration should apply.

Most companies do not have a line of credit to be used exclusively for the acquisition of equipment. However, if they did, the cost of borrowed funds would be the relevant discount rate for this specific evaluation situation. But for most companies, such a fund does not exist. In other words, the total borrowed funds that are available from any source, could be used to finance the expansion of existing income producing operations, to open new projects or to acquire equipment for existing projects. Assuming a finite amount of capital is available from all sources, the use of such funds to acquire equipment, means those same dollars can't be invested in other income producing alternatives. The opportunity cost of not realizing an economic return from investing available investment capital elsewhere is the relevant discount rate for all economic evaluations. Even if financing is considered to be unlimited, (which rarely if ever occurs due to perceived acceptable market or industry debt/equity ratios) making the opportunity cost of capital equal the financial cost of capital, it is not appropriate to use the cost of borrowed money as the discount rate. Many publicly traded companies use a financing cost equal to the weighted average cost of debt and common stock equity of capital from a financial model such as the Capital Asset Pricing Model (CAPM) which was introduced in Chapter 3. Generally, the cost of the equity component is far more costly than the cost of debt. With this in mind, why should the shareholders be asked to accept a lower return from capital tied up in the financing of equipment based on the cost of borrowed money? Even if you thought lease versus purchase implied a finance decision rather than an economic decision the weighted average cost of capital and not the cost of borrowed money would be the appropriate financing rate.

In another light, from an economic viewpoint, leasing compared to purchasing is analogous to replacement analysis in which case opportunity cost of capital has always been used. In replacement analysis, the decision to continue to provide service with old equipment that may have higher annual operating and maintenance costs is offset with the up front capital investment required for new equipment. This new equipment usually operates more efficiently with lower overall operating and maintenance costs over the necessary service period in comparison with older equipment. Leasing versus purchasing is directly analogous to capital intensive versus less capital intensive replacement analysis evaluations. Both involve an economic analysis, as well as a financing decision concerning the best way to provide a needed service.

Overall, whether to lease or purchase comes down to each individual investor's financial and tax situation and which alternative will provide the necessary service for the least cost over the desired service period. There are two alternative methods to evaluate such alternatives. First, a cost analysis on either a present, annual or future basis can be used. With this approach the objective is to minimize the cost of service between leasing or purchasing. Second, an incremental approach to assess the economics of the additional investment required for the more capital intensive purchase alternative over leasing can be used. Larger up front investments generally mean lower downstream operating costs and the reduction in such costs are the savings available to payoff the additional up front costs. Incremental evaluations typically rely on rate of return, net present value, or ratio analyses.

The following Example 10-2 illustrates present worth cost analysis for purchasing with cash or borrowed money compared to operating and capital leases. Then, Example 10-2A illustrates all the different analysis methods for purchasing for cash compared with an operating lease.

EXAMPLE 10-2 Leasing versus Purchasing an Asset

Consider a two year analysis of whether to purchase or lease an asset. The investor's effective income tax rate is 40% and other income exists against which to use deductions in the year they are generated. The asset qualifies as MACRS, five year depreciable property, assume the half year convention would apply when depreciation is applicable, with depreciation beginning in the year the asset is acquired. See the time diagrams for relevant purchasing and leasing data and determine whether the asset should be:

(A) Purchased with available cash:
(B) Leased under the following operating lease terms:
(C) Leased under the capital lease terms on diagrams:
(D) Purchased with 80% borrowed money at an effective annual interest rate of 9.0%, with two uniform and equal end of year one and two mortgage payments (MP).

For an after-tax, escalated dollar minimum rate of return of 15.0%, use present worth cost analysis to decide from an economic viewpoint, which alternative method of financing is preferred? Note: Monthly lease payments (LP) have been allocated to this annual period evaluation to correspond with yearly period discounting. Therefore, the first six months of payments are closer to time zero than the end of year one so they have been allocated to time zero. This leaves 12 months allocated to the end of year one, and six months at the end of year two. All values are in thousands of dollars; C = Capital Cost, L = Salvage, LP = Lease Payment, B = Borrowed Dollars, MP = Mortgage Payments.

A) Cash Purchase

C=350	—	L=150
0	1	2

B) Operating Lease

LP=60	LP=120	LP=60
0	1	2

C) Capital Lease

	0	1	2
	LP=100	LP=200	L=150 LP=100

D) Leveraged Purchase

	0	1	2
	B=280 C=350	MP=159	L=150 MP=159

Solution: This solution uses the income sign convention so all costs appear as negative values. All Values are in 000's.

A) Cash Purchase Cash Flow Analysis

Salvage			150.0
– Depreciation	–70.0	–112.0	–168.0
Taxable Income	–70.0	–112.0	–18.0
– Tax @ 40%	28.0	44.8	7.2
Net Income	–42.0	–67.2	–10.8
+ Depreciation	70.0	112.0	168.0
– Capital Cost	–350.0		
Cash Flow	–322.0	44.8	157.2

PW Cost @ 15.0% = –164.2

B) Operating Lease Cash Flow Analysis

Year	0	1	2
Salvage			0.0
– Lease Payments	–60.0	–120.0	–60.0
Taxable Income	–60.0	–120.0	–60.0
– Tax @ 40%	24.0	48.0	24.0
Net Income	–36.0	–72.0	–36.0
– Capital Cost	0.0		
Cash Flow	–36.0	–72.0	–36.0

PW Cost @ 15.0% = –125.8 (Least Cost Approach)

C) Capital Lease Cash Flow Analysis

* Imputed Interest Payments @ 9.0%

** PW Cost of Capital Lease Payments (Depreciable Basis):

PW Cost = 100 + 200($P/F_{9\%,1}$) + 100($P/F_{9\%,2}$) = \$368

	Payment	Interest	Principal	Balance
Yr 0	100	0	100	268
Yr 1	200	24	176	92
Yr 2	100	8	92	0

Year	0	1	2
Salvage			150.0
– Imputed Interest*		–24.0	–8.0
– Depreciation**	–74.0	–118.0	–176.0
Taxable Income	–74.0	–142.0	–34.0
– Tax @ 40%	29.6	56.8	13.6
Net Income	–44.4	–85.2	–20.4
+ Depreciation	74.0	118.0	176.0
– Capital Cost	–100.0	–176.0	–92.0
Cash Flow	–70.4	–143.2	63.6

PW Cost @ 15.0% = –146.8

D) 80% Borrowed Money, 20% Equity Cash Flow Analysis

Year	0	1	2
Salvage Revenue			150.0
– Interest		–25.2	–13.2
– Depreciation	–70.0	–112.0	–168.0
Taxable Income	–70.0	–137.2	–31.2
– Tax @ 40%	28.0	54.9	12.5
Net Income	–42.0	–82.3	–18.7
+ Depreciation	70.0	112.0	168.0
+ Loan Amount	280.0		
– Principal Payments		–134.0	–146.0
– Capital Cost	–350.0	0.0	0.0
Cash Flow	–42.0	–104.3	3.3

PW Cost @ 15.0% = –130.2

D) Loan Mortgage Payments = $280(A/P_{9\%,2}) = 159.2$

D) Loan Interest Amortization Schedule @ 9.0%

	Payment	Interest	Principal	Balance
Yr 0	0.0	0.0	0.0	280.0
Yr 1	159.2	25.2	134.0	146.0
Yr 2	159.2	13.2	146.0	0.0

The interest and principal payments were calculated by treating all payments as being discrete annual values.

EXAMPLE 10-2A Leasing Versus Purchase of Equipment

At present, a company is leasing equipment. Analysis is being made of whether to provide the service for the next 3 years by leasing with an operating lease or purchasing based on the following costs and salvage values:

Purchase	C=$10,000	OC=$1,000	OC=$1,500	OC=$2,000	L=$2,000
	0	1	2	3	

	Lease OC=$1,750	OC=$3,500	OC=$3,500	OC=$1,750	
Lease	—	OC=$1,000	OC=$1,500	OC=$2,000	L=0
	0	1	2	3	

Monthly lease payments in the first 6 months of year 1 are treated as time zero lease costs and lease payments in the last 6 months of year 3 are treated as year 3 costs, with full 12 month lease costs at years 1 and 2, to best account for the correct lease cost timing with annual periods. Operating costs are expensed for tax deduction purposes. Assume the equipment is purchased with cash (100% borrowed money financing is illustrated in Example 11-5) and the purchase cost will be depreciated starting in time zero using Modified ACRS rates for a 5 year life with the half-year convention. Assume other income exists against which to expense all operating costs in the years incurred. Use an effective tax rate of 40%. Which alternative is more economical for a minimum DCFROR of 15%?

A) Use incremental DCFROR analysis
B) Use incremental NPV analysis
C) Use present worth cost analysis
D) Use annual cost analysis

E) Use uniform annual equivalent revenue required analysis
F) Use break-even cost per unit of service analysis assuming 20,000 units are produced each year
G) Discuss the use of after-tax cost of borrowed money as the minimum discount rate in lease versus purchase analyses, instead of opprtunity cost of capital.

Solution: All values in Thousands of Dollars or Miles

C = Capital Costs, S = Savings, L = Salvage

Incremental Purchase – Lease	0	1	2	3
	C=10 S=1.75	S=3.5	S=3.5	S=1.75 L=2.0

Negative incremental operating costs are the same as positive savings and must be converted to cash flow each year. Do not net incremental operating costs and capital costs together at time zero since the incremental capital cost of 10 is depreciable while the incremental savings of 1.75 is equivalent to revenue that must be converted to cash flow. Only costs and revenues handled in the same manner for tax purposes may be netted together in after-tax analyses.

Incremental Cash Flows

Year	0	1	2	3
Revenue	1.75	3.50	3.50	3.75
–Depreciation	–2.00	–3.20	–1.92	–2.88*
Taxable Income	–0.25	0.30	1.58	0.87
–Tax @ 40%	0.10	–0.12	–0.63	–0.35
Net Income	–0.15	0.18	0.95	0.52
+Depreciation	2.00	3.20	1.92	2.88
–Capital Costs	–10.00			
Cash Flow	–8.15	3.38	2.87	3.40

* The book value write-off and year 3 depreciation are combined.

A) Incremental DCFROR Analysis

PW Eq: $0 = -8.15 + 3.38(P/F_{i,1}) + 2.87(P/F_{i,2}) + 3.40(P/F_{i,3})$

i = Incremental DCFROR = 8.95% by trial and error which is less than the minimum rate of return of 15%, so accept the lease alternative.

B) Incremental NPV Analysis

$$\text{Incremental NPV} = -8.15 + 3.38\overset{0.8696}{(P/F_{15\%,1})} + 2.87\overset{0.7561}{(P/F_{15\%,2})} + 3.40\overset{0.6575}{(P/F_{15\%,3})}$$

= –.80 which is less than 0 so reject purchase and accept the leasing alternative

Before considering the cost analyses to these two alternatives, look back at the before-tax incremental time diagram in this example and note the importance of recognizing the unique tax implications of the two costs in time zero. This analysis is based on the need to spend $10 thousand on depreciable equipment in order to save $1.75 thousand in time zero alone. The incremental analysis is not based on an incremental cost of $8.25 thousand creating subsequent savings. In all after-tax evaluations, it is very easy to incorrectly mix different before-tax expenditures. To avoid this type of error, investors might consider first determining the after-tax cost of each alternative and then making the incremental calculations from the resulting after-tax cash flows for each scenario as is addressed in the following:

C and D) Present Worth and Annual Worth Cost Analysis

Purchase Cash Flows

Year	0	1	2	3
Revenue				2.00
–Op. Costs		–1.00	–1.50	–2.00
–Depreciation	–2.00	–3.20	–1.92	–2.88
Taxable Income	–2.00	–4.20	–3.42	–2.88
–Tax @ 40%	0.80	1.68	1.37	1.15
Net Income	–1.20	–2.52	–2.05	–1.73
+Depreciation	2.00	3.20	1.92	2.88
–Capital Costs	–10.00			
Cash Flow	–9.20	0.68	–0.13	1.15

Lease Cash Flows

Year	0	1	2	3
Revenue				
–Op. Costs	–1.75	–4.50	–5.00	–3.75
Taxable Income	–1.75	–4.50	–5.00	–3.75
–Tax @ 40%	0.70	1.80	2.00	1.50
Net Income	–1.05	–2.70	–3.00	–2.25
–Capital Costs				
Cash Flow	–1.05	–2.70	–3.00	–2.25

$$\text{PW Purchase} = 9.20 - 0.68\overset{0.8696}{(P/F_{15\%,1})} + 0.13\overset{0.7561}{(P/F_{15\%,2})} - 1.15\overset{0.6575}{(P/F_{15\%,3})} = 7.95$$

$$\text{PW Lease} = 1.05 + 2.70\overset{0.8696}{(P/F_{15\%,1})} + 3.00\overset{0.7561}{(P/F_{15\%,2})} + 2.25\overset{0.6575}{(P/F_{15\%,3})} = 7.15$$

Select Lease to minimize cost of service. Notice that using an income sign convention where costs are negative and revenues are positive, present worth purchase minus present worth lease equals the incremental NPV of –0.80, so reject purchasing and select leasing. Remember the NPV sign convention is opposite the present worth cost sign convention.

Incremental NPV = –7.95 – (–7.15) = –0.80

$\text{AC Purchase} = 7.95(A/P_{15\%,3}) = 3.48$

$\text{AC Lease} = 7.15(A/P_{15\%,3}) = 3.13$

Select Lease to minimize cost of service per period.

Below, the cost analysis after-tax cash flows are summarized in order to revisit the incremental analysis. As previously illustrated, it is valid to derive incremental after-tax cash flows from the before-tax cost and savings, but the following methodology eliminates the possibility of incorrectly mixing different before-tax related capital expenditures that are depreciable and operating cost savings that would represent a component of taxable income.

Year	0	1	2	3
Purchase ATCF	–9.20	0.68	–0.13	1.15
Lease ATCF	–1.05	–2.70	–3.00	–2.25
Incremental ATCF	–8.15	3.38	2.87	3.40

These are the same incremental cash flows calculated earlier and must yield the same incremental economic conclusions described in cases A and B but this approach avoids the possibility of incorrectly handling the incremental tax issues.

E) Uniform Annual Equivalent Revenue Required (UAERR)

Since equivalent annual cost represents the after-tax annual cost each year necessary to provide service, UAERR represents the annual before-tax revenue necessary to cover the equivalent annual after-tax cost. The income tax adjustment is a simple calculation as shown below.

UAERR = Annual Cost / (1 - tax rate)

UAERR Purchase = 3.48/(1-0.4) = 5.80

UAERR Lease = 3.13/(1-0.4) = 5.21

Select leasing to minimize required break-even revenue.

F) Break-even Cost Per Unit Analysis

Similar to the handling of operating and lease costs, assume the 20,000 units per year are distributed uniformly during each year. The 10,000 units the first and last 6 month periods are treated as time 0 and year 3 values with 20,000 units at each of years 1 and 2.

Break-even Purchase Cost Per Unit Produced

= PW Cost Purchase Cost/[(PW Units)(1 - tax rate)]

$$= 7.95/[\{10 + 20\overset{1.626}{(P/A_{15,2})} + 10\overset{.6575}{(P/F_{15,3})}\}(1 - .4)]$$

= 7.95/[(49.095)(1 - .4)] = $0.27 per unit

Break-even Lease Cost Per Unit Produced

$$= 7.15/[\{10 + 20\overset{1.626}{(P/A_{15,2})} + 10\overset{.6575}{(P/F_{15,3})}\}(1 - .4)]$$

= 7.15/[(49.095)(1 - .4)] = $0.24 per unit

Select leasing with the smaller cost per unit produced.

G) Some companies view lease versus purchase investment decisions as finance decisions concerning whether to borrow money to purchase instead of leasing rather than as economic decisions. Therefore, the after-tax cost of borrowed money rather than opportunity cost of capital is used as the minimum discount rate. If this finance decision viewpoint is taken, it is very important to understand that the investor implicitly is assuming that a unique line of credit exists to borrow money to purchase assets instead of leasing and that this borrowing to purchase will have no effect on capital investment budget dollars now or in the future. In other words, borrowing today to purchase instead of lease will not affect budget dollars available to invest elsewhere at the opportunity cost of capital. Whether you agree or disagree with the validity of that assumption, implicitly that is the assumption being made. If the after-tax cost of borrowed money is used as the minimum discount rate, it assumes that you can borrow to purchase an asset instead of leasing, but you could not borrow that money to invest in other general investments.

10.3 Sunk Costs and Opportunity Costs Related to Replacement

As discussed earlier in section 9.4 sunk costs are not relevant to analyses since such costs occurred in the past and cannot be altered by present or future action. The concept that past costs are not relevant to investment evaluation studies is called the "sunk cost" concept. If you buy equipment for $3000 and use it two or three weeks before deciding that you do not like it and want to sell it you may find that $2000 is the best used equipment sales price that you can get. The $1000 loss is a sunk cost that resulted from a poor past decision that cannot be altered by present or future action. Economic decisions related to future action should not be permitted to be affected by sunk costs except for the remaining values and tax effects from the sunk costs, which are opportunity cost considerations. Examples 10-3 and 10-4 illustrate these considerations, but the following paragraphs present discussion related to the concepts.

Two considerations often confusing to replacement analysts are (1) proper handling of sunk costs, and (2) proper handling of opportunity costs (trade-in or secondhand sale values). Correct handling of these items is necessary for correct replacement analysis. Sunk costs must not be considered in evaluating expected future costs of one alternative versus another. Only sale value and tax considerations that remain to be realized from sunk costs should have an effect on economic analyses involving sunk costs. This means that actual value should be used in economic analyses rather than book value whenever actual values can be obtained. Also, actual tax considerations such as tax depreciation should always be used. If a machine originally costing $5,000 has been depreciated to a book value of $3,000 and has a current salvage value of $2,000 replacement analysis of this machine must be based on the current value of $2,000 because the difference of $1,000 between book value of $3,000 and actual value of $2,000 is a sunk cost that future action will not retrieve. However, depreciation for the analysis should be based on the $3,000 book value. A tax write-off benefit is the only potential value of a sunk cost other than salvage value. The owner has the choice of keeping the machine or holding $2,000 cash plus the potential tax write-off benefit, not $3,000 cash equal to book value.

Trade-in value involves two sources of confusion. These occur primarily because it is possible to make valid replacement analysis either working with costs and revenues handled from the accounting "receipts and disbursements" viewpoint or from the actual value viewpoint. It will be discussed and illustrated that either approach is valid as long as they are not mixed for different assets. First, from the accounting viewpoint, since no receipts or disbursements are necessary if an old asset is kept, nothing is paid out and analysts value the old asset at zero value for evaluation purposes. From the standpoint of calculating actual cost of service with the old asset, the asset has an actual cash value (true trade-in value or second hand market value) and that value should be used in a cost analysis, rather than zero. An example further illustrating the accountant's viewpoint using zero present value for trade-in assets will be discussed later in this chapter. Second, the trade-in value used must be the actual value of the used asset and not an artificially inflated trade-in price. If the true present value of a used asset is not used in the economic evaluation of that asset, then the economic evaluation criterion used will not reflect correctly the actual cost of using the asset for some projected future period of time.

To handle sunk costs and trade-in values correctly in replacement analyses it has been found that taking the "outsider viewpoint" helps clear the confusion regarding sunk costs and trade-in values. If you own an asset originally worth \$5,000, but now depreciated to \$3,000 with a present trade-in salvage value of \$2,000, an outsider can see that analysis of the old asset should be based on its actual \$2,000 value because that is what it is now worth regardless of whether you paid more or less for it and regardless of the amount of depreciation you may have already taken on it. After-tax analysis, however, should account for the tax deduction benefit from the full \$3,000 book value as a write-off if the old equipment is sold or traded, or as depreciation deductions if the old equipment is kept. It is also easy for the outsider to see that from an actual value analysis viewpoint the actual \$2,000 value should not be considered to be zero in the analysis just because no accounting transactions are made if the old asset is kept. The outsider can see that the new asset analysis should be based on actual cash value and not a fictitious trade-in value if you want to evaluate the true cost of operating the new asset for some future period of time. You may find it helpful to think in terms of selling the old asset for \$2,000 with an option to cancel the sale within 24 hours and then considering the following two alternatives: (1) apply the \$2,000 to repurchase the old asset; (2) apply the \$2,000 to the purchase price of a new asset. From an outsiders viewpoint you can see that the \$2,000 value of the present asset (net salvage value) is really available for use by either alternative. In other words, you incur an "opportunity cost" of \$2,000 if you keep the old equipment instead of selling it and having \$2,000 cash.

The following Examples, 10-3, 10-4 and 10-5, illustrate the handling of sunk costs and opportunity costs in service analysis evaluations.

EXAMPLE 10-3 Replacement Involving Sunk Cost and Opportunity Cost

Equipment that cost $7,000 two years ago has been depreciated to its present book value of $4,900 using straight line depreciation for a 5 year life with a half year 1 deduction. The present net salvage value of equipment is $3,500 (sale value minus removal costs) and operating costs for the next four years for which the equipment is needed are expected to be $3,000, $3,300, $3,600 and $3,900 respectively. The old equipment would have zero salvage value in four years. Consideration is being given to selling the existing old equipment and replacing it with new equipment that costs $9,000 and would be depreciated over seven years using the modified ACRS depreciation starting in year 1 with the half year convention. A write-off on remaining book value would be taken at the end of year four when the asset is sold for an estimated salvage value of zero. Operating costs with the new equipment are estimated to be $1,000, $1,100, $1,200 and $1,300 per year respectively over the next four years. Assume a 40% effective income tax rate and that other income exists against which to use tax deductions in any year. Also assume that the alternatives provide the same service. Use present worth cost analysis to compare the alternatives for a minimum escalated dollar DCFROR of 15%.

Solution:

When sunk costs and trade-in values are involved in economic analyses, as they usually are in replacement analyses, there are three different, equivalent, equally valid ways of handling the year 0 dollar values for correct economic analysis results. These three ways will be called Cases 1, 2 and 3.

	Actual Value Viewpoints		Accounting Viewpoint
	CASE 1	CASE 2	CASE 3
OLD	C=3500+560 tax saving	C=3500	C=0
	0 Book Value = 4900	0 Book Value = 4900	0 Book Value = 4900
NEW	C=9000	C=9000–560 tax saving	C=9000–560–3500=4940
	0 Book Value = 9000	0 Book Value = 9000	0 Book Value = 9000

The $7,000 cost of the old asset 2 years ago is a sunk cost that does not affect the analysis except for the tax effects of remaining tax book value of $4,900 yet to be deducted by depreciation. The $560 year 0 tax saving if the old asset is sold results because the sale value is proposed to be $1,400 less than the remaining tax book value ($3,500 sale value - $4,900 book value). This $1,400 loss would be written off against other income saving $560 in tax for the stated 40% effective income tax rate.

In Case 1, which represents "actual values", the $3,500 sale value and $560 tax savings from the write-off if the old asset is sold are treated as opportunity costs incurred by the owner if the old asset is kept instead of being sold. If the owner passes up the opportunity to sell the old asset in order to keep and use it he forgoes receiving the $4,060 cumulative sale and tax benefits, so this is a real cost, commonly called an "opportunity cost" for keeping and using the old equipment.

Case 2 is a variation of Case 1 based on handling the $560 tax saving as a reduction in the net cost of the new alternative instead of an additional opportunity cost associated with the old asset. Subtracting $560 from both Case 1 alternatives at year 0 gives Case 2.

Case 3 commonly is called the "accounting viewpoint" and it represents the net inflows and outflows of money (receipts and disbursements) if the old or new assets are utilized.

Notice the incremental New-Old year 0 cost is $4,940 for all cases, so incremental DCFROR, NPV or PVR analysis results would be identical for Cases 1, 2 and 3. With cost analysis, since both alternatives differ by the same values at year 0 as you go from Case 1, to Case 2, to Case 3, the alternatives are ranked the same with present, annual or future cost results for any of the 3 cases. Since the year 1 through 4 operating cost, depreciation, and salvage values are exactly the same for all cases, changing the year 0 cost by the same amount of money for both the Old and New alternatives must give the same economic conclusions for all cases. This is illustrated in the following Old versus New present worth costs analyses for the Case 1, 2, and 3 approaches to handling opportunity cost. In industry practice, about half of evaluation analysts use Case 1 or 2 "actual value" approaches to handle opportunity cost, and the other half use the Case 3 "accounting" viewpoint.

Old Machine Cash Flows

Case	1	2	3				
Year	0	0	0	1	2	3	4
Revenue							
–Op. Costs				–3.0	–3.3	–3.6	–3.9
–Depreciation				–1.4	–1.4	–1.4	–0.7
Taxable Income				–4.4	–4.7	–5.0	–4.6
–Tax @ 40%				1.8	1.9	2.0	1.8
Net Income				–2.6	–2.8	–3.0	–2.8
+Depreciation				1.4	1.4	1.4	0.7
–Capital Costs	–4.1	–3.5					
Cash Flow	–4.1	–3.5	0.0	–1.2	–1.4	–1.6	–2.1

$$\text{PW Cost, Case 1} = 4.1 + 1.2\overset{0.8696}{(P/F_{15\%,1})} + 1.4\overset{0.7561}{(P/F_{15\%,2})}$$

$$+ 1.6\overset{0.6575}{(P/F_{15\%,3})} + 2.1\overset{0.5718}{(P/F_{15\%,4})} = 8.45$$

PW Cost, Case 2 = 7.85, PW Cost, Case 3 = 4.35

New Machine Cash Flows

Case	1	2	3				
Year	0	0	0	1	2	3	4
Revenue							
–Op. Costs				–1.0	–1.1	–1.2	–1.3
–Depreciation				–1.3	–2.2	–1.6	–3.9*
Taxable Income				–2.3	–3.3	–2.8	–5.2
–Tax @ 40%				0.9	1.3	1.1	2.1
Net Income				–1.4	–2.0	–1.7	–3.1
+Depreciation				1.3	2.2	1.6	3.9
–Capital Costs	–9.0	–8.4	–4.9				
Cash Flow	–9.0	–8.4	–4.9	–0.1	0.2	–0.1	0.8

* The book value write-off and year 4 depreciations are combined.

$$\text{PW Cost, Case 1} = 9.0 + 0.1\overset{0.8696}{(P/F_{15\%,1})} - 0.2\overset{0.7561}{(P/F_{15\%,2})}$$

$$+ 0.1\overset{0.6575}{(P/F_{15\%,3})} - 0.8\overset{0.5787}{(P/F_{15\%,4})} = 8.54$$

PW Cost, Case 2 = 7.94, PW Cost, Case 3 = 4.44

The very slight present worth cost advantage of \$90 is favorable to the "Old" alternative for all three cases.

If you increase the minimum DCFROR in this analysis or any other comparison of either service producing or income producing alternatives, the more capital intensive alternative (New in this analysis) is always hurt more relative to the less capital intensive alternative with the smaller year 0 cost. To illustrate, change i^* to 25% from 15% for this analysis and note how Case 1 present worth costs change.

$$\text{PW Cost}_{OLD}\text{, Case 1} = 4.1 + 1.2\overset{0.8000}{(P/F_{25\%,1})} + 1.4\overset{0.6400}{(P/F_{25\%,2})}$$

$$+ 1.6\overset{0.5120}{(P/F_{25\%,3})} + 2.1\overset{0.4096}{(P/F_{25\%,4})} = 7.63$$

$$\text{PW Cost}_{NEW}\text{, Case 1} = 9.0 + 0.1\overset{0.8000}{(P/F_{25\%,1})} - 0.2\overset{0.6400}{(P/F_{25\%,2})}$$

$$+ 0.1\overset{0.5120}{(P/F_{25\%,3})} - 0.8\overset{0.4096}{(P/F_{25\%,4})} = 8.67$$

Notice now that the present worth cost advantage of the old equipment compared to the new has spread from \$90 to \$1,040.

10.4 Evaluation of Alternatives that Provide Different Service

When different service producing alternatives are projected to give different service per day, week or year (or other periods), it is necessary to get the alternatives on a common service-producing basis per period (as well as for a common evaluation life) before comparing the economics of the alternatives. The need to do this is tied to the assumption that extra service produced by an alternative (or alternatives) can be utilized. If the extra service cannot be utilized, the alternatives must be compared economically using the project costs as they are stated without adjustment, which has been the basis for all service-producing analyses done previously in the text.

However, if the extra service can be utilized, get alternatives that provide different service on a common service producing basis using one of the following approaches:

1) Add additional costs to the less productive alternative or alternatives to get service produced equivalent to the most productive alternative. Adjust all values including capital costs, operating costs, major repairs and salvage values.

2) Compare the less productive alternative or alternatives costs with the appropriate fraction of the more productive alternative costs. Adjust all values including capital costs, operating costs, major repairs and salvage values.

3) Charge the less productive alternative with a lost productivity opportunity cost from lower production or lower quality product that will be incurred if the less productive alternative is used. This opportunity cost represents projected lost or deferred profits.

While few people would neglect to account for different capacities of different sized assets such as haul trucks, compressors, or heat exchangers in economic analyses, the same people will often forget to account for differences in operating hours of service or number of units to be produced per period with the old assets compared to new. The following example relates to comparison of service-producing assets with the potential to provide different service.

EXAMPLE 10-4 Analysis of Alternatives That Provide Different Service

Three existing two year old machines have an open market sale or trade-in value of $65,000 each and remaining tax book value of $25,000 each. Replacement of the three existing machines with two new machines that each give 150% of the productivity per machine being realized with each old machine is being considered. The new machines would cost $120,000 each. The service of either the old or new machines is needed for the next four years so a four year evaluation life should be used. If the old machines are kept, remaining book value will be depreciated straight line at years 1 and 2. Salvage value of the old machines in four years from now is estimated to be zero but the machines are considered to be operable for four more years. Escalated dollar operating costs per machine for the old machines are projected to be $30,000 in year one, $35,000 in year two, $40,000 in year three and $45,000 in year four. Operating cost per machine for new machines is to be $25,000 in year one, $30,000 in year two, $35,000 in year three and $40,000 in year four.

The new machines would be depreciated using modified ACRS 7-year life depreciation starting in year 1 with the half-year convention. Salvage value is estimated to be $30,000 per machine in year four and taxable gain is taxed as ordinary income. The effective federal plus state tax rate is 40%. Other income exists against which to use all tax deductions in the year incurred. The minimum DCFROR is 15%. Evaluate whether the old machines should be replaced using present worth cost analysis. Then calculate break-even cost per unit of service for the old and new machines. Assume the old machines will give 2000 hours of service each year in years 1 through 4, and the new machine will give 3000 hours of service each year in years 1 through 4.

Solution: All Values in Thousands of Dollars or Hours

	Actual Value Viewpoints		Accounting Viewpoint
	CASE 1	CASE 2	CASE 3
"3"	C=195-48 tax if sold	C=195	C=0
OLD	0 Book Value = 75	0 Book Value = 75	0 Book Value = 75
"2"	C=240	C=240+48 tax if sold	C=240+48-195=93
NEW	0 Book Value = 240	0 Book Value = 240	0 Book Value = 240

The $48 tax if the 3 old assets are sold is based on taxing the $120 capital gain ($195 sale value - $75 book value) as ordinary income (taxed at the effective income tax rate of 40%).

The year 1 to 4 cash flow calculations for the OLD and NEW alternative are the same for each case. Only the year 0 costs differ from case to case. Also, notice the incremental NEW-OLD cost of $93 is identical for each case.

3 Old Machine Cash Flows

Year	(Case 1) 0	1	2	3	4
Revenue					
–Op. Costs		–90	–105	–120	–135
–Depreciation		–37.5	–37.5		
Taxable Income		–127.5	–142.5	–120	–135
–Tax @ 40%		51	57	48	54
Net Income		–76.5	–85.5	–72	–81
+Depreciation		37.5	37.5		
–Capital Costs	–147				
Cash Flow	–147	–39	–48	–72	–81

$$\text{Case 1 PW Cost}_{OLD} = 147 + 39\overset{0.8696}{(P/F_{15\%,1})} + 48\overset{0.7561}{(P/F_{15\%,2})}$$

$$+ 72\overset{0.6575}{(P/F_{15\%,3})} + 81\overset{0.5718}{(P/F_{15\%,4})} = \$310.8$$

$$\text{Case 2 PW Cost}_{OLD} = \text{Case 1 PW Cost}_{OLD} + 48 = \$358.8$$

$$\text{Case 3 PW Cost}_{OLD} = \text{Case 1 PW Cost}_{OLD} - 147 = \$163.8$$

2 New Machine Cash Flows

Year	(Case 1) 0	1	2	3	4
Revenue					60
–Op. Costs		–50	–60	–70	–80
–Depreciation		–34	–59	–42	–105
Taxable Income		–84	–119	–112	–125
–Tax @ 40%		34	48	45	50
Net Income		–50	–71	–67	–75
+Depreciation		34	59	42	105
–Capital Costs	–240				
Cash Flow	–240	–16	–12	–25	30

$$\text{Case 1 PW Cost}_{NEW} = 240 + 16(\overset{0.8696}{P/F_{15\%,1}}) + 12(\overset{0.7561}{P/F_{15\%,2}})$$

$$+ 25(\overset{0.6575}{P/F_{15\%,3}}) - 30(\overset{0.5718}{P/F_{15\%,4}}) = \$262.3$$

$$\text{Case 2 PW Cost}_{NEW} = \text{Case 1 PW Cost}_{NEW} + 48 = \$310.3$$

$$\text{Case 3 PW Cost}_{NEW} = \text{Case 1 PW Cost}_{NEW} - 147 = \$115.3$$

Providing the service with the NEW machines has a $48,500 present worth cost advantage for all cases, so select NEW. Notice that if you compared 1.5 old assets to 1 new asset, the advantage is similarly favorable to the new, but by $24,250 (a factor of two difference). Similar results occur for comparison of 1 old asset with 2/3 of a new asset.

Note that while the accounting approach leads to correct economic decisions, it does not give true equivalent annual cost. The accounting approach should not be used if you want to know what it actually costs to operate equipment in addition to obtaining valid economic replacement decisions because it combines trade-in financing with cost economics.

Break-even Cost Per Unit of Service Analysis

Use Case 1 actual value present worth cost results for "3 old machines" or "2 new machines" alternatives divided by after-tax present worth service units for 6000 hours of service per year. *Only the Case 1 cost analysis results give actual after-tax cost of service.* The Case 2 and 3 results are only useful for comparing relative differences between the alternatives.

"Old" Break-even Cost Per Hour

$$= 310.8/[(6.0)(\overset{2.855}{P/A_{15,4}})(1 - 0.4 \text{ tax rate})] = \$30.24 \text{ per hour}$$

"New" Break-even Cost Per Hour

$$= 262.3/[(6.0)(\overset{2.855}{P/A_{15,4}})(1 - 0.4 \text{ tax rate})] = \$25.52 \text{ per hour}$$

EXAMPLE 10-5 Exchange of Old Asset Versus Separate Sale

The solutions of Example 10-4 just presented (and all other replacement analysis solutions presented in this chapter) are all based on separate sale of the old machines and separate purchase of the new machines. *If old assets actually are traded in on new assets rather than being sold separately, existing tax law permits the investor to choose either the separate sale/separate purchase handling of tax considerations or adjustment of the book value of new assets to account for the gain or loss from trade-in of the old assets* as follows for the Example 10-4 assets.

There are only two different cases for laying out the old and new alternative time diagrams for a valid trade-in exchange analysis as shown in the solution. The Case 1 situation does not exist for exchange economics of the "Old" assets because there is no tax to be paid from selling the "Old". The Case 2 and Case 3 analysis of the "Old" assets is the same for exchange as in separate sale, separate purchase in Example 10-4.

Solution:

	CASE 2 (Actual Value Viewpoint)	CASE 3 (Accounting Viewpoint)
"3"	C=195	C=0
OLD	0 Book Value = 75	0 Book Value = 75
"2"	C=240	C=240–195=45
NEW	0 Book Value = 240-195+75=120	0 Book Value = 240-195+75=120

The "OLD" present worth costs for Cases 2 and 3 are identical to Cases 2 and 3 present worth cost "OLD" for Example 10-4. The "NEW" cash flows for Cases 2 and 3 are based on depreciating the initial new cost reduced by trade-in gain from "OLD".

Exchange of assets makes the "NEW" assets relatively more desirable than the "OLD" in comparison with separate sale/separate purchase. This is because exchanging eliminates immediate tax on gain from sale of the "OLD" which increases the opportunity cost of keeping the "OLD" asset rather than disposing of it by an exchange for "NEW".

"Exchange" Analysis of 3 Old for 2 New Machines

Year	0	1	2	3	4
Revenue					60
–Op. Costs		–50	–60	–70	–80
–Depreciation		–17	–29	–21	–52
Taxable Income		–67	–89	–91	–72
–Tax @ 40%		27	36	36	29
Net Income		–40	–53	–55	–43
+Depreciation		17	29	21	52
–Capital Costs	–240				
Cash Flow	–240	–23	–24	–34	9

$$\text{Case 2 PWCost}_{NEW} = 240 + 23\overset{0.8696}{(P/F_{15\%,1})} + 24\overset{0.7561}{(P/F_{15\%,2})}$$

$$+ 34\overset{0.6575}{(P/F_{15\%,3})} - 9\overset{0.5718}{(P/F_{15\%,4})} = \$295.4$$

$$\text{Case 3 PWCost}_{NEW} = \text{Case 2 PWCost}_{NEW} - 195 = \$100.4$$

Comparison of Case 2 present worth cost "NEW" of $295.4 to equivalent present worth cost "OLD" Case 2 of $358.8 gives a $63.4 present worth cost advantage to selecting "NEW". The same result is obtained comparing Case 3 present worth cost "NEW" of $100.4 to $163.8 present worth cost of "OLD".

10.5 Unequal Life Service Producing Alternatives

In Chapter 3, it was emphasized that to compare the economic differences between service producing alternatives with unequal lives you must determine a common study period for all alternatives before you can make the analysis. This is true after-tax as well as before-tax and is illustrated in Example 10-6, which is the after-tax analysis of the same alternatives analyzed on a before-tax basis in Example 3-29 in Chapter 3.

EXAMPLE 10-6 Comparison of Unequal Life Alternatives that Provide the Same Service

Three alternative processing methods "A", "B" and "C" with costs, salvage values and lives given on the time diagrams are being considered to carry out a processing operation for the next three years. It is expected that the process will not be needed after three years. A major repair costing $3,000 at the end of year two would extend the life alternative "A" through year three with a third year operating cost of $2,500 and the salvage equal to $1,000 at the end of year three instead of year two. The salvage of alternative "B" is estimated to be $3,000 at the end of year three and the salvage of alternative "C" is estimated to be $7,000 at the end of year three. For a minimum DCFROR of 15%, which alternative is economically best? Use after-tax equivalent annual cost analysis. Assume MACRS depreciation for a seven year life for all alternatives starting in year 0 with the half-year convention. Remaining book value is deducted against other income at the end of the evaluation lives. Assume sufficient income exists against which to use all deductions in the year incurred. The effective tax rate is 40%. Assume the $3,000 major repair at the end of year two for alternative "A" is expensed at the end of year two as an operating cost. Compare the alternatives for a three year evaluation life.

A)	C=$6,000	OC=$1,500	OC=$2,000 L=$1,000				
	0	1	2				
B)	C=$10,000	OC=$1,000	OC=$1,400	OC=$1,800	OC=$2,200 L=$2,000		
	0	1	2	3	4		
C)	C=$14,000	OC=$500	OC=$600	OC=$700	OC=$800	OC=$900 L=$5,000	
	0	1	2	3	4	5	

Solution: Diagrams For a 3 Year Evaluation Life

A)	C=$6,000	OC=$1,500	C=$3,000 OC=$2,000	OC=$2,500	L=$1,000
	0	1	2	3	
B)	C=$10,000	OC=$1,000	OC=$1,400	OC=$1,800	L=$3,000
	0	1	2	3	
C)	C=$14,000	OC=$500	OC=$600	OC=$700	L=$7,000
	0	1	2	3	

Case A Cash Flows

Year	0	1	2	3
Revenue				1,000
–Op. Costs		–1,500	–5,000	–2,500
–Depreciation	–857	–1,469	–1,050	–2,624*
Taxable Income	–857	–2,969	6,050	–4,124
–Tax @ 40%	343	1,188	2,420	1,650
Net Income	–514	–1,782	–3,630	–2,474
+Depreciation	857	1,469	1,050	2,624
–Capital Costs	–6,000			
Cash Flow	–5,657	–312	–2,580	150

* Book value write-off combined with year 3 depreciation

$$AC_A = [5{,}657 + 312\overset{0.8696}{(P/F_{15,1})} + 2{,}580\overset{0.7561}{(P/F_{15,2})}$$

$$- 150\overset{0.6575}{(P/F_{15,3})}]\overset{0.43798}{(A/P_{15,3})}$$

$$= \$3{,}408$$

Case B Cash Flows

Year	0	1	2	3
Revenue				3,000
–Op. Costs		–1,000	–1,400	–1,800
–Depreciation	–1,429	–2,449	–1,749	–4,373*
Taxable Income	–1,429	–3,449	–3,149	–3,173
–Tax @ 40%	571	1,380	1,260	1,269
Net Income	–857	–2,069	–1,890	–1,904
+Depreciation	1,429	2,449	1,749	4,373
–Capital Costs	–10,000			
Cash Flow	–9,429	380	–140	2,469

* Book value write-off combined with year 3 depreciation.

$$AC_B = \{9{,}429 - 380\overset{0.8696}{(P/F_{15,1})} + 140\overset{0.7561}{(P/F_{15,2})}$$

$$- 2{,}469\overset{0.6575}{(P/F_{15,3})}\}\overset{0.43798}{(A/P_{15,3})} = \$3{,}320$$

Case C Cash Flows

Year	0	1	2	3
Revenue				7,000
–Op. Costs		–500	–600	–700
–Depreciation	–2,000	–3,429	–2,449	–6,122*
Taxable Income	–2,000	–3,929	–3,049	178
–Tax @ 40%	800	1,571	1,220	–71
Net Income	–1,200	–2,357	–1,829	107
+Depreciation	2,000	3,429	2,449	6,122
–Capital Costs	–14,000			
Cash Flow	–13,200	1,071	620	6,229

* Book value write-off combined with year 3 depreciation

$$AC_C = [13{,}200 - 1{,}071\overset{0.8696}{(P/F_{15,1})} - 620\overset{0.7561}{(P/F_{15,2})}$$

$$- 6{,}229\overset{0.6575}{(P/F_{15,3})}]\overset{0.43798}{(A/P_{15,3})}$$

$$= \$3{,}374$$

Select Case "B" with the smallest equivalent annual cost although results are effectively break-even.

10.6 Optimum Replacement Life for Equipment

It frequently is necessary to replace equipment, vehicles, piping systems and other assets on a periodic basis. Determination of the optimum replacement life for these replacement situations is a very important type of evaluation problem. In general, it can be shown to be economically desirable to replace assets when the after-tax operating, maintenance and repair costs for the old assets are greater than the equivalent annual cost projected for the new assets. However, in many real situations the analysis becomes more complicated because new assets often have different productivity than old assets, requiring the prorating of costs in some manner to get all the alternatives on the basis of providing the same productivity or service. Also, if existing assets have a positive fair market value the incremental opportunity cost of using existing assets one more period must be accounted for in addition to operating type costs in a correct optimum replacement study. In other words, optimum replacement time calculations are dynamic by nature. Using yearly evaluation periods, every year you must estimate: (1) the second hand market value of existing assets (which determines the opportunity cost related to keeping the asset another year), (2) salvage a year later for the existing assets, (3) operating, maintenance and repair costs to operate the existing asset one more year, and (4) any major repair or rebuild costs to operate one more year. Using these values, calculate the annual cost of operating one more year with the existing asset. Compare the existing asset annual cost for one more year of operation with the equivalent annual cost of operating with a new (replacement) asset for the expected optimum useful life of the new asset. Replace when the after-tax annual cost of operating one more year with existing assets is projected to be greater than the equivalent cost of a new alternative for its optimum expected life. This criteria assumes that the annual cost of operating with existing assets will get bigger in future years due to asset age and obsolescence.

PROBLEMS

Excel solutions at Stermole.com

10-1 A machine produces 1000 units of product per day in an existing manufacturing operation. The machine has become obsolete due to tightened product quality standards. Two new replacement machines are being evaluated from an economic viewpoint. Replacement machine "A" will cost $15,000 and will produce the needed 1000 units of product per day for the next 3 years with annual escalated dollar operating costs projected to be $6,000 in year 1, $7,000 in year 2 and $8,000 in year 3 with a $2,000 escalated dollar salvage value at the end of year 3. Replacement machine "B" will cost $21,000 and can produce up to 1500 units of product per day for the next 3 years with annual escalated dollar operating costs of $5,000 in each of years 1, 2 and 3 for either 1000 or 1500 units per day, with a $3,000 escalated dollar salvage value at the end of year 3. Depreciate both machines using 5 year life Modified ACRS depreciation starting in year 0 with the half-year convention. Assume that other taxable income exists that will permit using all tax deductions in the year incurred. For an effective income tax rate of 40%, use present worth cost analysis and break-even cost per unit of service analysis, assuming 250 working days per year, for a minimum escalated dollar DCFROR of 20% to determine if machine "A" or "B" is economically best assuming:

A) no use exists for the extra 500 units of product per day that machine "B" can produce,

B) another division of the company can utilize the extra 500 units of product capacity per day of machine "B" and that division will pick up one third of machine "B" capital cost, operating costs, depreciation, salvage value and related tax effects.

10-2 An existing machine "A" has a $2,000 sale value at year 0 and an estimated 2 more years of useful life with end-of-year operating costs of $3,000 at year 1 and $4,000 at year 2 when the salvage value is expected to be 0. At year 2 a replacement machine "A" that would provide the same service is estimated to have a cost of $23,000 with annual operating costs of $2,000 in year 3, $2,500 in year 4 and $3,000 in year 5 when the salvage value is estimated to be $8,000. An alternative new machine "B" would cost $20,000 now and would provide the same service as the original replacement machine "A" and could be operated for an annual cost of $1,500 in year 1 escalating $500 per year in following years. Machine "B" is estimated to have a salvage value of $3,000 5 years from now. Use present worth cost analysis to compare these alternatives for a 5 year evaluation life and a minimum DCFROR of 15% for the following situations.

A) The service to be received from each machine is assumed to be the same. The existing machine "A" if fully depreciated and has a zero tax book value. Replacement machines "A" or "B" will be depreciated using the Modified ACRS depreciation for a 7-year life with depreciation starting in the year the costs are incurred with the half year convention. Other income exists against which to use deductions in the years incurred and the effective income tax rate is 40%.

B) If machine "B" provides the capability of giving 40% more productivity than machine "A" over each of the 5 years and we assume the additional productivity can be utilized, compare the economics of machines "A" and "B" if operating costs will be the same as in part 'A' for both machines.

10-3 A 4 year old machine has a remaining book value of $21,000 and a second-hand salvage value of $30,000. You need to analyze the cost of keeping this asset to lease to another party for the next 3 years. A major repair of $25,000 at year 0 that can be expensed for tax deduction purposes will extend the life of the old asset another 3 years. Operating costs in years 1, 2 and 3 are projected to be $15,000, $18,000 and $21,000 respectively. The salvage value at year 3 is estimated to be 0. The income tax rate is 40% and the minimum escalated dollar DCFROR is 20%. Other income exists against which to use deductions in any year.

A) Determine the after-tax actual value end-of-year equivalent annual cost of operating with the old machine for years 1, 2 and 3. Assume that the remaining book value of $21,000 will be deducted as depreciation at year 0 if the asset is kept.

B) Determine the three uniform and equal beginning-of-year lease payments (at years 0, 1 and 2) that will give the owner of the old machine a 20% DCFROR on invested dollars.

10-4 All values are in thousands of dollars.

A)

C=$50	OC=$12	OC=$15	OC=$18	OC=$21	OC=$24	L=$3
0	1	2	3	4	5	

B)

	C=$32	C=$50				
C=$15	OC=$20	OC=$16	OC=$3	OC=$4	OC=$5	L=$25
0	1	2	3	4	5	

The time diagrams show the capital costs (C), operating costs (OC) and salvage values (L) for two alternatives under consideration for providing needed processing operation service for the next 5 years. Alternative "A" involves acquisition of new equipment now with annual labor intensive operating costs and salvage values as shown. Alternative "B" involves buying used equipment now and replacing it with new labor saving equipment currently in the development stage, but expected to be available for installation in two stages at years 1 and 2 for costs and salvage values as shown. All new and used capital costs are to be depreciated using 7-year life modified ACRS depreciation starting in the years costs are incurred with the half-year convention, with the exception that the years 1 and 2 alternative "B" replacement costs go into service at year 2, so start depreciating the total $82,000 cost at year 2. Take write-offs on the remaining book values in the year assets are replaced or sold. Assume other income exists against which to use deductions in the year incurred. The effective income tax rate is 40%. For a minimum DCFROR of 15% use DCFROR Analysis to determine the economically better alternative.

10-5 Evaluate the economics of replacing a bulldozer using the following data. Compare the old dozer with a new using present worth cost analysis and break-even cost per unit of service analysis. The minimum DCFROR is 15%. Use a 5 year evaluation life. The new dozer purchase price is $460,000 with an estimated $140,000 salvage value in 5 years, while the old dozer has a $90,000 fair market value now and zero book value with an estimated zero salvage value in 5 years. The new dozer would be depreciated starting in time 0 with the half year convention using 7-year life Modified ACRS depreciation. The effective income tax rate is 40% and other income exists against which to use all deductions in the year incurred. Assume overhaul costs as well as operating costs given in the following table will be expensed in the year incurred. Assume the new dozer will give 130% of the service productivity given by the old and that: a) the extra service cannot be utilized, b) the extra service can be utilized. For break-even cost per unit of service analysis assume 2,000 units of service per year with the old and 2,600 units of service per year with the new.

	Non-Operator Cost per Operating Hr.		Operating Hrs.	Overhaul Costs ($)	
Year	Old	New	Both	Old	New
0	—	—	—	100,000	—
1	25.0	22.0	4000	50,000	—
2	28.0	24.0	4000	125,000	125,000
3	31.0	27.0	4000	60,000	—
4	35.0	31.0	4000	150,000	150,000
5	39.0	35.0	4000	—	—

10-6 A firm is considering the economics of whether to lease or purchase several small trucks. The total purchase cost of the trucks is $100,000 and they will be depreciable over 5 years starting in time 0 with the half-year convention, using Modified ACRS depreciation. Take a write-off on the remaining book value in the year the assets are sold. Salvage value of the trucks is expected to total $30,000 at year 3 when the trucks are expected to be sold. The operating, maintenance and insurance costs are considered to be the same whether the trucks are purchased or leased so they are left out of the analysis. The trucks can be leased for $36,000 per year on a 3 year contract with monthly payments. To best account for the timing of the lease payments with annual periods, assume the first 6 months of lease payments, $18,000, are at time 0, $36,000 lease costs are at years 1 and 2 and $18,000 at year 3. The effective income tax rate is 40% and the firm has other taxable income and tax obligations against which to use tax deductions in any year.

A) Use present worth cost analysis and verify the results with incremental DCFROR analysis to determine if leasing or purchasing is economically better for a minimum DCFROR of 15%.

B) What uniform end-of-period annual equal revenues are required (UAERR) to cover the cost of leasing or purchasing and give the investor a 15% DCFROR on invested dollars?

C) Re-analyze the alternatives from the viewpoint of an investor that must carry negative taxable income forward to year 3 when other income is expected to exist. Use present worth cost analysis.

10-7 You have been asked to evaluate whether it is economically desirable to replace three existing machines with two new machines that would provide the same service over the next 3 years. The existing machines cost $300,000 5 years ago and have been fully depreciated. The second-hand value of the existing machines is $80,000 per machine at this time. Keeping and using the existing machines will result in estimated operating costs per machine of $120,000 at year 1. $130,000 at year 2 and $140,000 at year 3. Year 3 existing machine salvage is estimated to be zero. Two new machines would cost $500,000 per machine. Operating costs per new machine are estimated to be $60,000 at year 1, $80,000 at year 2 and $100,000 at year 3. Salvage value per new machine is estimated to be $125,000 in year 3. The new machines would be depreciable over 5 years starting at year 0 with the half-year convention using Modified ACRS depreciation. Other taxable income exists against which to use deductions in any year. The effective income tax rate is 40%, the minimum escalated dollar DCFROR is 15%. Use equivalent annual cost analysis to determine whether to replace the existing machines. Then calculate the uniform annual equivalent revenue required per machine to provide the service with the existing machines compared to the new machines.

10-8 A company is trying to evaluate the economic merits of purchasing or leasing a plant. It can be purchased or installed on company land for $1,000,000 cash or leased for $200,000 per year at the beginning of each year on a ten year lease. Annual income is expected to be $800,000 with $200,000 annual operating costs at each of years 1 through 10. The life of the plant is estimated to be 10 years. The net salvage value of the plant is estimated to be $400,000 at the end of its

10 year life. The effective federal plus state tax rate is 40%. Depreciation of the purchased plant cost would be straight line over 10 years starting in year 0 with the half year convention. Determine the DCFROR that the company would receive on the \$1,000,000 year 0 investment that must be made to purchase rather than lease. If 10% is the minimum DCFROR, should the company lease or purchase? Verify the result with NPV and equivalent annual cost analysis.

10-9 A firm is considering the acquisition of a bulldozer. The list price is \$454,328 and sales tax of 7.1% is capitalized into the depreciation basis. Based on historical information the firm can expect to realize 30% of the list price in salvage in 5 years. Salvage will be taxed as ordinary income. Expected machine life is 15,000 hours: 4,000 hours each in years 1 and 2, 3,000 hours in year 3 and 2,000 hours in year 4 and 5. The machine will be depreciated using the modified ACRS depreciation for a 7-year life starting in time 0 with the half-year convention. State ownership taxes and permits are tax deductible as operating expenses and are estimated to be 2.3% of the list price of the machine in year 1, 1.5% in year 2, 1.25% in year 3, 1.0% in year 4 and 0.75% in year 5. (In practice, the state tax is based on 75% of cost, but to cover miscellaneous fees and permits in various counties, 100% of the list price is used.) Insurance is \$.55 per \$100 invested in year 1, escalating 6% per annum. Repairs will be \$15,000 in year 1, escalating 6% per annum. Major repairs of \$100,000 at the end of year 2, \$75,000 at the end of year 3 and \$125,000 at the end of year 4 will be necessary. In addition, \$20,000 will be spent at the end of year 5 to prepare the unit for auction. For tax purposes, major and minor repairs should be expensed as operating costs in the year incurred since these expenditures are not expected to add to the life of the machine or cause significant modifications to the unit.

Determine the before-tax standard cost per hour necessary to cover costs for a 15% after-tax minimum DCFROR. The effective state and federal income tax rate is 40%. It will be assumed that other income exists against which to use all deductions in the year incurred. Then measure the impact to the standard cost per hour of a variation to the production schedule. Assume the machine will operate 3,000 hours per year for 5 years with all other costs remaining constant.

Summary of Data:

Cost	$454,328
Sales Tax	$ 32,257

Year	0	1	2	3	4	5
Insurance	—	2,498	2,649	2,808	2,976	3,155
Taxes, Permits	—	10,450	6,815	5,679	4,543	3,407
Major Repairs	—	—	100,000	75,000	125,000	—
Minor Repairs	—	15,000	15,900	16,954	17,865	38,937
Salvage	—	—	—	—	—	136,298
Hours/Year	—	4,000	4,000	3,000	2,000	2,000
Alt. Hours/Year	—	3,000	3,000	3,000	3,000	3,000

10-10 A company has determined that from an economic viewpoint new automated equipment should replace existing labor intensive equipment. You must determine whether it is economically preferable to lease the new automated equipment or purchase it with cash equity. The year 0 cash cost for the new equipment will be $200,000. A year 3 salvage value of $50,000 is projected for a 3 year lease/purchase evaluation life. Operating costs and lease costs are expressed on a monthly basis for beginning of month costs. Make an annual period analysis by accounting for costs at the closest annual period to which the monthly costs are incurred (month 0 through 5 costs are year 0 costs, month 6 through 17 costs are year 1 costs, etc.). Verify the annual period results with a monthly period evaluation. Whether leasing or purchasing, operating costs are estimated to be $3,000 per month for months 0 through 11, $3,500 per month for months 12 through 23 and $4,000 per month for months 24 through 35. Lease costs for the lessee are projected to be $6,000 per month for months 0 through 35 and the lessor will retain ownership rights to the equipment at the end of month 36 when the lease will terminate. Assume the lease costs and operating costs will be expensed for tax purposes against other taxable income in the month or year incurred. If the equipment is purchased the $200,000 equipment cost will be depreciated starting in year 0 with the half-year convention for 5 year life Modified ACRS depreciation. For the monthly period analysis spread annual depreciation into 6 equal parts in years 0 and 5, and 12 equal parts in years 1 through 4. Assume a write-off will be taken on remaining book value at the end of year 3 (month 36) when salvage of $50,000 is realized. Use a 40% effective income tax rate, a 15% effective annual minimum DCFROR and apply present worth cost analysis to determine if leasing or purchasing is economically preferable. Verify your economic conclusion with incremental DCFROR analysis.

10-11 Capital intensive service-producing alternative "A" has a relatively high initial capital cost of $1,000 as shown on the time diagram below. Alternative "A" is being compared economically with less capital intensive service producing alternative "B" which has a zero initial capital cost. Both alternatives "A" and "B" are projected to provide the same service for each of evaluation years 1, 2 and 3 with operating costs and salvage values as shown on the time diagrams. The cost for alternative "A" will be depreciated using 5 year life MACRS depreciation starting at year 0 with the half year convention. The effective income tax rate is 40.0% and the minimum after-tax escalated dollar DCFROR is 15.0%. Use incremental DCFROR and NPV analysis to determine the economically preferable alternative. Verify your incremental analysis conclusions with present worth cost analysis, end-of-period equivalent annual cost analysis and beginning-of-period equivalent annual cost analysis. Assume other income exists against which to use negative taxable income in any year.

Should the appropriate minimum discount rate (15.0% as given for this analysis) be affected by whether this analysis involves lease versus purchase or an old asset to be replaced by a new asset?

Capital	OC=$100				
Intensive "A"	C=$1,000	OC=$200	OC=$200	OC=$100	L=$300
	0	1	2	3	

Less Capital					
Intensive "B"	OC=$275	OC=$550	OC=$550	OC=$275	L=$0
	0	1	2	3	

CHAPTER 10 AUXILIARY PROBLEMS

A10-1 Last year your company installed pumps with carbon steel impellors. A recent analysis has identified internal corrosion in the impellors that will cost the company an estimated $150,000 per year beginning next year (end of year 1) in injection and maintenance costs to maintain impellor integrity. It is estimated that these costs would escalate after year one at an average rate of 5.0% compounded per year. The existing pumps were 7-year MACRS depreciable property and the first half year of depreciation was taken in year –1, so 7 years of depreciation remain starting at time 0. The installed cost of the existing carbon steel pumps was $125,000 and the current salvage value today (time 0) is estimated at $40,000, while year 5 salvage is estimated to be zero.

Installation of new stainless steel impellors is being proposed to eliminate the need to incur the aforementioned injection and maintenance costs over the next 5 years. The installed cost of the new stainless impellors is estimated today at $400,000. The new pumps are also 7-year MACRS property which would be scheduled for depreciation beginning today, time zero. Write-off the remaining book value for each alternative when the pumps are salvaged. The year 5 new impellor salvage is estimated to be $80,000. The company effective tax rate is 40% and the minimum rate of return is 12%. Other income exists against which to use all deductions when incurred. Use present worth cost analysis to determine whether to replace the existing carbon steel pumps with stainless steel pumps.

A10-2 Suppose you want to acquire a computer for business use during the next three years. After identifying the machine, you are now considering whether it is economically better to purchase the unit with cash or to make beginning of month operating lease payments over the next 36 months (months 0–35). Sales tax is 7.0% and would apply to either the purchase price or the monthly lease payments. Shipping charges amount to $125 for either alternative and assume they would also be subject to sales tax. If you purchase the machine, the cost today is $2,400 and end of year 3 (month 36) salvage is estimated at $300.

If you choose to lease, the payment is $70 per month, beginning today plus shipping. Neglect any option to purchase upon termination of the lease. Your minimum rate of return is a nominal 12.0% compounded monthly. Use a 36 month-life and present a nominal (annualized) incremental rate of return analysis to determine which alternative is economically preferred. For annual cash flow calculations, assume month 0 through 5 lease payments are incurred at time zero, month 6 through 17 payments are allocated to the end of year 1, month 18–29 will be allocated to the end of year 2 with the remaining 6 payments allocated to the end of year 3. Expense all sales tax and shipping charges when incurred for each alternative. If purchased, the computer is 5-year MACRS property with depreciation beginning in time 0. Write off the remaining book value when the machine is sold a the end of the third year. Assume a 40% effective tax rate and that other income exists against which to utilize all deductions when incurred.

A10-3 Two used machines can be acquired for $60,000 per machine to provide necessary service for the next 2 years. The salvage of these machines is estimated at $20,000 per machine at the end of year 2 when the old machines will be replaced with one new machine capable of providing the same total service. The new machine would cost $350,000 at the end of year 2 and is anticipated to yield a salvage value of $170,000 at the end of year 4 when the service will no longer be required. Operating costs associated with the used machines are estimated at $60,000 per machine at year 1 and $70,000 per machine at year 2. Operating costs with a new machine purchased at year 2 are estimated to be $80,000 at year 3 and $85,000 at year 4.

Instead of buying the old machines and replacing them at year 2, a new machine providing the necessary service can be purchased today (time 0) for a cost of $300,000. Service with either the old or new machines is needed for the next 4 years; therefore, a 4-year evaluation life should be used. It is estimated that a new machine purchased at time 0 will yield a salvage value of $80,000 at year 4. Operating costs with a new machine purchased now (time 0) are estimated at $75,000 at year 1, $80,000 at year 2, $85,000 at year 3, and $90,000 at year 4. Assuming a minimum discount rate of 15%, use after-tax present worth cost analysis of each alternative to determine the least cost approach for providing the necessary service.

The escalated dollar after-tax minimum rate of return is 15%. The effective state and federal income tax rate is 40% and other income is assumed to exist against which to utilize all deductions. Any gain on salvage is taxed as ordinary income. All assets represent 5-year depreciable property. Use the MACRS depreciation method with a half year deduction in the first year. Start all depreciation in the period of acquisition.

A10-4 Two used machines can be rebuilt for $50,000 per machine to provide necessary service for the next 2 years. The current value of each machine is $10,000. If the units are rebuilt, the salvage of these machines is estimated at $30,000 per machine at the end of year 2 when the old machines will be replaced with one new machine capable of providing the same total service. The new machine would cost $340,000 at the end of year 2 and is anticipated to yield a salvage value of $200,000 at the end of year 4. Operating costs associated with the used machines are estimated at $50,000 per machine at year 1 and $60,000 per machine at year 2. Operating costs with a new machine purchased at year 2 are estimated to be $80,000 at year 3 and $85,000 at year 4.

Instead of rebuilding the old machines and replacing them at year 2, a new machine providing the necessary service can be purchased today (time 0) for a cost of $300,000. Service with either the old or new machines is needed for the next 4 years; therefore, a 4-year evaluation life should be used. It is estimated that a new machine purchased at time 0 will yield a salvage value of $80,000 at year 4. Operating costs with a new machine purchased now (time 0) are estimated at $75,000 at year 1, $80,000 at year 2, $85,000 at year 3, and $90,000 at year 4.

Other income exists against which to utilize all deductions. Expense all operating costs in the year incurred. The existing used machines are fully depreciated. All anticipated repairs and new equipment expenditures represent 5-year MACRS property with depreciation beginning in the year the costs are incurred. Write off all remaining book values whenever assets are sold. The effective state and federal income tax rate is 40%.

Assuming an escalated dollar after-tax minimum discount rate of 15%, use incremental net present value analysis and determine the economically preferred approach for providing the necessary service.

CHAPTER 11

EVALUATIONS INVOLVING BORROWED MONEY

11.1 Introduction of Leverage Applications

Most major investment projects that are undertaken anywhere in the world today involve at least some borrowed money. This makes the analysis of investments involving borrowed money a very important economic evaluation situation. The terms "leverage" and "gearing" often are used in referring to the economic effects on investments involving a combination of borrowed money and equity capital. The dictionary defines leverage as "increased means of accomplishing some purpose". We use a lever and fulcrum to get leverage to raise a heavy object such as a large rock, and we use someone else's money in addition to our own equity capital to leverage investment dollars to increase the profit we can generate with our equity. To illustrate this effect with a common example, consider that you have $10,000 to invest and that you pay cash for 1,000 shares of XYZ stock at $10 per share. Assume that the stock increases in price to $15 per share within a few months and you sell the 1,000 shares for $15,000. Neglecting stock broker commissions, your profit is $5,000 giving you a 50% return on your $10,000 equity investment over the period of time involved. Now assume that instead of paying cash for the stock, that you use your $10,000 cash as margin equity and borrow another $10,000, enabling you to purchase 2,000 shares of XYZ at $10 per share. Now you have $20,000 working for you instead of just your $10,000 equity. If the stock price goes to $15 per share and you sell the 2,000 shares, you receive $30,000 income of which $10,000 is used to repay the borrowed money, leaving $10,000 profit above recovery of your $10,000 equity. Neglecting stock broker commissions and also the borrowed money interest, this gives you a 100% return on your $10,000 initial equity investment over the period of time involved. The effect of 50% borrowed money or leverage has enabled us to double the profit we would receive per equity dollar invested. At this point it is appropriate and relevant to state a basic law of economics which is: "There ain't no free lunch." You are not getting something for nothing with borrowed money. Leverage can work against you in exactly the same manner that it works for you. To illustrate this, consider that the shares of XYZ stock drop in price to $5 per share from their initial $10 per share. If we paid cash for 1,000 shares, this is a $5,000 loss or a -50% return on our $10,000 equity investment. If we had used $10,000 borrowed money together with our $10,000 equity, we would have lost $5 per share on 2,000 shares or $10,000. This means we would have lost all of our equity because the $10,000 income from selling 2,000 shares at $5 per share would be needed in its entirety to repay the $10,000 borrowed money and we would have a minus 100% return on our equity investment. Note that leverage can and will work against us as well as for us in different situations.

We now want to demonstrate the handling of borrowed money in DCFROR and NPV analysis of various types of projects. As with the XYZ stock illustration just discussed, including leverage in analyses means we are calculating the rate of return or NPV based on our equity investment in a project rather than on the total investment value. All of the examples and problems presented in the text to this point have been for cash investment situations. *There are three basic differences between the analysis of cash investment alternatives and investment alternatives involving borrowed money. First, interest on borrowed money is an additional operating expense tax deduction that must be accounted for each evaluation period that mortgage payments are made. Second, loan principal payments are additional non-tax deductible capital costs that must be accounted for as after-tax outflows of money each evaluation period that mortgage payments are made. Third, investment capital costs must be adjusted for borrowed money inflows of money each evaluation period that loans are made.* These three adjustments are the basic evaluation considerations that must be accounted for in leveraged investment analyses that are not present in cash investment analyses.

Before illustrating the handling of a loan value and mortgage payment interest and principal in a leveraged discounted cash flow analysis, different methods for calculating mortgage payments on a loan are discussed. For illustration purposes, consider a $900 loan at 10.0% annual interest to be repaid over three years by four different loan amortization methods as follows (dollars in thousands):

1. Balloon Payment Loan.

   The \$900 loan is repaid with a single year three payment that is referred to as a balloon payment. This approach is more common with commercial loans than for consumer loans but is the basis for U.S. "E" Bond and U.S. Treasury Zero Coupon Bond (deep discount bond) payments. Sometimes, commercial or residential real estate loans will be structured with an amortization timeline that exceeds the life of the loan, thereby leaving a loan balance, or balloon payment, due at loan maturity that must be repaid with cash or new dept to refinance the balance. This represents risk to the borrower in that if the borrower cannot obtain additional debt or pay off the loan because of negative changes in market conditions or a weak liquid position, they may potentially face foreclosure. However, periodic payments are typically required under most commercial and consumer loan products, unlike U.S. "E" and Treasury Zero Coupon Bonds. An example of repayment schedule for these bonds is as follows:

Loan = \$900				
@ 10% Interest	—	—	—	Balloon Payment
0	1	2	3	= \$900(F/P$_{10\%,3}$)
				= \$1,198

   The year three repayment of the loan principal is \$900 while the accrued interest equals \$298 for a total amount due of \$1,198.

2. Interest Only Loan.

   An interest only loan is a variety of a balloon payment loan because the only payments that are made over the life of the loan are interest payments so the loan principal is paid in the full amount at maturity. This is analogous to conventional U.S. Treasury Bond and Corporate Bond payments.

Loan = \$900	Principal = \$0	\$0	\$900
@ 10% Interest	Interest = \$90	\$90	\$90
0	1	2	3

3. Constant Amortization Loan.

   In a constant amortization loan structure, a loan is repaid with equivalent periodic principal payments with interest varying depending upon the loan balance at the beginning of each respective period. Therefore, payments decline over the life of the loan and are fairly easy to calculate. This type of repayment schedule reduces risk to lenders and is particularly useful in situations where leverage may be issued to a higher degree than is customary. This is because the principal balance is reduced more rapidly in early years, inherently reducing the lenders exposure relative to collateral values.

Loan = \$900	Principal = \$300	\$300	\$300
@ 10% Interest	Interest = \$90	\$60	\$30
0	1	2	3

4. Constant Payment Loan.

   A constant payment loan structure entails repayment through uniform equal periodic payments and is the most common type of repayment schedule for both personal and corporate loans.

	Payment = \$361.9	\$361.9	\$361.9
	Principal = \$271.9	\$299.1	\$329.0
Loan = \$900	Interest = \$ 90.0	\$62.8	\$32.9
@ 10% Interest	Balance = \$628.1	\$329.0	\$0.0
0	1	2	3

   Periodic payments are calculated above as follows: $\$900(A/P_{10\%,3}) = \$361.90/\text{year}$. The interest component of each payment is determined based upon the outstanding loan balance at the beginning of each respective period. For example, interest in year one is calculated as \$900 multiplied by the interest rate of 10%, which equals \$90. Subtracting this interest component from the calculated payment of \$361.90 leaves us with the principal component, which is \$271.90.

These four approaches to amortizing a three year \$900 loan have been related to a fixed annual interest rate of 10% per year that did not vary over the loan life. Variable interest loans (or adjustable rate mortgages or ARM's) have the loan interest adjusted periodically, such as every six months, by keying the loan interest rate on either three month, six month or twelve month Treasury Bills, three year Treasury Bond rates, or some other index of interest rates plus some fixed percentage or other measure to calculate the loan interest rate. Any one of the four approaches presented here along with flat or add-on interest rate loans can be adapted to variable interest rate loan situations.

In Example 11-1 you will see how leveraging a project with borrowed money makes project economics look much better on a leveraged basis than on a cash equity investment basis. However, *do not compare leveraged investment economic results with cash equity investment economic results. Since leverage improves project economic results when borrowed money interest is less than the borrowed money earns in the project, you must look at all project economics with a common amount of leverage for economic results to be comparable for different investment projects.* Most companies make zero leverage, which is the cash equity analysis situation, the common leverage used for all income and service-producing discounted cash flow economic analyses.

EXAMPLE 11-1 Analysis of a Leveraged Investment

An investment project requires the year 0 investment of $100,000 for depreciable assets and $15,000 for working capital. The depreciable assets will be depreciated straight line for a 5 year life starting in year 0 with the half year convention. Annual project income is expected to be $65,000 with annual operating costs of $25,000, assuming a washout of escalation of annual income and operating costs. Year 4 asset salvage value and working capital return are estimated to be $35,000. The effective tax rate is 40% and other income exists against which to use tax deductions in any year.

A) Calculate project DCFROR assuming cash investments (100% Equity).
B) Calculate project DCFROR assuming $100,000 of the $115,000 investment will be borrowed at an interest rate of 10% per year with a four year loan to be paid off with uniform and equal mortgage payments at years 1, 2, 3 and 4.
C) Evaluate the sensitivity of the cash investment and leveraged investment DCFROR results to ±$10,000 per year change in year 1 through 4 revenues.
D) Convert the cash investment cash flow from part "A" to the leveraged cash flow in part "B" by adjusting for: 1) loan dollars, 2) after-tax interest, and 3) loan principal payments.

Solution: All Values in Thousands of Dollars

$100 borrowed at 10% annual interest on a 4 year loan gives annual mortgage payments of $\$100(A/P_{10,4}) = \$31.547$. Each mortgage payment must be broken into interest and principal components since only the interest portion of mortgage payments is tax deductible.

END OF YEAR	PRINCIPAL OWED DURING YEAR	MORTGAGE PAYMENT	INTEREST = 10% OF PRINCIPAL	AMOUNT APPLIED TO REDUCE PRINCIPAL	NEW PRINCIPAL OWED
1	$100.000	$31.547	$10.0000	$21.547	$78.453
2	78.453	31.547	7.8453	23.702	54.751
3	54.751	31.547	5.4751	26.072	28.679
4	28.679	31.547	2.8679	28.679	0
TOTALS		$126.188	$26.1883	$100.000	

I = Income, C = Capital Cost, OC = Operating Cost, Int=Interest,
P = Principal Payments, L = Salvage and Working Capital Return

Before-Tax Cash Investment Diagram

	I=65	I=65	I=65	I=65	
C=115	OC=25	OC=25	OC=25	OC=25	L=35
0	1	2	3	4	

Before-Tax Borrowed Money Diagram (or Loan Amortization Schedule)

	Int=10.00	Int= 7.85	Int= 5.48	Int= 2.87
I=100	P=21.55	P=23.70	P=26.07	P=28.68
0	1	2	3	4

Sum of Cash Investment and Loan Amortization Diagrams

	I=65	I=65	I=65	I=65	
	OC=25	OC=25	OC=25	OC=25	
	Int=10.00	Int= 7.85	Int= 5.48	Int= 2.87	
C=15	P=21.55	P=23.70	P=26.07	P=28.68	L=35
0	1	2	3	4	

Notice that exactly the same cumulative equity cost of $115,000 is paid for the borrowed money case "B" and the cash investment case "A" since the leveraged investment year 0 equity cost of $15,000 plus loan principal payments add up to $115,000. However, the use of borrowed money enables us to defer a significant portion of our equity cost into the future. With borrowed money the cost we pay for deferring equity costs is the interest charged each year. If the interest cost is less than the profit generated by the borrowed money, leverage works for us and our leveraged economic analysis results look better than the corresponding cash investment results.

A) Cash Investment Analysis

Year	0	1	2	3	4
Revenue		65	65	65	100*
–Op. Costs		–25	–25	–25	–25
–Depreciation	–10	–20	–20	–20	–20
–Write-off					–25**
Taxable Income	–10	20	20	20	30
–Tax @ 40%	4	–8	–8	–8	–12
Net Income	–6	12	12	12	18
+Depreciation	10	20	20	20	20
+Write-off					25
–Capital Costs	–115				
Cash Flow	–111	32	32	32	63

* Includes Salvage Value

** Includes $15 Working Capital and $10 Depreciation

PW Eq: $0 = -111 + 32(P/A_{i,3}) + 63(P/F_{i,4})$

i = Cash Investment DCFROR = 14.2%

At this point in the analysis *we can tell whether the effect of borrowed money leverage will work for us or against us by comparing the cash investment DCFROR to the after-tax cost of borrowed money*. Since interest is tax deductible every dollar of interest saves $0.40 in tax for a 40% income tax rate. This makes borrowing at 10% before-tax equivalent to an after-tax borrowed money interest rate of 6%. Borrowing money at an after-tax interest rate of 6% and putting it to work at the cash investment DCFROR of 14.2% makes leverage work for us. We expect the leveraged economic analysis results to look better than the cash investment results.

B) Leveraged Investment Analysis

Year	0	1	2	3	4
Revenue		65.00	65.00	65.00	100.00
–Op. Costs		–25.00	–25.00	–25.00	–25.00
–Depreciation	–10.00	–20.00	–20.00	–20.00	–20.00
–Write-off					–25.00
–Interest		–10.00	–7.85	–5.48	–2.87
Taxable Income	–10.00	10.00	12.15	14.52	27.13
–Tax @ 40%	4.00	–4.00	–4.86	–5.81	–10.85
Net Income	–6.00	6.00	7.29	8.71	16.28
+Depreciation	10.00	20.00	20.00	20.00	20.00
+Write-off					25.00
–Principal		–21.55	–23.70	–26.07	–28.68
–Capital Costs	–115.00				
+Borrowed	100.00				
Cash Flow	–11.00	4.45	3.59	2.64	32.60

PW Eq: $0 = -11.00 + 4.45(P/F_{i,1}) + 3.59(P/F_{i,2}) + 2.64(P/F_{i,3}) + 32.60(P/F_{i,4})$

i = Leveraged Investment DCFROR = 53.6%

This leveraged DCFROR represents after-tax rate of return on investor equity investments. Note that the leveraged DCFROR of 53.6% is much larger than the cash investment DCFROR of 14.2% although the leveraged positive cash flow is significantly smaller than the cash investment cash flow each year except year 4. The reason leverage works for us in this analysis is because borrowing money at an after-tax cost of 6% and putting it to work in this project which has a 14.2% cash investment DCFROR causes the negative leveraged cash flow at year 0 to be reduced proportionally more by the year 0 borrowed money than the positive leveraged cash flows are reduced in the revenue generating years by loan interest and principal payment costs. Leverage always works for an investor when the after-tax borrowed money interest rate is less than the cash investment project DCFROR.

To summarize this discussion, deferring equity cost by using borrowed money is always economically desirable as long as the borrowed money is earning more than it costs on an after-tax basis. However, the optimum amount of leverage for a given investor is really a financial decision rather than an economic decision. More leverage always makes the economics of investments look better if the after-tax cost of borrowed money is less than the cash investment DCFROR. Financially, an investor must consider the magnitude of mortgage payments that can be handled if investment economics turn bad. Bankruptcy proceedings are an unpleasant experience and getting over-extended on investment loans for investments that turn bad can have very negative financial as well as economic results.

People often talk about greater risk and uncertainty being associated with achieving leveraged investment results in comparison with cash investment results. What they usually mean is that leveraged results are more sensitive to changes in evaluation parameters than cash investment results are, because leveraged results in general always relate to smaller equity investment values. In other words, a given change in any evaluation parameter such as revenue or operating costs will cause a bigger magnitude change in leveraged evaluation results than in cash investment evaluation results. The Case "C" sensitivity analysis illustrates this consideration by showing that a given increase or decrease in project revenue for this example causes bigger magnitude change and percent change in leveraged DCFROR than in cash investment analysis.

C) Sensitivity Analysis of Cash and Leveraged Investments

The effect of increasing or decreasing revenue by $10,000 per year will be analyzed. Since tax deductions for this investment are the same regardless of revenue, increasing or decreasing revenue by $10,000 in years 1 through 4 will increase or decrease income tax at the 40% tax rate by $4,000 each year. The net effect of revenue and tax changes will increase or decrease cash flow by $6,000 each year for either the cash investment or leverage analysis. Making the $6,000 per year cash flow adjustment is an easy way of obtaining the sensitivity analysis cash flows that lead to the DCFROR results.

Cash Investment Sensitivity Analysis

	0	1	2	3	4	DCFROR
Base Case Cash Flows	–111	32	32	32	63	14.2%
$10,000 Revenue Increase Per Year	–111	38	38	38	69	21.0%
$10,000 Revenue Decrease Per Year	–111	26	26	26	57	7.2%

The changes in cash investment DCFROR due to increasing or decreasing revenue by $10,000 each year amount to ±50% changes from the base case 14.2% DCFROR.

Leveraged Investment Sensitivity Analysis

	0	1	2	3	4	DCFROR
Base Case Cash Flows	–11.0	4.45	3.59	2.64	32.60	53.7%
$10,000 Revenue Increase Per Year	–11.0	10.45	9.59	8.64	38.60	101.0%
$10,000 Revenue Decrease Per Year	–11.0	–1.55	–2.41	–3.36	26.60	12.4%

The changes in leveraged investment DCFROR due to increasing or decreasing revenue by $10,000 each year amount to +88% to -77% changes from the base case 53.7% DCFROR. The physical range of variation in leveraged DCFROR results from 101% to 12.4% is much greater than the 7.2% to 21% variation in cash investment results caused by the same ±$10,000 change in revenue. This greater range of variation in leveraged versus cash investment results relates to the greater risk and uncertainty that some people mention in discussing the attainment of leveraged results compared to the attainment of cash investment results.

Additionally, in a leveraged scenario with a downside sensitivity analysis as included herein, investors need to consider how cash balances will be replenished to continue operations financially in ensuing years in the event that this scenario becomes a reality. This may include bringing in a partner that could include an individual investor, a private equity firm, or some other form of ownership that can make a capital injection. Taking on additional debt likely is not an option as the business is already leveraged and a bank (or other lender) will not be interested in contributing any more capital to what may be a failing venture, even if there is additional collateral to be pledged. Lenders are under pressure from regulators to maintain high quality loan portfolios and adequately underwrite both existing and prospective loans, underscoring the need for investors and prospective borrowers to educate and prepare themselves for this line of thinking in a world where capital may be difficult to obtain.

D) Converting Cash Investment Cash Flow to Leveraged Cash Flow

By adjusting cash investment cash flows for the three considerations that differentiate cash investment and leveraged analyses, leveraged cash flow can be quickly obtained as the following analysis illustrates by converting part "A" cash flows to the leveraged part "B" cash flows.

Year	0	1	2	3	4
"A" Cash Invest. CF	-111.00	32.00	32.00	32.00	63.00
+Loan Amount	+100.00	—	—	—	—
–After-tax Interest*	—	–6.00	–4.71	–3.29	–1.72
–Loan Princ. Payment	—	–21.55	–23.70	–26.07	–28.68
"B" Leveraged CF	–11.00	+4.45	+3.59	+2.64	+32.60

* After-tax interest equals before-tax interest multiplied by the quantity one minus the tax rate.

Once either leveraged or cash investment project cash flow has been obtained, adjusting for loan dollars, after-tax interest and loan principal with the proper signs quickly and easily gives the other cash flow.

11.1a Joint Venture Analysis Considerations

Venture partners are a viable option for an investor to raise capital as an alternative to debt in the event that they do not already possess the necessary equity capital for development of an investment. However, investors should be aware of the following considerations when evaluating whether debt or equity may be the best way to raise capital in their particular situation:

1. If an investor does not have equity capital for development of an investment, an alternative to borrowing is to bring in a venture partner. If the project fails, a venture partner does not have to be repaid, but in most situations, a bank loan must be paid whether a project succeeds or not and the bank may have recourse to the investor if they have signed as a guarantor. Generally, the cost of equity is higher than debt, reflecting this additional risk taken on by active investors.

2. Equity dilutes ownership, requiring the original investor to give up more of the profits from the project. Debt may reduce profits through regular interest payments, which may be expensed, but this will not likely have the same magnitude of impact as a venture partner.

3. Debt creates contractual restrictions for a company. Equity may dilute ownership, but it does not create such restrictions. Within loan agreements, lenders will include various covenants, which may be financial or non-financial in nature. Financial covenants typically require a borrower to meet certain balance sheet or cash flow ratios, maintain a minimum balance of liquidity, or even maintain a minimum level of cash flow or net income. Non-financial ratios may restrict changes in management, methods of raising capital (including the ability to obtain debt from other lenders), require the preparation of certain types of financial statements, and other considerations.

4. The cost of equity is variable whereas the cost of debt is fixed. Dividend payments and distributions vary over time depending upon the performance of the project and the demands of the investors. Conversely, debt repayment schedules are typically fixed based upon the terms included in the promissory not that is signed at loan closing. An exception to this rule may be a cash flow recapture covenant which would require that a borrower contribute a certain percentage of cash flow above a specified level, usually calculated as EBITDA, to loan repayment. This is a common requirement in relatively high risk scenarios when the lender desires to have the loan paid down more quickly.

5. Dividend payments to partners are not tax deductible while the interest associated with debt is deductible. However, note that the principal portion of debt repayment is not deductible.

6. Both venture partners and debt allow investors to inject fewer capital dollars into a particular investment and spread liquidity over a number of investments to diversify a portfolio.

Based on the cash equity investment analysis results from Example 11-1, a 50-50 joint venture would give a 14.2% DCFROR to each venture partner where each partner incurs half of all costs and tax effects and receives half of all revenues and tax effects. Even if the developer has the money for 100% equity development, a 50-50 joint venture (or any other joint venture split) has the potential advantage of spreading investment risk over several projects instead of having a bigger investment in one project.

EXAMPLE 11-1A Joint Venture Analysis Variation of Example 11-1

Assume a joint venture partner will put up $100,000, which is approximately 87% of the time zero capital investment of $115,000. The venture partner will also incur 87% of operating costs and will receive 87% of all tax deductions. In return, the venture partner will receive 85% of all revenue, salvage value and working capital return. These numbers also suggest that the original owner of this project is now putting up 13.0% of all capital investments and operating costs for 15.0% of the gross revenues. For this joint venture proposal, calculate the DCFROR and NPV for i* of 12.0% for each joint venture partner to be referred to as "original owner" and "venture partners."

Solution: All Values in Thousands

Original Owner Cash Flow Analysis

Year	0	1	2	3	4
Revenue		9.75	9.75	9.75	15.00
– Oper. Costs		–3.25	–3.25	–3.25	–3.25
– Depreciation	–1.30	–2.61	–2.61	–2.61	–2.61
– Write-offs					–3.26
Taxable Income	–1.30	3.89	3.89	3.89	5.88
– Tax @ 40%	0.52	–1.56	–1.56	–1.56	–2.35
Net Income	–0.78	2.33	2.33	2.33	3.53
+ Depreciation	1.30	2.61	2.61	2.61	2.61
+ Write-offs					3.26
– Capital Cost	–15.00				
Cash Flow	–14.48	4.94	4.94	4.94	9.40

DCFROR = 21.5%

NPV @ 12.0% = $3.37

Venture Partner Cash Flow Analysis

Year	0	1	2	3	4
Revenue		55.25	55.25	55.25	85.00
– Oper. Costs		–21.75	–21.75	–21.75	–21.75
– Depreciation	–8.70	–17.40	–17.40	–17.40	–17.40
– Write-offs					–21.70
Taxable Income	–8.70	16.10	16.10	16.10	24.15
– Tax @ 40%	3.48	–6.44	–6.44	–6.44	–9.66
Net Income	–5.22	9.66	9.66	9.66	14.49
+ Depreciation	8.70	17.40	17.40	17.40	17.40
+ Write-offs					21.70
– Capital Cost	–100.00				
Cash Flow	–96.52	27.06	27.06	27.06	53.59

DCFROR = 13.1%

NPV @ 12.0% = $2.53

If the project is considered to be relatively risk free with upside revenue potential above the revenues built into this analysis, a venture partner might accept this venture split. Otherwise, the original owner may need to sweeten the pot by increasing the venture revenue fraction above 85.0% or by reducing the venture partner cost fraction below 87.0%. Joint ventures of this type usually involve some negotiation to satisfy the needs of the venture partners.

EXAMPLE 11-2 A Land Investment Analysis With Leverage (values in thousands)

Assume you have a chance to buy 2,000 acres of land of r$10,000 with a $3,500 down-payment to fulfill the lender's maximum advance rate of 65%, assuming that the property appraised for the contract amount. This produces a loan amount of $6,500 that will be on a constant amortization repayment schedule over five year amortization with annual end-of-year mortgage payments of $1,300 plus 5% interest on the unpaid principal. Assume further that you think the land can be sold for $15,000 cash three years from now and that the loan will be paid off through the sale proceeds. The effective federal and state income tax rate is 30% and all capital gains are assumed to be treated as ordinary income for this example. Calculate the DCFROR based upon:

A) Your 35% equity investment in the land
B) Paying cash for the land
C) Land selling price is $11,000 instead of $15,000
D) Land selling price is $8,000 in both unleveraged and leveraged scenarios
E) Calculate the break-even sale value at year 3 that would give a 25% escalated dollar leveraged DCFROR using Case A values.

Solution: C = Equity Capital Cost, i = interest, p = principal

Case A, 35% Equity Investment

Before Tax Diagram

	i=\$325	i= \$260	i= \$195	
C=\$3,500	p=\$1,300	p=\$1,300	p=\$3,900	L = \$15,000
0	1	2	3	

Assume that the interest is used as a tax write-off against other investment income each year, saving you \$0.30 in tax per \$1 of interest deduction. As previously discussed in this chapter, loan principal payments are not allowable tax deductions. The sale price of \$15,000 less \$10,000 cost gives a capital gain of \$5,000 taxed as ordinary income at the 30% ordinary income tax rate. The tax would be .30(5,000) or \$1,500 so sale cash flow at year 3 would be \$15,000 - \$1,500 tax or \$13,500. The cost of acquiring land is not depreciable or tax deductible in any way except against the sale value.

After-Tax Diagram

Year	0	1	2	3
Sale				15,000
– Interest		–325	–260	–195
– Basis Write-off				–10,000
Taxable Income		–325	–260	4,805
– Tax @ 30%		98	78	–1,442
Net Income		–228	–182	3,364
+ Basis Write-off				10,000
+/- Loan Principal	+6,500	–1,300	–1,300	–3,900
– Purchase Price	–10,000			
ATCF	–3,500	–1,528	–1,482	9,464

PW Eq: $0 = -3{,}500 - 1{,}528(P/F_{i,1}) - 1{,}482(P/F_{i,2}) + 9{,}464(P/F_{i,3})$

i = Leveraged Investment DCFROR = 17.17%

Observe that the -\$4,095 debt payment in year 3 fully repays the remaining loan balance in addition to the interest payment that is due at the end of the year.

Case B, Cash (100% Equity) Investment

If we assume a cash investment, no interest or principal payments are needed and the after-tax salvage value at the end of year 3 is the same \$13,500.

After-Tax Diagram

Year	0	1	2	3
Sale				15,000
– Basis Write-off				–10,000
Taxable Income				5,000
– Tax @ 30%				–1,500
Net Income				3,500
+ Basis Write-off				10,000
– Purchase Price	–10,000			
ATCF	–10,000	0	0	13,500

PW Eq: $0 = -3{,}500 + 13{,}500(P/F_{i,3})$

i = Cash Investment DCFROR = 10.83%

As Cases A and B illustrate, the introduction of borrowed money has a substantial impact on project economics with leveraged returns enhancing the economics depending upon the degree of leverage. The profit on the sale is the same in both the leveraged and cash investment cases, but it takes less of your dollars to generate the profit in a leveraged analysis offsetting the increased risk of using leverage. Quantitatively, this means that a given change in any parameter that affects the economic analysis will cause a larger variation in the leveraged DCFROR than in the cash investment DCFROR. To illustrate this, consider the "Case C" analysis that the land is sold for \$11,000 instead of \$15,000.

Case C, Reduced Sale Price of $11,000

Leveraged Investment

For the leveraged case, yearly interest and principal costs are the same while the new after-tax salvage is $11,000 less the tax of $1,000(.30) or $10,700.

Year	0	1	2	3
Sale				11,000
– Interest		–325	–260	–195
– Basis Write-off				–10,000
Taxable Income		–325	–260	805
– Tax @ 30%		98	78	–242
Net Income		–228	–182	563
+ Basis Write-off				10,000
+/- Loan Principal	+6,500	–1,300	–1,300	–3,900
– Purchase Price	–10,000			
ATCF	–3,500	–1,528	–1,482	6,663

PW Eq: $0 = -3{,}500 - 1{,}528(P/F_{i,1}) - 1{,}482(P/F_{i,2}) + 6{,}663(P/F_{i,3})$

The new leveraged investment DCFROR is 1.02%

Percent variation from base case result
(17.17 – 1.02)/17.17 x 100 = 94.08% decrease in DCFROR.

Cash Investment

Year	0	1	2	3
Sale				11,000
– Basis Write-off				–10,000
Taxable Income				1,000
– Tax @ 30%				–300
Net Income				700
+ Basis Write-off				10,000
– Purchase Price	–10,000			
ATCF	–10,000	0	0	10,700

PW Eq: $0 = -10{,}000 + 10{,}700(P/F_{i,3})$

The new cash investment DCFROR is 2.28%

Percent variation from base case result
(10.52 – 2.28)/10.52 x 100 = 78.32% decrease in DCFROR.

The 94% decrease in the leveraged DCFROR is greater than the 78% decrease in the cash investment analysis results, showing that investors' profits can decline more quickly with leverage just like they can make money more quickly with leverage.

Case D, Sale Price of $8,000

If the property is sold at $8,000 for a loss of $2,000 when compared to the purchase price, there is no tax due at the sale because there is no gain, but the loss can be used to shelter other investment income. For this example, it is assumed that other income exists.

Leveraged Investment

Year	0	1	2	3
Sale				8,000
– Interest		–325	–260	–195
– Basis Write-off				–10,000
Taxable Income		–325	–260	–2,195
– Tax @ 30%		98	78	659
Net Income		–228	–182	–1,536
+ Basis Write-off				10,000
+/- Loan Principal	+6,500	–1,300	–1,300	–3,900
– Purchase Price	–10,000			
ATCF	–3,500	–1,528	–1,482	4,564

PW Eq: $0 = -3{,}500 - 1{,}528(P/F_{i,1}) - 1{,}482(P/F_{i,2}) + 4{,}564(P/F_{i,3})$

i = Leveraged Investment DCFROR = 15.29%

Cash Investment

Year	0	1	2	3
Sale				8,000
– Basis Write-off				–10,000
Taxable Income				–2,000
– Tax @ 30%				600
Net Income				–1,400
+ Basis Write-off				10,000
– Purchase Price	–10,000			
ATCF	–10,000	0	0	8,600

PW Eq: $0 = -10{,}000 + 8{,}600(P/F_{i,3})$

i = Leveraged Investment DCFROR = –4.9%

Not only will profits rise or decline more quickly with the use of leverage, but so will losses. If the land is sold after three years at a $2,000 loss, the leveraged DCFROR is negatively amplified when compared to the cash investment DCFROR.

Case E, Break-Even Analysis for Case A Values

To achieve a 25% leveraged DCFROR on equity invested dollars, let "X" equal the break-even selling price in year three in the after-tax cash flow time diagram.

Year	0	1	2	3
Sale				X
– Interest		–325	–260	–195
– Basis Write-off				–10,000
Taxable Income		–325	–260	X–10,195
– Tax @ 30%		98	78	–0.3X+3,059
Net Income		–228	–182	–0.7X–7,136
+ Basis Write-off				10,000
+/- Loan Principal	+6,500	–1,300	–1,300	–3,900
– Purchase Price	–10,000			
ATCF	–3,500	–1,528	–1,482	0.7X–1,036

$$\text{PW Eq: } 0 = -3{,}500 - 1{,}528\overset{.8000}{(P/F_{25,1})} - 1{,}482\overset{.6400}{(P/F_{25,2})} + (0.7X - 1.036)\overset{.5120}{(P/F_{25,3})}$$

$$0 = -3{,}500 - 1{,}222 - 948 + 0.3584X - 530$$

$$0 = -6{,}200 + 0.3584X$$

$$6{,}200 = 0.3584X$$

$$17{,}299 = X$$

11.2 Considerations Related to Leveraged Investment Analysis

We have seen in Examples 11-1 and 11-2 that both the meaning of economic analysis results and the risk and uncertainty associated with leveraged and cash investment project economic analysis results are very different. This brings up the question concerning, "how should leveraged investments be evaluated for investment decision making purposes?" To reach a conclusion concerning the best answer to that question, consider the following comments:

1) Whenever possible always compare evaluation alternatives with the same or similar leverage, including the project alternatives that determine the minimum ROR. As will be shown in Section 11.4 your minimum ROR will be higher for leveraged project evaluations than for cash investment evaluations. Since the risks and uncertainties and meaning of economic results with different amounts of leverage are not the same, it is not reasonable for investment decision-making purposes to compare project analysis results based on different amounts of leverage. It may be debatable as to how to define the "same" or "similar" leverage as this could be considered as debt measured in total dollars or as percentage of total capital dollars required for a project. Herein it is suggested that it is most appropriate to use the percentage approach because this is how lenders will approach each project if there is a specific request for debt tied to it, which will be especially true for many smaller companies. However, it is also important to recognize that larger companies, especially those that are publicly traded, possess large revolving lines of credit with pools of banks that allow them to draw down funds as needed, making it especially easy to obtain 100% financing for many projects. Banks will typically monitor these lines and their collateral bases quaterly and underwrite them every 12 to 24 months.

2) Since more and more leverage gives higher and higher DCFROR results, the use of leveraged economic analysis results for decision making purposes can sometimes mislead the decision-maker into thinking a marginal project is a better project than it actually is. For this reason there is considerable merit in making zero leverage, the cash investment case as the common basis for comparing all investment opportunities. This approach is based on analyzing all projects from the viewpoint, "would I be willing to invest my cash in any or all of the projects considered if I had the money?" If the answer is yes, "which projects would be best?" The cash investment analysis approach is used by a majority of companies. Another advantage of this approach is that it does not require knowing the financing conditions when the analysis is made. Since financing arrangements often are not finalized until just before initiation of a project, using cash investment economic analysis eliminates the need to guess and make sensitivity analysis for different borrowed money assumptions. Remember, if the after-tax cost of borrowed money is less than the cash investment DCFROR, leverage will work for you and the leveraged DCFROR on your equity investment will be greater than the cash investment DCFROR for any and all investment projects. If the cash investment economic analysis results look satisfactory, the leveraged results will look even better if the after-tax borrowed money interest rate is less than the cash investment DCFROR.

3) There are exceptions to every rule. In cases where interest free non-recourse loans are made available by another company to be repaid out of production product, or revenue if a project is successful, the leverage considerations are not the same as we have been discussing. To illustrate this concept, in past years some companies needing natural gas reserves have funded drilling companies in this manner. If the obligation to repay the loan does not exist if the project fails, the risk and uncertainty conditions obviously are very different than when repayment of the loan must be made whether we succeed or fail. In the non-recourse loan analysis case we would want to verify that the net present value that we could get by tying up our assets in the leveraged interest free loan project would be at least as great as the net present value we could generate by putting our assets on other projects being considered. Comparing DCFROR results is of little or no value in this case because you get an infinite percent DCFROR with 100% borrowed money.

4) Different projects attract better financing than others because of relative risks and uncertainties involved with different projects in the eyes of the lender. Cash investment analysis does not take this consideration into account. Looking at projects on a cash investment basis is going to give you a good and probably the best basis for evaluating how a lender will view the economic potential and risk and uncertainty associated with projects, but it may be necessary to make a leveraged analysis comparison to take into account financing differences. Remember, the number one concern of a lender is, "Will there be sufficient project cash flow to cover the mortgage payments over the life of the project?"

For consumer loan products, cash flow and debt service obligations are compared using a Debt to Income Ratio (DTI), which is measured as your gross monthly income divided by recurring monthly debt. Recurring monthly debt could include mortgages, home equity credit lines, credit cards, student loans, auto loans, alimony, child support or other obligations that include regular payments. This standard definition encompasses all debts and is sometimes referred to as a back-end DTI ratio in underwriting. When underwriting mortgages, the Federal Housing Administration recommends a maximum back-end DTI ratio of 41%. Also considered in underwriting is what is referred to as a front-end DTI ratio that only compares gross income to housing costs, which include principal and interest payments, required insurance, property taxes, and mortgage insurance if applicable. Here, the FHA recommends a maximum ratio of 41%. Although the federal government closely monitors and regulates mortgage availability, note that these ratios are not fixed and may vary from lender to lender depending upon overall borrower leverage, liquidity, geographical risk, and other considerations.

For commercial loan products, cash flow and debt service obligations are compared using a Debt Service Coverage Ratio (DSCR), which is typically measured as Earnings Before Interest, Taxes, Depreciation and Amortization (EBITDA) divided by recurring monthly debt. EBITDA may be adjusted to reflect a term such as EBITDAX, where the X may include additional items that are added back include one-time expenses, depletion, or other non-cash considerations that may be the result of hedging or other operations. Recurring monthly debt could include capital lease obligations, lines of credit, equipment loans, real estate loans, and other such obligations. Depending upon the industry and the risk associated with it, lenders will typically look for DSC ratios between 1.15 and 1.35, possibly even higher, with these higher ratios being related to more risk.

5) Finally, the use of borrowed money relates to a finance decision as well as having an effect on economic evaluation results with and without leverage. Remember, we have been discussing how to determine the best projects from an economic viewpoint regardless of where the money is coming from to finance these projects. Now after it has been determined that given projects look satisfactory from a cash investment viewpoint, if we have the money to spend, it may also be necessary to analyze the projects from a leveraged viewpoint for financial as well as economic reasons if the financing terms are different for the different projects. This was mentioned in the previous paragraph. Remember to use the same leverage in all analysis cases and use incremental analysis if the alternatives are mutually exclusive. For non-mutually exclusive alternatives use cumulative NPV or use Growth DCFROR or Present Value Ratio to rank the projects that will maximize the profit on your available equity capital.

11.3 Current U.S. Tax Law Regarding Interest Deductions

Under the 1986 tax reform law, individual and corporate taxpayers in 2008 continue to be able to deduct interest on business debts incurred for the purpose of generating investment or business income. However, that same tax bill put significant restrictions on the kind of income that individuals can use interest deductions against and limits or eliminates the deductibility of certain interest by individuals. *Two major factors in the tax law for non-business taxpayers are: (1) interest on personal loans is non-deductible except for home mortgage loans on principal and second homes to the extent the debt does not exceed the purchase price plus improvements, which is the same restriction that applies to trade or business loans, (2) new limitations apply to the deduction of investment interest, limiting this deduction to the amount of net investment income for the year.*

Interest on personal loans such as car loans and unpaid credit card balances is not deductible. This category of non-deductible interest, referred to as "personal interest." includes all interest other than:

1) Interest incurred in connection with a trade or business.
2) Investment interest (there are restrictions on investment interest that are discussed in the next paragraph).
3) Qualified first and second home mortgage interest mentioned earlier.
4) Certain specialized interest categories such as deferred estate tax interest.

Investment interest limitations restrict investment interest deductions to the amount of net investment income for the year. There are three basic types of business investments: active, passive and portfolio. Interest on money borrowed to finance active investments can only be used against net active investment income. Similar restrictions apply to loan interest for passive or portfolio investments. This means investors may pay large tax on positive active investment taxable income but have to carry forward interest deductions on passive and portfolio investments if positive net investment income does not exist in those categories. For certain investment situations there is partial relief from some of these restrictions for lower tax bracket individuals. See a good tax manual for details. Net investment income is defined as the excess of investment income over investment expense. Investment expense will be calculated using actual operating expenses, tax depreciation, depletion and amortization deductions. Investment income includes the taxpayers share of income or loss attributable to any business interest and to include gain on investment property. Interest that is subject to the new investment interest limitations is defined as interest on debt incurred or continued to purchase or carry property held for investment. Property held for investment includes any property that produces income of the following types: interest, dividends, annuities or royalties not derived in the ordinary course of a trade or business. Investment interest does not include qualified residence interest or interest from a passive activity such as real estate rental property or limited partnerships which by definition are passive investments. Passive investment deductions may only be used against passive investment income. You should be getting the idea that the current tax law is very complicated with respect to the deductibility of different types of interest by different investors, so consultation with a good tax accountant is advisable before making new investments involving borrowed money.

EXAMPLE 11-3 A Leveraged Real Estate Investment Analysis

An individual investor is considering the purchase of a single family residence priced at $250,000. The property appraises for this purchase price and the investor is financing 80% of this cost ($200,000) with a 5.0% annual interest loan repayable with uniform and equal mortgage payments over ten years (constant payment mortgage). The investor plans to reinvest rental revenues each year for major repairs to fix up the property, which is in poor condition. It is expected that the property can and will be sold two years from now for \$375,000. The investor considers that this investment will be treated as a passive investment for tax purposes and no other passive investment income exists. Rental revenues are expected to be \$25,000 for year 1 and \$27,000 for year 2 with corresponding operating costs of \$30,000 in years 1 and 2. Consider that the house goes into service in the first month of year 1 and straight line, 27.5 year life depreciation is applicable to \$230,000 of the \$250,000 cost with \$20,000 allocated for land. Calculate the investor's leveraged DCFROR assuming the investor's effective income tax rate is 31%. Analyze the sensitivity of the DCFROR to reducing the year 2 sale value to \$300,000 from \$375,000. No other taxable income exists, so carry negative taxable income forward to be used against project taxable income. All income is assumed to be taxed as ordinary income at the effective tax rate of 31%.

Solution:

Loan Amortization Schedule:

Mortgage Payments = \$200,000$(A/P_{5\%,10})$ = \$25,900
Year 1 Interest = \$200,000(.05) = \$10,000
Year 1 Principal = \$25,900 – \$10,000 = \$15,900

New Loan Principal = \$200,000 – \$15,900 = \$184,100

Year 2 Interest = \$184,100(.05) = \$9,205
Year 2 Principal = \$25,900 – \$9,205 = \$16,695

New Loan Principal = \$184,100 – \$16,695 = \$167,405

Depreciation Schedule, Mid-Month Convention Applies

Year 1: \$230,000(1/27.5)(11.5/12) = \$8,015
Year 2: \$230,000(1/27.5) = \$8,364
Remaining Book Value = \$230,000 – 16,379 = \$213,621

Year	0	1	2
Revenue*		25,000	402,000
–Op. Cost		–30,000	–30,000
–Interest		–10,000	–9,205
–Depreciation		–8,015	–8,364
–Write-offs**			–233,621
–Loss Forward			–23,015
Taxable Income		–23,015	97,795
Tax @ 31%			–30,316
Net Income		–23,015	67,479
+Depreciation		8,015	8,364
+Write-off			233,621
+Loss Forward			23,015
+/–Loan Principal	200,000	–15,900	–184,100
–Capital Costs	–250,000		
Leveraged Cash Flow	–50,000	–30,900	148,379

* Includes rental revenue and terminal sale revenue.
** Write-off includes $20,000 for land plus depreciable book value.

Leveraged PW Eq: $0 = -50{,}000 - 30{,}900(P/F_{i,1}) + 148{,}379(P/F_{i,2})$

i = Leveraged DCFROR = 44.12%

Reducing salvage value revenue to $300,000 from $375,000 at year 2 will reduce cash flow by $51,750 since all deductions remain the same and 31% of the reduced $75,000 would be reduced tax. Reducing year 2 cash flow by $51,750 from $148,379 to $96,629 yields the following:

Leveraged PW Eq: $0 = -50{,}000 - 30{,}900(P/F_{i,1}) + 96{,}629(P/F_{i,2})$

i = Leveraged DCFROR = 11.51%

The leveraged DCFROR is very sensitive to changes in the final sale value.

11.4 Minimum Rate of Return and Leverage

NPV analysis at first glance seems to offer a leveraged analysis advantage over DCFROR analysis since NPV results, for a given minimum DCFROR, vary over a finite range as you go from zero to 100% borrowed money instead of the infinite range over which DCFROR results vary. *However, for leveraged NPV results to be valid for decision-making purposes, the minimum DCFROR used in NPV calculations must be based on the same or a similar amount of leverage as the project being analyzed. This means that you need a different minimum DCFROR for every NPV calculation based on different amounts of borrowed money.* More leverage makes DCFROR economics of projects look better as long as the after-tax cost of borrowed money is less than the cash investment DCFROR of the project in which the borrowed money is being used. *Since the minimum DCFROR represents the analysis of other opportunities for the investment of capital, it should be evident that it is desirable and necessary for valid economic analysis to evaluate the "other opportunities" on the same leverage basis as the project or projects being analyzed.*

It has been emphasized throughout this text that the opportunity cost of capital, which is the return on investment forgone if a new investment is accepted, is the appropriate "minimum rate of return" or "hurdle rate" to use in economic evaluations. In this section we want to examine the effect of leverage (borrowed money) on opportunity cost of capital. It will be shown that opportunity cost of capital is still the appropriate minimum rate of return (or discount rate) with leverage as with cash investments, but that the opportunity cost or discount rate increases as the proportion of borrowed dollars incorporated into the analysis of other opportunities increases. This assumes that the after-tax cost of borrowed funds is less than the cash investment DCFROR of the project or projects representing other investment opportunities so that leverage enhances the economic potential of these other investment opportunities.

To illustrate the effect of leverage on opportunity cost of capital, assume that the best alternative use of funds, or an investment typical of other cash investment opportunities, is represented by the initial investment of $100,000 in non-depreciable property, such as land, that will generate revenues of $70,000 per year and operating costs of $20,000 per year in each of the following years. Assume a 40% effective tax rate and salvage value of $100,000 at year 5. Calculate cash investment DCFROR.

Year	0	1–5	Salvage
Revenue		70,000	100,000
–Oper. Costs		–20,000	
–Write-off			–100,000
Taxable		50,000	0
–Tax @ 40%		–20,000	0
Net Income		30,000	0
–Capital Costs	–100,000		
+Write-off			+100,000
Cash Flow	–100,000	30,000	100,000

PW Eq: $0 = -100{,}000 + 30{,}000(P/A_{i,5}) + 100{,}000(P/F_{i,5})$

$i = \text{DCFROR} = 30.0\%$

This 30% DCFROR becomes our cash investment opportunity cost of capital, minimum DCFROR, hurdle rate, or discount rate if it represents our other investment opportunities.

If the investor was able to borrow 25% of the initial $100,000 capital cost at a 10% annual interest rate, the leveraged project DCFROR would be greater than 30% because the cash investment project DCFROR is greater than the after-tax cost of borrowed money devoted to it. (Borrowing at 10% interest before-tax gives 6% interest after-tax for a 40% tax rate.) Assuming that a $25,000, 5 year loan at 10% interest per year is amortized with 5 equal mortgage payments of $6,600, the leveraged DCFROR is calculated as follows:

All Values are in Thousands of Dollars

Year	0	1	2	3	4	5
Revenue		70	70	70	70	170
–Oper. Costs		–20	–20	–20	–20	–20
–Interest		–2.5	–2.09	–1.64	–1.14	–0.6
–Write-off						–100.00
Taxable		47.5	47.91	48.36	48.86	49.4
–Tax @ 40%		–19.00	–19.16	–19.34	–19.54	–19.76
Net Income		28.50	28.75	29.02	29.32	29.64
±Loan Principal	25.00	–4.10	–4.51	–4.96	–5.46	–6.00
–Capital Costs	–100.00					
+Write-off						+100.00
Lever. Cash Flow	–75.00	24.40	24.24	24.06	23.86	123.64

An alternative, reasonably quick, way of getting the leveraged cash flows for different amounts of borrowed money is to adjust the cash investment cash flows for, (1) loan income in the year or years of borrowing, (2) after-tax interest cost which is before-tax interest multiplied by one minus the tax rate, (3) loan principal payments.

Year	0	1	2	3	4	5
Cash Investment Cash Flow	–100.00	30.00	30.00	30.00	30.00	130.00
+Loan Income	25.00					
–After-Tax Interest		–1.50	–1.25	–0.98	–0.68	–0.36
–Loan Principal Payments		–4.10	–4.51	–4.96	–5.46	–6.00
Lever. Cash Flow	–75.00	24.40	24.24	24.06	23.86	123.64

$$\text{PW Eq: } 0 = -75 + 24.40(P/F_{i,1}) + 24.24(P/F_{i,2}) + 24.06(P/F_{i,3}) + 23.86(P/F_{i,4}) + 123.64(P/F_{i,5})$$

$$i = \text{Leveraged Investment DCFROR} = 35.5\%$$

This result is 5.5% higher than the 30% cash investment DCFROR. Increasing the borrowed money leverage proportion increases the leveraged DCFROR. These results demonstrate that the opportunity cost that defines the after-tax minimum rate of return is a function of the leverage proportion associated with the investment. Because the use of leverage will increase the project DCFROR, the minimum rate of return or hurdle rate that the project investment must equal or exceed for acceptance must also be increased to reflect the increased leverage incorporated in the investment. If the minimum DCFROR is not increased to reflect the increased leverage proportion, almost any project can be made to look economically attractive simply by increasing the proportion of borrowed money devoted to the project. However, just because economics can be improved by increasing the degree of leverage, that does,'t mean that it is really a feasible scenario. In the lending environment in the real world, most businesses, especially smaller businesses, will be limited in the amount of leverage they can obtain depending upon the value of the collateral and its desirability, the liquidity of the borrower, the overall cash flow of the borrower, the health of the broad economy, and other considerations.

Also, as discussed earlier in Example 11-1, leveraged DCFROR results have different uncertainty associated with their meaning compared to the meaning of cash investment DCFROR results. This is because cash investment DCFROR results relate to larger unamortized investments every year compared to the corresponding meaning of leveraged DCFROR results, which always relate to smaller unamortized investments each year. This always causes sensitivity analysis of any project parameter to give greater total variations in leveraged results compared to cash investment results. This means that both the physical meaning and the uncertainty meaning are different for DCFROR results based on different amounts of leverage. One of the most important considerations in economic analysis work is to be consistent in the assumptions and handling of different investment analyses.

11.5 Capitalization of Interest in Certain Leveraged Investments

A capitalized cost is deductible for tax purposes over a period of time greater than a year by deductions such as depreciation, amortization or depletion, while an expensed cost is deductible in the year incurred as an operating cost type of expense. *Capitalization of interest payments on borrowed money means deducting the interest over the tax deductible life of the asset to which the interest relates by allowable tax deductions such as depreciation, amortization or write-offs against a terminal sale or liquidation value.* The rational for capitalization of interest is that it is required under U.S. tax law in certain instances discussed in the next paragraph.

Under special interest capitalization rules, interest on a debt must be capitalized if the debt is incurred or continued to finance the construction, building, installation, manufacture, development, or improvement of real or tangible personal property that is produced by the taxpayer and that has, (1) a long useful life, which means a depreciable life of 15 years or more under the 1986 tax reform act, (2) an estimated production period exceeding two years, or, (3) an estimated production period exceeding one year and a cost exceeding one million dollars.

The following example illustrates capitalization of borrowed money interest during the construction period of a project to be deducted by depreciation over the allowable project depreciation life.

EXAMPLE 11-4 Capitalization of Construction Interest in Investment Analysis

A natural gas pipeline is to be constructed over a right-of-way that will cost $500,000 at year 0 with construction costs of $600,000 at year 0, $700,000 at year 1 and $800,000 at year 2. The pipeline is expected to go into service at the beginning of year 3, so straight line depreciation for a 15 year life will start in year 3 with the half-year convention. Construction borrowed money interest will be capitalized and depreciated with pipeline cost. 100% of the year 0, 1 and 2 construction costs (not the right-of-way cost) will be borrowed at 10% annual interest with all loan interest and principal capitalized to year 2 to be paid off by ten equal mortgage payments at years 3 through 12. However, it is expected that the pipeline will be sold at year 4 for $4 million with a write-off on remaining book value taken at year 4 against the sale income. The loan will also be paid off in year 4. Pipeline revenues are projected to be $400,000 at year 3 and $450,000 at year 4 with operating costs of $150,000 at year 3 and $160,000 at year 4. Other income exists against which to use deductions in the years incurred and the effective income tax rate is 40%.

Solution: All Values in Thousands of Dollars

Loan Amortization Schedule:

Year 1 Interest = .10($600) = $60

Year 2 Interest = .10($600 + $700 + $60) = $136

Year 2 Capitalized Interest and Cost

= $600 + $700 + $800 + $60 + $136 = $2,296

Year 3-12 Mortgage Payments = $2,296($A/P_{10,10}$) = $373.67

Year 3 Interest = .10($2,296) = $229.60

Year 3 Principal = $373.67 - $229.60 = $144.07

Year 4 Principal Owed = $2,296 - $144.07 = $2,151.93

Year 4 Interest = .10($2,151.93) = $215.19

Depreciation Schedule:

Year 3 = (\$2,296)(1/15)(1/2)	= \$ 76.53
Year 4 = (\$2,296)(1/15)	= \$ 153.06
Remaining Book Value Write-off	= \$2,066.44

Cash Flow Calculations:

Year	0	1	2	3	4
Income				400.0	4,450.0
–Oper Costs				–150.0	–160.0
–Post Prod. Interest				–229.6	–215.2
–Depreciation				–76.5	–153.1
–Write-off					–2,066.4
Taxable Income				–56.1	1,855.3
–Tax @ 40%				22.4	–742.1
Net Income				–33.7	1,113.2
+Deprec/Write-off				76.5	2,219.5
±Loan Principal	600	760	936	–144.1	–2,151.9
–Capital Costs	–1,100	–760	–936		
Cash Flow	–500	0	0	–101.3	1,180.8

PW Eq: $0 = -500 - 101.3(P/F_{i,3}) + 1{,}180.8(P/F_{i,4})$

i = Leveraged DCFROR = 20.6%

11.6 Leveraged Purchase Versus Lease Analysis

Comparison of leasing versus purchasing of assets and facilities from an economic analysis viewpoint is the same as the analysis of any service-producing alternatives as was illustrated previously in Chapter 10, Section 10.2. However, lease versus purchase analysis is such a common important analysis to people in all types of industries and organizations that it merits special attention here again to illustrate a leveraged purchase versus operating lease analysis.

When leveraged purchase of an asset is to be compared with leasing the asset, build the appropriate borrowed money leverage into the purchased asset cash flow calculations analogous to earlier leveraged evaluations presented. Use a leveraged after-tax minimum DCFROR that represents other leveraged investment opportunities. Example 11-5 illustrates a typical leveraged purchase compared to leasing analysis, plus break-even lease payments analysis to make leasing economically equivalent to the leveraged purchase alternative for different discount rates.

Example 11-5 Leveraged Purchase Versus Lease Analysis and Break-even Lease Payment Analysis

Evaluate Chapter 10, Example 10-2A operating lease versus cash equity purchase assuming the purchased asset is financed with 100% borrowed money at 10% annual interest with mortgage payments of $3,000 loan principal plus interest at years 1 and 2, and $4,000 loan principal plus interest at year 3. The time diagrams are reproduced here for convenience.

Purchase	C=$10,000	OC = $1,000	OC = $1,500	OC = $2,000	L = $2,000
	0	1	2	3	

	Lease OC = $1750	OC = $3,500	OC = $3,500	OC = $1,750	
Lease		OC = $1,000	OC = $1,500	OC = $2,000	L = 0
	0	1	2	3	

Depreciation of the $10,000 purchase cost starts in year 0 with a half-year deduction using 5 year life Modified ACRS rates. Other income is assumed to exist against which to use deductions in any year. The effective income tax rate is 40%. Use present worth cost analysis and incremental NPV analysis assuming the leveraged minimum discount rate is 15% as in the cash investment analysis for Example 10-2A. Calculate the break-even lease payments that would make leasing equivalent to the leveraged purchase for minimum discount rates of 10%, 15% and 20%. Consider why the break-even lease payments get smaller instead of larger as the discount rate is increased from 10% to 20%. In rationalizing the break-even lease payment results for different discount rates, keep in mind that when revenue or positive cash flow is followed by cost or negative cash flow, the discount rate has rate of reinvestment meaning rather than rate of return meaning. This is the key to correct understanding and explaining of the break-even lease payment changes that occur.

Solution: All Values in Thousands of Dollars

Leveraged Purchase Cash Flows

Year	0	1	2	3
Revenue				2.00
–Op. Costs		–1.00	–1.50	–2.00
–Interest		–1.00	–0.70	–0.40
–Depreciation	–2.00	–3.20	–1.92	–2.88*
Taxable	–2.00	–5.20	–4.12	–3.28
–Tax @ 40%	+0.80	+2.08	+1.65	+1.31
Net Income	–1.20	–3.12	–2.47	–1.97
+Depreciation	+2.00	+3.20	+1.92	+2.88
–Capital Cost	–10.00			
+Loan	+10.00			
–Loan Principal		–3.00	–3.00	–4.00
Leveraged CF	+0.80	–2.92	–3.55	–3.09

* Book value write-off combined with year 3 depreciation.

$$\text{Lev. PW Cost Purchase} = -0.80 + 2.92(\overset{.8696}{P/F_{15,1}}) + 3.55(\overset{.7561}{P/F_{15,2}})$$

$$+ 3.09(\overset{.6575}{P/F_{15,3}}) = 6.45$$

Lease Cash Flows

Year	0	1	2	3
Revenue				
–Op. Costs	–1.75	–4.50	–5.00	–3.75
Taxable	–1.75	–4.50	–5.00	–3.75
–Tax @ 40%	+0.70	+1.80	+2.00	+1.50
Net Income	–1.05	–2.70	–3.00	–2.25
–Capital Cost				
Cash Flow	–1.05	–2.70	–3.00	–2.25

$$\text{PW Cost Lease} = 1.05 + 2.70(\overset{.8696}{P/F_{15,1}}) + 3.00(\overset{.7561}{P/F_{15,2}})$$

$$+ 2.25(\overset{.6575}{P/F_{15,3}}) = 7.14$$

The leveraged purchase present worth cost is less, so select leveraged purchase over leasing for a 15% leveraged discount rate. This economic conclusion is opposite the conclusion that was reached in Example 10-2A where the analysis was done on a cash equity investment basis. If the leveraged minimum discount rate is increased to 25%, purchasing is still the better economic choice.

Leveraged PW Cost @ i* = 25% = 5.39, select minimum
Leasing PW Cost @ i* = 25% = 6.28

The incremental cash flows for incremental NPV analysis can be obtained either by analyzing the incremental differences in the after-tax leveraged purchase and leasing cash flows, or by looking at the difference in the before-tax purchase and lease time diagram numbers and converting the incremental purchase–lease costs and savings and salvage to after-tax cash flow. The former approach is left to the reader with the before-tax incremental values converted to cash flow here.

C = Capital Cost, S = Savings, L = Salvage Value

Before-tax	C = 10.00				
Incremental	S = 1.75	S = 3.50	S = 3.50	S = 1.75	L = 2.00
Purchase/Lease	0	1	2	3	

Negative incremental operating costs give the positive savings each year and these savings must be converted to after-tax cash flow each year. Net incremental operating costs and capital costs should not be netted against each other in year 0 since these costs are treated very differently for income tax deduction purposes.

Incremental Leveraged Cash Flow Calculations

Year	0	1	2	3
Savings	1.75	3.50	3.50	3.75
–Depreciation	–2.00	–3.20	–1.92	–2.88*
–Interest		–1.00	–0.70	–0.40
Taxable	–0.25	–0.70	+0.88	+0.47
–Tax @ 40%	+0.10	+0.28	–0.35	–0.19
Net Income	–0.15	–0.42	+0.53	+0.28
+Depreciation	+2.00	+3.20	+1.92	+2.88
–Capital Cost	–10.00			
+Loan	+10.00			
–Loan Principal		–3.00	–3.00	–4.00
Leveraged CF	+1.85	–0.22	–0.55	–0.84

* Book value write-off combined with year 3 depreciation.

$$\text{Lev. NPV} = +1.85 - 0.22(\overset{.8696}{P/F_{15,1}}) - 0.55(\overset{.7561}{P/F_{15,2}}) - 0.84(\overset{.6575}{P/F_{15,3}})$$

$$= \$0.69$$

Note that positive leveraged cash flow in year 0 is followed by negative cash flow in years 1,2 and 3. Rate of reinvestment requirement, rather than rate of return meaning, is associated with the 15% minimum discount rate. It would be impossible to calculate DCFROR for this incremental analysis without going to either growth ROR or present worth cost modified ROR analysis to get negative cash flow followed by positive cash flow which is a requirement to calculate rate of return.

Break-even Lease Payments for Equivalence to Leveraged Purchase

To calculate the break-even lease payments we work with the incremental cash flow numbers except the annual savings are a function of the break-even lease payments. Since operating costs are the same whether we lease or purchase, the incremental savings are entirely due to the lease payments. The analysis follows.

Break-even Lease Payment Cash Flow

Year	0	1	2	3
Savings	x/2	x	x	x/2+2.0
–Depreciation	–2.00	–3.20	–1.92	–2.88
–Interest		–1.00	–0.70	–0.40
Taxable	x/2–2.0	x–4.2	x–2.62	x/2–1.28
–Tax @ 40%	–.4x/2+.8	–.4x+1.68	–.4x+1.05	–.4x/2+.51
Net Income	.6x/2-1.2	.6x-2.52	.6x-1.57	.6x/2-.77
+Depreciation	+2.00	+3.20	+1.92	+2.88
–Capital Cost	–10.00			
+Loan	+10.00			
–Loan Principal		–3.00	–3.00	–4.00
Leveraged CF	.3x+.80	.6x-2.32	.6x-2.65	.3x-1.89

$$NPV = 0 = .3x + 0.80 + (.6x - 2.32)\overset{.8696}{(P/F_{15,1})} + (.6x - 2.65)\overset{.7561}{(P/F_{15,2})}$$

$$+(.3x - 1.89)\overset{.6575}{(P/F_{15,3})} = 1.4727x - 4.4638, \; x = 3.03$$

Once again positive cash flow in year 0 is followed by negative cash flow in years 1, 2 and 3 so rate of reinvestment meaning (rather than rate of return) is associated with the minimum discount rate. Therefore, we should expect and observe that increasing the discount rate reduces rather than increases the break-even payments. The greater the reinvestment rate, the less the savings from lease payments that are needed to cover years 1, 2 and 3 interest and income tax costs. Of course the converse applies also.

$$i^* = 20\%, 0 = .3x + .80 + (.6x - 2.32)(.8333) + (.6x - 2.65)(.6944) + (.3x - 1.89)(.5787)$$

$$0 = 1.3902x - 4.067, \; x = 2.92$$

$$i^* = 10\%, 0 = .3x + .8 + (.6x - 2.32)(.9091) + (.6x - 2.65)(.8264) + (.3x - 1.89)(.7513)$$

$$0 = 1.5667x - 4.9190, \; x = 3.14$$

For $i^* = 15\%$, $x = 3.03$ by interpolation between the 10% and 20% results.

In leveraged analyses, the combination of borrowed money and tax savings from tax deductions in the early years often causes positive cash flow to be followed by negative cash flow, giving rate of reinvestment requirement rather than rate of return meaning to the discount rate. Proper understanding of this fact is necessary to calculate and interpret break-even results correctly. People are used to thinking a large discount rate is going to give the greatest, and therefore the best, break-even revenue from an NPV type equation. That is not the case when positive cash flow is followed by negative cash flow due to rate of reinvestment requirement instead of rate of return meaning for the discount rate as we have seen. In this case the smaller discount rate gave the best results for the lessor of the property. This is a very important break-even valuation principle to understand.

11.7 Summary

In summarizing this chapter on leverage, the following point is considered to be pertinent. Do not borrow money when you have a sufficient treasury to finance investments on a 100% equity basis unless the portion of your treasury equal to the borrowed money amount can be put to work at a DCFROR which is more than the after-tax cost of borrowed money.

PROBLEMS
Excel solutions at Stermole.com

11-1 Your corporation is considering the purchase of mountain recreation land for a cost of \$60,000 and you estimate that 5 years from now it will be possible to sell the land for \$150,000. Assume that your corporation is in the 40% effective ordinary tax bracket and that profit from the sale of the land in 5 years will be taxed as ordinary income. Determine your corporation DCFROR on its equity in the investment for:

A) Paying cash for the land,

B) Borrowing \$50,000 of the \$60,000 purchase cost at 10% interest per year with a mortgage agreement to pay back \$10,000 principal plus interest on the unpaid principal at each of years 1 through 5. Assume interest costs each year are expenses against other income.

11-2 An investor purchased land 2 years ago for \$1 million and the land has since been zoned for a commercial shopping center development. The investor has received an offer of \$7 million cash for the land now at year 0 and gain would be taxed as an individual long term capital gain. Assume the individual ordinary income effective tax rate is 35%. Keeping the property and developing it starting now at time 0 will involve costs and revenues shown on the following diagram.

All values are in millions of dollars.

C Bldgs.=30	Income/Yr.=65	70	75	
C Equip.= 5	OpCost/Yr.=25	30	35	L=40
0 (Now)	1	2	3	

To finance the development, \$5 million of cash equity will be invested at year zero and \$30 million will be borrowed at year zero at 12% annual interest with the loan set up to be repaid over 5 years with equal mortgage payments at the end of years 1 through 5. However, if the property is sold at year 3 the remaining loan principal will be paid off at that time. The buildings will be depreciated over a 31.5 year life using straight line depreciation starting in month 1 of year 1 with the mid-month convention. The equipment will be depreciated using 7-year life Modified ACRS depreciation starting in year 1 with the half-year convention. Assume any taxable gain on the terminal value (L) is taxed as ordinary income. For a leveraged minimum DCFROR of 20% determine whether selling or developing is economically better.

11-3 A major petroleum company spent \$3 million last year acquiring the mineral rights to a property surrounded by producing oil wells. Probability of successful development is considered to be 100%. An offer of \$5 million cash now at time 0 has been received for the property from another investor and gain from the sale would be taxed as ordinary income. It is projected that if we fully develop the property and produce it over the next 3 years that a sale value of \$6.5 million for the property and all production assets can be realized 3 years from now with any sale taxable gain assumed to be taxed as ordinary income. To develop the property the company must borrow \$4 million at 12% annual interest now (at time 0) to be paid off over 5 years with 5 equal end-of-year mortgage payments. However, if the property is sold at the end of year 3, the remaining loan principal will be paid off then. The minimum DCFROR is 25% for leveraged investments of this type. Make a DCFROR analysis to determine whether it is better to sell now or develop and sell 3 years from now based on the development data given on the following diagram.

All values are in millions of dollars.

	Revenue =7.0	11.0	9.0	
	Op. Costs=1.2	2.5	2.1	
Cost Tangibles =1.5	Tangibles=1.0			
Cost Intangibles=2.0	Intang =2.0			
				L=6.5
0	1	2	3	

Royalties are 15% of revenues each year. Operating costs include all severance and excise tax. 10% of total initial reserves are produced in year 1, 16% in year 2 and 14% in year 3. Assume intangible well costs are incurred in the first month of the year in which they occur. Tangible well costs are depreciated over 7 years using the Modified ACRS rates starting in the year tangible costs are incurred with the half-year convention. Use a 40% effective income tax rate and assume other taxable income exists against which to use deductions in any year.

11-4 You are to evaluate for a corporation the economics of purchasing a silver property now at year 0 for a $2 million mineral rights acquisition cost. Mining equipment costs of $3 million will be incurred at year 0 but put into service in year 1 with mineral development costs of $1.5 million spent during year 1. Consider that the mineral development costs are incurred in the seventh month of year 1 for tax deduction purposes. Other income exists against which to use negative taxable income in any year so credit the project with tax savings in the year deductions are taken. Mining equipment will be depreciated starting in year 1 with the half-year convention using Modified ACRS depreciation for a 7-year life. Production is estimated to be 300,000 ounces of silver per year with silver prices projected to be $15 per ounce in year 1, $20 per ounce in year 2 and $25 per ounce in year 3. Total silver reserves are estimated to be 3,000,000 ounces. Operating costs are estimated to be $10 per ounce in year 1, $11.25 per ounce in year 2 and $12.50 per ounce in year 3. The effective income tax rate is 40%. Assume the mine will be sold at the end of year 3 for $6 million and that any taxable gain from the sale will be taxed as ordinary income. Calculate the leveraged project DCFROR assuming $4 million is borrowed at year 0 at a 10% annual interest rate. Loan mortgage payments will be uniform and equal over year 1 to 10. Assume the remaining unpaid loan principal will be paid off at the end of year 3 when the mine is sold.

11-5 An investor is evaluating the purchase of 200 acres of land for a $200,000 purchase price now with plans to sell the land for a profit one year from now. The investor plans to pay for the property with $40,000 cash equity and $160,000 borrowed money at a 10% annual interest rate with the loan to paid in full when the property is sold. What escalated dollar sale value must the land have one year after purchase to give the investor a constant dollar leveraged DCFROR of 30% on investor equity if the annual inflation rate is projected to be 10%? Assume that the capital gain from the land sale will be taxed as ordinary income with an effective ordinary income tax rate of 34%.

11-6 A business is considering the purchase of an excavating machine for a cost of $150,000 at year 0. An additional $10,000 working capital investment will be required at time 0 for spare parts inventory. It is projected that rental of the machine will generate annual escalated dollar sales revenues of $150,000, $180,000 and $210,000 in years 1, 2 and 3 and escalated dollar operating costs of $50,000, $70,000 and $90,000 for years 1, 2 and 3 respectively. The machine will be depreciated using 7-year life Modified ACRS depreciation starting at year 0 with the half-year convention. It is estimated that the machine will be used for 3 years and sold for a $50,000 escalated dollar salvage value. To pay for the machine $120,000 will be borrowed from a bank at time 0 at 10% interest per year on unpaid principal amounts with equal principal payments of $40,000 plus interest made at the end of years 1, 2 and 3. Consider the effective tax rate to be 40%. Assuming an average annual inflation rate of 10% per year calculate the constant dollar DCFROR on the business equity investment over the 3 year evaluation life for the leverage conditions stated. What is the leveraged escalated dollar DCFROR that corresponds to the leveraged constant dollar DCFROR?

11-7 A depreciable investment of $100,000 is required at time 0 to develop a new product with an expected 5 year market life. A development cost of $10,000, to be expensed against other income, is also required at time 0 along with $30,000 for working capital. Sales of $150,000 per year are expected in year 1 with operating costs of $118,000. Escalation of sales and operating costs are expected to be a washout in years 2 through 5. Working capital return of $30,000 and equipment salvage of $0 are expected to be realized at the end of year 5 when the project is terminated. The effective income tax rate is 40%. Depreciation is straight line over 5 years starting in year 0 with the half-year convention. Compare the cash investment DCFROR with the leveraged DCFROR for borrowing $100,000 at time 0 at 12% interest per year with $20,000 loan principal payments each year plus interest paid off each year.

11-8 Work Problem 10-10 assuming 75% of the $200,000 equipment cost will be financed at year 0 with a 10% interest rate on borrowed money. The loan is to be paid off over 3 years with mortgage payments of interest plus $50,000 principal made at each of years 1, 2 and 3. The effective annual leveraged minimum DCFROR is 25%.

11-9 A non-mineral project has been analyzed to have the following cash investment after-tax cash flow stream:

Cash	CF	–$800,000	+$400,000	+$500,000	+550,000
Investment		0	1	2	3

Convert the cash investment cash flow to leveraged cash flow assuming $500,000 is borrowed at year 0 for 12.0% interest per year with the loan to be paid off with three uniform and equal mortgage payments at year 1, 2 and 3. Assume a 40.0% effective ordinary income tax rate. A) Calculate the leveraged project DCFROR. B) How much could be paid at year 0 to acquire the rights to develop the leveraged project and achieve a 25.0% leveraged DCFROR on equity invested dollars? The acquisition cost is considered to be amortizable over 3 years beginning in year 1 with three equal deductions.

CHAPTER 11 AUXILIARY PROBLEMS

A11-1 A non-mineral project with the following cash investment after-tax cash flow stream has been analyzed.

–800,000	+400,000	+500,000	+500,000
0	1	2	3

A) Convert the cash investment cash flow to leveraged cash flow assuming $500,000 is borrowed at time 0 with a 12% compound interest rate per year. The loan will be paid off in three uniform and equal mortgage payments at years 1, 2, and 3. Assume a 40% effective ordinary income tax rate and income exists to use all deductions when incurred.

B) Calculate the leveraged project DCFROR.

C) Determine the amount that could be paid at time 0 to acquire the rights to develop the leveraged project and realize a 25% leveraged DCFROR on equity dollars. Assume the acquisition cost is amortizable over three years (in each of years 1, 2, and 3).

A11-2 You are to determine the investment DCFROR that an investor who pays $400,000 time zero would realize on equity investment based on the following data. $360,000 of the $400,000 will be for the building that goes into service in the first month of year 1, (business buildings are real property and, therefore, depreciable straight line over 39 years and subject to the mid-month convention in the first year). The remaining 10% ($40,000) of the acquisition is for land, which is deductible only against the terminal sale value estimated at $500,000 for both assets at the end of year 2. Any year 2 taxable gain would be taxed as ordinary income. Financing this investment will involve a loan of $320,000 made at time 0. This loan has a nominal 10% interest rate compounded annually with the loan paid off over 5 years with uniform and equal mortgage payments. Assume unpaid portion of the loan principal will be paid off at the end of year 2 when the property is sold. Revenues are projected to be $80,000 in year 1 and $85,000 in year 2. Operating costs are estimated at $30,000 in year 1 and $35,000 in year 2. The effective ordinary income tax rate is 40% and other income exists against which to use deductions in any year negative taxable income exists.

A) Calculate the leveraged investment DCFROR.

B) Calculate the cash investment DCFROR that corresponds to the leveraged DCFROR calculated in part A for the $400,000 investment price.

A11-3 For a loan today of $250,000 and a nominal interest rate of 8.0%, develop the before-tax loan amortization schedules to pay off the loan amount over 3-years based on the following terms:

A) The loan is repaid with 3 equal total mortgage payments at the end of years 1, 2 and 3.

B) The loan is repaid with 3 equal principal payments in years 1, 2 and 3 along with the appropriate accrued interest.

C) The loan is an interest only loan with interest payments made each year and a single balloon payment made at the end of year 3.

D) The loan involves negative amortization. Therefore, assume no payments are made until the end of year 3 when the principal and accrued interest are paid off with one check.

CHAPTER 12

PERSONAL INVESTMENTS AND HEDGING

12.1 Introduction

Individuals and businesses have many investment opportunities in which they can put available investment capital to work. Bank savings accounts, money market accounts, certificates of deposit and purchase of a home to live in are the most common investments for the average individual. However, businesses and many individuals that have cash to invest above their savings account and home purchase requirements generally want to achieve a rate of return on invested capital greater than can be achieved on government guaranteed bank account type investments. There is a seemingly unending list of possible individual or business investments with varying degrees of risk. Some of these investments might include common stock, options on common stock, bonds, debentures, mortgage loans, commodity futures, options on commodity futures, real estate (such as apartment buildings, office buildings, rental properties, farm and ranch or undeveloped land), manufacturing and production projects including oil and gas and mining development to name a few common investments. There are very significant differences in the risk associated with the previous mentioned investments. *All investments involve risk but some involve much higher levels of risk than others.* Trading options on common stock, foreign currency or options on futures are examples of investments involving higher levels of risk. You may double or triple your investment capital quickly in option and futures investments but it is equally likely that you may lose all of your investment capital. Seldom is there a free lunch. If you get the opportunity to make money fast in investments such as options and futures, you also run the risk of losing money fast in these investments. Once a majority of people understand the risks associated with options and futures investments, they usually conclude that these are not appropriate investments for their situation. However, options and futures investments are very legitimate and important for business and individual investment hedging purposes. As an example, a commodity producer can fix the price to be received for commodity product expected to be produced over the next year by appropriate sale of commodity futures or acquisition of put options on futures. A refiner or breakfast cereal company can pin down raw material prices for crude oil or grain over the next year by appropriate purchase of crude oil or grain futures or call options on futures. *The use of options and futures for business hedging purposes involves very important every day transactions in many companies today.* Therefore, it is very important for company managers and potential managers to be familiar with option and futures contract trading to understand how their companies use these investments to mitigate financial and economic risk in different company investment situations. Individuals can in some cases use the same option and futures investment strategies to hedge investment risk. Put and call options and futures contracts are described in detail in the sections 12.3 and 12.4 of this chapter. Discussion of various hedging strategies using options and futures is also presented along with discussion of upside and downside potential associated with different hedging strategies.

Buying on margin is an alternative to options and futures that increases the risk associated with achieving the economic objective of any investment. *"Margin" is the equity capital that, when combined with borrowed money, will cover investment cost.* A 40.0% margin means the investor puts up 40.0% equity combined with 60.0% debt to cover an investment cost. Investments with less than 100.0% margin involve financial leverage. It was demonstrated in Example 11-1c that leveraged investments always have greater sensitivity than cash equity investments to a given change in any evaluation parameter such as cost or revenue. Leveraged investments compared to cash investments are somewhat analogous to options and futures contracts on assets compared to direct purchase of the assets. Leveraged investments make money faster for investors than cash equity investments when things go right, but leveraged investments lose money faster for investors than cash equity investments when things go bad. Once again, seldom is there a free lunch.

Each investor must recognize that all investments involve some risk. Even government guaranteed bank savings and money market account investments involve the risk that the government could go bankrupt and be unable to cover losses from a bank failure. We all have to recognize the risks inherent in different investments and to select investments that are consistent with the level of risk that still enables us to sleep well. Some investors do not sleep well with any amount of debt while others feel they should be leveraged to the greatest extent possible as a hedge against inflation. However, for all investors, regardless of their risk aversion tendencies, *it is very important to understand the worst that can happen from a given investment. Then, only invest an amount of money that would not affect your standard of living or investment strategy if the worst case scenario occurs.* In other words, keep your money in the bank rather than investing in common stock or real estate or other business ventures if you feel you can not afford a significant loss of investment capital. No matter how confident you are about an investment , remember there generally is a significant downside risk that you must discipline yourself to consider.

Diversification of investments can be very important in the management of risk. Instead of investing in the common stock of just one company, spread your common stock investments over at least four or five companies assuming the sum of money to be invested is sufficient to make that sensible and feasible when commissions are considered. With a diversified common stock portfolio, bad news that depresses the price of stock for one company or industry may be offset by good news that accelerates the price rise in another stock. The same principles apply to bond investments. No matter how good and secure a common stock or bond investment may seem, do not overload your portfolio with any one type of investment. The financial collapse and bankruptcy of companies like Lehman Brothers and General Motors are classic examples of investments that seemed very safe and secure just a few short years ago. Portfolio diversification within common stock, bond or other investment areas can be a very effective hedge against risk of failure. Once your investment capital is sufficiently large, you should consider having a combination of common stock, bonds, real estate and other investments of interest. In the 1980's and 1990's common stock and bond investments did very well while real estate investments in many parts of the country had mixed performance. In the 1970's real estate investments in general did very well in most regions, while stock and bond investments fared poorly. Diversification of your investments over several investment areas gives you a hedge (not a guarantee) against failure of all of your investments at the same time. Every investor must determine the mix of investments that is appropriate for his or her financial needs.

Common stock and bond mutual funds give investors a means of investing in very diversified stock and bond portfolios. For individuals to achieve mutual fund type diversification on individual stock and bond investments requires a larger amount of capital than most people have to invest. However, keep in mind that four or five good individual stock or bond investments may give you adequate diversification and give you equivalent or better performance than many mutual funds. If you decide to go the mutual fund investment route, analysis of the many common stock and bond mutual funds requires careful analysis of past performance and the potential for good future performance. This is exactly what needs to be done to select individual common stock investments. Also, with mutual funds you need to be careful to consider initial investment fixed fee charges which are referred to as "*load*". Loads can vary from 1% to 9% of initial investment in load funds and are 0% in "*no-load*" funds. In addition, annual management fees are charged that typically range from 1/2% to 1% of your fund asset value each year. Also, some funds have liquidation penalty fees that may be several percent of fund value. Sometimes the magnitude of these liquidation fees is a function of the length of time your money has been invested in the fund. You will also have a stock broker commission to pay if you acquire mutual fund shares through a broker. In general, you need to have a long term investment horizon for mutual fund investments to make sense but that is true for individual stock and bond investments as well. You must do your homework carefully in selecting a mutual fund if you decide that mutual fund management fees are less than the potential benefits relative to making your own stock and bond investments.

Many people adopt the attitude that they either do not know much about or are not interested in managing their own personal investments. Therefore, they conclude they will stick to mutual fund investments or let a professional money manager handle their investments. This is not an unreasonable approach for some people, but how do you select a competent money manager or a good mutual fund without having considerable general investment analysis knowledge? People spend years in high school and college and continuing education classes learning to make money, but often they do not spend days or hours learning how to manage their hard earned cash. When compounded over many years, what seems like a very small difference in investment annual rate of return or "yield" can become very significant. For example, $10,000 invested in a manner that causes it to grow at 12% compounded annually grows to about $300,000 in 30 years, while the same $10,000 invested so that it grows at 15% per year grows to about $660,000 in 30 years. This is a very significant difference in future value benefits for you, your family or heirs. If you make good investment decisions at an early age, the time value of money is working for you for many years through the effect of compound interest. This maximizes the likelihood that you will accumulate a personal net worth that will enable you to cover special financial requirements such as sending children to college, meeting major illness costs, taking special vacations, retiring early or retiring at the normal time on a good income.

As the years go by a person's investment objectives often change from capital accumulation to annual income generation. When a person's age is in the 20's or 30's, capital accumulation for the purposes previously mentioned usually is the primary investment objective. People in their 40's and 50's frequently have mixed capital accumulation and income generation as investment objectives. For the average person over 60, income generation for retirement living purposes tends to become a much higher priority consideration. Understanding what your investment objectives are and how different kinds of investments may best enable you to achieve your objectives is a very important key to potential financial security. The following sections of this chapter present more detail about the mechanics and risks associated with common stock, options, futures, options on futures, bonds and certificate of deposit investments. The first eleven chapters of the text have addressed the mechanics of calculating and applying the discounted cash flow criteria for proper analysis and comparison of alternative general business investments in any industry. The last section of this chapter will illustrate comparison of the economic potential of general stock and bond investments and tax deferred investments.

12.2 Common Stock Investments

The key to all successful investments is buying "low" and selling "high". To achieve that objective in common stock investments over the long term requires investing in companies with consistently increasing common stock prices. Since common stock price changes typically reflect changes in net income and cash flow earnings per share of common stock, *long term success in common stock investing is directly related to finding and investing in companies with consistent annual increases in net income and cash flow earnings per share of common stock.* Without regard to economic projections, stock market forecasts, interest rate predictions, balance of payments results or inflation estimates, if you systematically invest in companies with net income and cash flow growth, you have a very high probability of long term common stock investment success. Following are six rules considered appropriate for successful common stock investing.

Rule 1. *Decide whether you should invest in common stocks at all due to inherent common stock ownership risks.* Volatility in stock prices requires that you be prepared financially and mentally to ride out market declines. It may be several years before increasing earnings and cash flow in the companies in which you invest are reflected in higher stock prices. If your future plans include a need to pull your money out of the market to buy a car or house you may not be ready for common stock investments.

Rule 2. *Invest with a long-term prospective.* No one has a crystal ball to consistently predict future stock market moves. Over the short term (less than a year), the stock market as a whole, and the individual stocks that make up the market, may go up or down in price or remain unchanged. However, over the long run of many years, increasing company earnings have historically always lead to higher stock prices eventually.

Rule 3. *Do your homework to find companies with long term net income and cash flow earnings growth prospects.* Utilize brokerage house information, company annual and quarterly reports, Standard and Poor's reports and five year earnings data, stock investment service reports and data, and any other source of information to find companies with at least five years of consistent past net income and cash flow earnings growth that exceeds 10 to 12 percent per year. Then use your judgement to select the companies that have the greatest potential to continue their earnings growth in the future.

Rule 4. *Do not worry about forecasts for the general economy, stock market or interest rates.* Over the past thirty years the common stocks of companies with consistently good earnings growth have had consistent increases in stock price during both good and bad economic times. Of course, everyone wants to buy at the bottom of a stock price decline and to sell at the top. There is no question that over the short term, business cycles, interest rate changes and other factors may affect stock prices. However, in practice no one has the clairvoyant vision to predict when stock market tops and bottoms will occur. Systematic investing in the common stock of companies with projected future earnings that are expected to consistently increase is the best key to successful common stock investing.

Rule 5. *Diversify your investments over no fewer than four and no more than twenty common stocks or invest in a growth stock mutual fund.* An unexpected negative earnings report by a company can cause a fast decline in the price of most any company stock. Diversifying your investments over several companies reduces the downside impact of negative performance by one stock. There is a price to be paid for this reduction of risk by diversification. The upside impact on your common stock portfolio is reduced from a better than expected performance by one stock. In other words, with diversification, you accept reduction in maximum profit potential to reduce the maximum expected loss.

Rule 6. *Continue to monitor your common stock investments after you buy.* Monitor your investments on a regular basis for the increasing net income and cash flow earnings performance that have been the basis of your investment. If earnings prospects turn negative for the long term, sell, even if the stock has declined in price. It probably will go even lower in price if earnings turn sour. The Wall Street axiom "take your losses and let your winnings ride" is based on this logic.

Past performance is certainly no guarantee of similar future performance, but consistently increasing earnings in the 12% per year or higher range is a very strong indicator of excellent management, which is key to future performance. Investing in companies that have a proven growth record in net income and cash flow earnings per share of common stock of 12% per year for at least five years is a good foundation, but still not a guarantee, for solid growth potential in the future.

At different times all stocks tend to be priced either low *("over-sold")*, average or high *("over-bought")* in comparison with what one might consider an historical normal price. *"Price-Earnings Ratio"* is a common measure of whether stock price is high, low or normal. It represents the price of one share of common stock divided by the net income earnings per share for a twelve month period. If a given stock over the last thirty years has traded in a range of price-earnings ratios from ten to twenty with an average of fifteen, you might conclude that the stock currently is fairly valued or undervalued if the current price-earnings ratio is fifteen or less. A price-earnings ratio greater than fifteen may indicate that the stock is overvalued. Price-earnings ratio is just one measure of relative stock value and must always be considered in conjunction with future earnings growth potential. A higher price-earnings ratio may be justified for a stock with high earnings growth rate potential. An excellent source of net income earnings, stock price, and dividends paid annually over the past thirty-five years (or twelve years or twenty-two months in different books) is SRC Five Trend Security Charts by Securities Research Company listed in the references.

Cash flow earnings information must be obtained from company annual reports and various brokerage company research and analysis reports. To find or calculate cash flow information on companies generally requires more work than is required to obtain net income information. With large blue chip growth companies, cash flow growth and net income growth are usually similar. It is in looking for undervalued stock situations or in analyzing new smaller companies that there are sometimes differences in financial report net income and cash flow earnings. For example, a small or large company with large sunk costs from marginal investments many years ago may be doing very well economically now with rapidly growing annual revenue cash flow. However, current net income financial earnings may be depressed by financial depreciation still being taken on sunk costs. Remember that "sunk costs" are costs that have been incurred in the past and cannot be affected by anything done now or in the future. If cash flow growth in recent years has been better than net income growth an undervalued stock price situation may exist, while cash flow growth lagging net income growth may be indicative of an overvalued stock price. In general, it is desirable to check net income trends against revenue cash flow (net income plus non-cash depreciation, depletion, amortization, deferred tax deductions) for several recent years for any major trend differences.

When you buy common stock shares in order to profit from an expected increase in stock price, you are said to be *"long"* in the common stock. The term *"long"* signifies stock ownership. A *"bull market"* is an advancing market and investors who are long in common stock investments generally make money in bull markets. On the other hand, a *"bear market"* is a declining market and investors who are *"short"* in common stock investments generally make money in bear markets. An investor who is *"short"* in the common stock of a company has made a *short sale* in the company's stock. A *"short sale"* involves selling stock that you do not own with the expectation of being able to buy it back later at a lower price. A short sale is made by having a broker borrow shares from someone else so delivery of stock can be made to the buyer of the stock from the short sale. Remember that a profit is always made by buying low and selling high. The normal order of "buying first and selling second" is switched when a short sale is made. If it is anticipated that the price of a stock will decline, making a short sale involves selling first at what you think is a high price with the expectation that you will *"cover your short sale"* (buy back the common stock security previously sold short) at a lower price. The Wall Street axiom "he who sells what isn't his'n, buys it back or goes to prison" is based on the fact that every short sale must eventually be covered. Loss potential is unlimited from short sale transactions if stock price goes up instead of down. "*Short position*" is the amount of stock that investors are short and not covered on a given date. Following is an illustration of profit or loss resulting from a *"round lot"* (100 shares of common stock) long and short sale transaction.

EXAMPLE 12-1 "Long" and "Short Sale" Transaction Profit or Loss

Consider the economic consequences of 1) buying (going long) and 2) selling short (going short) one round lot (100 shares) of XYZ Corporation common stock at $50 per share if A) the stock price goes up to $60 per share or B) the stock price goes down to $40 per share when you close out your investment position by either selling or covering your short position.

Solution:

1A) Buying at $50 per share and selling at $60 per share results in a $10 per share profit multiplied by 100 shares equalling a $1000 profit.

2A) Selling short at $50 per share and covering the short at $60 per share results in a $10 per share loss multiplied by 100 shares equalling a $1000 loss.

1B) Buying at $50 per share and selling at $40 per share results in a $10 per share loss multiplied by 100 shares equalling a $1000 loss.

2B) Selling short at $50 per share and covering the short at $40 per share results in a $10 per share profit multiplied by 100 shares equalling a $1000 profit.

Short sales may be made for speculative reasons in an attempt to profit from an expected future decline in stock price or a short sale may be made for hedging purposes on stock that you already own to lock in a profit. Assume you own shares of a stock that has advanced significantly in price. Further assume that you feel the stock price has peaked, but to avoid having the sale profit on this year's tax return you do not want to sell now. *"Selling against the box"* involves making a short sale on stock that you own to lock in the profit. If the stock price drops, money is made on the short sale but an equal sum is lost on the stock you own. If the stock price goes up, you profit on the stock you own but lose an equal sum on the short sale. The *"selling against the box"* technique gives a hedging method of locking in profit on stock or other assets which you own and in which short sale transactions can be made. As a result of the Tax Revenue Act of 1997, "selling against the box" to defer tax on the sale of a security was made illegal.

Prior to July 2007, the SEC imposed a limitation on short sales to only executing short positions when a stock previously traded on an uptick or higher price. This provision was intended to prevent a stock from being excessively driven down in value simply due to short trades. Since July of 2007, short sales were no longer subject to the uptick limitation and some believe this has led to increased volatility on down days in the market. In 2008 some restrictions were reinstated. *"Up-tick"* is a term used to designate a transaction made at a price higher than the previous transaction. Conversely, *"down-tick"* is a term used to designate a transaction made at a price lower than the preceding trade. *"Even tick"* is a term used to designate a transaction made at a price equal to the preceding trade. The reason for restricting short sale transactions to up-tick trades is to prevent short sellers from depressing stock prices in a down market. This happened in the 1929 stock market crash.

Commissions must be paid for the purchase, sale and short sale of common stock, mutual funds, exchange traded funds and options to name a few. Brokers executing your trade can be separated into full service, full service discount, discount and deep discount traders. Most if not all offer electronic trading and competition has forced many of these commissions to $20 or less per trade. Usually the price you pay is a function of the size of your account and the level of investment activity. Above certain trade thresholds, the more trades you make each month, generally, the better the price you can expect per transaction.

12.3 Put and Call Option Investments

Put and call options may be traded in equities (stock), indexes, exchange traded funds, interest rates, futures, and other structured products. Long-term Equity Anticipation Securities (LEAPS) allow investors to establish positions in a stock for an extended period up to 3 years. Today, beyond the options listed, there are a variety of options that allow for speculation or insurance on various forms of credit, market movement and virtually any type of financial security. The Chicago Board of Options Exchange www.cboe.com is a great source for information on all the various forms of options that exist in the market today.

Many of the risks of buying and selling options are the same for all types of options, although some special risks may apply separately to each type. *"Put and call options" are legal contracts that give the owner the right to sell (a put) or buy (a call) a specified amount of an underlying asset at a specified price (called the exercise price or strike price) for a specified time.* Options that can be exercised at any time before they expire are commonly called *"American-style options"*. They are different than *"European-style options"* which can be exercised only during a specified period before expiration. The discussion in this text relates primarily to American-style options.

The "*option buyer*" is the person who obtains the rights conveyed by the option for a fee called a "*premium*". The buyer is sometimes referred to as the "*holder*" or "*owner*". Since options are legal contracts there must be an option writer. For receipt of the option premium fee the writer of an option is obligated, if and when he or she is assigned an option exercise, to perform according to the terms of the option. The "*option writer*" sometimes is referred to as the "*option seller*" and may be an individual, corporation, trust or other organization. Option writers have an obligation to deliver which adds an element of risk relative to the investor's position. For example, the writer of a call option must deliver the security to the option buyer if the option is exercised. Correspondingly, the writer of a put option must purchase the underlying security when exercised. Option writers or sellers are taking an opposite position to the buyer for a variety of reasons. This section will focus on the buyer who acquires a right to buy or sell the underlying security, at the exercise or strike price.

Call (and put) options on common stock give the holder the right to buy (or sell) 100 shares of common stock at a specified strike price for a specified time. The terms "*contract*" and "*option*" are interchangeable and involve rights to buy (call) or sell (put) 100 shares of common stock. Call holders usually only make money if the price of the underlying asset increases since that generally causes the price of the call option to increase. Put holders usually only make money if the price of the underlying asset decreases since that generally causes the price of the put option to increase. Investors in options can profit directly or indirectly from their investment by either 1) selling the right associated with the option position to another investor in the market place or, 2) by actually exercising the option. In either case, this action must occur prior to the option expiration date at which time; the option literally expires and becomes worthless.

EXAMPLE 12-2 Put and Call Transaction Profit and Loss

Assume that in January the price of XYZ common stock is $49 per share. A person acquires 1) an April XYZ call option at a $50 strike price for a premium of $2 per share, or 2) an April XYZ put option at a $50 strike price for a premium of $3 per share. In February the price of XYZ stock has risen to $55 per share and A) the call price is $6 per share when it is sold, or B) the put price is $0.50 per share when it is sold. Calculate the profit or loss from these call and put transactions.

Solutions: Each put and call option contract controls 100 shares of stock

1A) Buying the call option for $2 per share multiplied by 100 shares equals $200 cost plus commission. (A table of typical discount broker commissions is presented at the end of Section 12.2). Selling the call option for $6 per share multiplied by 100 shares equals $600 income minus commission. Neglecting commissions, the call transaction profit = $600 - $200 = $400. Note it is the option price and not the underlying asset stock price that is used in determining profit and loss on options. We are interested in the underlying asset stock price movement because it is the driving force that caused the call price to increase and give the investor the $400 profit.

1B) Buying the put option for $3 per share multiplied by 100 shares cost $300 plus commission. Selling the put option for $0.50 per share multiplied by 100 shares equals $50 income less commissions. Neglecting commissions, the put transaction loss or negative profit equals $50 - $300 = -$250. If the stock price had dropped from $49 per share to $45 per share instead of rising to $55 per share, the put option transaction would have generated a profit and the call transaction would have generated a loss. To explain this, the concept of *intrinsic value* and *time value* must be introduced.

"Intrinsic value" is the value that the holder of an option would realize for exercising the option, that is, the amount, if any, by which the option is *"in-the-money"*. By definition, an *"in-the-money"* option has positive intrinsic value. An *"out-of-the-money"* option has zero intrinsic value. *"Time value"* (or *"speculative value"*) is whatever value an option has in addition to its intrinsic value. Time value reflects what a buyer would be willing to pay above intrinsic value for an option to obtain the speculative right to benefit from a possible favorable change in the price of the underlying asset before its expiration. The concepts of intrinsic value and time value apply only to American-style options since you must be able to exercise options at any time to realize intrinsic value.

EXAMPLE 12-3 Put and Call Intrinsic Value and Time Value

Determine the intrinsic value and time value for initial and final put, call and stock prices described in Example 12-2. Initial January XYZ stock price was $49 per share when a person acquired 1) an April XYZ call at a $50 strike price for a premium of $2 per share or 2) and April XYZ put option at a $50 strike price for a premium of $3 per share. Final February XYZ stock price was $55 per share when A) the call price was $6 per share and B) the put price was $0.50 per share.

Solution:

The initial call premium of $2 is entirely time value since intrinsic value is zero. A call giving the right to buy XYZ at a strike price of $50 has no intrinsic value when the stock can be bought in the open market at the current XYZ market price per share of $49 per share.

The initial XYZ put premium (price) of $3 per share is partially time value and partially intrinsic value. The right to sell XYZ stock at a strike price of $50 per share is worth $1 per share when the stock would have to be sold at $49 per share in the open market, therefore intrinsic value equals $1 per share. The difference in the $3 put premium and the $1 intrinsic value is $2 per share time value.

The final XYZ call price of $6 per share is $5 per share intrinsic value and $1 per share time value. With the XYZ stock price at $55 per share, the call giving the right to buy stock at $50 per share could be exercised with the purchased stock simultaneously sold at the $55 per share market price. This gives a $5 per share intrinsic value that could be realized from exercising the call option. The difference in the $6 per share premium price and $5 per share intrinsic value is the $1 per share time value.

The final XYZ put price of $0.50 per share is entirely time value. When stock can be sold in the open market at $55 per share, the right to sell at $50 per share through use of the put has no intrinsic value.

EXAMPLE 12-4 Comparison of Buying Stock, Selling Short or Buying Options

Assume the price of XYZ common stock is $30 per share and you have $3000 to invest. Consider one of the following four alternatives: 1) buying 100 shares of the XYZ stock, or 2) acquiring call options at a $30 strike price for $2 per share, assuming that you expect the XYZ stock price to increase. Alternatively, if you expect the XYZ stock price to decline, you could use the $3000 as a reserve for, 3) covering potential loss from the short sale of 100 shares, or 4) acquiring put options at a $30 strike price for $2 per share. Calculate the potential profit or loss from the four possible transactions if:

A) The stock price rises to $40 per share, the call price increases to $10 per share and the put price declines to zero.

B) The stock price drops to $20 per share, the call price drops to zero and the put price increases to $10 per share.

Solution:

The stock price increases to $40 per share for 1A through 4A.

1A) Buy Stock Profit = ($40 sale price-$30 initial cost)(100 shares)
= $1,000 profit
($1,000 profit/$3,000 cost)(100%) = 33.3% gain

2A) Call Option Profit = ($10 sale price-$2 initial cost)(1500 shares)
= $12,000 profit
($12,000 profit/$3,000 cost)(100%) = 400% gain

3A) Short Sale Loss = ($30 sale price-$40 cover cost)(100 shares)
= $1,000 loss
($1,000 loss/$3000 cost)(100%) = 33.3% loss

4A) Put Option Loss = ($0 sale price-$2 initial cost)(1500 shares)
= $3,000 loss
($3,000 loss/$3,000 cost)(100%) = 100% loss

The stock price decreases to $20 per share for 1B through 4B.

1B) Buy Stock Loss = ($20 sale price-$30 initial cost)(100 shares)
= $1,000 loss
($1,000 loss/$3,000 cost)(100%) = 33.3% loss

2B) Call Option Loss = ($0 sale price-$2 initial cost)(1500 shares)
= $3,000 loss
($3,000 loss/$3,000 cost)(100%) = 100% loss

3B) Short Sale Profit = ($30 sale price-$20 cover cost)(100 shares)
= $1,000 profit
($1,000 profit/$3,000 cost)(100%) = 33.3% gain

4B) Put Option Profit = ($10 sale price-$2 initial cost)(1500 shares)
= $12,000 profit
($12,000 profit/$3,000 cost)(100%) = 400% gain

It is clear that acquiring the XYZ stock or call options on the stock makes money if the XYZ stock price goes up, while selling short or buying put options makes money if the XYZ stock price drops. Also notice that the leverage associated with options compared to buying or short selling (control of 1500 shares versus 100 shares in this case for the same $3,000 investment) causes a much higher percentage gain and loss with options. Options give the investor the opportunity to make money faster and to lose money faster than with direct buy or short sale transactions.

12.3a Writing Put and Call Option Contracts

There are two sides to every legal contract. For every buyer there must be a seller. With options, the *seller is the "option writer"* who receives a premium for granting the buyer the right to buy (call) or sell (put) 100 shares of common stock at a specified exercise price for a specified period of time. The primary reason for writing options is not necessarily highly speculative. It often appeals to the investor in quest of enhanced income from available investment capital. The buyer of options may have a variety of reasons for purchasing options including outright speculation, insuring profits, limiting losses, tax considerations and so forth. The seller or writer of options usually has just one motivation, to earn extra income on investment capital through the premium received for writing options.

EXAMPLE 12-5 Writing (Selling) a Put Option

Consider that you have a "bullish" view of the market and wish to enhance your return on available investment capital. You feel that the XYZ stock price is going to increase from its current price of $40 per share. You write a 95 day put option on XYZ at a strike price of $40 for which you receive a $250 premium. If the stock price goes up as you project, the put option will not be exercised and you will realize a $250 profit. If your judgement is consistently correct you can, in theory, do this four times per year and gain $1000 extra premium income. This can be used against a possible outlay of $4000 to exercise the put if the XYZ stock price drops instead of going up. Discuss the transaction economics if the XYZ stock price drops to $30 near the expiration date of the put option and you are required to exercise the option.

Solution:

You have written a put option agreeing to buy 100 shares of XYZ at $40 per share. If your option is exercised you must pay $4000 for 100 shares of XYZ. A premium of $250 was received for writing the option making your net cost per share $37.50. The market is now valuing the stock at $30 per share so you will have a $7.50 per share loss or a total loss of $750 if you sell the stock.

This example has illustrated the loss to the writer from exercising the option near its expiration. Both writers and buyers of options can limit losses or take profits without going through the exercise procedure. They can simply liquidate their positions at any time before the option expires. The option buyer sells an option with the same strike price and expiration as the one being held. Likewise, the option writer buys an option to cancel the one he wrote to liquidate his position.

EXAMPLE 12-6 Writing (Selling) A Call Option

In selling a call option, the "*option writer*" commits to selling the optioned stock at a specified strike price for a specified period of time, at the discretion of the call buyer. The objective generally is to enhance income on stock already owned. Assume you own 100 shares of ABC stock currently priced at $40 per share and yields about 5% in annual dividends. You do not expect the stock to increase in price over the next 3 months, so you sell a 95 day call on ABC at a $40 strike price and receive a premium of $300 (premiums on call options generally are a little higher than on put options due to supply-demand). If the price of ABC stays at $40 per share or below, the call option will not be exercised and you pocket the premium. Doing this four times a year would yield $1200 in addition to the annual dividends of $200. However, analyze your economic situation if the stock price jumps to $50 per share and you are required to exercise the option.

Solution:

Exercising your option requires you to deliver the stock to the option holder for $40 per share. You also received a premium fee of $3 per share, so you receive a total of $43 per share instead of the $50 per share that you could have sold at if you had not written the call option. This is an implicit loss of $7 per share or a total loss of $700 per contract.

When the call writer owns the stock that the option is written against, the call option is referred to as a "*covered option*". When the call writer does not own the stock against which the option is written, the writer must buy the stock in the open market if the option is exercised and the call option is referred to as a "*naked option*". Naked option writing is the riskiest form of option writing with unlimited loss potential.

There are two types of combination option positions which involve positions in more than one option at the same time. A "*straddle*" involves writing or buying both a put and a call on the same underlying asset, with the options having the same exercise price and expiration date. A *"spread"* involves being both the writer and the buyer of the same type option (put or call) on the same underlying asset, with the options having different exercise prices and/or expiration dates.

The *"option expiration date"* for common stock put and call options on individual stocks and indexes of stocks is the Saturday immediately following the third Friday of the option expiration month.

"Rights" and *"Warrants"* are similar to call options but generally are issued to provide investor incentive that enhances new fund raising potential. When a company wants to raise funds by issuing additional securities it sometimes gives its existing stockholders the *"right"* to buy the new securities ahead of other investors in proportion to the number of shares owned. The document evidencing this privilege is called a *"right"*. *Rights* usually give stockholders the right to buy new stock below the market value, so *rights* have a market value of their own, are actively traded and usually have a relatively short life. *"Warrants"* are similar to *rights* but may be good perpetually instead of for a finite period.

Stock splits and stock dividends usually are accounted for in options trading by adjusting the number of options shares proportional to the stock split or dividend. A *"stock dividend"* is a common stock dividend paid in securities rather than cash. A *"stock split"* is a division of the outstanding common stock shares of a corporation into a larger number of shares. With a three-for-one split by a company, each shareholder gets two new shares for each existing share, so the shareholder ends up with a total of three shares for each one existing share. On the day the three-for-one stock split is effective, the price per share of common stock is reduced to one-third the closing price at the close of trading on the previous day. The investor owns three times as many shares at one-third the price, so value is unchanged. Put and call options are adjusted similarly. On the day a three-for-one option is effective, each old put or call option controls three-hundred shares at one-third the strike price of the original one-hundred share put or call option contract. The Options Clearing Corporation has the final decision on option adjustments for stock splits and stock dividends but option adjustments normally are proportional to the common stock adjustments. In the case of a 25% stock dividend which would involve a company issuing twenty-five new shares for each existing one-hundred shares, old put and call contracts would control one-hundred-twenty-five shares after the stock dividend at a strike price of four-fifths of the original strike price.

12.3b Index Options

A "*common stock index*" is a measure of the value of a group of stocks. Other indexes have been developed to cover a variety of interests such as debt securities, foreign currencies, and the cost of living. However, only *stock indexes* are currently the subject of option trading. Different stock indexes are calculated in different ways. Often the market prices of the stocks in the index group are "value weighted". That is, in calculating the index value, the market price of each common stock is multiplied by the number of shares outstanding. Another method is to add up the prices of the stocks in the index and divide by the number of stocks, disregarding numbers of shares outstanding. No matter how the index is calculated, investors should keep in mind that an index responds only to price movements in stocks on which it is based. No index gives a true reflection of the total stock market. *When an index option is exercised, the exercise is settled by payment of cash, not by delivery of stock.*

EXAMPLE 12-7 Exercising An Index Option

Assume that the holder of a May $300 strike price call on the XYZ Index chooses to exercise it on a date when the exercise settlement value of the index is $325. If the multiplier for options on the XYZ Index is 100, the assigned call option writer would be obligated to pay the call option holder $2,500 in cash.

$2,500 = ($325 liquidation price – $300 strike price)(100)

The multipliers for options on different indexes may be different. Persons interested in trading index options should make sure that they know the applicable multiplier for each index involved in the trading. This affects the investment magnitude and financial exposure and risk. Index put options can be useful as an insurance type hedging mechanism that can reduce the negative financial impact on a common stock portfolio due to a sharp stock market decline. The following example illustrates this concept.

EXAMPLE 12-8 Index Put Options for Portfolio Insurance

Suppose that in February an investor wants to hedge a $100,000 common stock portfolio against a spring decline in the stock market. After examining the characteristics of the major stock indexes, the investor concludes that the Standard & Poor's 100 Index comes closest to matching the portfolio. Assume the S&P 100 Index stands at 272 and the multiplier is 100. The value then for one index option contract is $27,200, requiring four put contracts to approximate the $100,000 portfolio value. The investor might decide to buy four May $260 strike price puts. Since these puts are "out-of-money" by 12 points they are relatively cheap at about $4, or $400 per contract. Four put contracts would cost $1,600 or 1.6% of the portfolio value.

Suppose the market drops 20% bringing the Standard & Poor's 100 Index down to 218. Each May 260 put would have intrinsic value of 42 points ($260-$218) or $4,200 per contract. Four contracts would be worth $16,800 leaving $15,200 in profit after subtracting the $1,600 cost of the four puts. A 20% market decline would reduce the value of the $100,000 portfolio by $20,000 so the index put option insurance covered about 75% of the loss. By acquiring put options 12 points below market price (strike price of $260 when market price is $272), the investor effectively insured the portfolio against losses incurred after the first 12 points of the index's decline. Had the investor been willing to bear more of the market risk, the cost of the insurance could have been reduced by purchasing puts with a lower strike price. Another way to reduce the insurance cost is to sell the put options before they expire. Out-of-the-money put options (strike price below the market price) often lose most of their value in the final six weeks before expiration. Selling the insurance put options every month or two and replacing them with longer life options may reduce the hedging cost.

Index options also are utilized in trading strategies that attempt to apply *arbitrage* techniques. *"Arbitrage"* is a technique employed to take advantage of differences in price to lock in a profit. *"Programmed trading"* involves monitoring the prices and values of the stocks that make up a stock index as well as the value of the index. Sometimes differences occur in the values of the index and underlying common stock values so that simultaneous sale of the index and purchase of the underlying stock (or purchase of the index and simultaneous sale of the underlying stock) will lock in a profit. To handle these transactions fast enough to make them effectively simultaneous, they are computerized. Thus the term *"programmed trading"*.

12.3c Foreign Currency and Debt Options

Foreign currency and debt options provide a basis for hedging against foreign currency exchange rate or interest rate changes. *"Debt options"* are options on U.S. Treasury securities that require delivery of the underlying securities upon exercise of the options. *"Foreign currency options"* are traded on the currencies of many individual nations and also on the European Currency Unit (ECU), which is the official medium of exchange of the European Economic Community's Monetary System. Option contract sizes on foreign currencies vary from 62,500 West German marks or Swiss francs per contract to 50,000 Canadian or Australian dollars per contract, 6,250,000 Japanese yen per contract or 31,250 British pounds per contract. Debt options on U.S. Treasury Bonds and Notes cover a $100,000 principal amount of underlying Treasury securities.

"Exercise prices of debt options" are expressed as a percent of par. For example, a Treasury Bond call with an exercise price of 102 would entitle the holder to purchase the underlying bond for $102,000 (102% of $100,000) plus accrued interest on the bond from the date of issue or the last interest payment date, whichever is later, through and including the exercise settlement date.

"Exercise prices on foreign currencies" are expressed in U.S. cents per unit of foreign currency, with the exception of the Japanese yen which is expressed in hundredths of U.S. cents per yen. For example, a put covering 62,500 West German marks with an exercise price of 60 would entitle the put holder to sell 62,500 marks for a price of $37,500 ($.60 multiplied by 62,500). The *"expiration date for foreign currency"* options is the Saturday immediately preceding the third Wednesday of the expiration month. Refer to your broker for debt option expiration dates.

"Premiums for Treasury Bond and Note options" are expressed in terms of points and 32nds, with each 1/32 representing 1/32 of 1% of the unit of trading. For example, if a Treasury Note option is purchased at a premium of 2 16/32, the cost of the option will be $2,500 (2 1/2% of $100,000).

"Premiums on foreign currency" are expressed the same as exercise price, in U.S. cents per unit of foreign currency, again with the exception of the Japanese yen, which is expressed in hundredths of U.S. cents per yen.

EXAMPLE 12-9 Foreign Currency Options Illustrated

Suppose that the Australian dollar exchange rate is 75.5 cents U.S. per 100 cents Australian now (February). Assume that you can

A) acquire a June put at a 75 strike price for a premium of 2.60 cents or B) acquire a June call at a 75 strike price for a premium of 3.50 cents. Neglect commissions and calculate the profit or loss that will result from either transaction if the options are exercised on the June expiration date and 1) in June the Australian dollar exchange rate is 78 cents or 2) in June the Australian dollar exchange rate is 72 cents.

Solution: 1 Australian dollar = 1 unit with 50,000 units/contract

There will be no option time value at the expiration date so premium value and exercise value both equal intrinsic value at the expiration date.

A1) The right to sell Australian dollars at 75 cents is worthless when they can be sold in the open market at 78 cents. The final put value is therefore $0. Loss is: ($.026 initial cost/unit)(50,000 units) = $1300

A2) The right to sell Australian dollars at 75 cents is worth 3 cents per unit intrinsic value when the market value is 72 cents.
Profit/unit = ($.03 - $.026 initial cost) = 0.4 cents or $.004/unit
Total Profit = ($.004/unit)(50,000 units) = $200

B1) The right to buy Australian dollars at 75 cents is worth 3 cents per unit in intrinsic value when they cost 78 cents in the open market. However, the original call cost 3.5 cents per unit so we have a loss.
Loss/unit = $.03 final price - $.035 initial cost = -$.005 profit
Total Loss = ($.005/unit)(50,000 units) = $250
Even though the Australian dollar strengthened you lost money on this call because the 3 cent per unit time value in the call premium was greater than the 2.5 cent increase in intrinsic value.

B2) The right to buy Australian Dollars at 75 cents is worthless when they can be bought in the open market at 72 cents, so the June call premium value is $0.
Total Loss = ($0.035/unit)(50,000 units) = $1750

It is important to emphasize that the buyer of a put or call option acquires "the right" to sell or buy at the strike price until the option expires, but that no assets have actually been sold or bought unless and until the option is exercised. This is important because it limits an investor's maximum loss to the amount invested in the option. In the next section futures contracts are described as legal contracts involving the actual purchase or sale of assets for delivery at a specified future time. Since you are actually buying or selling for future delivery with futures contracts, maximum loss potential is unlimited. Not being able to lose more money than your initial investment in put and call options contracts often is considered to be a significant advantage over dealing in futures contracts with unlimited loss potential.

12.4 Futures Contract Transactions

Unlike common stock investments, futures contract investments, like option investments, have finite lives. Futures are primarily used for either; 1) hedging commodity price fluctuation risks or 2) price speculation for taking advantage of potential commodity price movements.

The "*buyer of a futures contract*" (the party with a long position) agrees on a fixed purchase price to buy the underlying commodity (for example, gold, wheat or T-Bonds) from the seller at a future contract expiration date. The "*seller of a futures contract*" (the party with a short position) agrees to sell the underlying commodity to the buyer at a fixed sale price at a future contract expiration date.

"*Futures contracts*" are legal contracts to buy or sell a specified amount of some commodity at a specified price for delivery at a future contract expiration date. However, in most cases, delivery never takes place. Instead, both the buyer and seller, acting independently of each other, usually liquidate their long and short positions before the contract expires. This is done by the buyer selling an equivalent futures contract and the seller buying an equivalent futures contract.

Each futures market and contract has characteristics described by answers to the following six questions:

1. What commodity do the contracts represent?
2. How much of that commodity and what grade of the commodity do the futures contract represent?
3. Which exchange handles the futures trades?
4. In what month and on what day do the contracts expire?
5. What is the monetary value of the smallest move the contract can make?
6. What is the maximum move the contract is allowed to make during one day?

EXAMPLE 12-10 A Gold Futures Contract Illustration

Suppose the price of gold is $420 per ounce in May and you feel: (A) the price is going to move up sharply in the future months so you buy an October gold contract for a futures contract settle price of $440 per ounce, or (B) the price is going to move down so you sell an October gold contract for $440 per ounce. Calculate the profit or loss from these transactions if the contracts are liquidated in September when the October gold future settle price is 1) $500 per ounce, 2) $400 per ounce.

Solution: (Gold futures contracts cover 100 troy ounces.)

A1) Buying gold at $440 per ounce and selling at $500 per ounce gives a $60 per ounce profit, times 100 ounces equals $6,000 profit.

A2) Buying gold at $440 per ounce and selling at $400 per ounce gives a $40 per ounce loss, times 100 ounces equals a $4,000 loss.

B1) Selling gold at $440 per ounce and buying it back at $500 per ounce results in a loss of $60 per ounce, times 100 ounces equals a $6,000 loss.

B2) Selling gold at $440 per ounce and buying it back at $400 per ounce gives a $40 per ounce profit, times 100 ounces equals a $4,000 profit.

Commodity Exchange transactions do not have to be paid for in cash. For most futures transactions an investor must deposit a "*margin*" in the amount of 10% to 15% of the underlying futures contract dollar value. Some brokers refer to the margin requirement on futures as a "good faith deposit" since there is no cost incurred until the future transaction is completed by either executing the futures contract or making an offsetting transaction. Minimum margins are set by the exchanges for different commodities and may be adjusted periodically due to commodity volatility changes. Notice that in the last Example 12-10, the investor bought or sold gold futures at $440 per ounce, so each 100 ounce contract had a value of $44,000. With a 10% margin requirement the investor put up $4,400 equity margin to realize a 136% return ($6,000/$4,400)(100%) on equity investment in "A1" and 136% loss (-$6,000/$4,400)(100%) on equity investment in "B1". It can be seen that percentage gain or loss on your equity investment in futures contracts can be very large and is limited only by commodity price movement.

"Hedgers" and *"speculators"* are the two basic categories of futures contract investors. In general *"hedgers"* use futures for protection against adverse future price movements in the underlying commodity. The rationale of hedging is based upon the demonstrated tendency of cash commodity spot prices and futures prices to move in tandem. Hedgers are often businesses or individuals who deal in the underlying commodity. Take for example a breakfast cereal producer that requires wheat and oats for cereal processing throughout the year. For protection against higher wheat and oat prices that could occur due to drought in the farm belt or increased sales to a foreign country the processor can "hedge" the risk exposure by buying wheat and oats contracts to cover the amount of grain that is expected to be bought in the future. If grain prices rise, profits on the futures contracts will offset the higher cost of grain, locking the price in at today's future contract price. Financial institutions, pension funds, insurance companies and corporations hedge their common stock and bond portfolios against market down turns by selling stock index futures, T-Bond or T-Bill futures. This is analogous to the use of index put options for portfolio insurance discussed in Example 12-8. If these same organizations have future financing requirements they can hedge against interest rate increases by buying T-Bond or T-Bill futures.

"Speculators" typically do not deal in the commodities underlying the futures they trade. Instead, they are in the market to profit by buying futures contracts they expect will rise in price and by selling futures contracts they expect will fall. Successful speculators usually are disciplined traders who study the market carefully. They know when to cut their losses or when to let their profits run. Otherwise they quickly are forced into another line of work.

12.4a Options on Futures

So far we have discussed and illustrated how speculators and hedgers buy or sell futures contracts depending on their views and objectives. You may also wish to participate in the futures market by buying or writing (selling) options on futures. Trading of options on futures began in 1983. As the name implies, "*options on futures*" are options to buy (a call) or sell (a put) a specified amount of commodity futures at a specified price for a specified time. "*Options on futures*" generally expire a few days before the underlying futures contracts expire so that futures positions created by exercise of an option can be reversed before the futures contract expires.

Options on futures offer the trader four investment position choices: buying or writing a call, or buying or writing a put. Direct futures trading only offers the investor two basic choices: buying or selling a futures contract. It is important to note that by investing in buying options on futures you cannot lose more than you invest whereas by buying futures contracts directly you have unlimited loss potential. *The buyer of options on futures* can profit greatly if his view is correct and the market continues to move in the direction he expected. If he is wrong he cannot lose more money than the premium he paid up front to the option writer.

On the other hand, the *writer of options on futures* contracts whose view is correct gets to keep the premium payment received from the buyer. This is the most he can make. If the writer is wrong he may lose part or all of the premium or if the buyer exercises the option before it expires, the writer may be assigned a losing position in the futures market. Furthermore, the writer whose position moves against him is *"marked to the market daily"* which means he must put up new investment money daily to cover losses.

Note the sharp differences in the risk profiles of options buyers and writers (sellers). The option buyer will profit if his view is correct and suffer limited losses if he is wrong. For this potential advantage, he pays the writer a premium. On the other hand the writer has limited profit potential (the premium is the maximum profit) and is exposed to unlimited losses if he is wrong.

Both writers and buyers of options can limit losses or take profits at any time by liquidating their positions at any time before the option expires. To do this, the option buyer sells an option with the same strike price and expiration as the one he is holding and the option writer buys an option to cancel the one he wrote.

EXAMPLE 12-11 Options on Futures Illustration

In August, Light Sweet Crude Oil was trading at $63.25 per barrel and on the same day, a November futures contract was trading at $64.48 per barrel. You are bullish and expect the price of crude oil to continue to rise above the current November pricing. The New York Mercantile Exchange (NYMEX™) futures contract involves trading 1,000 barrels per contract. If you purchase one Light Sweet Crude Oil contract, you would have a cost of:

Initial Investment (Cost Basis)

Buy 1 November Contract = 1,000 bbl * $64.48 / bbl = $64,480

As previously discussed, you would generally purchase this contract on margin and put up say, 10% as a good faith deposit to cover the position, which would cost $6,448 plus a commission when you cover by executing an offsetting position. If the November Light Sweet Crude Oil price continues to move up to $70, the investor could sell an offsetting contract in their account. The resulting buy and sell orders cancel in units, and any obligation to deliver, but would result in the following profit.

Cover Position

Sell 1 November Contract = 1,000 bbl * $70.00 / bbl = $70,000

Profit = $70,000 – $64,480 =
$5,520 less the commission when covering.

Instead of purchasing a November futures contract, the investor could purchase a November 6500 Call Option. This option would give an investor the right to buy one November crude contract at a strike price of $65.00 per bbl and is trading at a premium price of $3.43 per bbl. The cost basis in this position would be:

Initial Investment (Cost Basis)

1,000 bbl * $3.43 / bbl = $3,430 plus commission

If in the next few weeks, crude oil moved to $70.00 per barrel, the right to buy it for November delivery would increase by at least $5.00 ($70 market – $65 strike). Assuming the contract contained no additional speculative value, the premium might be $8.43 per barrel. The investor could then sell that right in the market and realize the following:

November Option Sale Value

1,000 bbls × $8.43 / bbl =
$8,430 per contract offset by the commission

Profit from position: $8,430 – $3.430 = $5,000 less commission.

With option investments, you cannot lose more than you invested in the option premium plus commission, whereas losses in futures investments are potentially unlimited and may end up being many times bigger than the initial investment. Hedging or speculating in futures almost always involves a margin type of account and the use of borrowed money. Investing in options may or may not involve the use of borrowed funds. Borrowing to extend any position works for investors that guess right, and can work against those who guess wrong!

12.5 Net Worth, Stock Equity, Bonds and Debentures

The *"net worth"* of a person, corporation or other organization equals total assets minus total liabilities. From an economic viewpoint, positive net worth is a desirable attribute of all entities. The net worth of corporations represents the corporate "equity" value, where *"equity" is the ownership interest of common and preferred stockholders in a company.* Whenever a person, corporation or other organization applies for a loan, they usually are required to provide information that determines their net worth for the lender. Since the concept of net worth relates to a variety of investment situations in different ways, it is very important to develop a good understanding of net worth and how to explicitly determine it. The following terms and discussion are intended to enhance understanding of net worth.

"Total assets" represent the value of everything a person, corporation or other organization owns or has due it. "Total assets" generally are broken into two components called current assets and fixed assets. *"Current assets" are convertible into cash within a year by normal operations.* They typically include cash, accounts receivable on realized sales, inventories, and short term loans due to the investor within one year. *"Fixed assets" are assets that in the normal course of business will not be converted to cash within one year such as land, mineral rights, buildings, equipment and business interests.*

"Total liabilities" are all the financial claims against an individual, corporation or other organization, and are generally broken into two components called current (short term) liabilities and long term liabilities. *"Current" or "short term liabilities" are accounts payable, notes and loans due within one year. "Long term liabilities"(also called "funded debt") are the bond, debenture and long-term loan financing payable more than one year in the future, not including common and preferred stock, which are equity ownership securities rather than debt securities.*

Total assets minus total liabilities gives "net worth" which represents the combined preferred and common stock equity value of a corporation. "Common stock" securities represent an ownership interest in a corporation.

If the corporation has also issued "preferred stock", both common and preferred stock holders have ownership rights, but the preferred stock holder normally has first claim on dividends, and assets in the event of liquidation. Preferred stock dividends normally are paid at a specified rate while common stock dividends fluctuate with the earnings of the corporation. Common stock holders, therefore, assume the greater risk, but generally exercise greater control through voting right preferences over preferred stock. "Voting rights" on common stock usually are one vote per share. Preferred shareholders usually only vote if preferred dividends are in default.

There are several different categories of preferred stock. *"Cumulative preferred stock"* has a provision that states if one or more dividends are omitted, the omitted dividends must be paid before any dividends may be paid on the company's common stock. *"Non-cumulative preferred stock"* does not allow for the accrual of unpaid dividends so omitted dividends are essentially non-recoverable. *"Participating preferred stock"* is entitled to its stated dividend and also to additional dividends on a specified basis upon payment of dividends on the common stock of the company.

In the event of a corporate liquidation, bond holders are at the head of the creditor line to be paid off with available funds, debenture holders are second, preferred stock holders third, and common stock holders are last. Common stock investment gives the greatest reward potential from possible increasing dividends and capital appreciation in common stock value. This greater reward potential is offset by greater risk of losing the investment principal in comparison with bond, debenture or preferred stock investments.

"Bonds" are promissory notes of a corporation or government entity usually issued in multiples of $1000. A bond is evidence of a debt for which the issuer promises to pay the bondholder a specified amount of interest for a specified length of time, and then to repay the bond face value on the expiration date. In every case a bond represents debt, which means the bond holder is a creditor and not a part owner as is the case of a common or preferred stock holder. Property or securities that have been pledged by a borrower to secure repayment of a loan is called *"collateral"*. Bonds are backed by the assets of a company as collateral.

"Debentures" are similar to bonds except that they are backed only by the general credit and name of the issuing company and not by the assets of the company. To entice investors to accept the greater risk associated with debenture investments, debentures typically have higher dividend rates than bonds. *"Convertible debentures"* are debentures that may be exchanged by

the owner for common stock or another security of the same company in accordance with the terms of the issue. *"Convertible bonds"* and *"convertible preferred stock"* have characteristics similar to those of *"convertible debentures"*.

An *"indenture"* is a written agreement under which bonds, debentures and preferred stock are issued, setting forth interest or dividend rates, maturity dates, sinking fund requirements, etc. A *"sinking fund"* holds money set aside regularly by a company to redeem bonds, debentures or preferred stock in accordance with the indenture.

Bonds, debentures, preferred and common stock investments generally are considered to be very *"liquid"* investments because they are easily converted to cash. When a very large block of common stock of a company is sold, often it is done through a secondary distribution. A *"secondary distribution"* involves redistribution of a large block of common stock sometime after the initial *"primary distribution"* by the issuing company. The secondary distribution sale is handled by a securities firm or group of firms, and the shares usually are offered at a fixed price which is related to the current price of the stock. In a *"thin market"* in which there are comparatively few bids to buy or offers to sell, it may be more difficult to liquidate bond, debenture or stock investments at "your" price than in a *"liquid market"* where there are many bids to buy and offers to sell. Bonds are either traded "flat" or "and interest". Most bonds are traded *"and interest"* which means the buyer pays to the seller the bond market price plus accrued interest since the last dividend payment date. *"Flat"* means that the bond price includes consideration for all unpaid accrued interest.

Bonds are a very popular method of debt financing for corporations and government organizations so there are many different types of bonds. As presented in Chapter 3, Section 3.5, *"U.S. Treasury Bonds"* are securities issued by the U.S. government with lives greater than 10 years. *"U.S. Treasury Notes"* have lives of one to ten years and *"U.S. Treasury Bills"* have three, six or twelve month maturity dates. Treasury Bond, Note and Bill investments are perceived to be among the safest investments in the world today and, as a result, are often used as the basis for a risk free rate. Conventional Treasury or corporate bond interest rates are paid semi-annually with maturity value equal to the face value of the bond. All bonds issued since the mid-1980's are *registered bonds. "Registered bonds"* are bonds that are registered on the books of the issuing company or government organization in the name of the owner and can only be transferred to a new owner when endorsed by the registered owner. *"Bearer bonds"* are not registered on the books of the issuing company, so the bearer of the bond is the owner. No signature is necessary to transfer ownership; they are *"negotiable"* like cash. In the mid 1980's Congress outlawed the issuance of new bearer bonds, but bonds in existence at the time of the law change will be traded for another twenty to twenty-five years. *Bearer bonds* are *"coupon bonds"*; bonds with coupons attached. The coupons are clipped as they come due and are presented by the holder for payment of interest (usually through a local bank).

"Zero coupon bonds" are bonds that pay no semi-annual dividends; the dividend coupons have a value of zero. Zero coupon bonds can be created by stripping the dividends from the maturity value and selling the two components separately, or by setting up a new bond issue on a zero coupon bond basis. Zero coupon bonds are sold at a discount from face value.

EXAMPLE 12-12 Conventional and Zero Coupon Bonds

A conventional $10,000 U.S. Treasury, 30 year bond will pay interest at a rate of 8% compounded semi-annually. What are the present values of the interest stream and the maturity value respectively?

Solution:

Conventional Bond C=$10,000 Int=$400 . . . . Int=$400
Maturity Value = $10,000
0 1 . . . . 60 semi-annual periods

$$\text{PW Int.} = \$400\overset{22.623}{(P/A_{4,60})} = \$9{,}049$$

$$\text{PW Maturity Value} = \$10{,}000\overset{.0951}{(P/F_{4,60})} = \$951$$

Total Conventional Bond Present Value = $9,049 + $951 = $10,000

If you sell the year 30 maturity value of $10,000.00 separately for $951.00 at year 0, it is a zero coupon bond transaction.

By selling the interest stream and the maturity value separately, retired people looking for maximum annual income achieve their objective by buying the interest stream and not having to pay for the maturity value, which they might not expect to live long enough to utilize. Pension funds for individuals, corporations or government organizations acquire zero coupon bonds to obtain investments that lock in the bond interest rate at the investment rate of growth over the life of the zero coupon bond. Individuals in the U.S. often do not find zero coupon bonds attractive investments for non-pension fund or non-tax deferred annuity investment funds. This is because individuals must pay tax on accrued interest each year whether the accrued interest is physically received or not. People often have an aversion to paying tax on revenue they do not actually receive until a later date.

Bond investment values can be very sensitive to interest rate changes. Many people do not realize that they can lose money in the bond market just as fast or faster than in the stock market.

EXAMPLE 12-13 Bond Value Sensitivity to Interest Rates

Assume that you invest \$10,000 in a 30 year, U.S. Treasury Bond paying 8% interest compounded semi-annually. You invest another \$10,000 in a 30 year, U.S Treasury zero coupon bond paying 8% interest compounded semi-annually, giving a year 30 maturity value of \$105,196 (\$10,000 x $F/P_{4,60}$). Further assume that one week after you buy these bonds, a major change occurs in financial markets, interest rates jump to 10% per year compounded semi-annually. You need to sell these bonds to meet other financial obligations. Calculate your one-week percent loss from each bond investment.

Solution: Bond sale values are based on 5% per semi-annual period interest at the time of the sale (10% compounded semi-annually).

Regular Bond	C=\$10,000	Int=\$400 . . . . Int=\$400	Maturity Value = \$10,000
	0	1 . . . . 60 semi-annual periods	

One week later, present worth is:

$$= \$400(\overset{18.929}{P/A_{5,60}}) + \$10{,}000(\overset{.0535}{P/F_{5,60}}) = \$8{,}107$$

Percent Loss = [(\$10,000 – \$8,107)/\$10,000](100%) = 18.93%

Zero Coupon Bond	C=\$10,000	— . . . . —	Maturity Value = \$105,196
	0	1 . . . . 60 semi-annual periods	

One week later, present worth is:

$$= \$105{,}196(P/F_{5,60}^{.0535}) = \$5{,}628$$

Percent Loss = [(\$10,000 - \$5,628)](100%) = 43.72%

These are very significant percent changes in investment values. In this case and in general, zero coupon bond values are much more sensitive to interest rate changes than conventional bonds. Unless investments are long-term to lock-in a satisfactory rate of money growth, zero coupon investment are very speculative investments that can either lose or make money quickly over the short term. It is wise to choose very high rated A plus zero coupon bond investments. Since no money is received until far into the future, you want to be certain about investment security. The only zero coupon bond investments recommended here are U.S. Treasury zero coupon bonds.

U.S. Government Savings Bonds, Series EE are directly analogous to zero coupon bonds except for one very significant income tax difference. Tax on accrued interest on EE Savings Bonds is deferred to the future point in time when you cash them, while zero coupon bond accrued interest is taxed annually. However, to offset the tax advantage of Series EE Savings Bonds, a lower interest rate is paid than on conventional bonds.

EXAMPLE 12-14 Zero Coupon Bonds and Series EE Savings Bonds

Compare the after-tax future value accumulated 5 years in the future from investment of \$10,000 in a 9% annual interest rate, 5 year zero coupon bond, or a 7.65% Series EE Savings Bond. The 7.65% rate is 85% of the 9% rate. Effective annual interest rates and annual interest payments are assumed here for simplicity of calculations rather than using the actual semi-annual period rates that apply to bonds. Assume a 32% effective federal plus state income tax rate for an individual. Assume the money paid in tax every year on accrued interest on the zero coupon bond would be invested in additional new EE savings bonds at 7.65% interest per year if that alternative were elected.

Solution:

	Accrued Taxable Interest Per Year						
Zero Coupon Bond, 9%/yr	C=$10,000	$900	$981	$1,069	$1,166	$1,270	Maturity Value=$15,386
	0	1	2	3	4	5	
Income Tax @ 38%		$288	$314	$342	$373	$406	

The tax to be paid every year is additional outside investment necessary to generate the $15,386 year 5 zero coupon bond maturity value which is after-tax cash flow. Assume money equivalent in amount and timing to the zero coupon bond interest tax payments is invested in Series EE Savings Bonds each year for a fair comparison.

Series EE Bond, 7.65% yr	C=$10,000	$288	$314	$342	$373	$406	Maturity Value=?
	0	1	2	3	4	5	

$$\text{Maturity Value} = \$10{,}000(\overset{1.4457}{F/P_{7.65,5}}) + 288(\overset{1.3429}{F/P_{7.65,4}})$$

$$+ 314(\overset{1.2475}{F/P_{7.65,3}}) + 342(\overset{1.1589}{F/P_{7.65,2}})$$

$$+ 373(\overset{1.0765}{F/P_{7.65,1}}) + 406 = \$16{,}033$$

The difference in the $16,033 maturity value and cumulative investment amount is taxable at 32%.

Income Tax = ($16,033 - $11,723 Cum. Cost)(.32) = $1,379

After-tax Series EE year 5 CF = $16,033 - $1,379 = $14,654

This Series EE Savings Bond future value of $14,654 after taxes is less than the zero coupon bond future value of $15,386 after tax, so the zero coupon investment is economically preferable. Remember that these numbers are to illustrate general concepts and methods only. The analysis should be re-run for actual savings bond and zero coupon bond rates that are applicable at the time of your investment decision.

"Municipal bonds" (or "tax exempt bonds") are the bonds of state, city, county and other public authorities specified under federal law, the interest

on which is either wholly or partly exempt from federal income tax and sometimes exempt from state income tax. Whereas the accrued interest on Series EE savings bonds is tax deferred to the future time when the bonds are sold, municipal bond interest is "tax-free". The only exception is related to municipal bonds that are subject to alternative minimum tax. If the funds from municipal bonds are used for private development purposes rather that public purposes, those municipal bonds are subject to alternative minimum tax rules for individuals or corporations, which may cause part or all of municipal bond interest to be taxable. It is advisable to check with a tax accountant or knowledgeable broker concerning alternative minimum tax status of specific municipal bond issues before investing.

As in comparing the tax savings of Series EE Savings Bonds to zero coupon bonds, *the potential tax savings of "tax free" municipal bonds are not really tax-free. Investors accept interest rates in municipal bond investments that typically are several percentage points less than can be obtained in conventional taxable bond investments. Therefore, implicit tax is actually being paid on municipal bonds.* The public municipalities benefit from the lower interest rates that investors are willing to accept to avoid paying tax on the interest.

EXAMPLE 12-15 A Municipal Bond Investment Compared to a Taxable Zero Coupon Bond Investment

Compare the Example 12-14 $10,000 cost, 9% annual interest 5 year zero coupon bond investment which had after-tax future value of $15,383 with the future value of a municipal bond investment. Consider investing the initial $10,000 and the annual tax that would be paid on annual accrued interest on the zero coupon bond investment in municipal bonds paying 7.5% interest per year. Assume annual municipal bond interest can be reinvested every year in other municipal bonds paying 7.5% interest per year. Assume the municipal bond is not subject to alternative minimum tax.

Solution:

Zero Coupon Bond Year 5 Value = \$15,386 after-tax, from Example 12-14

Municipal Bond Year 5 Value

$$= \$10{,}000(F/P_{7.5,5})^{1.4356} + 288(F/P_{7.5,4})^{1.3355} + 314(F/P_{7.5,3})^{1.2423} + 342(F/P_{7.5,2})^{1.1556}$$

$$+ 373(F/P_{7.5,1})^{1.075} + 406 = \$15{,}927 \text{ after-tax}$$

For the assumed rates in this analysis the municipal bond investment is projected to give the greater future value by \$541. For relatively high tax bracket individuals, municipal bond investments often are preferable to other taxable fixed interest rate bond, debenture, preferred stock, certificate of deposit or money market account type investments. However, for tax deferred annuities and pension funds where income tax does not have to be paid until the funds are liquidated, the lower municipal bond interest rate is a disadvantage. Each investment analysis situation must be analyzed carefully with special attention paid to income tax considerations and risk differences.

The final bond subject concerns *junk bonds. "Junk bonds"* are the bonds of highly leveraged corporations that have questionable ("junky") assets backing the bonds as collateral. Although bonds are ahead of debenture and preferred and common stock creditors, they follow long term loans in the creditor pecking order in the event of bankruptcy liquidation. The highly leveraged buy-outs of major companies in recent years have been carried out with such large amounts of long term debt, that bonds previously thought to be safe, secure and high rated have been pushed down to the risky "junk bond" category after leveraged buy-outs. Today, investors must be aware that a leveraged buy-out can cause the bonds of almost any company to take on the "junk bond" label overnight. This makes the security of U.S. Treasury Notes and Bonds look especially good today. Bond investments can be much riskier than many people realize, making "high quality" of utmost importance.

12.6 Placing Orders to Buy or Sell Stocks, Bonds, Debentures, Options and Futures

To maximize the likelihood that you will achieve your objective in buying or selling stocks, bonds, debentures, options, futures or other securities, it is desirable to be aware that there are many different ways of placing orders to buy or sell. The most common order utilized is a *market order*. A *"market order"* is an order to buy or sell a stated amount of a security at the most advantageous price obtainable after the order is represented in the *Trading Crowd*. The *"Trading Crowd"* is the group of traders at the trading locations where securities are bought and sold on the floor of the New York Stock Exchange or other stock, bond, option or commodity futures exchanges. Brokers and the broker's stock exchange representative are legally obligated under Securities and Exchange Commission (SEC) law to obtain the best price possible for their clients when a market order is placed. A *"limit order"* is an order to buy or sell a stated amount of a security at a specified price, or at a better price if obtainable, after the order is represented in the Trading Crowd. The terms *"limited order"* and *"limited price order"* are interchangeable with *"limit order"*. Limit orders enable investors to specify the price they are willing to pay to buy or sell securities. Especially when you are buying or selling stocks in the *over-the-counter* market it is desirable to consider placing limit orders rather than market orders. The *"over-the-counter"* market is a market for securities conducted primarily by telephone by securities dealers who may or may not be members of a securities exchange. When investors place limit orders they reduce the necessity to rely on the integrity of brokers they do not know. A large majority of brokers represent their clients well with the highest level of integrity. However, in any walk of life, there is a small percent of people who will "take you to the cleaners" and separate you from your financial capital if you give them the opportunity. Limit orders reduce this likelihood in securities transactions. With respect to the over-the-counter market in stocks, the prices of more widely traded common stocks are reported on the National Association of Securities Dealers Automated Quotation (NASDAQ) system. This is an automated communications system that allows securities dealers throughout the country to see quickly the bid and asked price quotation range of all brokers making a market in a specific issue. The *"bid and asked"* price or *"quotation"* or *"quote"* is the highest price anyone wants to pay to buy (the bid) and the lowest price anyone wants to sell for at the same time (the asked). Many small company stocks are not regularly reported on the NASDAQ stock listings.

There are many variations of market and limit orders to achieve specific trading objectives with specified timing constraints. A *"good till cancelled order"* or *"open order"* is an order to buy or sell which remains in effect until it is either executed or cancelled. An *"order good until a specified time"* is a market or limit order which is to be represented in the Trading Crowd until a specified time, after which such order, or portion thereof, not executed is to be treated as though it were cancelled. A *"day order"* is an order to buy or sell which, if not executed , expires at the end of the trading day on which it was entered. An *"at the opening order"* or *"at the opening only order"* is a market or limit order which is to be executed at the opening (the initial trade of the day) of the stock or not at all, and any such order, or portion thereof, not so executed is treated as cancelled. An *"at the close order"* is a market order which is to be executed at the close, or as near the close as practicable. A *"time order"* is an order to buy or sell which becomes a market or limit order at a specified time.

A *"fill or kill order"* is a market or limit order that is to be executed in its entirety as soon as it is represented to the Trading Crowd. If not so executed, the order is treated as cancelled. An *"all or none order"* is a market or limit order which is to be executed in its entirety or not at all. Unlike a "fill or kill" order, it is not treated as a cancelled order if not executed as soon as it is represented in the Trading Crowd.

A *"stop order"* is an order to buy (or sell) which becomes an executable market order to buy (or sell) when a transaction in the security occurs at or above (or below with a stop order to sell) the stop price. Stop orders may be used in an effort to protect paper profit, or to try and limit loss to a certain amount, or to take advantage of perceived technical or fundamental considerations affecting the market. The term *"technical analysis"* applies to various internal factors affecting the market such as the size of the short interest, whether the market has had a sustained advance or decline without interruption, whether sharp advances or declines have occurred on small or large volume and so forth. *"Fundamental analysis"* relates to fundamental economic factors such as current earnings, earnings trends, new orders, dividends, current and projected interest rates, economic conditions and so forth.

A *"stop limit order"* is an order to buy (or sell) which becomes an executable limit order to buy (or sell) when a transaction in the security occurs at or above (or below with a stop limit order to sell) the stop price. An *"alternative order"*, sometimes called an *"either/or order"* is an order to do either of two alternatives, such as either sell (or buy) a particular stock at a limit price or sell (or buy) on a stop order. If the order is executed upon the happening of one alternative, the order on the other alternative is treated as cancelled. If the order is for an amount of securities larger than one unit of trading, the number of units executed determines the amount of the alternative order to be treated as cancelled.

12.7 Comparison of Alternative Personal Investments

Individuals can make many different types of investments with widely varying tax ramifications. For example, any person with available capital has a choice of investing in common or preferred stocks, bonds, debentures, bank money market accounts and certificates of deposit, insurance annuities, leasing ventures, real estate, farm and ranch or raw land, mining or petroleum developments or tax deferred annuities, pension plans and individual retirement accounts to name some of the common possibilities. This makes personal investment analyses of alternative investment choices as complicated, or *more* complicated than many corporate analyses. As with general business analyses, personal investment evaluations may involve the analysis of either mutually exclusive or non-mutually exclusive alternatives. Like business analyses, all personal investment analyses must be done after-tax, consistently using either escalated or constant dollars. However, escalated dollar analysis is recommended. Consistent leverage (borrowed money to equity ratio) must also be used in all evaluations if they are not being done on a cash equity (100% margin) investment basis. Fair analysis comparison of tax deferred, tax free and taxable investments requires very careful handling of the after-tax analysis income tax considerations.

For investors in all tax brackets the tax deferred aspects of investments in a traditional individual retirement account (IRA), tax deferred annuities and pension plans create very complex and competitive alternatives with many other taxable income alternatives from earned interest in bonds or CD's or taxable income from investment opportunities. The Roth IRA is somewhat inverted to a traditional IRA. With traditional IRA's, initial investments up to the limit amount are deductible from ordinary taxable income in that year and withdrawals after age 59½ are taxed as ordinary income. With a Roth IRA, initial investments are not tax deductible and withdrawals after 59½ are not taxed. In fact, you can withdraw the equity invested in a Roth at any time and not be subject to tax or penalties. Below is a summary of some of the principal features differentiating a Roth IRA from a Regular IRA:

Traditional IRA

- A combined total investment of $5,500 may be invested in 2014 in Traditional or Roth IRA accounts. This amount is indexed for inflation in $500 dollar annual increments. Various adjustments are made to the maximum contribution level for individuals in different age brackets. With these deposits all federal income tax is deferred until withdrawals are realized beginning at age 59½.
- With few exceptions, any withdrawal prior to age 59½ is subject to a 10% penalty in addition to the ordinary income tax due on the amount withdrawn.
- Mandatory minimum distributions enforced at age 70½.
- No contributions allowed after age 70½.
- For anybody other than a spouse that might inherit an IRA, the amount of the IRA may be subject to both estate taxes and ordinary income tax on any subsequent withdrawals from the account.
- In qualifying to contribute to a traditional IRA individuals and married couples are subject to constraints on their Adjusted Gross Income and any participation in an employee sponsored retirement program.

Roth IRA

- A combined total investment of $5,500 may be invested in 2014 in Traditional or Roth IRA accounts. This amount is indexed for inflation in $500 dollar annual increments. Various adjustments are made to the maximum contribution level for individuals in different age brackets. Deposits are not deductible in the year incurred so the annual amount deposited is subject to state and federal income taxes the year the deposit is made.
- Investors may withdraw 100% of the accumulated investment (equity) at any time and not be subject to any penalty or tax. Only the accrued interest or wealth must remain in the account or these funds are subject to a 10% penalty. Some exceptions may apply related to first time home ownership.
- A child with earned income can invest each year in a Roth IRA the lesser of their earned taxable income for the year or $5,500. If a child has no earned income for a year, then no Roth IRA deposit can be made. However, the deposit to a Roth IRA could come from a gift from parents or grandparents and still qualify provided the child's earned income really exists! For children under 18 the creation of a Roth IRA

will require a custodial account and proof of income such as check receipts, W4 or W2 forms. Each broker will likely have their own proof of income requirements to establish the account.

- At age 59½, any amount may be withdrawn from a Roth tax free. However, because of this benefit, married and single taxpayers may only contribute to a Roth if their adjustable gross income is less than $178,000 or $112,000, respectively, in 2014. There are reduced allowable contributions up to $188,000 for married taxpayers and $127,000 for individual taxpayers. All of these amounts are indexed for inflation.
- There are no mandatory minimum distributions at 70½.
- Contributions may continue to be made after age 70½ if you have earned income.
- Heirs to a Roth account get a tax deduction for federal estate taxes paid on any withdrawals the heirs make from the account.

To qualify to contribute to a Roth IRA single individuals and married couples are subject to constraints on their adjusted gross incomes for various scenarios.

Decisions on whether you qualify for an IRA, and which account to establish, can be difficult. Not because of time value of money issues but more due to the complexity of the tax code, estate considerations, the flexibility of anticipated withdrawals during the retirement years, etc. This is clearly an area where the financial and intangible considerations addressed in Chapter 1 are relevant.

The following example illustrates some of the time value of money basics for the different types of savings alternatives you might be considering for feathering your retirement nest egg.

EXAMPLE 12-16 Traditional IRA, Roth IRA and Taxable Savings Plans

Consider a 40-year-old individual with $2,000 of annual before-tax salary that is being considered for investment. Assume the first deposit (investment) would be made one year from today. The investor is currently in a 31% effective federal plus state tax bracket but upon retirement 20 years from today, the corresponding tax rate on ordinary income should drop to 18% as the income level drops. Develop the appropriate time diagrams and compare the after-tax future value that would be available 20 years from today by investing the money in the following alternatives:

A) The individual opens a traditional IRA and invests the before-tax salary in a conservative government bond mutual fund that is anticipated to earn 8.0% before taxes per year for the next 20 years. Tax on any income is deferred until the account is liquidated which is assumed to occur 20 years from today.

B) The individual opens the same traditional IRA but invests the before-tax salary in a growth fund that is anticipated to grow at 12.0% per year for the next 20 years before taxes.

C) The individual opens a Roth IRA and invests the after-tax money in a conservative government bond mutual fund that is anticipated to earn 8.0% before taxes per year for the next 20 years. Tax on any account accrued income is eliminated by tax code definition of a Roth IRA.

D) The individual opens the same Roth IRA but invests in a growth fund that is anticipated to grow at 12.0% per year for the next 20 years before-taxes.

E) Suppose this individual can't qualify for either IRA and considers investing the $2,000 of before-tax salary in the stock market. The stock to be acquired pays no dividend and will hopeful grow at the 12.0% average growth rate similar to the other fund. However, in this case, if the stock is sold after 20 years, it will qualify for long-term capital gains at an assumed tax rate of 15%. (Currently stock investments made after year 2000 and held for at least 5 years qualify for a maximum long-term capital gain tax rate of 18.0%).

Solution:

A) Traditional IRA, Earning 8.0% Per Year

With the traditional IRA, taxpayers have the ability to keep 100% of their tax dollars working until retirement 20 years from now.

–	$2,000	$2,000 . . $2,000
0	1	2 20

$$F = \$2,000(F/A_{8\%,20}) \quad [45.7620]$$
$$= \$91,524$$

Year 20 ATCF = $91,524(1 – 0.18 year 20 tax rate) = $75,050

Note: If the Year 20 tax rate remained at 31%, ATCF = 63,152

B) Traditional IRA, Earning 12.0% Per Year

Again, With the traditional IRA, taxpayers have the ability to keep 100% of their tax dollars working until retirement 20 years from now.

–	\$2,000	\$2,000 . . \$2,000
0	1	2 20

$$F = \$2{,}000(F/A_{12\%,20}) = \$144{,}105 \quad (72.0524)$$

Year 20 ATCF = \$144,105(1 – 0.18 year 20 tax rate) = \$118,166

Note: If the Year 20 tax rate remained at 31%, ATCF = 99,432

C) Roth IRA, Earning 8.0% Per Year

The disadvantage of the Roth IRA is the loss of available dollars working for you due to income taxes – until retirement 20 years from now. For an investor with an anticipated tax rate of 31.0%, the after-tax income available to invest would be:

Year	1–20
Taxable Salary	2,000
– Income Taxes @ 31%	– 620
After-Tax Salary (ATCF)	1,380

–	\$1,380	\$1,380 . . \$1,380
0	1	2 20

$$F = \$1{,}380(F/A_{8\%,20}) = \$63{,}152 \quad (45.7620)$$

Year 20 ATCF = \$63,152

Note this result is identical to the Case A traditional IRA result for a 31% tax rate in year 20.

D) Roth IRA, Earning 12.0% Per Year

Again, the only change in this analysis from Case C is the increase in the annual interest or rate of growth for the account as follows:

–	\$1,380	\$1,380 . . \$1,380
0	1	2 20

$$F = \$1{,}380(F/A_{12\%,20}) = \$99{,}432 \quad (72.0524)$$

Year 20 ATCF = \$99,432

This result is the same as the Case B traditional IRA result for a 31% tax rate in year 20.

E) Ordinary Taxable Investment in Common Stock

The disadvantage here is that not only is your salary still taxable, but now the gain realized 20 years from today would also be taxable at the applicable long-term capital gains tax rate assumed to be 15.0% for this example.

Year	1–20
Taxable Salary	2,000
– Income Taxes @ 31%	– 620
After-Tax Salary (ATCF)	1,380

–	\$1,380	\$1,380 . . . . \$1,380
0	1	2 20

$$F = \$1{,}380(F/A_{12\%,20}) = \$99{,}432 \quad (F/A_{12\%,20} = 72.0524)$$

Year	20
Stock Sale Value	99,432
– Stock Book Value	–27,600
Long-Term Capital Gain	71,832
– Income Taxes @ 15%	–10,775
Net Income	61,057
+ Stock Book Value	27,600
ATCF	88,657

Note that due to the double taxation of salary and stock appreciation, the after-tax value of this opportunity is diminished relative to investing in either the traditional IRA or the Roth IRA.

Looking back at cases A, B, C and D you can see that the biggest impact has more to do with the forecasted tax rates and the timing of withdrawals at retirement. If tax rates are held the same, the same after-tax cash flow is generated with each alternative. Forecasted higher future tax rates would favor the Roth while lower future tax rates favor the traditional IRA as illustrated in this example.

For investors who feel that it is reasonable to expect to be able to select common stock investments analogous to those listed in Section 12.2 with the potential to grow at 12% per year or better in the foreseeable future, common stock investments are very competitive with conventional and municipal bond investments for long term capital accumulation purposes. However, as the economic "gloom and doom" advocates continually remind us, an economic crash worse than any seen since 1929 could be just around the corner. Therefore, maintaining a diversified investment portfolio in the highest quality common stocks, bonds, real estate and other investments of interest probably is best.

12.7a Life Insurance Alternatives

There are two primary situations where an individual may need life insurance. The first situation is when a person has dependents such as a spouse and children that would financially suffer if the person died without life insurance. The second situation is where a relatively wealthy and older person has a significantly large estate tied up in illiquid assets and therefore, wants to leave the estate enough cash flow to cover estate taxes upon death.

A significant tax consideration related to life insurance is that beneficiaries owe no income tax on policy values received upon death of the insured. There may, however be estate tax. By handling the establishment of a life insurance policy and payment of policy premiums in a legally appropriate manner, the beneficiary may avoid estate tax as well as income tax upon death of the insured. Good legal counsel is necessary to achieve this objective.

By far the most common need for life insurance relates to a person wanting to leave their spouse and children in reasonable financial shape if unexpected death of the person occurs. It is important to keep in mind in this situation that the insurance death benefit is the needed coverage for this situation. Accumulating a cash value in the insurance policy is a secondary consideration.

There are two basic types of life insurance policies with many variations of each: 1) term insurance, and 2) whole life, ordinary life, or universal life insurance. Term insurance is pure insurance on the insured's life with no cash value accrued at any time during the policy. Whole life, ordinary life and universal life insurance involve a combination of insurance and a savings plan that has a future after-tax value. Therefore, annual premiums are greater for whole life type policies than term insurance. Whole life and ordinary life insurance policies generally have uniform annual premiums over the policy life and specified cash values at different future points in time. Universal life insurance is a modern day variation of whole life insurance. The key difference is with universal life insurance policies you can vary your premiums from year to year. Of course this affects your death benefit and cash value from year to year rather than having fixed benefits and cash values as with whole life insurance.

The least expensive life insurance is term insurance. If the primary objective is to provide insurance death benefit to beneficiaries upon unexpected death, term insurance is best in most situations. For those under 50 years of age, buying term insurance and investing extra dollars elsewhere in stocks, bonds or real estate usually will give greater future cash value than paying higher premiums annually for a whole life, ordinary life or universal life type policy. This generally is true even considering tax on the annual accrued interest component of whole life policy cash value is deferred. For either term or whole life policies, paying extra premium for increased accidental death benefit often makes sense, since unexpected death by accident is a major reason for life insurance.

To quantitatively evaluate the economic differences between term and whole life type insurance policies, you must compare insurance premiums and cash values for equal levels of insurance over the same period of time. Incremental analysis of the difference in values for whole life versus term insurance gives the incremental values that the incremental insurance premium costs generate for whole life versus term insurance.

EXAMPLE 12-17 Term Versus Whole Life Insurance Analysis

Consider a 35 year old person wanting $250,000 of life insurance over the next 30 years. Under a universal life policy, that coverage can be obtained for beginning of year premiums of $1,600.00 per year. At the end of year 30, the lump sum cash value of the policy is estimated to be $162,150.00. Assuming a lump sum withdrawal is made at the end of year 30, taxes would be owed on the difference between the cash value and the cumulative premium payments over 30 years (30 * $1,600.00 = $48,000). The alternative is to acquire guaranteed renewable term insurance with premiums increasing every ten years. With beginning of period premium payments, the payments are estimated to be $328.00 at years 0 through 9. At years 10 through 19 the payments are expected to be $616.00 per year and those premiums will increase to $1,346.00 at years 20 through 29. Assume a 35.0% effective federal plus state tax rate for an after-tax cash flow analysis.

Solution:

Whole Life:

–$1,600	–$1,600	–$1,600	–$1,600	–$1,600	–$1,600	–$1,600	$162,150
0	1. 9		10 19		20 29		30

Term:

–$328	–$328	–$328	–$616	–$616	–1,346	–$1,346	$0
0	1. 9		10 19		20 29		30

Whole Life-Term:

–$1,272	–$1,272	–$1,272	–$984	–$984	–$254	–$254	+$162,150
0	1. 9		10 19		20 29		30

Before-tax, Incremental ROR = 9.04%

Assuming the cumulative sum of the 30 universal life premiums will be deductible against the year 30 cash value of $162,150, the after-tax cash flow at year 30 will be:

Year 30 CF = $162,150 – ($162,150-$48,000)(0.35 tax rate)
= $122,198

This gives after-tax DCFROR of 7.71% on the incremental premium investments. If the 7.71% after-tax incremental investment is competitive with other opportunities for investing capital now and in the future over the next 30 years, then acceptance of the incremental universal life policy investments is indicated.

12.7b Home Purchase Versus Renting

One of the most common major investment decisions that people face in their working careers is deciding whether to rent or buy a residence. Many factors affect this decision. From an intangible viewpoint, most people want their own home. On the other hand, if you travel a lot, not having to worry about home maintenance may override the satisfaction of home ownership. If you expect to move in a year or two, renting and not having to worry about selling your home to move may be perceived to be a big intangible benefit regardless of economics. As discussed earlier in the text, a combination of intangible and financial factors along with economic considerations usually impact investment decisions. Although the importance of intangible and financial factors is recognized, a proper economic analysis of renting versus buying a home should be done.

Economic parameters that need to be accounted for in a valid after-tax rent versus buy analysis include, but are not limited to:

- Home purchase price, inclusive of all financing and closing fees, points, etc.
- Projected ownership life
- Estimated future sale value
- Sale commission to be paid
- Initial equity required to purchase
- Loan amount*
- Loan interest rate and mortgage payments
- Cost of annual property taxes
- Cost of annual homeowners insurance
- Cost of annual maintenance and upkeep costs
- Annual rental expense for an equivalent property

* *Annual salary income times three is a basic rule of thumb for determining the maximum amount you can borrow on a first home mortgage.*

Tax savings from allowable deductions needs to be taken into account in a proper after-tax analysis. However, after selling, under year 2008 tax law, if you have lived in a home for two of the past five years, a single person may be able to exclude home sale gain up to $250,000 and a married couple may be able to exclude $500,000 of gain. You cannot realize this tax benefit more often than every two years. If you sell for a loss, you may be able to deduct the loss as business loss. Check with a good tax accountant for possibilities in that regard.

If you buy a home and finance it at least partially with a loan, the annual borrowed money interest component of your mortgage payments is tax deductible as an itemized deduction. Also your property taxes are deductible as an itemized deduction so tax savings from these deductions must be taken into account.

If you are renting and not itemizing deductions, taxpayers take a standard deduction against income to determine taxable income. Itemizing deductions after purchasing a home would result in incremental benefits for those deductions in excess of the standard deduction. Rental payments are not tax deductible if you rent, so after-tax rent costs equals the before-tax rent cost. A rent versus buy analysis is illustrated in Example 12-18.

EXAMPLE 12-18 Home Purchase Versus Rental

A five year life present worth cost of home service is to be made by a married couple to compare purchase of a $150,000 home with renting. The purchase cost would be covered with $30,000 cash equity and a $120,000 thirty year loan at 10.0% interest per year. Assume yearly end-of-year mortgage payments for simplicity. Assume the loan will be paid off at the end of year 5 when it is estimated that the home will be sold for $180,000. A 7.0% real estate sales commission is estimated to be paid on the sale value. Annual property taxes are estimated to be $1,500 in year 1, escalating $50 per year through year 5. Annual house insurance is estimated to be $500 with annual maintenance estimated to be $1,000. Home maintenance and insurance costs are not allowable itemized deductions, but the home loan interest and property tax will be taken as itemized deductions for federal and state income tax calculation purposes in lieu of using the married joint return standard deduction of $7,350. Assume the individual effective federal plus state tax rate is 30.0% Assume that the year 5 sale value of $180,000 less real estate sale commission is not taxable per current tax law. The couple assumes that other places exist to invest money at 10.0% per year after-taxes and that the risk in those investments is equivalent to investing in the home. If the couple rents, assume end-of-year annual rent costs of $12,000 in years 1 and 2, $13,200 in years 3 and 4, and $14,000 in year 5.

Solution:

Home Purchase Cash Flow Analysis

Annual 30 year mortgage payments = $\$120,000(A/P_{10,30})$ = $12,730. These annual mortgage payments break down into annual interest and equity principal amounts each year shown in the cash flow calculations.

Year	0	1	2	3	4	5
– Mortgage Interest		–12,000	–11,927	–11,847	–11,758	–11,661
– Property Tax		–1,500	–1,550	–1,600	–1,650	–1,700
Taxable Inc.		–13,500	–13,477	–13,447	–13,408	–13,361
– Tax @ 30%		4,050	4,043	4,034	4,022	4,008
Net Income		–9,450	–9,434	–9,413	–9,386	–9,353
– Insurance		–500	–500	–500	–500	–500
– Maintenance		–1,000	–1,000	–1,000	–1,000	–1,000
– Principal		–730	–803	–883	–972	–1,069
+ Loan Amount	120,000					–114,543
– Purchase Price	–150,000					
+ Sale Value						180,000
– Commission (7%)						–12,600
Cash Flow	–30,000	–11,680	–11,737	–11,796	–11,858	40,935

Purchase Present Worth Cost @ 10.0%:

$30{,}000 + 11{,}680(P/F_{10,1}) + 11{,}737(P/F_{10,2}) + 11{,}796(P/F_{10,3})$
$+ 11{,}858(P/F_{10,4}) - 40{,}935(P/F_{10,5})$
$= \$41{,}862$

Rental Cash Flow Analysis

Year	0	1	2	3	4	5
Annual Rent = CF	0	–12,000	–12,000	–13,200	–13,200	–14,400

Rental Present Worth Cost @ 10.0%:

$12{,}000(P/A_{10,2}) + 13{,}200(P/A_{10,2})(P/F_{10,2}) + 14{,}400(P/F_{10,5})$
$= \$48{,}700$

The smaller present worth cost of 5 years of housing service is "purchase," so purchasing is the economic choice. That conclusion, however, neglects the fact that itemizing tax deductions causes loss of the married joint return standard deduction of $7,350 (in 2000). If deductions are itemized, in addition to home loan interest and property tax, several other costs can be deducted such as annual auto ownership taxes, state income tax and charitable contributions. Assume the license taxes and state income tax and charitable deductions would be $2,200 per year, so the difference in the $7,350 standard deduction and $2,200 is a foregone $5,150 deduction if a home is bought and deductions are itemized. A $5,150 deduction in each of years 1 through 5 would save $5,150(0.30 tax rate) or $1,545 per year in tax savings. The present worth of these tax savings is $1,545(P/A_{10,5}) = $5,858. If the present worth home purchase cost is increased by the $5,858 opportunity cost from foregone tax savings due to itemized versus standard deduction, the adjusted present worth purchase cost is $47,720, which is closer to the $48,700 rent present worth cost. Carefully accounting for all costs, revenues and tax effects along with the proper timing of these items is very important to all analyses, including home purchase versus rent analyses.

12.7c Personal Auto Purchase versus Lease

Individuals do not get depreciation tax deductions or lease payment expense deductions on personal automobile costs. Interest paid on money borrowed to finance personal autos is not tax deductible under current tax. Therefore, the after-tax cost of providing automobile service is the same as the before-tax cost for purchasing with cash, purchasing with borrowed money, or leasing. This is very different than the business analysis of auto lease versus purchase analysis presented in Example 10-2 where the tax savings from depreciation and operating lease payments were taken into account as allowable tax deductions. The following example illustrates several decision criteria that can be used to evaluate the leasing versus purchase of a personal automobile. These techniques are the same for all types of vehicles.

EXAMPLE 12-19 Personal Auto Purchase Versus Lease

Three alternatives are being considered for the personal use of a luxury automobile over the next 36 months based on actual lease cost and purchase cost data. The manufacturer's suggested retail price (MSRP) is $71,850.00. When applicable, the year 3 salvage is estimated at $0.50 on the dollar, or $35,925.00 for the base cases A & B (realized at the end of the 36th month). The alternatives follow:

(A) Purchase the car with cash now, at time zero, for $71,850.00.

(B) Purchase the car by putting 20% down at time zero and borrowing the remaining 80% of the MSRP at an annual interest rate of 10% compounded monthly. The loan will be paid off in 36 end-of-month payments, starting in month one.

For both (A) and (B) the salvage value is as stated earlier.

(C) Lease the car with beginning-of-month payments of $977.81 and an additional 10% of the MSRP when you pick up the vehicle at time zero.

The minimum rate of return is 12% annual interest compounded monthly. Assume all insurance and operating costs will be the same for each method of financing, so they can be omitted in the analysis. Use present worth cost and incremental rate of return or NPV to determine which alternative of financing is the economic choice. Then, since few people pay the MSRP when acquiring a vehicle, determine the break-even purchase price for alternatives 1 & 2 that would make you indifferent between purchasing or leasing. All other criteria remain the same.

Solution:

(1) Present Worth Cost

A) Cash C=$71,850 — Salvage = $35,925

0. 36

$$PWC = 71{,}850 - 35{,}925\overset{0.69892}{(P/F_{1\%,36})} = \underline{\underline{\$46{,}741.12}}$$

B) Borrow 80% at 10% per annum compounded monthly.

20% Equity C=$14,370 C=$1,854.72 . . . . C=$1,854.72 Salv.= $35,925

0 1. 36

where:

$$\text{Loan Payment} = [0.8(71{,}850)]\overset{0.03227}{(A/P_{0.8333\%,36})} = \$1{,}854.72$$

$$PWC = 14{,}370 + 1{,}854\overset{30.1075}{(P/A_{1\%,36})} - 35{,}925\overset{0.69892}{(P/F_{1\%,36})} = \underline{\underline{\$45{,}102.28}}$$

C) Lease

LP=$977.81

C=$7,185 LP=$977.81 . . . LP=$977.81 —

0 1. . . . . 35 36

$$PWC = 8{,}162.81 + 977.81\overset{29.4086}{(P/A_{1\%,35})} = \underline{\underline{\$36{,}918.81}}$$

Sensitivity of PWC Results to Discount Rate Changes:

Nominal Discount Rate	Cash PW Cost	Borrow PW Cost	Lease PW Cost
0%	$35,295	$45,215	$42,386
4%	39,981	45,322	40,415
5%	40,919	45,323	39,946
6%	41,829	45,316	39,487
7%	42,712	45,300	39,038
8%	43,568	45,275	38,597
9%	44,398	45,243	38,165
10%	45,203	45,203	37,741
11%	45,984	45,156	37,326
12%	46,741	45,102	36,919
13%	47,476	45,042	36,520
14%	48,188	44,975	36,128
15%	48,879	44,903	35,745
20%	52,036	44,463	33,934

(2) Incremental Analysis

Borrow-Lease:

ΔC=$6,207 ΔC=$876.91 ΔC=$876.91 . . . ΔC=$1,854.72 L=$35,925

0 1 35. 36

ΔROR = –4.6%, therefore reject borrowing at 10%

Cash-Lease:

ΔC=$63,687.19 S=$977.81 . . . . . . S=$977.81 — L=$35,925

0 1 . . . . 35 36

ΔROR = 4.31% < 12% so leasing is economically preferable

Since leasing is preferred to both forms of purchasing:
What is the break-even cash purchase price if other opportunities exist to invest your money at 12% before taxes?

PW Cost of leasing = $36,919. Let X = the break-even cash purchase price.

$$X - 0.5X\overset{0.69892}{(P/F_{1\%,36})} = \$36,919$$

$X = \underline{\underline{\$56,751}}$ This break-even price is 79% of the MSRP.

Leveraged Break-even:

$$0.2X + 0.8X\overset{0.03227}{(A/P_{0.8333\%,36})}\overset{30.1075}{(P/A_{1\%,36})} - 0.5X\overset{0.69892}{(P/F_{1\%,36})} = 36,919$$

$0.6285X = 36,919;$ $X = \underline{\underline{\$58,741}}$

If the dealer wanted a 15% return on his or her investment, based on the given one time front-end payment, the monthly lease payments and the final salvage value, what is the dealer cost basis in the vehicle?

$$7,185.00 + 977.81 + 977.81\overset{28.2079}{(P/A_{1.25\%,35})} + 35,925.00\overset{0.6394}{(P/F_{1.25\%,36})}$$

$= \underline{\underline{\$58,715.22}}$

12.8 Summary of Selected Investment Terminology

American-Style options: an option that may be exercised at any time from the date of purchase until the expiration date.
Annual percentage rate (APR): Annualized cost of borrowing money reflecting the nominal interest rate (typically compounded monthly) and closing costs such as points that are related to the loan.
Annual percentage yield (APY): A compound interest rate that when applied once at the end of the year will yield equivalent interest to a nominal interest rate compounded "m" times throughout the year. Also known as effective interest in many engineering economy texts.
At-the-money: an option whose strike price equals the market price of the underlying security.
Bearer bonds: (also known as coupon bonds) were not registered. These bonds made grandparents famous for "clipping coupons." So, the owner or holder of a bearer bond had interest (from the coupons deposited at a bank) income not easily traced by the Internal Revenue Service. Bearer bonds are no longer issued today.
Bonds: are promissory notes of a corporation or government entity.
Call option: an option contract that gives the holder the right to buy a specified amount of an underlying security (stock, commodity, index, interest rate, etc.) at a specified price (strike price) for a specified period of time (expiration date).
Call privileges: are instruments included in most corporate and municipal bonds. This gives the issuer of the debt the right to call the bond before the normal maturity date. If executed, call privileges usually reduce the yield on a bond return for its holder.
Common stock: represents an ownership interest in a corporation or business.
Common stock index: is a measure of value for a group of stocks. Some of the more notable indexes would include the Dow Jones Industrials (DJIA), Nasdaq, Nasdaq 100, S&P 500, Fortune 500, NYSE Composite, Russell 1000 and the list goes on. Indexes are traded in the markets today much like any other stock and may offer some trading advantages.
Convertible debentures: may be exchanged by the holder for common stock or another security of the same company in accordance with the terms of the issue.
Coupon yield: The nominal compound interest rate of return an investor would realize if a bond could be purchased at face value and held till its normal maturity. When the purchase price is equal to the face value of the

bond, the coupon yield is a measure of both a compound interest and an add-on or flat interest rate and will be identical to the bond Yield to Maturity (YTM).

Cumulative preferred stock: includes a provision that states if one or more dividends are omitted, the omitted dividends must be paid before any dividends may be paid on the company's common stock.

Current assets: are convertible into cash within a year in normal operations.

Current yield: The nominal add-on or flat rate of return an investor would realize when a bond is purchased and held till its normal maturity. Current yield is determined by dividing the annual interest received by the purchase price.

Debentures: are similar to bonds with the exception that they are backed only by the general credit and name of the issuing company and not by any specific assets of the company. As such, debentures carry more financial risk than bonds and as a result, generally offer slightly higher yields depending on the issuer.

Deep discount bonds: see "zero coupon bond."

Derivative: a security whose value is derived in part from the value and characteristics of an underlying security. Put and call options and futures contracts are examples of financial derivatives.

Downtick: is a term used to designate a transaction made at a price less than the preceding trade.

European Style options: an option with a limited exercise window during a specified period just prior to expiration.

Equity options: put or call options related to an individual common stock.

Even-tick: is a term used to designate a transaction made at a price equal to the preceding trade.

Exercise: to execute the right entitled to the holder of an option.

Exercise price: the price at which the option is to be executed. Also known as a strike price.

Expiration date: the date at which an option contract becomes null and void or a futures contract is to be exercised.

Face value: The value at which the coupon yield is established. Generally bonds are sold in face value increments of $1,000.00

Fixed assets: are assets that in the normal course of business will not be converted to cash within one year.

Futures contracts: are legal contracts to buy or sell a specified amount of some commodity at a specified price for delivery at a future contract expiration date.

Hedging: a strategy to limit the loss or capture a gain from movement in the value of a security, currency, index, interest rate or commodity.
Holder: the buyer or purchaser of an option.
Index options: options related to an index representing a group of common stocks such as the Dow Jones Industrials Average. Options related to the Dow are known as DJX options – many other index options exist as well.
Indenture: is a written agreement under which bonds, debentures and preferred stock are issued, setting forth the interest or dividend rates, maturity dates, call dates and other conditions such as conversion terms, sinking fund requirements and so forth.
In-the-money: is a term related to the option premium. A call option premium is in-the-money if the strike price is less than the current market price of the underlying security. A put option premium is in the money if the strike price is greater than the current market price for the underlying security.
Intrinsic Value: the actual physical value of an option if exercised. Also defined as the amount by which an option premium is said to be "in-the-money."
Junk bonds: are issued by highly leveraged corporations that may have questionable assets backing them as collateral.
Leaps: Long-term equity anticipation securities are options with a life of 2 to 3 years or basically, long-term options.
Long position: an investment whose holder believes the underlying security is likely to move higher in the future. In options, the number of contracts bought would exceed the number of contracts sold.
Margin: the cash an investor must deposit in a leveraged account, the actual amount is typically computed daily by the broker. Margin can also be defined as the equity capital that, when combined with the borrowed money, will cover the cost of an investment.
Municipal bonds: are issued by a state, city or county – the interest is either wholly or partially exempt from federal and or state income tax.
Naked call option: is a call option for which the writer does not own an equivalent position in the underlying security for the options he or she has written.
Option buyer: is also known as the holder. The buyer is the person obtaining the rights conveyed by the call option for a fee called a premium.
Market Orders:
- **All-or-none:** is an order to be executed in its entirety, or not at all.
- **Day:** is an order to buy or sell a stated amount of a security that, if not executed, will expire at the end of the trading day.

Fill-or-fill: is a market or limit order that is to be executed in its entirety as soon as it is represented to the trading crowd, or not at all.

Good-till-Canceled: is an order to buy or sell which remains in effect until either executed or canceled.

Limit: is an order to buy or sell a stated amount of a security at a specified price, or at a better price after the order is presented to the trading crowd.

Market: is an order to buy or sell a stated amount of a security at the most advantageous price obtainable when presented to the trading crowd.

Stop: is an order to buy at or above a specified price (the "stop" price), or to sell at or below a specified price (the "stop" price). Once the stop price level is realized, the order becomes a market order.

Out-of-the-money: is a term related to an option premium. For a call option, the premium is out-of-the-money if the strike price is greater than the market price of the underlying security. For a put option, the premium is said to be out-of-the-money if the strike price is less than the market price of the underlying security.

Participating preferred stock: holders of this stock are entitled to any stated dividend and also to additional dividends on a specified basis upon payment of dividends on the common stock of the company.

Preferred stock: represents a special class of stock that does not represent an ownership interest in the company. Preferred stock dividends are typically paid at a specified rate.

Premium: is usually described as the price per unit of an option contract. For equity options, the premium is expressed per share. Each option contract controls 100 shares, so, 100 times the premium gives the value of one equity option contract.

Price Earnings Ratio: financial measure of performance based on the following formula:

P/E Ratio = Price of Common Stock / Earnings Per Share of Common Stock

Earnings refer to the financial "net income" generated for a given period. Some analysts base earnings on the most recently reported 4 quarters, while others look forward at the forecasted next 4 quarters of anticipated earnings.

Put option: an option contract that gives the holder the right to sell a specified amount of an underlying security or asset at a specified price (strike price) for a specified period of time (expiration date).

Registered bonds: are uniquely different from bearer bonds in that the bond is registered by the issuing corporation or government in the name of the owner or holder. This information is then provided to the Internal Revenue Service. All bonds issued today are registered.

Short position: the number of common stock shares sold short at a given time. Although short sellers usually are negative concerning prospects for stock price, analysts often consider a high short position in a stock to be bullish for stock prices because shares sold short must eventually be repurchased which may drive the price higher.

Short sale: involves selling a stock that an investor may not own, with the expectation of being able to buy it back later at a lower price.

Sinking fund: holds money set aside regularly by a company or government entity to redeem bonds, debentures or preferred stock in accordance with the indenture.

Speculative value: see time value.

Spread: involves the simultaneous purchase and writing of options on the same underlying security. These options may have different strike prices and or expiration dates. The purpose of a spread is to minimize risk and also create the possibility for increased profits above that possible by simply owning the underlying security.

Straddle: involves the simultaneous purchase and sale of the same number of calls and puts with identical strike prices and expiration dates.

Strips: see "zero coupon bond."

Term Insurance: a pure form of life insurance in the sense that the policy provides life insurance only over a limited number of years into the future and is not in any way a savings plan.

Time value: the portion of an option's premium that is speculative and related to the amount of time remaining before an option expires. Time value will diminish to zero as an option approaches its expiration date.

Treasury bills (T-bills): are securities issued by the U.S. government with lives ranging from three to six months. In the past, one-year t-bills have also been available but they are scheduled to be phased out in early 2001 due to the declining U.S. debt.

Treasury notes: are securities issued by the U.S. government with lives ranging from one to five years.

Treasury bonds: are securities issued by the U.S. government with lives ranging from five to thirty years.

Universal life insurance: see whole life insurance.

Up-tick: is a term used to designate a transaction made at a price higher than the preceding trade.

Whole life insurance: (also known as universal life) this involves a combination of term life insurance and savings plan that has a separate after-tax value.

Writing a covered call: a strategy by which a person writes (or sells) call options while simultaneously owning the underlying security. The writer receives the premium from the buyer of the call.

Writing a covered put: a strategy by which a person sells put options and simultaneously creates a short sale position in an equivalent number of shares in the underlying security. The writer receives the premium from the buyer of the puts.

Yield: the compound interest equivalent of stock dividends per share divided by the purchase price of the stock (also known as a dividend yield) or, in the bond market, the annual interest divided by the purchase price (commonly known as current yield).

Yield to call: The nominal compound interest rate of return an investor would realize if a bond is repurchased (called) on the first available call date. Current yield would remain the same since that calculation is not influenced by the timing of payments or the overall payments received.

Yield to maturity: is the bond markets definition of the nominal compound interest rate of return being received on a bond investment if held to maturity with or without call privileges.

Zero coupon bonds: also known as "deep discount bonds" or "strips," these bonds pay the owner a single lump sum of money called "maturity value" at a future time referred to as the bond "maturity date." Zero coupon bonds do not pay interest annually or semi-annually like normal registered bonds and therefore, are sold at a discount to the bond maturity value (maturity value may also be referred to as "face value").

APPENDICES

A: Discrete Interest, Discrete Value Factors (i = ½% to i = 200%)

B: Continuous Interest, Discrete Value Factors

C: Continuous Interest, Continuous Flowing Value Factors

D: Production Cost Variations and Break-even Analysis

E: Arithmetic Gradient Series Factor Development

APPENDIX A

DISCRETE INTEREST, DISCRETE VALUE FACTORS

Discrete Compounding Interest Factors, i = ½% to i = 200%

Single Payment Compound Amount Factor $= F/P_{i,n} = (1+i)^n$

Single Payment Present Worth Factor $= P/F_{i,n} = \frac{1}{(1+i)^n}$

Uniform Series Compound Amount Factor $= F/A_{i,n} = \frac{(1+i)^n - 1}{i}$

Sinking Fund Deposit Factor $= A/F_{i,n} \quad \frac{i}{(1+i)^n - 1}$

Capital Recovery Factor $= A/P_{i,n} = \frac{i(1+i)^n}{(1+i)^n - 1}$

Uniform Series Present Worth Factor $= P/A_{i,n} = \frac{(1+i)^n - 1}{i(1+i)^n}$

Arithmetic Gradient Series Factor $= A/G_{i,n} = \frac{1}{i} - \frac{n}{(1+i)^n - 1}$

i = 0.50%

n	F/Pi,n	P/Fi,n	F/Ai,n	A/Fi,n	A/Pi,n	P/Ai,n
1	1.0050	0.9950	1.0000	1.00000	1.00500	0.9950
2	1.0100	0.9901	2.0050	0.49875	0.50375	1.9851
3	1.0151	0.9851	3.0150	0.33167	0.33667	2.9702
4	1.0202	0.9802	4.0301	0.24813	0.25313	3.9505
5	1.0253	0.9754	5.0503	0.19801	0.20301	4.9259
6	1.0304	0.9705	6.0755	0.16460	0.16960	5.8964
7	1.0355	0.9657	7.1059	0.14073	0.14573	6.8621
8	1.0407	0.9609	8.1414	0.12283	0.12783	7.8230
9	1.0459	0.9561	9.1821	0.10891	0.11391	8.7791
10	1.0511	0.9513	10.2280	0.09777	0.10277	9.7304
11	1.0564	0.9466	11.2792	0.08866	0.09366	10.6770
12	1.0617	0.9419	12.3356	0.08107	0.08607	11.6189
13	1.0670	0.9372	13.3972	0.07464	0.07964	12.5562
14	1.0723	0.9326	14.4642	0.06914	0.07414	13.4887
15	1.0777	0.9279	15.5365	0.06436	0.06936	14.4166
16	1.0831	0.9233	16.6142	0.06019	0.06519	15.3399
17	1.0885	0.9187	17.6973	0.05651	0.06151	16.2586
18	1.0939	0.9141	18.7858	0.05323	0.05823	17.1728
19	1.0994	0.9096	19.8797	0.05030	0.05530	18.0824
20	1.1049	0.9051	20.9791	0.04767	0.05267	18.9874
21	1.1104	0.9006	22.0840	0.04528	0.05028	19.8880
22	1.1160	0.8961	23.1944	0.04311	0.04811	20.7841
23	1.1216	0.8916	24.3104	0.04113	0.04613	21.6757
24	1.1272	0.8872	25.4320	0.03932	0.04432	22.5629
25	1.1328	0.8828	26.5591	0.03765	0.04265	23.4456
26	1.1385	0.8784	27.6919	0.03611	0.04111	24.3240
27	1.1442	0.8740	28.8304	0.03469	0.03969	25.1980
28	1.1499	0.8697	29.9745	0.03336	0.03836	26.0677
29	1.1556	0.8653	31.1244	0.03213	0.03713	26.9330
30	1.1614	0.8610	32.2800	0.03098	0.03598	27.7941
31	1.1672	0.8567	33.4414	0.02990	0.03490	28.6508
32	1.1730	0.8525	34.6086	0.02889	0.03389	29.5033
33	1.1789	0.8482	35.7817	0.02795	0.03295	30.3515
34	1.1848	0.8440	36.9606	0.02706	0.03206	31.1955
35	1.1907	0.8398	38.1454	0.02622	0.03122	32.0354
36	1.1967	0.8356	39.3361	0.02542	0.03042	32.8710
48	1.2705	0.7871	54.0978	0.01849	0.02349	42.5803
60	1.3489	0.7414	69.7700	0.01433	0.01933	51.7256
72	1.4320	0.6983	86.4089	0.01157	0.01657	60.3395
84	1.5204	0.6577	104.0739	0.00961	0.01461	68.4530
96	1.6141	0.6195	122.8285	0.00814	0.01314	76.0952
120	1.8194	0.5496	163.8793	0.00610	0.01110	90.0735
180	2.4541	0.4075	290.8187	0.00344	0.00844	118.5035
240	3.3102	0.3021	462.0409	0.00216	0.00716	139.5808
360	6.0226	0.1660	1004.5150	0.00100	0.00600	166.7916

i = 1.00%

n	F/Pi,n	P/Fi,n	F/Ai,n	A/Fi,n	A/Pi,n	P/Ai,n
1	1.0100	0.9901	1.0000	1.00000	1.01000	0.9901
2	1.0201	0.9803	2.0100	0.49751	0.50751	1.9704
3	1.0303	0.9706	3.0301	0.33002	0.34002	2.9410
4	1.0406	0.9610	4.0604	0.24628	0.25628	3.9020
5	1.0510	0.9515	5.1010	0.19604	0.20604	4.8534
6	1.0615	0.9420	6.1520	0.16255	0.17255	5.7955
7	1.0721	0.9327	7.2135	0.13863	0.14863	6.7282
8	1.0829	0.9235	8.2857	0.12069	0.13069	7.6517
9	1.0937	0.9143	9.3685	0.10674	0.11674	8.5660
10	1.1046	0.9053	10.4622	0.09558	0.10558	9.4713
11	1.1157	0.8963	11.5668	0.08645	0.09645	10.3676
12	1.1268	0.8874	12.6825	0.07885	0.08885	11.2551
13	1.1381	0.8787	13.8093	0.07241	0.08241	12.1337
14	1.1495	0.8700	14.9474	0.06690	0.07690	13.0037
15	1.1610	0.8613	16.0969	0.06212	0.07212	13.8651
16	1.1726	0.8528	17.2579	0.05794	0.06794	14.7179
17	1.1843	0.8444	18.4304	0.05426	0.06426	15.5623
18	1.1961	0.8360	19.6147	0.05098	0.06098	16.3983
19	1.2081	0.8277	20.8109	0.04805	0.05805	17.2260
20	1.2202	0.8195	22.0190	0.04542	0.05542	18.0456
21	1.2324	0.8114	23.2392	0.04303	0.05303	18.8570
22	1.2447	0.8034	24.4716	0.04086	0.05086	19.6604
23	1.2572	0.7954	25.7163	0.03889	0.04889	20.4558
24	1.2697	0.7876	26.9735	0.03707	0.04707	21.2434
25	1.2824	0.7798	28.2432	0.03541	0.04541	22.0232
26	1.2953	0.7720	29.5256	0.03387	0.04387	22.7952
27	1.3082	0.7644	30.8209	0.03245	0.04245	23.5596
28	1.3213	0.7568	32.1291	0.03112	0.04112	24.3164
29	1.3345	0.7493	33.4504	0.02990	0.03990	25.0658
30	1.3478	0.7419	34.7849	0.02875	0.03875	25.8077
31	1.3613	0.7346	36.1327	0.02768	0.03768	26.5423
32	1.3749	0.7273	37.4941	0.02667	0.03667	27.2696
33	1.3887	0.7201	38.8690	0.02573	0.03573	27.9897
34	1.4026	0.7130	40.2577	0.02484	0.03484	28.7027
35	1.4166	0.7059	41.6603	0.02400	0.03400	29.4086
36	1.4308	0.6989	43.0769	0.02321	0.03321	30.1075
48	1.6122	0.6203	61.2226	0.01633	0.02633	37.9740
60	1.8167	0.5504	81.6697	0.01224	0.02224	44.9550
72	2.0471	0.4885	104.7099	0.00955	0.01955	51.1504
84	2.3067	0.4335	130.6723	0.00765	0.01765	56.6485
96	2.5993	0.3847	159.9273	0.00625	0.01625	61.5277
120	3.3004	0.3030	230.0387	0.00435	0.01435	69.7005
180	5.9958	0.1668	499.5802	0.00200	0.01200	83.3217
240	10.8926	0.0918	989.2554	0.00101	0.01101	90.8194
360	35.9496	0.0278	3494.9641	0.00029	0.01029	97.2183

i = 2.00%

n	F/Pi,n	P/Fi,n	F/Ai,n	A/Fi,n	A/Pi,n	P/Ai,n	A/Gi,n
1	1.0200	0.9804	1.0000	1.00000	1.02000	0.9804	n/a
2	1.0404	0.9612	2.0200	0.49505	0.51505	1.9416	0.4950
3	1.0612	0.9423	3.0604	0.32675	0.34675	2.8839	0.9868
4	1.0824	0.9238	4.1216	0.24262	0.26262	3.8077	1.4752
5	1.1041	0.9057	5.2040	0.19216	0.21216	4.7135	1.9604
6	1.1262	0.8880	6.3081	0.15853	0.17853	5.6014	2.4423
7	1.1487	0.8706	7.4343	0.13451	0.15451	6.4720	2.9208
8	1.1717	0.8535	8.5830	0.11651	0.13651	7.3255	3.3961
9	1.1951	0.8368	9.7546	0.10252	0.12252	8.1622	3.8681
10	1.2190	0.8203	10.9497	0.09133	0.11133	8.9826	4.3367
11	1.2434	0.8043	12.1687	0.08218	0.10218	9.7868	4.8021
12	1.2682	0.7885	13.4121	0.07456	0.09456	10.5753	5.2642
13	1.2936	0.7730	14.6803	0.06812	0.08812	11.3484	5.7231
14	1.3195	0.7579	15.9739	0.06260	0.08260	12.1062	6.1786
15	1.3459	0.7430	17.2934	0.05783	0.07783	12.8493	6.6309
16	1.3728	0.7284	18.6393	0.05365	0.07365	13.5777	7.0799
17	1.4002	0.7142	20.0121	0.04997	0.06997	14.2919	7.5256
18	1.4282	0.7002	21.4123	0.04670	0.06670	14.9920	7.9681
19	1.4568	0.6864	22.8406	0.04378	0.06378	15.6785	8.4073
20	1.4859	0.6730	24.2974	0.04116	0.06116	16.3514	8.8433
21	1.5157	0.6598	25.7833	0.03878	0.05878	17.0112	9.2760
22	1.5460	0.6468	27.2990	0.03663	0.05663	17.6580	9.7055
23	1.5769	0.6342	28.8450	0.03467	0.05467	18.2922	10.1317
24	1.6084	0.6217	30.4219	0.03287	0.05287	18.9139	10.5547
25	1.6406	0.6095	32.0303	0.03122	0.05122	19.5235	10.9745
26	1.6734	0.5976	33.6709	0.02970	0.04970	20.1210	11.3910
27	1.7069	0.5859	35.3443	0.02829	0.04829	20.7069	11.8043
28	1.7410	0.5744	37.0512	0.02699	0.04699	21.2813	12.2145
29	1.7758	0.5631	38.7922	0.02578	0.04578	21.8444	12.6214
30	1.8114	0.5521	40.5681	0.02465	0.04465	22.3965	13.0251
35	1.9999	0.5000	49.9945	0.02000	0.04000	24.9986	14.9961
36	2.0399	0.4902	51.9944	0.01923	0.03923	25.4888	15.3809
40	2.2080	0.4529	60.4020	0.01656	0.03656	27.3555	16.8885
45	2.4379	0.4102	71.8927	0.01391	0.03391	29.4902	18.7034
50	2.6916	0.3715	84.5794	0.01182	0.03182	31.4236	20.4420
55	2.9717	0.3365	98.5865	0.01014	0.03014	33.1748	22.1057
60	3.2810	0.3048	114.0515	0.00877	0.02877	34.7609	23.6961
65	3.6225	0.2761	131.1262	0.00763	0.02763	36.1975	25.2147
70	3.9996	0.2500	149.9779	0.00667	0.02667	37.4986	26.6632
75	4.4158	0.2265	170.7918	0.00586	0.02586	38.6771	28.0434
80	4.8754	0.2051	193.7720	0.00516	0.02516	39.7445	29.3572
85	5.3829	0.1858	219.1439	0.00456	0.02456	40.7113	30.6064
90	5.9431	0.1683	247.1567	0.00405	0.02405	41.5869	31.7929
95	6.5617	0.1524	278.0850	0.00360	0.02360	42.3800	32.9189
100	7.2446	0.1380	312.2323	0.00320	0.02320	43.0984	33.9863

i = 3.00%

n	F/Pi,n	P/Fi,n	F/Ai,n	A/Fi,n	A/Pi,n	P/Ai,n	A/Gi,n
1	1.0300	0.9709	1.0000	1.00000	1.03000	0.9709	n/a
2	1.0609	0.9426	2.0300	0.49261	0.52261	1.9135	0.4926
3	1.0927	0.9151	3.0909	0.32353	0.35353	2.8286	0.9803
4	1.1255	0.8885	4.1836	0.23903	0.26903	3.7171	1.4631
5	1.1593	0.8626	5.3091	0.18835	0.21835	4.5797	1.9409
6	1.1941	0.8375	6.4684	0.15460	0.18460	5.4172	2.4138
7	1.2299	0.8131	7.6625	0.13051	0.16051	6.2303	2.8819
8	1.2668	0.7894	8.8923	0.11246	0.14246	7.0197	3.3450
9	1.3048	0.7664	10.1591	0.09843	0.12843	7.7861	3.8032
10	1.3439	0.7441	11.4639	0.08723	0.11723	8.5302	4.2565
11	1.3842	0.7224	12.8078	0.07808	0.10808	9.2526	4.7049
12	1.4258	0.7014	14.1920	0.07046	0.10046	9.9540	5.1485
13	1.4685	0.6810	15.6178	0.06403	0.09403	10.6350	5.5872
14	1.5126	0.6611	17.0863	0.05853	0.08853	11.2961	6.0210
15	1.5580	0.6419	18.5989	0.05377	0.08377	11.9379	6.4500
16	1.6047	0.6232	20.1569	0.04961	0.07961	12.5611	6.8742
17	1.6528	0.6050	21.7616	0.04595	0.07595	13.1661	7.2936
18	1.7024	0.5874	23.4144	0.04271	0.07271	13.7535	7.7081
19	1.7535	0.5703	25.1169	0.03981	0.06981	14.3238	8.1179
20	1.8061	0.5537	26.8704	0.03722	0.06722	14.8775	8.5229
21	1.8603	0.5375	28.6765	0.03487	0.06487	15.4150	8.9231
22	1.9161	0.5219	30.5368	0.03275	0.06275	15.9369	9.3186
23	1.9736	0.5067	32.4529	0.03081	0.06081	16.4436	9.7093
24	2.0328	0.4919	34.4265	0.02905	0.05905	16.9355	10.0954
25	2.0938	0.4776	36.4593	0.02743	0.05743	17.4131	10.4768
26	2.1566	0.4637	38.5530	0.02594	0.05594	17.8768	10.8535
27	2.2213	0.4502	40.7096	0.02456	0.05456	18.3270	11.2255
28	2.2879	0.4371	42.9309	0.02329	0.05329	18.7641	11.5930
29	2.3566	0.4243	45.2189	0.02211	0.05211	19.1885	11.9558
30	2.4273	0.4120	47.5754	0.02102	0.05102	19.6004	12.3141
35	2.8139	0.3554	60.4621	0.01654	0.04654	21.4872	14.0375
36	2.8983	0.3450	63.2759	0.01580	0.04580	21.8323	14.3688
40	3.2620	0.3066	75.4013	0.01326	0.04326	23.1148	15.6502
45	3.7816	0.2644	92.7199	0.01079	0.04079	24.5187	17.1556
50	4.3839	0.2281	112.7969	0.00887	0.03887	25.7298	18.5575
55	5.0821	0.1968	136.0716	0.00735	0.03735	26.7744	19.8600
60	5.8916	0.1697	163.0534	0.00613	0.03613	27.6756	21.0674
65	6.8300	0.1464	194.3328	0.00515	0.03515	28.4529	22.1841
70	7.9178	0.1263	230.5941	0.00434	0.03434	29.1234	23.2145
75	9.1789	0.1089	272.6309	0.00367	0.03367	29.7018	24.1634
80	10.6409	0.0940	321.3630	0.00311	0.03311	30.2008	25.0353
85	12.3357	0.0811	377.8570	0.00265	0.03265	30.6312	25.8349
90	14.3005	0.0699	443.3489	0.00226	0.03226	31.0024	26.5667
95	16.5782	0.0603	519.2720	0.00193	0.03193	31.3227	27.2351
100	19.2186	0.0520	607.2877	0.00165	0.03165	31.5989	27.8444

i = 4.00%

n	F/Pi,n	P/Fi,n	F/Ai,n	A/Fi,n	A/Pi,n	P/Ai,n	A/Gi,n
1	1.0400	0.9615	1.0000	1.00000	1.04000	0.9615	n/a
2	1.0816	0.9246	2.0400	0.49020	0.53020	1.8861	0.4902
3	1.1249	0.8890	3.1216	0.32035	0.36035	2.7751	0.9739
4	1.1699	0.8548	4.2465	0.23549	0.27549	3.6299	1.4510
5	1.2167	0.8219	5.4163	0.18463	0.22463	4.4518	1.9216
6	1.2653	0.7903	6.6330	0.15076	0.19076	5.2421	2.3857
7	1.3159	0.7599	7.8983	0.12661	0.16661	6.0021	2.8433
8	1.3686	0.7307	9.2142	0.10853	0.14853	6.7327	3.2944
9	1.4233	0.7026	10.5828	0.09449	0.13449	7.4353	3.7391
10	1.4802	0.6756	12.0061	0.08329	0.12329	8.1109	4.1773
11	1.5395	0.6496	13.4864	0.07415	0.11415	8.7605	4.6090
12	1.6010	0.6246	15.0258	0.06655	0.10655	9.3851	5.0343
13	1.6651	0.6006	16.6268	0.06014	0.10014	9.9856	5.4533
14	1.7317	0.5775	18.2919	0.05467	0.09467	10.5631	5.8659
15	1.8009	0.5553	20.0236	0.04994	0.08994	11.1184	6.2721
16	1.8730	0.5339	21.8245	0.04582	0.08582	11.6523	6.6720
17	1.9479	0.5134	23.6975	0.04220	0.08220	12.1657	7.0656
18	2.0258	0.4936	25.6454	0.03899	0.07899	12.6593	7.4530
19	2.1068	0.4746	27.6712	0.03614	0.07614	13.1339	7.8342
20	2.1911	0.4564	29.7781	0.03358	0.07358	13.5903	8.2091
21	2.2788	0.4388	31.9692	0.03128	0.07128	14.0292	8.5779
22	2.3699	0.4220	34.2480	0.02920	0.06920	14.4511	8.9407
23	2.4647	0.4057	36.6179	0.02731	0.06731	14.8568	9.2973
24	2.5633	0.3901	39.0826	0.02559	0.06559	15.2470	9.6479
25	2.6658	0.3751	41.6459	0.02401	0.06401	15.6221	9.9925
26	2.7725	0.3607	44.3117	0.02257	0.06257	15.9828	10.3312
27	2.8834	0.3468	47.0842	0.02124	0.06124	16.3296	10.6640
28	2.9987	0.3335	49.9676	0.02001	0.06001	16.6631	10.9909
29	3.1187	0.3207	52.9663	0.01888	0.05888	16.9837	11.3120
30	3.2434	0.3083	56.0849	0.01783	0.05783	17.2920	11.6274
35	3.9461	0.2534	73.6522	0.01358	0.05358	18.6646	13.1198
36	4.1039	0.2437	77.5983	0.01289	0.05289	18.9083	13.4018
40	4.8010	0.2083	95.0255	0.01052	0.05052	19.7928	14.4765
45	5.8412	0.1712	121.0294	0.00826	0.04826	20.7200	15.7047
50	7.1067	0.1407	152.6671	0.00655	0.04655	21.4822	16.8122
55	8.6464	0.1157	191.1592	0.00523	0.04523	22.1086	17.8070
60	10.5196	0.0951	237.9907	0.00420	0.04420	22.6235	18.6972
65	12.7987	0.0781	294.9684	0.00339	0.04339	23.0467	19.4909
70	15.5716	0.0642	364.2905	0.00275	0.04275	23.3945	20.1961
75	18.9453	0.0528	448.6314	0.00223	0.04223	23.6804	20.8206
80	23.0498	0.0434	551.2450	0.00181	0.04181	23.9154	21.3718
85	28.0436	0.0357	676.0901	0.00148	0.04148	24.1085	21.8569
90	34.1193	0.0293	827.9833	0.00121	0.04121	24.2673	22.2826
95	41.5114	0.0241	1012.7846	0.00099	0.04099	24.3978	22.6550
100	50.5049	0.0198	1237.6237	0.00081	0.04081	24.5050	22.9800

i = 5.00%

n	F/Pi,n	P/Fi,n	F/Ai,n	A/Fi,n	A/Pi,n	P/Ai,n	A/Gi,n
1	1.0500	0.9524	1.0000	1.00000	1.05000	0.9524	n/a
2	1.1025	0.9070	2.0500	0.48780	0.53780	1.8594	0.4878
3	1.1576	0.8638	3.1525	0.31721	0.36721	2.7232	0.9675
4	1.2155	0.8227	4.3101	0.23201	0.28201	3.5460	1.4391
5	1.2763	0.7835	5.5256	0.18097	0.23097	4.3295	1.9025
6	1.3401	0.7462	6.8019	0.14702	0.19702	5.0757	2.3579
7	1.4071	0.7107	8.1420	0.12282	0.17282	5.7864	2.8052
8	1.4775	0.6768	9.5491	0.10472	0.15472	6.4632	3.2445
9	1.5513	0.6446	11.0266	0.09069	0.14069	7.1078	3.6758
10	1.6289	0.6139	12.5779	0.07950	0.12950	7.7217	4.0991
11	1.7103	0.5847	14.2068	0.07039	0.12039	8.3064	4.5144
12	1.7959	0.5568	15.9171	0.06283	0.11283	8.8633	4.9219
13	1.8856	0.5303	17.7130	0.05646	0.10646	9.3936	5.3215
14	1.9799	0.5051	19.5986	0.05102	0.10102	9.8986	5.7133
15	2.0789	0.4810	21.5786	0.04634	0.09634	10.3797	6.0973
16	2.1829	0.4581	23.6575	0.04227	0.09227	10.8378	6.4736
17	2.2920	0.4363	25.8404	0.03870	0.08870	11.2741	6.8423
18	2.4066	0.4155	28.1324	0.03555	0.08555	11.6896	7.2034
19	2.5270	0.3957	30.5390	0.03275	0.08275	12.0853	7.5569
20	2.6533	0.3769	33.0660	0.03024	0.08024	12.4622	7.9030
21	2.7860	0.3589	35.7193	0.02800	0.07800	12.8212	8.2416
22	2.9253	0.3418	38.5052	0.02597	0.07597	13.1630	8.5730
23	3.0715	0.3256	41.4305	0.02414	0.07414	13.4886	8.8971
24	3.2251	0.3101	44.5020	0.02247	0.07247	13.7986	9.2140
25	3.3864	0.2953	47.7271	0.02095	0.07095	14.0939	9.5238
26	3.5557	0.2812	51.1135	0.01956	0.06956	14.3752	9.8266
27	3.7335	0.2678	54.6691	0.01829	0.06829	14.6430	10.1224
28	3.9201	0.2551	58.4026	0.01712	0.06712	14.8981	10.4114
29	4.1161	0.2429	62.3227	0.01605	0.06605	15.1411	10.6936
30	4.3219	0.2314	66.4388	0.01505	0.06505	15.3725	10.9691
31	4.5380	0.2204	70.7608	0.01413	0.06413	15.5928	11.2381
32	4.7649	0.2099	75.2988	0.01328	0.06328	15.8027	11.5005
33	5.0032	0.1999	80.0638	0.01249	0.06249	16.0025	11.7566
34	5.2533	0.1904	85.0670	0.01176	0.06176	16.1929	12.0063
35	5.5160	0.1813	90.3203	0.01107	0.06107	16.3742	12.2498
36	5.7918	0.1727	95.8363	0.01043	0.06043	16.5469	12.4872
37	6.0814	0.1644	101.6281	0.00984	0.05984	16.7113	12.7186
38	6.3855	0.1566	107.7095	0.00928	0.05928	16.8679	12.9440
39	6.7048	0.1491	114.0950	0.00876	0.05876	17.0170	13.1636
40	7.0400	0.1420	120.7998	0.00828	0.05828	17.1591	13.3775
48	10.4013	0.0961	188.0254	0.00532	0.05532	18.0772	14.8943
50	11.4674	0.0872	209.3480	0.00478	0.05478	18.2559	15.2233

i = 6.00%

n	F/Pi,n	P/Fi,n	F/Ai,n	A/Fi,n	A/Pi,n	P/Ai,n	A/Gi,n
1	1.0600	0.9434	1.0000	1.00000	1.06000	0.9434	n/a
2	1.1236	0.8900	2.0600	0.48544	0.54544	1.8334	0.4854
3	1.1910	0.8396	3.1836	0.31411	0.37411	2.6730	0.9612
4	1.2625	0.7921	4.3746	0.22859	0.28859	3.4651	1.4272
5	1.3382	0.7473	5.6371	0.17740	0.23740	4.2124	1.8836
6	1.4185	0.7050	6.9753	0.14336	0.20336	4.9173	2.3304
7	1.5036	0.6651	8.3938	0.11914	0.17914	5.5824	2.7676
8	1.5938	0.6274	9.8975	0.10104	0.16104	6.2098	3.1952
9	1.6895	0.5919	11.4913	0.08702	0.14702	6.8017	3.6133
10	1.7908	0.5584	13.1808	0.07587	0.13587	7.3601	4.0220
11	1.8983	0.5268	14.9716	0.06679	0.12679	7.8869	4.4213
12	2.0122	0.4970	16.8699	0.05928	0.11928	8.3838	4.8113
13	2.1329	0.4688	18.8821	0.05296	0.11296	8.8527	5.1920
14	2.2609	0.4423	21.0151	0.04758	0.10758	9.2950	5.5635
15	2.3966	0.4173	23.2760	0.04296	0.10296	9.7122	5.9260
16	2.5404	0.3936	25.6725	0.03895	0.09895	10.1059	6.2794
17	2.6928	0.3714	28.2129	0.03544	0.09544	10.4773	6.6240
18	2.8543	0.3503	30.9057	0.03236	0.09236	10.8276	6.9597
19	3.0256	0.3305	33.7600	0.02962	0.08962	11.1581	7.2867
20	3.2071	0.3118	36.7856	0.02718	0.08718	11.4699	7.6051
21	3.3996	0.2942	39.9927	0.02500	0.08500	11.7641	7.9151
22	3.6035	0.2775	43.3923	0.02305	0.08305	12.0416	8.2166
23	3.8197	0.2618	46.9958	0.02128	0.08128	12.3034	8.5099
24	4.0489	0.2470	50.8156	0.01968	0.07968	12.5504	8.7951
25	4.2919	0.2330	54.8645	0.01823	0.07823	12.7834	9.0722
26	4.5494	0.2198	59.1564	0.01690	0.07690	13.0032	9.3414
27	4.8223	0.2074	63.7058	0.01570	0.07570	13.2105	9.6029
28	5.1117	0.1956	68.5281	0.01459	0.07459	13.4062	9.8568
29	5.4184	0.1846	73.6398	0.01358	0.07358	13.5907	10.1032
30	5.7435	0.1741	79.0582	0.01265	0.07265	13.7648	10.3422
31	6.0881	0.1643	84.8017	0.01179	0.07179	13.9291	10.5740
32	6.4534	0.1550	90.8898	0.01100	0.07100	14.0840	10.7988
33	6.8406	0.1462	97.3432	0.01027	0.07027	14.2302	11.0166
34	7.2510	0.1379	104.1838	0.00960	0.06960	14.3681	11.2276
35	7.6861	0.1301	111.4348	0.00897	0.06897	14.4982	11.4319
36	8.1473	0.1227	119.1209	0.00839	0.06839	14.6210	11.6298
37	8.6361	0.1158	127.2681	0.00786	0.06786	14.7368	11.8213
38	9.1543	0.1092	135.9042	0.00736	0.06736	14.8460	12.0065
39	9.7035	0.1031	145.0585	0.00689	0.06689	14.9491	12.1857
40	10.2857	0.0972	154.7620	0.00646	0.06646	15.0463	12.3590
48	16.3939	0.0610	256.5645	0.00390	0.06390	15.6500	13.5485
50	18.4202	0.0543	290.3359	0.00344	0.06344	15.7619	13.7964

i = 7.00%

n	F/Pi,n	P/Fi,n	F/Ai,n	A/Fi,n	A/Pi,n	P/Ai,n	A/Gi,n\
1	1.0700	0.9346	1.0000	1.00000	1.07000	0.9346	n/a
2	1.1449	0.8734	2.0700	0.48309	0.55309	1.8080	0.4831
3	1.2250	0.8163	3.2149	0.31105	0.38105	2.6243	0.9549
4	1.3108	0.7629	4.4399	0.22523	0.29523	3.3872	1.4155
5	1.4026	0.7130	5.7507	0.17389	0.24389	4.1002	1.8650
6	1.5007	0.6663	7.1533	0.13980	0.20980	4.7665	2.3032
7	1.6058	0.6227	8.6540	0.11555	0.18555	5.3893	2.7304
8	1.7182	0.5820	10.2598	0.09747	0.16747	5.9713	3.1465
9	1.8385	0.5439	11.9780	0.08349	0.15349	6.5152	3.5517
10	1.9672	0.5083	13.8164	0.07238	0.14238	7.0236	3.9461
11	2.1049	0.4751	15.7836	0.06336	0.13336	7.4987	4.3296
12	2.2522	0.4440	17.8885	0.05590	0.12590	7.9427	4.7025
13	2.4098	0.4150	20.1406	0.04965	0.11965	8.3577	5.0648
14	2.5785	0.3878	22.5505	0.04434	0.11434	8.7455	5.4167
15	2.7590	0.3624	25.1290	0.03979	0.10979	9.1079	5.7583
16	2.9522	0.3387	27.8881	0.03586	0.10586	9.4466	6.0897
17	3.1588	0.3166	30.8402	0.03243	0.10243	9.7632	6.4110
18	3.3799	0.2959	33.9990	0.02941	0.09941	10.0591	6.7225
19	3.6165	0.2765	37.3790	0.02675	0.09675	10.3356	7.0242
20	3.8697	0.2584	40.9955	0.02439	0.09439	10.5940	7.3163
21	4.1406	0.2415	44.8652	0.02229	0.09229	10.8355	7.5990
22	4.4304	0.2257	49.0057	0.02041	0.09041	11.0612	7.8725
23	4.7405	0.2109	53.4361	0.01871	0.08871	11.2722	8.1369
24	5.0724	0.1971	58.1767	0.01719	0.08719	11.4693	8.3923
25	5.4274	0.1842	63.2490	0.01581	0.08581	11.6536	8.6391
26	5.8074	0.1722	68.6765	0.01456	0.08456	11.8258	8.8773
27	6.2139	0.1609	74.4838	0.01343	0.08343	11.9867	9.1072
28	6.6488	0.1504	80.6977	0.01239	0.08239	12.1371	9.3289
29	7.1143	0.1406	87.3465	0.01145	0.08145	12.2777	9.5427
30	7.6123	0.1314	94.4608	0.01059	0.08059	12.4090	9.7487
31	8.1451	0.1228	102.0730	0.00980	0.07980	12.5318	9.9471
32	8.7153	0.1147	110.2182	0.00907	0.07907	12.6466	10.1381
33	9.3253	0.1072	118.9334	0.00841	0.07841	12.7538	10.3219
34	9.9781	0.1002	128.2588	0.00780	0.07780	12.8540	10.4987
35	10.6766	0.0937	138.2369	0.00723	0.07723	12.9477	10.6687
36	11.4239	0.0875	148.9135	0.00672	0.07672	13.0352	10.8321
37	12.2236	0.0818	160.3374	0.00624	0.07624	13.1170	10.9891
38	13.0793	0.0765	172.5610	0.00580	0.07580	13.1935	11.1398
39	13.9948	0.0715	185.6403	0.00539	0.07539	13.2649	11.2845
40	14.9745	0.0668	199.6351	0.00501	0.07501	13.3317	11.4233
48	25.7289	0.0389	353.2701	0.00283	0.07283	13.7305	12.3447
50	29.4570	0.0339	406.5289	0.00246	0.07246	13.8007	12.5287

i = 8.00%

n	F/Pi,n	P/Fi,n	F/Ai,n	A/Fi,n	A/Pi,n	P/Ai,n	A/Gi,n
1	1.0800	0.9259	1.0000	1.00000	1.08000	0.9259	n/a
2	1.1664	0.8573	2.0800	0.48077	0.56077	1.7833	0.4808
3	1.2597	0.7938	3.2464	0.30803	0.38803	2.5771	0.9487
4	1.3605	0.7350	4.5061	0.22192	0.30192	3.3121	1.4040
5	1.4693	0.6806	5.8666	0.17046	0.25046	3.9927	1.8465
6	1.5869	0.6302	7.3359	0.13632	0.21632	4.6229	2.2763
7	1.7138	0.5835	8.9228	0.11207	0.19207	5.2064	2.6937
8	1.8509	0.5403	10.6366	0.09401	0.17401	5.7466	3.0985
9	1.9990	0.5002	12.4876	0.08008	0.16008	6.2469	3.4910
10	2.1589	0.4632	14.4866	0.06903	0.14903	6.7101	3.8713
11	2.3316	0.4289	16.6455	0.06008	0.14008	7.1390	4.2395
12	2.5182	0.3971	18.9771	0.05270	0.13270	7.5361	4.5957
13	2.7196	0.3677	21.4953	0.04652	0.12652	7.9038	4.9402
14	2.9372	0.3405	24.2149	0.04130	0.12130	8.2442	5.2731
15	3.1722	0.3152	27.1521	0.03683	0.11683	8.5595	5.5945
16	3.4259	0.2919	30.3243	0.03298	0.11298	8.8514	5.9046
17	3.7000	0.2703	33.7502	0.02963	0.10963	9.1216	6.2037
18	3.9960	0.2502	37.4502	0.02670	0.10670	9.3719	6.4920
19	4.3157	0.2317	41.4463	0.02413	0.10413	9.6036	6.7697
20	4.6610	0.2145	45.7620	0.02185	0.10185	9.8181	7.0369
21	5.0338	0.1987	50.4229	0.01983	0.09983	10.0168	7.2940
22	5.4365	0.1839	55.4568	0.01803	0.09803	10.2007	7.5412
23	5.8715	0.1703	60.8933	0.01642	0.09642	10.3711	7.7786
24	6.3412	0.1577	66.7648	0.01498	0.09498	10.5288	8.0066
25	6.8485	0.1460	73.1059	0.01368	0.09368	10.6748	8.2254
26	7.3964	0.1352	79.9544	0.01251	0.09251	10.8100	8.4352
27	7.9881	0.1252	87.3508	0.01145	0.09145	10.9352	8.6363
28	8.6271	0.1159	95.3388	0.01049	0.09049	11.0511	8.8289
29	9.3173	0.1073	103.9659	0.00962	0.08962	11.1584	9.0133
30	10.0627	0.0994	113.2832	0.00883	0.08883	11.2578	9.1897
31	10.8677	0.0920	123.3459	0.00811	0.08811	11.3498	9.3584
32	11.7371	0.0852	134.2135	0.00745	0.08745	11.4350	9.5197
33	12.6760	0.0789	145.9506	0.00685	0.08685	11.5139	9.6737
34	13.6901	0.0730	158.6267	0.00630	0.08630	11.5869	9.8208
35	14.7853	0.0676	172.3168	0.00580	0.08580	11.6546	9.9611
36	15.9682	0.0626	187.1021	0.00534	0.08534	11.7172	10.0949
37	17.2456	0.0580	203.0703	0.00492	0.08492	11.7752	10.2225
38	18.6253	0.0537	220.3159	0.00454	0.08454	11.8289	10.3440
39	20.1153	0.0497	238.9412	0.00419	0.08419	11.8786	10.4597
40	21.7245	0.0460	259.0565	0.00386	0.08386	11.9246	10.5699
48	40.2106	0.0249	490.1322	0.00204	0.08204	12.1891	11.2758
50	46.9016	0.0213	573.7702	0.00174	0.08174	12.2335	11.4107

i = 9.00%

n	F/Pi,n	P/Fi,n	F/Ai,n	A/Fi,n	A/Pi,n	P/Ai,n	A/Gi,n
1	1.0900	0.9174	1.0000	1.00000	1.09000	0.9174	n/a
2	1.1881	0.8417	2.0900	0.47847	0.56847	1.7591	0.4785
3	1.2950	0.7722	3.2781	0.30505	0.39505	2.5313	0.9426
4	1.4116	0.7084	4.5731	0.21867	0.30867	3.2397	1.3925
5	1.5386	0.6499	5.9847	0.16709	0.25709	3.8897	1.8282
6	1.6771	0.5963	7.5233	0.13292	0.22292	4.4859	2.2498
7	1.8280	0.5470	9.2004	0.10869	0.19869	5.0330	2.6574
8	1.9926	0.5019	11.0285	0.09067	0.18067	5.5348	3.0512
9	2.1719	0.4604	13.0210	0.07680	0.16680	5.9952	3.4312
10	2.3674	0.4224	15.1929	0.06582	0.15582	6.4177	3.7978
11	2.5804	0.3875	17.5603	0.05695	0.14695	6.8052	4.1510
12	2.8127	0.3555	20.1407	0.04965	0.13965	7.1607	4.4910
13	3.0658	0.3262	22.9534	0.04357	0.13357	7.4869	4.8182
14	3.3417	0.2992	26.0192	0.03843	0.12843	7.7862	5.1326
15	3.6425	0.2745	29.3609	0.03406	0.12406	8.0607	5.4346
16	3.9703	0.2519	33.0034	0.03030	0.12030	8.3126	5.7245
17	4.3276	0.2311	36.9737	0.02705	0.11705	8.5436	6.0024
18	4.7171	0.2120	41.3013	0.02421	0.11421	8.7556	6.2687
19	5.1417	0.1945	46.0185	0.02173	0.11173	8.9501	6.5236
20	5.6044	0.1784	51.1601	0.01955	0.10955	9.1285	6.7674
21	6.1088	0.1637	56.7645	0.01762	0.10762	9.2922	7.0006
22	6.6586	0.1502	62.8733	0.01590	0.10590	9.4424	7.2232
23	7.2579	0.1378	69.5319	0.01438	0.10438	9.5802	7.4357
24	7.9111	0.1264	76.7898	0.01302	0.10302	9.7066	7.6384
25	8.6231	0.1160	84.7009	0.01181	0.10181	9.8226	7.8316
26	9.3992	0.1064	93.3240	0.01072	0.10072	9.9290	8.0156
27	10.2451	0.0976	102.7231	0.00973	0.09973	10.0266	8.1906
28	11.1671	0.0895	112.9682	0.00885	0.09885	10.1161	8.3571
29	12.1722	0.0822	124.1354	0.00806	0.09806	10.1983	8.5154
30	13.2677	0.0754	136.3075	0.00734	0.09734	10.2737	8.6657
31	14.4618	0.0691	149.5752	0.00669	0.09669	10.3428	8.8083
32	15.7633	0.0634	164.0370	0.00610	0.09610	10.4062	8.9436
33	17.1820	0.0582	179.8003	0.00556	0.09556	10.4644	9.0718
34	18.7284	0.0534	196.9823	0.00508	0.09508	10.5178	9.1933
35	20.4140	0.0490	215.7108	0.00464	0.09464	10.5668	9.3083
36	22.2512	0.0449	236.1247	0.00424	0.09424	10.6118	9.4171
37	24.2538	0.0412	258.3759	0.00387	0.09387	10.6530	9.5200
38	26.4367	0.0378	282.6298	0.00354	0.09354	10.6908	9.6172
39	28.8160	0.0347	309.0665	0.00324	0.09324	10.7255	9.7090
40	31.4094	0.0318	337.8824	0.00296	0.09296	10.7574	9.7957
48	62.5852	0.0160	684.2804	0.00146	0.09146	10.9336	10.3317
50	74.3575	0.0134	815.0836	0.00123	0.09123	10.9617	10.4295

i = 10.00%

n	F/Pi,n	P/Fi,n	F/Ai,n	A/Fi,n	A/Pi,n	P/Ai,n	A/Gi,n
1	1.1000	0.9091	1.0000	1.00000	1.10000	0.9091	n/a
2	1.2100	0.8264	2.1000	0.47619	0.57619	1.7355	0.4762
3	1.3310	0.7513	3.3100	0.30211	0.40211	2.4869	0.9366
4	1.4641	0.6830	4.6410	0.21547	0.31547	3.1699	1.3812
5	1.6105	0.6209	6.1051	0.16380	0.26380	3.7908	1.8101
6	1.7716	0.5645	7.7156	0.12961	0.22961	4.3553	2.2236
7	1.9487	0.5132	9.4872	0.10541	0.20541	4.8684	2.6216
8	2.1436	0.4665	11.4359	0.08744	0.18744	5.3349	3.0045
9	2.3579	0.4241	13.5795	0.07364	0.17364	5.7590	3.3724
10	2.5937	0.3855	15.9374	0.06275	0.16275	6.1446	3.7255
11	2.8531	0.3505	18.5312	0.05396	0.15396	6.4951	4.0641
12	3.1384	0.3186	21.3843	0.04676	0.14676	6.8137	4.3884
13	3.4523	0.2897	24.5227	0.04078	0.14078	7.1034	4.6988
14	3.7975	0.2633	27.9750	0.03575	0.13575	7.3667	4.9955
15	4.1772	0.2394	31.7725	0.03147	0.13147	7.6061	5.2789
16	4.5950	0.2176	35.9497	0.02782	0.12782	7.8237	5.5493
17	5.0545	0.1978	40.5447	0.02466	0.12466	8.0216	5.8071
18	5.5599	0.1799	45.5992	0.02193	0.12193	8.2014	6.0526
19	6.1159	0.1635	51.1591	0.01955	0.11955	8.3649	6.2861
20	6.7275	0.1486	57.2750	0.01746	0.11746	8.5136	6.5081
21	7.4002	0.1351	64.0025	0.01562	0.11562	8.6487	6.7189
22	8.1403	0.1228	71.4027	0.01401	0.11401	8.7715	6.9189
23	8.9543	0.1117	79.5430	0.01257	0.11257	8.8832	7.1085
24	9.8497	0.1015	88.4973	0.01130	0.11130	8.9847	7.2881
25	10.8347	0.0923	98.3471	0.01017	0.11017	9.0770	7.4580
26	11.9182	0.0839	109.1818	0.00916	0.10916	9.1609	7.6186
27	13.1100	0.0763	121.0999	0.00826	0.10826	9.2372	7.7704
28	14.4210	0.0693	134.2099	0.00745	0.10745	9.3066	7.9137
29	15.8631	0.0630	148.6309	0.00673	0.10673	9.3696	8.0489
30	17.4494	0.0573	164.4940	0.00608	0.10608	9.4269	8.1762
31	19.1943	0.0521	181.9434	0.00550	0.10550	9.4790	8.2962
32	21.1138	0.0474	201.1378	0.00497	0.10497	9.5264	8.4091
33	23.2252	0.0431	222.2515	0.00450	0.10450	9.5694	8.5152
34	25.5477	0.0391	245.4767	0.00407	0.10407	9.6086	8.6149
35	28.1024	0.0356	271.0244	0.00369	0.10369	9.6442	8.7086
36	30.9127	0.0323	299.1268	0.00334	0.10334	9.6765	8.7965
37	34.0039	0.0294	330.0395	0.00303	0.10303	9.7059	8.8789
38	37.4043	0.0267	364.0434	0.00275	0.10275	9.7327	8.9562
39	41.1448	0.0243	401.4478	0.00249	0.10249	9.7570	9.0285
40	45.2593	0.0221	442.5926	0.00226	0.10226	9.7791	9.0962
48	97.0172	0.0103	960.1723	0.00104	0.10104	9.8969	9.5001
50	117.3909	0.0085	1163.9085	0.00086	0.10086	9.9148	9.5704

i = 12.00%

n	F/Pi,n	P/Fi,n	F/Ai,n	A/Fi,n	A/Pi,n	P/Ai,n	A/Gi,n
1	1.1200	0.8929	1.0000	1.00000	1.12000	0.8929	n/a
2	1.2544	0.7972	2.1200	0.47170	0.59170	1.6901	0.4717
3	1.4049	0.7118	3.3744	0.29635	0.41635	2.4018	0.9246
4	1.5735	0.6355	4.7793	0.20923	0.32923	3.0373	1.3589
5	1.7623	0.5674	6.3528	0.15741	0.27741	3.6048	1.7746
6	1.9738	0.5066	8.1152	0.12323	0.24323	4.1114	2.1720
7	2.2107	0.4523	10.0890	0.09912	0.21912	4.5638	2.5515
8	2.4760	0.4039	12.2997	0.08130	0.20130	4.9676	2.9131
9	2.7731	0.3606	14.7757	0.06768	0.18768	5.3282	3.2574
10	3.1058	0.3220	17.5487	0.05698	0.17698	5.6502	3.5847
11	3.4785	0.2875	20.6546	0.04842	0.16842	5.9377	3.8953
12	3.8960	0.2567	24.1331	0.04144	0.16144	6.1944	4.1897
13	4.3635	0.2292	28.0291	0.03568	0.15568	6.4235	4.4683
14	4.8871	0.2046	32.3926	0.03087	0.15087	6.6282	4.7317
15	5.4736	0.1827	37.2797	0.02682	0.14682	6.8109	4.9803
16	6.1304	0.1631	42.7533	0.02339	0.14339	6.9740	5.2147
17	6.8660	0.1456	48.8837	0.02046	0.14046	7.1196	5.4353
18	7.6900	0.1300	55.7497	0.01794	0.13794	7.2497	5.6427
19	8.6128	0.1161	63.4397	0.01576	0.13576	7.3658	5.8375
20	9.6463	0.1037	72.0524	0.01388	0.13388	7.4694	6.0202
21	10.8038	0.0926	81.6987	0.01224	0.13224	7.5620	6.1913
22	12.1003	0.0826	92.5026	0.01081	0.13081	7.6446	6.3514
23	13.5523	0.0738	104.6029	0.00956	0.12956	7.7184	6.5010
24	15.1786	0.0659	118.1552	0.00846	0.12846	7.7843	6.6406
25	17.0001	0.0588	133.3339	0.00750	0.12750	7.8431	6.7708
26	19.0401	0.0525	150.3339	0.00665	0.12665	7.8957	6.8921
27	21.3249	0.0469	169.3740	0.00590	0.12590	7.9426	7.0049
28	23.8839	0.0419	190.6989	0.00524	0.12524	7.9844	7.1098
29	26.7499	0.0374	214.5828	0.00466	0.12466	8.0218	7.2071
30	29.9599	0.0334	241.3327	0.00414	0.12414	8.0552	7.2974
31	33.5551	0.0298	271.2926	0.00369	0.12369	8.0850	7.3811
32	37.5817	0.0266	304.8477	0.00328	0.12328	8.1116	7.4586
33	42.0915	0.0238	342.4294	0.00292	0.12292	8.1354	7.5302
34	47.1425	0.0212	384.5210	0.00260	0.12260	8.1566	7.5965
35	52.7996	0.0189	431.6635	0.00232	0.12232	8.1755	7.6577
36	59.1356	0.0169	484.4631	0.00206	0.12206	8.1924	7.7141
37	66.2318	0.0151	543.5987	0.00184	0.12184	8.2075	7.7661
38	74.1797	0.0135	609.8305	0.00164	0.12164	8.2210	7.8141
39	83.0812	0.0120	684.0102	0.00146	0.12146	8.2330	7.8582
40	93.0510	0.0107	767.0914	0.00130	0.12130	8.2438	7.8988
48	230.3908	0.0043	1911.5898	0.00052	0.12052	8.2972	8.1241
50	289.0022	0.0035	2400.0182	0.00042	0.12042	8.3045	8.1597

i = 15.00%

n	F/Pi,n	P/Fi,n	F/Ai,n	A/Fi,n	A/Pi,n	P/Ai,n	A/Gi,n
1	1.1500	0.8696	1.0000	1.00000	1.15000	0.8696	n/a
2	1.3225	0.7561	2.1500	0.46512	0.61512	1.6257	0.4651
3	1.5209	0.6575	3.4725	0.28798	0.43798	2.2832	0.9071
4	1.7490	0.5718	4.9934	0.20027	0.35027	2.8550	1.3263
5	2.0114	0.4972	6.7424	0.14832	0.29832	3.3522	1.7228
6	2.3131	0.4323	8.7537	0.11424	0.26424	3.7845	2.0972
7	2.6600	0.3759	11.0668	0.09036	0.24036	4.1604	2.4498
8	3.0590	0.3269	13.7268	0.07285	0.22285	4.4873	2.7813
9	3.5179	0.2843	16.7858	0.05957	0.20957	4.7716	3.0922
10	4.0456	0.2472	20.3037	0.04925	0.19925	5.0188	3.3832
11	4.6524	0.2149	24.3493	0.04107	0.19107	5.2337	3.6549
12	5.3503	0.1869	29.0017	0.03448	0.18448	5.4206	3.9082
13	6.1528	0.1625	34.3519	0.02911	0.17911	5.5831	4.1438
14	7.0757	0.1413	40.5047	0.02469	0.17469	5.7245	4.3624
15	8.1371	0.1229	47.5804	0.02102	0.17102	5.8474	4.5650
16	9.3576	0.1069	55.7175	0.01795	0.16795	5.9542	4.7522
17	10.7613	0.0929	65.0751	0.01537	0.16537	6.0472	4.9251
18	12.3755	0.0808	75.8364	0.01319	0.16319	6.1280	5.0843
19	14.2318	0.0703	88.2118	0.01134	0.16134	6.1982	5.2307
20	16.3665	0.0611	102.4436	0.00976	0.15976	6.2593	5.3651
21	18.8215	0.0531	118.8101	0.00842	0.15842	6.3125	5.4883
22	21.6447	0.0462	137.6316	0.00727	0.15727	6.3587	5.6010
23	24.8915	0.0402	159.2764	0.00628	0.15628	6.3988	5.7040
24	28.6252	0.0349	184.1678	0.00543	0.15543	6.4338	5.7979
25	32.9190	0.0304	212.7930	0.00470	0.15470	6.4641	5.8834
26	37.8568	0.0264	245.7120	0.00407	0.15407	6.4906	5.9612
27	43.5353	0.0230	283.5688	0.00353	0.15353	6.5135	6.0319
28	50.0656	0.0200	327.1041	0.00306	0.15306	6.5335	6.0960
29	57.5755	0.0174	377.1697	0.00265	0.15265	6.5509	6.1541
30	66.2118	0.0151	434.7451	0.00230	0.15230	6.5660	6.2066
31	76.1435	0.0131	500.9569	0.00200	0.15200	6.5791	6.2541
32	87.5651	0.0114	577.1005	0.00173	0.15173	6.5905	6.2970
33	100.6998	0.0099	664.6655	0.00150	0.15150	6.6005	6.3357
34	115.8048	0.0086	765.3654	0.00131	0.15131	6.6091	6.3705
35	133.1755	0.0075	881.1702	0.00113	0.15113	6.6166	6.4019
36	153.1519	0.0065	1014.3457	0.00099	0.15099	6.6231	6.4301
37	176.1246	0.0057	1167.4975	0.00086	0.15086	6.6288	6.4554
38	202.5433	0.0049	1343.6222	0.00074	0.15074	6.6338	6.4781
39	232.9248	0.0043	1546.1655	0.00065	0.15065	6.6380	6.4985
40	267.8635	0.0037	1779.0903	0.00056	0.15056	6.6418	6.5168
48	819.4007	0.0012	5456.0047	0.00018	0.15018	6.6585	6.6080
50	1083.6574	0.0009	7217.7163	0.00014	0.15014	6.6605	6.6205

i = 18.00%

n	F/Pi,n	P/Fi,n	F/Ai,n	A/Fi,n	A/Pi,n	P/Ai,n	A/Gi,n
1	1.1800	0.8475	1.0000	1.00000	1.18000	0.8475	n/a
2	1.3924	0.7182	2.1800	0.45872	0.63872	1.5656	0.4587
3	1.6430	0.6086	3.5724	0.27992	0.45992	2.1743	0.8902
4	1.9388	0.5158	5.2154	0.19174	0.37174	2.6901	1.2947
5	2.2878	0.4371	7.1542	0.13978	0.31978	3.1272	1.6728
6	2.6996	0.3704	9.4420	0.10591	0.28591	3.4976	2.0252
7	3.1855	0.3139	12.1415	0.08236	0.26236	3.8115	2.3526
8	3.7589	0.2660	15.3270	0.06524	0.24524	4.0776	2.6558
9	4.4355	0.2255	19.0859	0.05239	0.23239	4.3030	2.9358
10	5.2338	0.1911	23.5213	0.04251	0.22251	4.4941	3.1936
11	6.1759	0.1619	28.7551	0.03478	0.21478	4.6560	3.4303
12	7.2876	0.1372	34.9311	0.02863	0.20863	4.7932	3.6470
13	8.5994	0.1163	42.2187	0.02369	0.20369	4.9095	3.8449
14	10.1472	0.0985	50.8180	0.01968	0.19968	5.0081	4.0250
15	11.9737	0.0835	60.9653	0.01640	0.19640	5.0916	4.1887
16	14.1290	0.0708	72.9390	0.01371	0.19371	5.1624	4.3369
17	16.6722	0.0600	87.0680	0.01149	0.19149	5.2223	4.4708
18	19.6733	0.0508	103.7403	0.00964	0.18964	5.2732	4.5916
19	23.2144	0.0431	123.4135	0.00810	0.18810	5.3162	4.7003
20	27.3930	0.0365	146.6280	0.00682	0.18682	5.3527	4.7978
21	32.3238	0.0309	174.0210	0.00575	0.18575	5.3837	4.8851
22	38.1421	0.0262	206.3448	0.00485	0.18485	5.4099	4.9632
23	45.0076	0.0222	244.4868	0.00409	0.18409	5.4321	5.0329
24	53.1090	0.0188	289.4945	0.00345	0.18345	5.4509	5.0950
25	62.6686	0.0160	342.6035	0.00292	0.18292	5.4669	5.1502
26	73.9490	0.0135	405.2721	0.00247	0.18247	5.4804	5.1991
27	87.2598	0.0115	479.2211	0.00209	0.18209	5.4919	5.2425
28	102.9666	0.0097	566.4809	0.00177	0.18177	5.5016	5.2810
29	121.5005	0.0082	669.4475	0.00149	0.18149	5.5098	5.3149
30	143.3706	0.0070	790.9480	0.00126	0.18126	5.5168	5.3448
31	169.1774	0.0059	934.3186	0.00107	0.18107	5.5227	5.3712
32	199.6293	0.0050	1103.4960	0.00091	0.18091	5.5277	5.3945
33	235.5625	0.0042	1303.1253	0.00077	0.18077	5.5320	5.4149
34	277.9638	0.0036	1538.6878	0.00065	0.18065	5.5356	5.4328
35	327.9973	0.0030	1816.6516	0.00055	0.18055	5.5386	5.4485
36	387.0368	0.0026	2144.6489	0.00047	0.18047	5.5412	5.4623
37	456.7034	0.0022	2531.6857	0.00039	0.18039	5.5434	5.4744
38	538.9100	0.0019	2988.3891	0.00033	0.18033	5.5452	5.4849
39	635.9139	0.0016	3527.2992	0.00028	0.18028	5.5468	5.4941
40	750.3783	0.0013	4163.2130	0.00024	0.18024	5.5482	5.5022
48	2820.5665	0.0004	15664.2586	0.00006	0.18006	5.5536	5.5385
50	3927.3569	0.0003	21813.0937	0.00005	0.18005	5.5541	5.5428

i = 20.00%

n	F/Pi,n	P/Fi,n	F/Ai,n	A/Fi,n	A/Pi,n	P/Ai,n	A/Gi,n
1	1.2000	0.8333	1.0000	1.00000	1.20000	0.8333	n/a
2	1.4400	0.6944	2.2000	0.45455	0.65455	1.5278	0.4545
3	1.7280	0.5787	3.6400	0.27473	0.47473	2.1065	0.8791
4	2.0736	0.4823	5.3680	0.18629	0.38629	2.5887	1.2742
5	2.4883	0.4019	7.4416	0.13438	0.33438	2.9906	1.6405
6	2.9860	0.3349	9.9299	0.10071	0.30071	3.3255	1.9788
7	3.5832	0.2791	12.9159	0.07742	0.27742	3.6046	2.2902
8	4.2998	0.2326	16.4991	0.06061	0.26061	3.8372	2.5756
9	5.1598	0.1938	20.7989	0.04808	0.24808	4.0310	2.8364
10	6.1917	0.1615	25.9587	0.03852	0.23852	4.1925	3.0739
11	7.4301	0.1346	32.1504	0.03110	0.23110	4.3271	3.2893
12	8.9161	0.1122	39.5805	0.02526	0.22526	4.4392	3.4841
13	10.6993	0.0935	48.4966	0.02062	0.22062	4.5327	3.6597
14	12.8392	0.0779	59.1959	0.01689	0.21689	4.6106	3.8175
15	15.4070	0.0649	72.0351	0.01388	0.21388	4.6755	3.9588
16	18.4884	0.0541	87.4421	0.01144	0.21144	4.7296	4.0851
17	22.1861	0.0451	105.9306	0.00944	0.20944	4.7746	4.1976
18	26.6233	0.0376	128.1167	0.00781	0.20781	4.8122	4.2975
19	31.9480	0.0313	154.7400	0.00646	0.20646	4.8435	4.3861
20	38.3376	0.0261	186.6880	0.00536	0.20536	4.8696	4.4643
21	46.0051	0.0217	225.0256	0.00444	0.20444	4.8913	4.5334
22	55.2061	0.0181	271.0307	0.00369	0.20369	4.9094	4.5941
23	66.2474	0.0151	326.2369	0.00307	0.20307	4.9245	4.6475
24	79.4968	0.0126	392.4842	0.00255	0.20255	4.9371	4.6943
25	95.3962	0.0105	471.9811	0.00212	0.20212	4.9476	4.7352
26	114.4755	0.0087	567.3773	0.00176	0.20176	4.9563	4.7709
27	137.3706	0.0073	681.8528	0.00147	0.20147	4.9636	4.8020
28	164.8447	0.0061	819.2233	0.00122	0.20122	4.9697	4.8291
29	197.8136	0.0051	984.0680	0.00102	0.20102	4.9747	4.8527
30	237.3763	0.0042	1181.8816	0.00085	0.20085	4.9789	4.8731
31	284.8516	0.0035	1419.2579	0.00070	0.20070	4.9824	4.8908
32	341.8219	0.0029	1704.1095	0.00059	0.20059	4.9854	4.9061
33	410.1863	0.0024	2045.9314	0.00049	0.20049	4.9878	4.9194
34	492.2235	0.0020	2456.1176	0.00041	0.20041	4.9898	4.9308
35	590.6682	0.0017	2948.3411	0.00034	0.20034	4.9915	4.9406
36	708.8019	0.0014	3539.0094	0.00028	0.20028	4.9929	4.9491
37	850.5622	0.0012	4247.8112	0.00024	0.20024	4.9941	4.9564
38	1020.6747	0.0010	5098.3735	0.00020	0.20020	4.9951	4.9627
39	1224.8096	0.0008	6119.0482	0.00016	0.20016	4.9959	4.9681
40	1469.7716	0.0007	7343.8578	0.00014	0.20014	4.9966	4.9728
48	6319.7487	0.0002	31593.7436	0.00003	0.20003	4.9992	4.9924
50	9100.4382	0.0001	45497.1908	0.00002	0.20002	4.9995	4.9945

i = 25.00%

n	F/Pi,n	P/Fi,n	F/Ai,n	A/Fi,n	A/Pi,n	P/Ai,n	A/Gi,n
1	1.2500	0.8000	1.0000	1.00000	1.25000	0.8000	n/a
2	1.5625	0.6400	2.2500	0.44444	0.69444	1.4400	0.4444
3	1.9531	0.5120	3.8125	0.26230	0.51230	1.9520	0.8525
4	2.4414	0.4096	5.7656	0.17344	0.42344	2.3616	1.2249
5	3.0518	0.3277	8.2070	0.12185	0.37185	2.6893	1.5631
6	3.8147	0.2621	11.2588	0.08882	0.33882	2.9514	1.8683
7	4.7684	0.2097	15.0735	0.06634	0.31634	3.1611	2.1424
8	5.9605	0.1678	19.8419	0.05040	0.30040	3.3289	2.3872
9	7.4506	0.1342	25.8023	0.03876	0.28876	3.4631	2.6048
10	9.3132	0.1074	33.2529	0.03007	0.28007	3.5705	2.7971
11	11.6415	0.0859	42.5661	0.02349	0.27349	3.6564	2.9663
12	14.5519	0.0687	54.2077	0.01845	0.26845	3.7251	3.1145
13	18.1899	0.0550	68.7596	0.01454	0.26454	3.7801	3.2437
14	22.7374	0.0440	86.9495	0.01150	0.26150	3.8241	3.3559
15	28.4217	0.0352	109.6868	0.00912	0.25912	3.8593	3.4530
16	35.5271	0.0281	138.1085	0.00724	0.25724	3.8874	3.5366
17	44.4089	0.0225	173.6357	0.00576	0.25576	3.9099	3.6084
18	55.5112	0.0180	218.0446	0.00459	0.25459	3.9279	3.6698
19	69.3889	0.0144	273.5558	0.00366	0.25366	3.9424	3.7222
20	86.7362	0.0115	342.9447	0.00292	0.25292	3.9539	3.7667
21	108.4202	0.0092	429.6809	0.00233	0.25233	3.9631	3.8045
22	135.5253	0.0074	538.1011	0.00186	0.25186	3.9705	3.8365
23	169.4066	0.0059	673.6264	0.00148	0.25148	3.9764	3.8634
24	211.7582	0.0047	843.0329	0.00119	0.25119	3.9811	3.8861
25	264.6978	0.0038	1054.7912	0.00095	0.25095	3.9849	3.9052
26	330.8722	0.0030	1319.4890	0.00076	0.25076	3.9879	3.9212
27	413.5903	0.0024	1650.3612	0.00061	0.25061	3.9903	3.9346
28	516.9879	0.0019	2063.9515	0.00048	0.25048	3.9923	3.9457
29	646.2349	0.0015	2580.9394	0.00039	0.25039	3.9938	3.9551
30	807.7936	0.0012	3227.1743	0.00031	0.25031	3.9950	3.9628
31	1009.7420	0.0010	4034.9678	0.00025	0.25025	3.9960	3.9693
32	1262.1774	0.0008	5044.7098	0.00020	0.25020	3.9968	3.9746
33	1577.7218	0.0006	6306.8872	0.00016	0.25016	3.9975	3.9791
34	1972.1523	0.0005	7884.6091	0.00013	0.25013	3.9980	3.9828
35	2465.1903	0.0004	9856.7613	0.00010	0.25010	3.9984	3.9858
36	3081.4879	0.0003	12321.9516	0.00008	0.25008	3.9987	3.9883
37	3851.8599	0.0003	15403.4396	0.00006	0.25006	3.9990	3.9904
38	4814.8249	0.0002	19255.2994	0.00005	0.25005	3.9992	3.9921
39	6018.5311	0.0002	24070.1243	0.00004	0.25004	3.9993	3.9935
40	7523.1638	0.0001	30088.6554	0.00003	0.25003	3.9995	3.9947

i = 30.00%

n	F/Pi,n	P/Fi,n	F/Ai,n	A/Fi,n	A/Pi,n	P/Ai,n	A/Gi,n
1	1.3000	0.7692	1.0000	1.00000	1.30000	0.7692	n/a
2	1.6900	0.5917	2.3000	0.43478	0.73478	1.3609	0.4348
3	2.1970	0.4552	3.9900	0.25063	0.55063	1.8161	0.8271
4	2.8561	0.3501	6.1870	0.16163	0.46163	2.1662	1.1783
5	3.7129	0.2693	9.0431	0.11058	0.41058	2.4356	1.4903
6	4.8268	0.2072	12.7560	0.07839	0.37839	2.6427	1.7654
7	6.2749	0.1594	17.5828	0.05687	0.35687	2.8021	2.0063
8	8.1573	0.1226	23.8577	0.04192	0.34192	2.9247	2.2156
9	10.6045	0.0943	32.0150	0.03124	0.33124	3.0190	2.3963
10	13.7858	0.0725	42.6195	0.02346	0.32346	3.0915	2.5512
11	17.9216	0.0558	56.4053	0.01773	0.31773	3.1473	2.6833
12	23.2981	0.0429	74.3270	0.01345	0.31345	3.1903	2.7952
13	30.2875	0.0330	97.6250	0.01024	0.31024	3.2233	2.8895
14	39.3738	0.0254	127.9125	0.00782	0.30782	3.2487	2.9685
15	51.1859	0.0195	167.2863	0.00598	0.30598	3.2682	3.0344
16	66.5417	0.0150	218.4722	0.00458	0.30458	3.2832	3.0892
17	86.5042	0.0116	285.0139	0.00351	0.30351	3.2948	3.1345
18	112.4554	0.0089	371.5180	0.00269	0.30269	3.3037	3.1718
19	146.1920	0.0068	483.9734	0.00207	0.30207	3.3105	3.2025
20	190.0496	0.0053	630.1655	0.00159	0.30159	3.3158	3.2275
21	247.0645	0.0040	820.2151	0.00122	0.30122	3.3198	3.2480
22	321.1839	0.0031	1067.2796	0.00094	0.30094	3.3230	3.2646
23	417.5391	0.0024	1388.4635	0.00072	0.30072	3.3254	3.2781
24	542.8008	0.0018	1806.0026	0.00055	0.30055	3.3272	3.2890
25	705.6410	0.0014	2348.8033	0.00043	0.30043	3.3286	3.2979
26	917.3333	0.0011	3054.4443	0.00033	0.30033	3.3297	3.3050
27	1192.5333	0.0008	3971.7776	0.00025	0.30025	3.3305	3.3107
28	1550.2933	0.0006	5164.3109	0.00019	0.30019	3.3312	3.3153
29	2015.3813	0.0005	6714.6042	0.00015	0.30015	3.3317	3.3189
30	2619.9956	0.0004	8729.9855	0.00011	0.30011	3.3321	3.3219
31	3405.9943	0.0003	11349.9811	0.00009	0.30009	3.3324	3.3242
32	4427.7926	0.0002	14755.9755	0.00007	0.30007	3.3326	3.3261
33	5756.1304	0.0002	19183.7681	0.00005	0.30005	3.3328	3.3276
34	7482.9696	0.0001	24939.8985	0.00004	0.30004	3.3329	3.3288
35	9727.8604	0.0001	32422.8681	0.00003	0.30003	3.3330	3.3297

i = 40.00%

n	F/Pi,n	P/Fi,n	F/Ai,n	A/Fi,n	A/Pi,n	P/Ai,n	A/Gi,n
1	1.4000	0.7143	1.0000	1.00000	1.40000	0.7143	n/a
2	1.9600	0.5102	2.4000	0.41667	0.81667	1.2245	0.4167
3	2.7440	0.3644	4.3600	0.22936	0.62936	1.5889	0.7798
4	3.8416	0.2603	7.1040	0.14077	0.54077	1.8492	1.0923
5	5.3782	0.1859	10.9456	0.09136	0.49136	2.0352	1.3580
6	7.5295	0.1328	16.3238	0.06126	0.46126	2.1680	1.5811
7	10.5414	0.0949	23.8534	0.04192	0.44192	2.2628	1.7664
8	14.7579	0.0678	34.3947	0.02907	0.42907	2.3306	1.9185
9	20.6610	0.0484	49.1526	0.02034	0.42034	2.3790	2.0422
10	28.9255	0.0346	69.8137	0.01432	0.41432	2.4136	2.1419
11	40.4957	0.0247	98.7391	0.01013	0.41013	2.4383	2.2215
12	56.6939	0.0176	139.2348	0.00718	0.40718	2.4559	2.2845
13	79.3715	0.0126	195.9287	0.00510	0.40510	2.4685	2.3341
14	111.1201	0.0090	275.3002	0.00363	0.40363	2.4775	2.3729
15	155.5681	0.0064	386.4202	0.00259	0.40259	2.4839	2.4030
16	217.7953	0.0046	541.9883	0.00185	0.40185	2.4885	2.4262
17	304.9135	0.0033	759.7837	0.00132	0.40132	2.4918	2.4441
18	426.8789	0.0023	1064.6971	0.00094	0.40094	2.4941	2.4577
19	597.6304	0.0017	1491.5760	0.00067	0.40067	2.4958	2.4682
20	836.6826	0.0012	2089.2064	0.00048	0.40048	2.4970	2.4761
21	1171.3556	0.0009	2925.8889	0.00034	0.40034	2.4979	2.4821
22	1639.8978	0.0006	4097.2445	0.00024	0.40024	2.4985	2.4866
23	2295.8569	0.0004	5737.1423	0.00017	0.40017	2.4989	2.4900
24	3214.1997	0.0003	8032.9993	0.00012	0.40012	2.4992	2.4925
25	4499.8796	0.0002	11247.1990	0.00009	0.40009	2.4994	2.4944

i = 50.00%

n	F/Pi,n	P/Fi,n	F/Ai,n	A/Fi,n	A/Pi,n	P/Ai,n	A/Gi,n
1	1.5000	0.6667	1.0000	1.00000	1.50000	0.6667	n/a
2	2.2500	0.4444	2.5000	0.40000	0.90000	1.1111	0.4000
3	3.3750	0.2963	4.7500	0.21053	0.71053	1.4074	0.7368
4	5.0625	0.1975	8.1250	0.12308	0.62308	1.6049	1.0154
5	7.5938	0.1317	13.1875	0.07583	0.57583	1.7366	1.2417
6	11.3906	0.0878	20.7813	0.04812	0.54812	1.8244	1.4226
7	17.0859	0.0585	32.1719	0.03108	0.53108	1.8829	1.5648
8	25.6289	0.0390	49.2578	0.02030	0.52030	1.9220	1.6752
9	38.4434	0.0260	74.8867	0.01335	0.51335	1.9480	1.7596
10	57.6650	0.0173	113.3301	0.00882	0.50882	1.9653	1.8235
11	86.4976	0.0116	170.9951	0.00585	0.50585	1.9769	1.8713
12	129.7463	0.0077	257.4927	0.00388	0.50388	1.9846	1.9068
13	194.6195	0.0051	387.2390	0.00258	0.50258	1.9897	1.9329
14	291.9293	0.0034	581.8585	0.00172	0.50172	1.9931	1.9519
15	437.8939	0.0023	873.7878	0.00114	0.50114	1.9954	1.9657
16	656.8408	0.0015	1311.6817	0.00076	0.50076	1.9970	1.9756
17	985.2613	0.0010	1968.5225	0.00051	0.50051	1.9980	1.9827
18	1477.8919	0.0007	2953.7838	0.00034	0.50034	1.9986	1.9878
19	2216.8378	0.0005	4431.6756	0.00023	0.50023	1.9991	1.9914
20	3325.2567	0.0003	6648.5135	0.00015	0.50015	1.9994	1.9940

i = 70.00%

n	F/Pi,n	P/Fi,n	F/Ai,n	A/Fi,n	A/Pi,n	P/Ai,n	A/Gi,n
1	1.7000	0.5882	1.0000	1.00000	1.70000	0.5882	n/a
2	2.8900	0.3460	2.7000	0.37037	1.07037	0.9343	0.3704
3	4.9130	0.2035	5.5900	0.17889	0.87889	1.1378	0.6619
4	8.3521	0.1197	10.5030	0.09521	0.79521	1.2575	0.8845
5	14.1986	0.0704	18.8551	0.05304	0.75304	1.3280	1.0497
6	24.1376	0.0414	33.0537	0.03025	0.73025	1.3694	1.1693
7	41.0339	0.0244	57.1912	0.01749	0.71749	1.3938	1.2537
8	69.7576	0.0143	98.2251	0.01018	0.71018	1.4081	1.3122
9	118.5879	0.0084	167.9827	0.00595	0.70595	1.4165	1.3520
10	201.5994	0.0050	286.5706	0.00349	0.70349	1.4215	1.3787
11	342.7190	0.0029	488.1699	0.00205	0.70205	1.4244	1.3964
12	582.6222	0.0017	830.8889	0.00120	0.70120	1.4261	1.4079
13	990.4578	0.0010	1413.5111	0.00071	0.70071	1.4271	1.4154
14	1683.7783	0.0006	2403.9690	0.00042	0.70042	1.4277	1.4203
15	2862.4231	0.0003	4087.7472	0.00024	0.70024	1.4281	1.4233

i = 90.00%

n	F/Pi,n	P/Fi,n	F/Ai,n	A/Fi,n	A/Pi,n	P/Ai,n	A/Gi,n
1	1.900	0.5263	1.0000	1.00000	1.90000	0.5263	n/a
2	3.610	0.2770	2.9000	0.34483	1.24483	0.8033	0.3448
3	6.859	0.1458	6.5100	0.15361	1.05361	0.9491	0.5991
4	13.032	0.0767	13.3690	0.07480	0.97480	1.0259	0.7787
5	24.761	0.0404	26.4011	0.03788	0.93788	1.0662	0.9007
6	47.046	0.0213	51.1621	0.01955	0.91955	1.0875	0.9808
7	89.387	0.0112	98.2080	0.01018	0.91018	1.0987	1.0319
8	169.836	0.0059	187.5951	0.00533	0.90533	1.1046	1.0637
9	322.688	0.0031	357.4308	0.00280	0.90280	1.1077	1.0831
10	613.107	0.0016	680.1185	0.00147	0.90147	1.1093	1.0948
11	1164.903	0.0009	1293.2251	0.00077	0.90077	1.1102	1.1017
12	2213.315	0.0005	2458.1277	0.00041	0.90041	1.1106	1.1057
13	4205.298	0.0002	4671.4426	0.00021	0.90021	1.1108	1.1080
14	7990.067	0.0001	8876.7410	0.00011	0.90011	1.1110	1.1094
15	15181.127	0.0001	16866.8078	0.00006	0.90006	1.1110	1.1101

i = 110.00%

n	F/Pi,n	P/Fi,n	F/Ai,n	A/Fi,n	A/Pi,n	P/Ai,n	A/Gi,n
1	2.100	0.4762	1.0000	1.00000	2.10000	0.4762	n/a
2	4.410	0.2268	3.1000	0.32258	1.42258	0.7029	0.3226
3	9.261	0.1080	7.5100	0.13316	1.23316	0.8109	0.5459
4	19.448	0.0514	16.7710	0.05963	1.15963	0.8623	0.6923
5	40.841	0.0245	36.2191	0.02761	1.12761	0.8868	0.7836
6	85.766	0.0117	77.0601	0.01298	1.11298	0.8985	0.8383
7	180.109	0.0056	162.8262	0.00614	1.10614	0.9040	0.8700
8	378.229	0.0026	342.9351	0.00292	1.10292	0.9067	0.8879
9	794.280	0.0013	721.1637	0.00139	1.10139	0.9079	0.8977
10	1667.988	0.0006	1515.4437	0.00066	1.10066	0.9085	0.9031
11	3502.775	0.0003	3183.4318	0.00031	1.10031	0.9088	0.9059
12	7355.828	0.0001	6686.2068	0.00015	1.10015	0.9090	0.9075

i = 130.00%

n	F/Pi,n	P/Fi,n	F/Ai,n	A/Fi,n	A/Pi,n	P/Ai,n	A/Gi,n
1	2.300	0.43478	1.0000	1.00000	2.30000	0.4348	n/a
2	5.290	0.18904	3.3000	0.30303	1.60303	0.6238	0.3030
3	12.167	0.08219	8.5900	0.11641	1.41641	0.7060	0.5006
4	27.984	0.03573	20.7570	0.04818	1.34818	0.7417	0.6210
5	64.363	0.01554	48.7411	0.02052	1.32052	0.7573	0.6903
6	148.036	0.00676	113.1045	0.00884	1.30884	0.7640	0.7284
7	340.483	0.00294	261.1404	0.00383	1.30383	0.7670	0.7486
8	783.110	0.00128	601.6230	0.00166	1.30166	0.7682	0.7590
9	1801.153	0.00056	1384.7328	0.00072	1.30072	0.7688	0.7642
10	4142.651	0.00024	3185.8855	0.00031	1.30031	0.7690	0.7668
11	9528.098	0.00010	7328.5366	0.00014	1.30014	0.7692	0.7681
12	21914.624	0.00005	16856.6342	0.00006	1.30006	0.7692	0.7687

i = 150.00%

n	F/Pi,n	P/Fi,n	F/Ai,n	A/Fi,n	A/Pi,n	P/Ai,n	A/Gi,n
1	2.500	0.40000	1.0000	1.00000	2.50000	0.4000	n/a
2	6.250	0.16000	3.5000	0.28571	1.78571	0.5600	0.2857
3	15.625	0.06400	9.7500	0.10256	1.60256	0.6240	0.4615
4	39.063	0.02560	25.3750	0.03941	1.53941	0.6496	0.5616
5	97.656	0.01024	64.4375	0.01552	1.51552	0.6598	0.6149
6	244.141	0.00410	162.0938	0.00617	1.50617	0.6639	0.6420
7	610.352	0.00164	406.2344	0.00246	1.50246	0.6656	0.6552
8	1525.879	0.00066	1016.5859	0.00098	1.50098	0.6662	0.6614
9	3814.697	0.00026	2542.4648	0.00039	1.50039	0.6665	0.6643
10	9536.743	0.00010	6357.1621	0.00016	1.50016	0.6666	0.6656
11	23841.858	0.00004	15893.9053	0.00006	1.50006	0.6666	0.6662
12	59604.645	0.00002	39735.7632	0.00003	1.50003	0.6667	0.6665

i = 200.00%

n	F/Pi,n	P/Fi,n	F/Ai,n	A/Fi,n	A/Pi,n	P/Ai,n	A/Gi,n
1	3.000	0.33333	1.0000	1.00000	3.00000	0.3333	n/a
2	9.000	0.11111	4.0000	0.25000	2.25000	0.4444	0.2500
3	27.000	0.03704	13.0000	0.07692	2.07692	0.4815	0.3846
4	81.000	0.01235	40.0000	0.02500	2.02500	0.4938	0.4500
5	243.000	0.00412	121.0000	0.00826	2.00826	0.4979	0.4793
6	729.000	0.00137	364.0000	0.00275	2.00275	0.4993	0.4918
7	2187.000	0.00046	1093.0000	0.00091	2.00091	0.4998	0.4968
8	6561.000	0.00015	3280.0000	0.00030	2.00030	0.4999	0.4988
9	19683.000	0.00005	9841.0000	0.00010	2.00010	0.5000	0.4995
10	59049.000	0.00002	29524.0000	0.00003	2.00003	0.5000	0.4998

APPENDIX B

CONTINUOUS INTEREST, DISCRETE VALUE FACTORS

B.1 Factor Development

In Chapter 2 it was shown that compounding interest an infinite number of times per year leads to what is called "continuous compounding of interest." In this appendix, the compound interest formulas are derived for continuous interest with end of period payments. In the next appendix the formulas are developed for continuous interest with the continuous flow of money.

The following symbols will be used in the formulas to be developed:

r = the nominal annual continuous interest rate

n = the number of years

P, A, and F are defined as used throughout the text.

If a principal, P, is drawing continuous compound interest, an incremental interest amount, ΔP, is accumulated in incremental time, Δt. Writing an incremental dollar balance as shown in equation B-1 gives P at time t + Δt – P at time t equals P times r times the incremental time, Δt.

$$P|t+\Delta t - P|t = Pr\Delta t \quad \text{or} \quad \frac{P|t+\Delta t - P|t}{\Delta t} = Pr \qquad \text{B-1}$$

Taking the limit as Δt approaches zero gives

$$\lim_{\Delta t \to 0} \frac{P|t+\Delta t - P|t}{\Delta t} = \frac{dP}{dt} = Pr \qquad \text{B-2}$$

since the left side of Equation B-2 is the definition of the derivative of P with respect to t.

Separating the variables and integrating Equation B-2 yields

$$\int_{P=P}^{P=F} \frac{dP}{P} = \int_{t=0}^{t=n} r\,dt \qquad \text{B-3}$$

$$\ln P\Big|_{P}^{F} = rt\Big|_{o}^{n} \quad \text{or} \quad \ln F/P = rn \qquad \text{B-4}$$

Taking the antilog of Equation B-4 gives

$$F = Pe^{rn} = P\left(F/P_{r,n}\right) \qquad \text{B-5}$$

The factor e^{rn} is the continuous interest single payment compound amount factor. Solving Equation B-5 for P gives:

$$P = F\left(1/e^{rn}\right) = F\left(P/F_{r,n}\right) \qquad \text{B-6}$$

The factor $1/e^{rn}$ is the continuous interest single payment present worth factor.

As we did in Chapter 2 for discrete period compound interest we can now develop a uniform series compound amount factor for continuous interest with equal end of period payments. Treating each term of the series of payments individually yields the equation

$$F = A + Ae^{r} + Ae^{2r} + \ldots + Ae^{r(n-2)} + Ae^{r(n-1)} \qquad \text{B-7}$$

Multiplying each side of Equation B-7 by e_r yields

$$Fe^{r} = Ae^{r} + Ae^{2r} + Ae^{3r} + \ldots + Ae^{r(n-1)} + Ae^{rn} \qquad \text{B-8}$$

Subtracting Equation B-7 from B-8 gives

$$Fe^{r} - F = Ae^{rn} - A$$

or

$$F = A\left[\frac{e^{rn} - 1}{e^{r} - 1}\right] = A\left(F/A_{r,n}\right) \qquad \text{B-9}$$

where the factor $(e^{rn} - 1)/(e^{r} - 1)$ is the continuous interest discrete end-of-period payment uniform series compound amount factor.

Rearranging Equation B-9 gives

$$A = F\left[\frac{e^{r}-1}{e^{rn}-1}\right] = F\left(A/F_{r,n}\right) \qquad \text{B-10}$$

where the factor $(e^r - 1)/(e^{rn} - 1)$ is the continuous interest discrete end-of-period payment sinking fund deposit factor.

Formulas relating A and P result by combining Equations B-5 and B-9 to eliminate F.

$$P = A\left[\frac{e^{rn}-1}{\left(e^{r}-1\right)e^{rn}}\right] = A\left(P/A_{r,n}\right) \qquad \text{B-11}$$

where $(e^{rn} - 1)/(e^r - 1)e^{rn}$ is the continuous interest discrete end-of-period payment uniform series present worth factor. Rearranging Equation B-11 gives

$$A = P\left[\frac{\left(e^{r}-1\right)e^{rn}}{e^{rn}-1}\right] = P\left(A/P_{r,n}\right) \qquad \text{B-12}$$

where $(e^r - 1)e^{rn}/(e^{rn} - 1)$ is the continuous interest discrete end-of-period payment capital recovery factor.

Table B1 gives tabulated values of these continuous interest, discrete dollar value factors.

B.2 Applications

EXAMPLE B-1 Continuous Interest Compared to Annual and Effective Interest.

Calculate the future worth 6 years from now of a present sum of $1000 if interest is:

a) 10% per year compounded continuously
b) 10% per year compounded annually
c) an effective annual rate for 10% compounded continuously.

Solution:

a) $1000

0 1 - - - - 6 $F = 1000\ (F/P_{r,6})$ for $r = 0.10$

from Appendix B, $F/P_{r,6} = e^{6r} = e^{0.60} = 1.822$
therefore, F = 1000 (1.822) = \$1822

1.772
b) $F = 1000\,(F/P_{i,6}) = 1772$ for i = 10%

c) Same result as "a", i.e., effective continuous interest gives the identical result with continuous compounding of the nominal rate. The effective rate is $E = e^r - 1 = e^{0.1} - 1 = 1.1052 - 1 = 0.1052$ or 10.52%. This rate compounded annually gives the same result as 10% compounded continuously.

EXAMPLE B-2 Continuous Interest for Uniform Series

Determine the uniform series of end of year payments required to amortize a \$10,000 loan in 10 years if interest is

a) r = 6% per year compounded continuously
b) i = 6% per year compounded annually
c) E = An effective annual rate for 6% compounded continuously.

Solution:

a) \$10,000 A A
0 1– – – – 6

.1370
so $A = 10{,}000\,(A/P_{r,10}) = \$1370$

where $A/P_{r,10} = (e^{.06} - 1)e^{.60}/(e^{.60} - 1) = \dfrac{(0.0618)(1.8221)}{0.8221}$

.1359
b) $A = 10{,}000\,(A/P_{i,10}) = \$1359$

c) Same result as "a", since compounding "r" continuously gives the same total annual interest as compounding the effective rate, $E = e^r - 1$, annually.

Continuous Interest Factors for Lump Sum End-of-Period Payments:

$F/P_{r,n} = e^{rn}$

$P/F_{r,n} = 1/e^{rn}$

$F/A_{r,n} = (e^{rn} - 1)/(e^r - 1)$

$A/F_{r,n} = (e^r - 1)/(e^{rn} - 1)$

$P/A = (e^{rn} - 1)/(e^r - 1)e^{rn}$

$A/P_{r,n} = (e^r - 1)e^{rn}/(e^{rn} - 1)$

r = 10.00%

n	F/Pr,n	P/Fr,n	F/Ar,n	A/Fr,n	A/Pr,n	P/Ar,n
1	1.10517	0.90484	1.00000	1.00000	1.10517	0.90484
2	1.22140	0.81873	2.10517	0.47502	0.58019	1.72357
3	1.34986	0.74082	3.32657	0.30061	0.40578	2.46439
4	1.49182	0.67032	4.67643	0.21384	0.31901	3.13471
5	1.64872	0.60653	6.16826	0.16212	0.26729	3.74124
6	1.82212	0.54881	7.81698	0.12793	0.23310	4.29005
7	2.01375	0.49659	9.63910	0.10374	0.20892	4.78663
8	2.22554	0.44933	11.65285	0.08582	0.19099	5.23596
9	2.45960	0.40657	13.87839	0.07205	0.17723	5.64253
10	2.71828	0.36788	16.33799	0.06121	0.16638	6.01041
11	3.00417	0.33287	19.05628	0.05248	0.15765	6.34328
12	3.32012	0.30119	22.06044	0.04533	0.15050	6.64448
13	3.66930	0.27253	25.38056	0.03940	0.14457	6.91701
14	4.05520	0.24660	29.04986	0.03442	0.13959	7.16361
15	4.48169	0.22313	33.10506	0.03021	0.13538	7.38674
16	4.95303	0.20190	37.58674	0.02661	0.13178	7.58863
17	5.47395	0.18268	42.53978	0.02351	0.12868	7.77132
18	6.04965	0.16530	48.01372	0.02083	0.12600	7.93662
19	6.68589	0.14957	54.06337	0.01850	0.12367	8.08618
20	7.38906	0.13534	60.74927	0.01646	0.12163	8.22152
21	8.16617	0.12246	68.13832	0.01468	0.11985	8.34398
22	9.02501	0.11080	76.30449	0.01311	0.11828	8.45478
23	9.97418	0.10026	85.32951	0.01172	0.11689	8.55504
24	11.02318	0.09072	95.30369	0.01049	0.11566	8.64576
25	12.18249	0.08208	106.32686	0.00940	0.11458	8.72784
26	13.46374	0.07427	118.50936	0.00844	0.11361	8.80211
27	14.87973	0.06721	131.97310	0.00758	0.11275	8.86932
28	16.44465	0.06081	146.85283	0.00681	0.11198	8.93013
29	18.17415	0.05502	163.29747	0.00612	0.11129	8.98515
30	20.08554	0.04979	181.47162	0.00551	0.11068	9.03494
35	33.11545	0.03020	305.36438	0.00327	0.10845	9.22121
40	54.59815	0.01832	509.62900	0.00196	0.10713	9.33418
45	90.01713	0.01111	846.40443	0.00118	0.10635	9.40270
50	148.41316	0.00674	1401.65325	0.00071	0.10588	9.44427
55	244.69193	0.00409	2317.10378	0.00043	0.10560	9.46947
60	403.42879	0.00248	3826.42655	0.00026	0.10543	9.48476
65	665.14163	0.00150	6314.87910	0.00016	0.10533	9.49404

r = 12.00%

n	F/Pr,n	P/Fr,n	F/Ar,n	A/Fr,n	A/Pr,n	P/Ar,n
1	1.12750	0.88692	1.00000	1.00000	1.12750	0.88692
2	1.27125	0.78663	2.12750	0.47004	0.59753	1.67355
3	1.43333	0.69768	3.39875	0.29423	0.42172	2.37122
4	1.61607	0.61878	4.83208	0.20695	0.33445	2.99001
5	1.82212	0.54881	6.44815	0.15508	0.28258	3.53882
6	2.05443	0.48675	8.27027	0.12092	0.24841	4.02557
7	2.31637	0.43171	10.32470	0.09686	0.22435	4.45728
8	2.61170	0.38289	12.64107	0.07911	0.20660	4.84018
9	2.94468	0.33960	15.25277	0.06556	0.19306	5.17977
10	3.32012	0.30119	18.19744	0.05495	0.18245	5.48097
11	3.74342	0.26714	21.51756	0.04647	0.17397	5.74810
12	4.22070	0.23693	25.26098	0.03959	0.16708	5.98503
13	4.75882	0.21014	29.48168	0.03392	0.16142	6.19516
14	5.36556	0.18637	34.24050	0.02921	0.15670	6.38154
15	6.04965	0.16530	39.60606	0.02525	0.15275	6.54684
16	6.82096	0.14661	45.65570	0.02190	0.14940	6.69344
17	7.69061	0.13003	52.47666	0.01906	0.14655	6.82347
18	8.67114	0.11533	60.16727	0.01662	0.14412	6.93880
19	9.77668	0.10228	68.83841	0.01453	0.14202	7.04108
20	11.02318	0.09072	78.61509	0.01272	0.14022	7.13180
21	12.42860	0.08046	89.63827	0.01116	0.13865	7.21226
22	14.01320	0.07136	102.06686	0.00980	0.13729	7.28362
23	15.79984	0.06329	116.08007	0.00861	0.13611	7.34691
24	17.81427	0.05613	131.87991	0.00758	0.13508	7.40305
25	20.08554	0.04979	149.69418	0.00668	0.13418	7.45283
26	22.64638	0.04416	169.77972	0.00589	0.13339	7.49699
27	25.53372	0.03916	192.42610	0.00520	0.13269	7.53616
28	28.78919	0.03474	217.95982	0.00459	0.13208	7.57089
29	32.45972	0.03081	246.74901	0.00405	0.13155	7.60170
30	36.59823	0.02732	279.20873	0.00358	0.13108	7.62902
35	66.68633	0.01500	515.19963	0.00194	0.12944	7.72572
40	121.51042	0.00823	945.20309	0.00106	0.12855	7.77878
45	221.40642	0.00452	1728.72046	0.00058	0.12808	7.80791
50	403.42879	0.00248	3156.38220	0.00032	0.12781	7.82389
55	735.09519	0.00136	5757.75150	0.00017	0.12767	7.83266
60	1339.43076	0.00075	10497.75541	0.00010	0.12759	7.83748
65	2440.60197	0.00041	19134.60564	0.00005	0.12755	7.84012

r = 15.00%

n	F/Pr,n	P/Fr,n	F/Ar,n	A/Fr,n	A/Pr,n	P/Ar,n
1	1.16183	0.86071	1.00000	1.00000	1.16183	0.86071
2	1.34986	0.74082	2.16183	0.46257	0.62440	1.60153
3	1.56831	0.63763	3.51169	0.28476	0.44660	2.23915
4	1.82212	0.54881	5.08001	0.19685	0.35868	2.78797
5	2.11700	0.47237	6.90212	0.14488	0.30672	3.26033
6	2.45960	0.40657	9.01912	0.11088	0.27271	3.66690
7	2.85765	0.34994	11.47873	0.08712	0.24895	4.01684
8	3.32012	0.30119	14.33638	0.06975	0.23159	4.31803
9	3.85743	0.25924	17.65650	0.05664	0.21847	4.57727
10	4.48169	0.22313	21.51392	0.04648	0.20832	4.80040
11	5.20698	0.19205	25.99561	0.03847	0.20030	4.99245
12	6.04965	0.16530	31.20259	0.03205	0.19388	5.15775
13	7.02869	0.14227	37.25224	0.02684	0.18868	5.30003
14	8.16617	0.12246	44.28092	0.02258	0.18442	5.42248
15	9.48774	0.10540	52.44709	0.01907	0.18090	5.52788
16	11.02318	0.09072	61.93483	0.01615	0.17798	5.61860
17	12.80710	0.07808	72.95801	0.01371	0.17554	5.69668
18	14.87973	0.06721	85.76511	0.01166	0.17349	5.76389
19	17.28778	0.05784	100.64484	0.00994	0.17177	5.82173
20	20.08554	0.04979	117.93262	0.00848	0.17031	5.87152
21	23.33606	0.04285	138.01816	0.00725	0.16908	5.91437
22	27.11264	0.03688	161.35423	0.00620	0.16803	5.95125
23	31.50039	0.03175	188.46686	0.00531	0.16714	5.98300
24	36.59823	0.02732	219.96726	0.00455	0.16638	6.01032
25	42.52108	0.02352	256.56549	0.00390	0.16573	6.03384
26	49.40245	0.02024	299.08657	0.00334	0.16518	6.05408
27	57.39746	0.01742	348.48902	0.00287	0.16470	6.07151
28	66.68633	0.01500	405.88648	0.00246	0.16430	6.08650
29	77.47846	0.01291	472.57281	0.00212	0.16395	6.09941
30	90.01713	0.01111	550.05127	0.00182	0.16365	6.11052
35	190.56627	0.00525	1171.36068	0.00085	0.16269	6.14674
40	403.42879	0.00248	2486.67270	0.00040	0.16224	6.16385
45	854.05876	0.00117	5271.18827	0.00019	0.16202	6.17193
50	1808.04241	0.00055	11166.00777	0.00009	0.16192	6.17574
55	3827.62582	0.00026	23645.34077	0.00004	0.16188	6.17755
60	8103.08392	0.00012	50064.08891	0.00002	0.16185	6.17840
65	17154.22878	0.00006	105992.57917	0.00001	0.16184	6.17880

r = 20.00%

n	F/Pr,n	P/Fr,n	F/Ar,n	A/Fr,n	A/Pr,n	P/Ar,n
1	1.22140	0.81873	1.00000	1.00000	1.22140	0.81873
2	1.49182	0.67032	2.22140	0.45017	0.67157	1.48905
3	1.82212	0.54881	3.71323	0.26931	0.49071	2.03786
4	2.22554	0.44933	5.53535	0.18066	0.40206	2.48719
5	2.71828	0.36788	7.76089	0.12885	0.35025	2.85507
6	3.32012	0.30119	10.47917	0.09543	0.31683	3.15627
7	4.05520	0.24660	13.79929	0.07247	0.29387	3.40286
8	4.95303	0.20190	17.85449	0.05601	0.27741	3.60476
9	6.04965	0.16530	22.80752	0.04385	0.26525	3.77006
10	7.38906	0.13534	28.85717	0.03465	0.25606	3.90539
11	9.02501	0.11080	36.24622	0.02759	0.24899	4.01620
12	11.02318	0.09072	45.27124	0.02209	0.24349	4.10691
13	13.46374	0.07427	56.29441	0.01776	0.23917	4.18119
14	16.44465	0.06081	69.75815	0.01434	0.23574	4.24200
15	20.08554	0.04979	86.20280	0.01160	0.23300	4.29178
16	24.53253	0.04076	106.28833	0.00941	0.23081	4.33255
17	29.96410	0.03337	130.82086	0.00764	0.22905	4.36592
18	36.59823	0.02732	160.78496	0.00622	0.22762	4.39324
19	44.70118	0.02237	197.38320	0.00507	0.22647	4.41561
20	54.59815	0.01832	242.08438	0.00413	0.22553	4.43393
21	66.68633	0.01500	296.68253	0.00337	0.22477	4.44893
22	81.45087	0.01228	363.36886	0.00275	0.22415	4.46120
23	99.48432	0.01005	444.81973	0.00225	0.22365	4.47125
24	121.51042	0.00823	544.30405	0.00184	0.22324	4.47948
25	148.41316	0.00674	665.81447	0.00150	0.22290	4.48622
26	181.27224	0.00552	814.22762	0.00123	0.22263	4.49174
27	221.40642	0.00452	995.49987	0.00100	0.22241	4.49626
28	270.42641	0.00370	1216.90628	0.00082	0.22222	4.49995
29	330.29956	0.00303	1487.33269	0.00067	0.22208	4.50298
30	403.42879	0.00248	1817.63225	0.00055	0.22195	4.50546
35	1096.63316	0.00091	4948.59760	0.00020	0.22160	4.51254
40	2980.95798	0.00034	13459.44381	0.00007	0.22148	4.51514
45	8103.08392	0.00012	36594.32242	0.00003	0.22143	4.51610
50	22026.46576	0.00005	99481.44253	0.00001	0.22141	4.51645

r = 25.00%

n	F/Pr,n	P/Fr,n	F/Ar,n	A/Fr,n	A/Pr,n	P/Ar,n
1	1.28403	0.77880	1.00000	1.00000	1.28403	0.77880
2	1.64872	0.60653	2.28403	0.43782	0.72185	1.38533
3	2.11700	0.47237	3.93275	0.25428	0.53830	1.85770
4	2.71828	0.36788	6.04975	0.16530	0.44932	2.22558
5	3.49034	0.28650	8.76803	0.11405	0.39808	2.51208
6	4.48169	0.22313	12.25837	0.08158	0.36560	2.73521
7	5.75460	0.17377	16.74006	0.05974	0.34376	2.90899
8	7.38906	0.13534	22.49466	0.04445	0.32848	3.04432
9	9.48774	0.10540	29.88372	0.03346	0.31749	3.14972
10	12.18249	0.08208	39.37146	0.02540	0.30942	3.23181
11	15.64263	0.06393	51.55395	0.01940	0.30342	3.29573
12	20.08554	0.04979	67.19658	0.01488	0.29891	3.34552
13	25.79034	0.03877	87.28212	0.01146	0.29548	3.38429
14	33.11545	0.03020	113.07246	0.00884	0.29287	3.41449
15	42.52108	0.02352	146.18791	0.00684	0.29087	3.43801
16	54.59815	0.01832	188.70899	0.00530	0.28932	3.45633
17	70.10541	0.01426	243.30714	0.00411	0.28814	3.47059
18	90.01713	0.01111	313.41255	0.00319	0.28722	3.48170
19	115.58428	0.00865	403.42969	0.00248	0.28650	3.49035
20	148.41316	0.00674	519.01397	0.00193	0.28595	3.49709
21	190.56627	0.00525	667.42713	0.00150	0.28552	3.50234
22	244.69193	0.00409	857.99340	0.00117	0.28519	3.50642
23	314.19066	0.00318	1102.68533	0.00091	0.28493	3.50961
24	403.42879	0.00248	1416.87599	0.00071	0.28473	3.51208
25	518.01282	0.00193	1820.30478	0.00055	0.28457	3.51401
26	665.14163	0.00150	2338.31761	0.00043	0.28445	3.51552
27	854.05876	0.00117	3003.45924	0.00033	0.28436	3.51669
28	1096.63316	0.00091	3857.51800	0.00026	0.28428	3.51760
29	1408.10485	0.00071	4954.15116	0.00020	0.28423	3.51831
30	1808.04241	0.00055	6362.25600	0.00016	0.28418	3.51886
35	6310.68810	0.00016	22215.22346	0.00005	0.28407	3.52025
40	22026.46576	0.00005	77547.51676	0.00001	0.28404	3.52065
45	76879.91962	0.00001	270676.19698	0.00000	0.28403	3.52077
50	268337.28595	0.00000	944761.52569	0.00000	0.28403	3.52080

r = 30.00%

n	F/Pr,n	P/Fr,n	F/Ar,n	A/Fr,n	A/Pr,n	P/Ar,n
1	1.34986	0.74082	1.00000	1.00000	1.34986	0.74082
2	1.82212	0.54881	2.34986	0.42556	0.77542	1.28963
3	2.45960	0.40657	4.17198	0.23969	0.58955	1.69620
4	3.32012	0.30119	6.63158	0.15079	0.50065	1.99739
5	4.48169	0.22313	9.95170	0.10049	0.45034	2.22052
6	6.04965	0.16530	14.43339	0.06928	0.41914	2.38582
7	8.16617	0.12246	20.48303	0.04882	0.39868	2.50828
8	11.02318	0.09072	28.64920	0.03490	0.38476	2.59900
9	14.87973	0.06721	39.67238	0.02521	0.37507	2.66620
10	20.08554	0.04979	54.55211	0.01833	0.36819	2.71599
11	27.11264	0.03688	74.63765	0.01340	0.36326	2.75287
12	36.59823	0.02732	101.75029	0.00983	0.35969	2.78020
13	49.40245	0.02024	138.34852	0.00723	0.35709	2.80044
14	66.68633	0.01500	187.75097	0.00533	0.35519	2.81543
15	90.01713	0.01111	254.43730	0.00393	0.35379	2.82654
16	121.51042	0.00823	344.45443	0.00290	0.35276	2.83477
17	164.02191	0.00610	465.96485	0.00215	0.35200	2.84087
18	221.40642	0.00452	629.98676	0.00159	0.35145	2.84539
19	298.86740	0.00335	851.39317	0.00117	0.35103	2.84873
20	403.42879	0.00248	1150.26057	0.00087	0.35073	2.85121
21	544.57191	0.00184	1553.68937	0.00064	0.35050	2.85305
22	735.09519	0.00136	2098.26128	0.00048	0.35034	2.85441
23	992.27471	0.00101	2833.35647	0.00035	0.35021	2.85542
24	1339.43076	0.00075	3825.63118	0.00026	0.35012	2.85616
25	1808.04241	0.00055	5165.06194	0.00019	0.35005	2.85672
26	2440.60197	0.00041	6973.10436	0.00014	0.35000	2.85712
27	3294.46807	0.00030	9413.70633	0.00011	0.34997	2.85743
28	4447.06674	0.00022	12708.17440	0.00008	0.34994	2.85765
29	6002.91221	0.00017	17155.24114	0.00006	0.34992	2.85782
30	8103.08392	0.00012	23158.15335	0.00004	0.34990	2.85794

r = 40.00%

n	F/Pr,n	P/Fr,n	F/Ar,n	A/Fr,n	A/Pr,n	P/Ar,n
1	1.49182	0.67032	1.00000	1.00000	1.49182	0.67032
2	2.22554	0.44933	2.49182	0.40131	0.89314	1.11965
3	3.32012	0.30119	4.71737	0.21198	0.70381	1.42084
4	4.95303	0.20190	8.03748	0.12442	0.61624	1.62274
5	7.38906	0.13534	12.99051	0.07698	0.56880	1.75808
6	11.02318	0.09072	20.37957	0.04907	0.54089	1.84879
7	16.44465	0.06081	31.40275	0.03184	0.52367	1.90960
8	24.53253	0.04076	47.84739	0.02090	0.51272	1.95037
9	36.59823	0.02732	72.37992	0.01382	0.50564	1.97769
10	54.59815	0.01832	108.97816	0.00918	0.50100	1.99600
11	81.45087	0.01228	163.57631	0.00611	0.49794	2.00828
12	121.51042	0.00823	245.02718	0.00408	0.49591	2.01651
13	181.27224	0.00552	366.53759	0.00273	0.49455	2.02203
14	270.42641	0.00370	547.80984	0.00183	0.49365	2.02573
15	403.42879	0.00248	818.23624	0.00122	0.49305	2.02820
16	601.84504	0.00166	1221.66504	0.00082	0.49264	2.02987
17	897.84729	0.00111	1823.51007	0.00055	0.49237	2.03098
18	1339.43076	0.00075	2721.35736	0.00037	0.49219	2.03173
19	1998.19589	0.00050	4060.78813	0.00025	0.49207	2.03223
20	2980.95798	0.00034	6058.98402	0.00017	0.49199	2.03256
21	4447.06674	0.00022	9039.94200	0.00011	0.49194	2.03279
22	6634.24400	0.00015	13487.00874	0.00007	0.49190	2.03294
23	9897.12904	0.00010	20121.25274	0.00005	0.49187	2.03304
24	14764.78154	0.00007	30018.38178	0.00003	0.49186	2.03311
25	22026.46576	0.00005	44783.16333	0.00002	0.49185	2.03315
26	32859.62562	0.00003	66809.62908	0.00001	0.49184	2.03318
27	49020.80105	0.00002	99669.25470	0.00001	0.49183	2.03320
28	73130.44170	0.00001	148690.05575	0.00001	0.49183	2.03322
29	109097.79906	0.00001	221820.49744	0.00000	0.49183	2.03323
30	162754.79109	0.00001	330918.29650	0.00000	0.49183	2.03323

r = 50.00%

n	F/Pr,n	P/Fr,n	F/Ar,n	A/Fr,n	A/Pr,n	P/Ar,n
1	1.64872	0.60653	1.00000	1.00000	1.64872	0.60653
2	2.71828	0.36788	2.64872	0.37754	1.02626	0.97441
3	4.48169	0.22313	5.36700	0.18632	0.83504	1.19754
4	7.38906	0.13534	9.84869	0.10154	0.75026	1.33288
5	12.18249	0.08208	17.23775	0.05801	0.70673	1.41496
6	20.08554	0.04979	29.42024	0.03399	0.68271	1.46475
7	33.11545	0.03020	49.50578	0.02020	0.66892	1.49494
8	54.59815	0.01832	82.62123	0.01210	0.66082	1.51326
9	90.01713	0.01111	137.21938	0.00729	0.65601	1.52437
10	148.41316	0.00674	227.23651	0.00440	0.65312	1.53111
11	244.69193	0.00409	375.64967	0.00266	0.65138	1.53519
12	403.42879	0.00248	620.34160	0.00161	0.65033	1.53767
13	665.14163	0.00150	1023.77040	0.00098	0.64970	1.53918
14	1096.63316	0.00091	1688.91203	0.00059	0.64931	1.54009
15	1808.04241	0.00055	2785.54519	0.00036	0.64908	1.54064
16	2980.95798	0.00034	4593.58760	0.00022	0.64894	1.54098
17	4914.76883	0.00020	7574.54558	0.00013	0.64885	1.54118
18	8103.08392	0.00012	12489.31441	0.00008	0.64880	1.54130
19	13359.72681	0.00007	20592.39833	0.00005	0.64877	1.54138
20	22026.46576	0.00005	33952.12514	0.00003	0.64875	1.54142
21	36315.50261	0.00003	55978.59090	0.00002	0.64874	1.54145
22	59874.14160	0.00002	92294.09351	0.00001	0.64873	1.54147
23	98715.77082	0.00001	152168.23511	0.00001	0.64873	1.54148
24	162754.79109	0.00001	250884.00593	0.00000	0.64873	1.54148
25	268337.28595	0.00000	413638.79702	0.00000	0.64872	1.54149
26	442413.39104	0.00000	681976.08297	0.00000	0.64872	1.54149
27	729416.36818	0.00000	1124389.47401	0.00000	0.64872	1.54149
28	1202604.28132	0.00000	1853805.84219	0.00000	0.64872	1.54149
29	1982759.25868	0.00000	3056410.12352	0.00000	0.64872	1.54149
30	3269017.36419	0.00000	5039169.38220	0.00000	0.64872	1.54149

APPENDIX C

CONTINUOUS INTEREST, CONTINUOUS FLOWING VALUE FACTORS

C.1 Factor Development

Since receipts and disbursements flow somewhat continuously in many real business situations, to account for this situation as realistically as possible, it sometimes is deemed to be desirable to have compound interest formulas based upon the continuous flow of funds rather than end of period lump sums. Since the interest rate compounding must correspond to the periods used, continuous interest must be used with the continuous flow of funds, i.e., an infinite number of payment periods require an interest rate with an infinite number of compounding periods.

The following symbols will be used in the formulas to be developed:

r = the nominal continuous interest rate

n = the number of years

$\overline{A}$ = the single total amount of funds flowing continuously during a period, in a uniform series of n equal payments. In the equations developed in this text, it is assumed that A is an input. A is often called a "funds flow" term.

P and F are defined as used throughout the text.

F* = the single total amount of funds flowing continuously during a period in a single equivalent payment for the year occurring at the end of the funds flow payment period.

Writing an incremental dollar balance shows that money accumulates from two sources: interest on invested principal, and the continuous inflow from $\overline{A}$. The incremental equation is:

$$P\big|_{t+\Delta t} - P\big|_{t} = Pr\,\Delta t + \overline{A}\Delta t \qquad \text{C-1}$$

Dividing by Δt and taking the limit as Δt approaches zero yields

$$P\big|_{t+\Delta t} - P\big|$$

Separating the variables and integrating gives

$$\int_{P=P}^{P=F} \frac{rdP}{Pr+\overline{A}} = \int_{t=0}^{t=n} rdt \quad \text{or} \quad \ln\left(Pr+\overline{A}\right)\Big|_{P}^{F} = rt\Big|_{o}^{n} \qquad \text{C-2}$$

Substituting the limits gives

$$\ln\left(Fr+\overline{A}\right)\Big/\left(Pr+\overline{A}\right) = rn \qquad \text{C-3}$$

so

$$\frac{Fr+\overline{A}}{Pr+\overline{A}} = e^{rn} \qquad \text{C-4}$$

When there are no continuous uniform annual payments, $\overline{A} = 0$ and $F = Pe^{rn}$, the same as Equation B-5 developed in Appendix B for continuous interest with lump sum payments. The present worth equation $P = F\,(1/e^{rn})$ is the same as Equation B-6.

The four factors for $F/\overline{A}_{r,n}$; $\overline{A}/F_{r,n}$; $P/\overline{A}_{r,n}$; and $\overline{A}/P_{r,n}$ all differ from the factors developed in Appendix B. These factors result from the following developments:

1. To relate F and $\overline{A}$, assume P = 0 in Equation C-4. This makes Equation C-4 yield

$$F = \overline{A}\left(e^{rn}-1\right)\Big/r = \overline{A}\left(F/\overline{A}_{r,n}\right) \qquad \text{C-5}$$

where $(e^{rn} - 1)/r$ is the funds flow uniform series compound amount factor. Rearranging

$$\overline{A} = Fr\Big/\left(e^{rn}-1\right) = F\left(\overline{A}/F_{r,n}\right) \qquad \text{C-6}$$

where $r/(e^{rn} - 1)$ is the funds flow sinking fund deposit factor. Note that F, $\overline{A}$, and the $F/\overline{A}_{r,n}$ and $\overline{A}/F_{r,n}$ factors are positive.

2. To relate P and $\overline{A}$, assume F = 0 in Equation C-4. This makes Equation C-4 yield

$$\overline{A} = \text{Pr}\,e^{rn}\Big/\left(1-e^{rn}\right) = P\left(\overline{A}/P_{r,n}\right) \qquad \text{C-7}$$

where $re^{rn}/(1 - e^{rn})$ is the funds flow capital recovery factor. Note that it is negative since $(1 - e^{rn})$ will always be negative for all real values of r and n. $\overline{A}$ is negative in Equation C-7 since it is an output of money (a payment) required to recover the initial principal, P, plus interest due. Since $\overline{A}$ is the annual mortgage payment necessary to repay P in n years. we can see that this sign convention is consistent and logical.

Rearranging Equation C-7 gives

$$P = \overline{A}\left(1-e^{rn}\right)\Big/\left(re^{rn}\right) = \overline{A}\left(P/\overline{A}_{r,n}\right) \qquad \text{C-8}$$

where $(1 - e^{rn})/re^{rn}$ is the funds flow uniform series present worth factor. Note that both $\overline{A}$ and $P/\overline{A}_{r,n}$ are negative in Equation C-8 to give a positive present value, P. It is normal to switch $1 - e^{rn}$ to $e^{rn} - 1$ so that funds flow factors are always positive. This is done in the remainder of this text.

These factors based on the funds flow concept find relatively wide usage by companies in making economic analyses of alternative investment possibilities. It is felt by many economic analysts that because receipts and disbursements flow somewhat continuously, that the funds flow assumption is better than the end-of-period payments assumption with discrete compound interest. This is true in some cases, but in most practical evaluation cases. both lump sum payments and continuous receipts and disbursements are involved. Therefore, using either method alone gives some error and the best result would come from a combination of the methods. Computer programming gets complicated when funds flow and discrete payments are both considered in the same problem, so it is common for companies to use one method or the other, but not a combination of both. Typical percent differences that result between using the two methods are illustrated by the following examples.

C.2 Applications

EXAMPLE C-1 Funds Flow Compared to End of Period Payments

Calculate the present worth of 10 uniform $1000 payments if

a) interest is 10% per year compounded continuously and payments are end-of-year
b) interest is 10% per year compounded continuously and payments are continuous

c) what is the percent change in results from a) to b)?

Solution:

a) P=? A=1000 A=1000

0 1 – – – n=10

$$\text{so} \quad P = 1000(\overset{6.00}{P/A_{r,10}}) = \$6000 \quad \text{for} \quad r = 0.10$$

$$\text{where} \quad P/A_{r,10} = (e^{1.0} - 1)/(e^{.1} - 1)e^{1.0}$$

$$= 1.7183/(0.1052)(2.718) = 6.00$$

b) P=? $\bar{A}$=1000 $\bar{A}$=1000

0 1 – – – n=10

$$\text{so} \quad P = 1000(\overset{6.325}{P/\bar{A}_{r,10}}) = \$6325 \quad \text{for} \quad r = 0.10$$

$$\text{where} \quad P/\bar{A}_{r,10} = (e^{1.0} - 1)/0.1\, e^{1.0} = (1.7183)/0.27183 = 6.325$$

c) $\% \text{ change a) to b)} = \dfrac{6325 - 6000}{6000} \times 100 =$ 5. 41% deviation between results.

EXAMPLE C-2 Analysis Involving Both Lump Sum and Funds Flow Payments

Development of an investment project involves the following cash outlays: three lump sum payments of \$70,000 at time zero and at the end of the first and second years, and uniform funds flow payments of \$50,000 during each of the first three years. Assume a nominal annual continuous interest rate of 10% and calculate the present worth of all payments:

a) assuming the funds flow payments to be end-of-year payments
b) assuming the lump sum payments to be funds flow payments during the prior year
c) properly combining both lump sum and funds flow calculations as appropriate.

Solution:

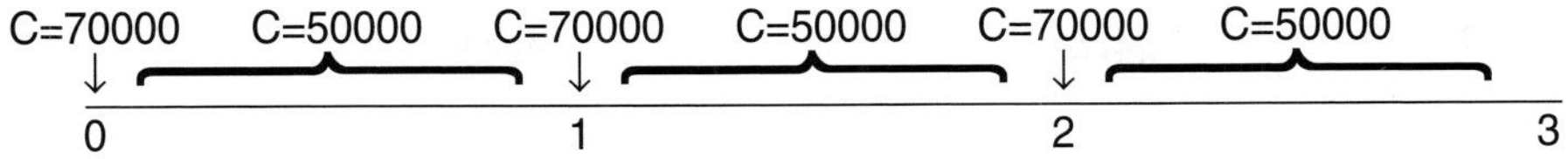

$r = 10\%$

a) Assume all costs are end-of-period costs.

$$\text{Present Worth} = 70{,}000 + 120{,}000\overset{1.720}{(P/A_{r,2})} + 50{,}000\,\overset{.741}{(P/F_{r,3})} = \$313{,}500$$

where $P/A_{r,2} = (e^{.2} - 1)/(e^{.1} - 1)e^{.2} = (.2214)/(.1052)\,(1.2214) = 1.720$

$P/F_{r,3} = 1/e^{.3} = 1/1.3499 = 0.741$

b) Assume all costs are funds flow.

$$\text{Present Worth} = 70{,}000 + 50{,}000\,\overset{2.594}{(P/\bar{A}_{r,3})} + 70{,}000\,\overset{1.810}{(P/\bar{A}_{r,2})} = \$326{,}200$$

where $P\bar{A}_{r,3} = (e^{.3} - 1)/0.1e^{.3} = (0.3499)/0.13499 = 2.594$

$P/\bar{A}_{r,2} = e^{.2} - 1/0.1e^{.2} = (2214)/0.12214 = 1.810$

Alternate Solution for b):

$$\text{P.W.} = 70{,}000 + 120{,}000(P/\bar{A}_{r,2}) + 50{,}000\overset{.952}{(P/\bar{A}_{r,1})}\,\overset{.818}{(P/F_{r,2})} = \$326{,}200$$

where $P/\bar{A}_{r,1} = (e^{.1} - 1)/0.1\,e^{.1} = 0.1052/0.11052 = 0.952$

$P/F_{r,2} = 1/e^{.2} = 1/1.2214 = 0.818$

c) $\text{P.W.} = 70{,}000 + 70{,}000\overset{1.720}{(P/A_{r,2})} + 50{,}000\overset{2.594}{(P/\bar{A}_{r,3})} = \$320{,}100$

Note that a) and b) results both differ from c), with the correct result, "c", between the results for "a" and "b".

C.3 Discount Factors to Time Zero for Single Funds Flow Payments

To find the present worth of a funds flow single cash payment or receipt which we will call F*, made during the nth year as illustrated

P=?						| – F* – |	
0	1	–	–	–	–	n–1	n

on the diagram, it is common to combine the appropriate funds flow factor and end-of-period continuous interest factor as follows:

The sum of money at time n-1 equivalent to F* is

$F^* \, (P/\bar{A}_{r,1})$

The present worth, P, of the sum of money $F^* \, (P/\bar{A}_{r,1})$ is

$$P = \left(P/F_{r,n-1}\right)\left(F^*\right)\left(P/\bar{A}_{r,1}\right) = \left(\frac{F^*}{e^{r(n-1)}}\right)\left(\frac{e^r - 1}{re^r}\right)$$

$$= F^*\left(\frac{e^r - 1}{re^{rn}}\right) = F^*\left(P/F^*_{r,n}\right) \quad \text{where} \quad P/F^*_{r,n} = \frac{e^r - 1}{re^{rn}}$$

Continuous Interest Factors for Continuous Flowing Funds:

$F/A^*_{r,n} = (e^{rn} - 1)/r$

$A/F^*_{r,n} = r/(e^{rn} - 1)$

$A/P^*_{r,n} = re^{rn}/(e^{rn} - 1)$

$P/A^*_{r,n} = (e^{rn} - 1)/re^{rn} = [(e^{rn} - 1)/r][1/e^{rn}]$

$P/F^*_{r,n} = (e^r - 1)/re^{rn} = [(e^r - 1)/r][1/e^{rn}]$

$F/P^*_{r,n} = ((e^r - 1)/r)\,(e^{r(n-1)}) = [(e^r - 1)/r][e^{r(n-1)}]$

***r = 10.00%**

n	F/P*r,n	P/F*r,n	F/A*r,n	A/F*r,n	A/P*r,n	P/A*r,n
1	1.05171	0.95163	1.05171	0.95083	1.05083	0.95163
2	1.16232	0.86107	2.21403	0.45167	0.55167	1.81269
3	1.28456	0.77913	3.49859	0.28583	0.38583	2.59182
4	1.41966	0.70498	4.91825	0.20332	0.30332	3.29680
5	1.56897	0.63789	6.48721	0.15415	0.25415	3.93469
6	1.73398	0.57719	8.22119	0.12164	0.22164	4.51188
7	1.91634	0.52226	10.13753	0.09864	0.19864	5.03415
8	2.11788	0.47256	12.25541	0.08160	0.18160	5.50671
9	2.34062	0.42759	14.59603	0.06851	0.16851	5.93430
10	2.58679	0.38690	17.18282	0.05820	0.15820	6.32121
11	2.85884	0.35008	20.04166	0.04990	0.14990	6.67129
12	3.15951	0.31677	23.20117	0.04310	0.14310	6.98806
13	3.49180	0.28662	26.69297	0.03746	0.13746	7.27468
14	3.85903	0.25935	30.55200	0.03273	0.13273	7.53403
15	4.26489	0.23467	34.81689	0.02872	0.12872	7.76870
16	4.71343	0.21234	39.53032	0.02530	0.12530	7.98103
17	5.20915	0.19213	44.73947	0.02235	0.12235	8.17316
18	5.75700	0.17385	50.49647	0.01980	0.11980	8.34701
19	6.36247	0.15730	56.85894	0.01759	0.11759	8.50431
20	7.03162	0.14233	63.89056	0.01565	0.11565	8.64665
21	7.77114	0.12879	71.66170	0.01395	0.11395	8.77544
22	8.58844	0.11653	80.25013	0.01246	0.11246	8.89197
23	9.49169	0.10544	89.74182	0.01114	0.11114	8.99741
24	10.48994	0.09541	100.23176	0.00998	0.10998	9.09282
25	11.59318	0.08633	111.82494	0.00894	0.10894	9.17915
26	12.81244	0.07811	124.63738	0.00802	0.10802	9.25726
27	14.15994	0.07068	138.79732	0.00720	0.10720	9.32794
28	15.64915	0.06395	154.44647	0.00647	0.10647	9.39190
29	17.29499	0.05787	171.74145	0.00582	0.10582	9.44977
30	19.11392	0.05236	190.85537	0.00524	0.10524	9.50213
35	31.51352	0.03176	321.15452	0.00311	0.10311	9.69803
40	51.95701	0.01926	535.98150	0.00187	0.10187	9.81684
45	85.66263	0.01168	890.17131	0.00112	0.10112	9.88891
50	141.23379	0.00709	1474.13159	0.00068	0.10068	9.93262

***r = 12.00%**

n	F/P*r,n	P/F*r,n	F/A*r,n	A/F*r,n	A/P*r,n	P/A*r,n
1	1.06247	0.94233	1.06247	0.94120	1.06120	0.94233
2	1.19794	0.83577	2.26041	0.44240	0.56240	1.77810
3	1.35067	0.74126	3.61108	0.27693	0.39693	2.51936
4	1.52287	0.65744	5.13395	0.19478	0.31478	3.17681
5	1.71704	0.58310	6.85099	0.14596	0.26596	3.75990
6	1.93595	0.51716	8.78694	0.11381	0.23381	4.27706
7	2.18278	0.45868	10.96972	0.09116	0.21116	4.73575
8	2.46108	0.40681	13.43080	0.07446	0.19446	5.14256
9	2.77486	0.36081	16.20566	0.06171	0.18171	5.50337
10	3.12864	0.32001	19.33431	0.05172	0.17172	5.82338
11	3.52754	0.28382	22.86184	0.04374	0.16374	6.10721
12	3.97729	0.25173	26.83913	0.03726	0.15726	6.35894
13	4.48438	0.22326	31.32351	0.03192	0.15192	6.58220
14	5.05612	0.19802	36.37963	0.02749	0.14749	6.78022
15	5.70076	0.17563	42.08040	0.02376	0.14376	6.95584
16	6.42759	0.15577	48.50799	0.02062	0.14062	7.11161
17	7.24709	0.13815	55.75508	0.01794	0.13794	7.24976
18	8.17107	0.12253	63.92615	0.01564	0.13564	7.37229
19	9.21286	0.10867	73.13900	0.01367	0.13367	7.48096
20	10.38747	0.09639	83.52647	0.01197	0.13197	7.57735
21	11.71184	0.08549	95.23831	0.01050	0.13050	7.66284
22	13.20506	0.07582	108.44336	0.00922	0.12922	7.73866
23	14.88866	0.06725	123.33202	0.00811	0.12811	7.80590
24	16.78692	0.05964	140.11894	0.00714	0.12714	7.86554
25	18.92720	0.05290	159.04614	0.00629	0.12629	7.91844
26	21.34036	0.04692	180.38650	0.00554	0.12554	7.96536
27	24.06118	0.04161	204.44768	0.00489	0.12489	8.00697
28	27.12891	0.03691	231.57659	0.00432	0.12432	8.04387
29	30.58776	0.03273	262.16435	0.00381	0.12381	8.07660
30	34.48760	0.02903	296.65195	0.00337	0.12337	8.10564
35	62.84051	0.01593	547.38609	0.00183	0.12183	8.20837
40	114.50287	0.00874	1004.25348	0.00100	0.12100	8.26475
45	208.63784	0.00480	1836.72014	0.00054	0.12054	8.29570
50	380.16293	0.00263	3353.57328	0.00030	0.12030	8.31268

***r = 15.00%**

n	F/P*r,n	P/F*r,n	F/A*r,n	A/F*r,n	A/P*r,n	P/A*r,n
1	1.07889	0.92861	1.07889	0.92687	1.07687	0.92861
2	1.25350	0.79927	2.33239	0.42874	0.57874	1.72788
3	1.45636	0.68793	3.78875	0.26394	0.41394	2.41581
4	1.69204	0.59211	5.48079	0.18246	0.33246	3.00792
5	1.96587	0.50963	7.44667	0.13429	0.28429	3.51756
6	2.28402	0.43865	9.73069	0.10277	0.25277	3.95620
7	2.65365	0.37755	12.38434	0.08075	0.23075	4.33375
8	3.08311	0.32496	15.46745	0.06465	0.21465	4.65871
9	3.58206	0.27969	19.04950	0.05249	0.20249	4.93840
10	4.16176	0.24073	23.21126	0.04308	0.19308	5.17913
11	4.83527	0.20720	28.04653	0.03566	0.18566	5.38633
12	5.61778	0.17834	33.66432	0.02971	0.17971	5.56467
13	6.52693	0.15350	40.19125	0.02488	0.17488	5.71817
14	7.58322	0.13212	47.77447	0.02093	0.17093	5.85029
15	8.81044	0.11371	56.58491	0.01767	0.16767	5.96401
16	10.23627	0.09788	66.82118	0.01497	0.16497	6.06188
17	11.89285	0.08424	78.71403	0.01270	0.16270	6.14612
18	13.81752	0.07251	92.53154	0.01081	0.16081	6.21863
19	16.05367	0.06241	108.58521	0.00921	0.15921	6.28104
20	18.65170	0.05372	127.23691	0.00786	0.15786	6.33475
21	21.67018	0.04623	148.90710	0.00672	0.15672	6.38099
22	25.17716	0.03979	174.08426	0.00574	0.15574	6.42078
23	29.25169	0.03425	203.33595	0.00492	0.15492	6.45503
24	33.98561	0.02948	237.32156	0.00421	0.15421	6.48451
25	39.48565	0.02537	276.80721	0.00361	0.15361	6.50988
26	45.87578	0.02184	322.68299	0.00310	0.15310	6.53172
27	53.30005	0.01880	375.98305	0.00266	0.15266	6.55052
28	61.92583	0.01618	437.90887	0.00228	0.15228	6.56670
29	71.94755	0.01393	509.85642	0.00196	0.15196	6.58062
30	83.59112	0.01199	593.44754	0.00169	0.15169	6.59261
35	176.96241	0.00566	1263.77512	0.00079	0.15079	6.63168
40	374.62942	0.00267	2682.85862	0.00037	0.15037	6.65014
45	793.09049	0.00126	5687.05842	0.00018	0.15018	6.65886
50	1678.97258	0.00060	12046.94943	0.00008	0.15008	6.66298

***r = 20.00%**

n	F/P*r,n	P/F*r,n	F/A*r,n	A/F*r,n	A/P*r,n	P/A*r,n
1	1.10701	0.90635	1.10701	0.90333	1.10333	0.90635
2	1.35211	0.74205	2.45912	0.40665	0.60665	1.64840
3	1.65147	0.60754	4.11059	0.24327	0.44327	2.25594
4	2.01711	0.49741	6.12770	0.16319	0.36319	2.75336
5	2.46370	0.40725	8.59141	0.11640	0.31640	3.16060
6	3.00918	0.33343	11.60058	0.08620	0.28620	3.49403
7	3.67542	0.27299	15.27600	0.06546	0.26546	3.76702
8	4.48916	0.22350	19.76516	0.05059	0.25059	3.99052
9	5.48308	0.18299	25.24824	0.03961	0.23961	4.17351
10	6.69704	0.14982	31.94528	0.03130	0.23130	4.32332
11	8.17979	0.12266	40.12507	0.02492	0.22492	4.44598
12	9.99081	0.10043	50.11588	0.01995	0.21995	4.54641
13	12.20281	0.08222	62.31869	0.01605	0.21605	4.62863
14	14.90454	0.06732	77.22323	0.01295	0.21295	4.69595
15	18.20445	0.05511	95.42768	0.01048	0.21048	4.75106
16	22.23497	0.04512	117.66265	0.00850	0.20850	4.79619
17	27.15785	0.03694	144.82050	0.00691	0.20691	4.83313
18	33.17067	0.03025	177.99117	0.00562	0.20562	4.86338
19	40.51475	0.02476	218.50592	0.00458	0.20458	4.88815
20	49.48483	0.02028	267.99075	0.00373	0.20373	4.90842
21	60.44091	0.01660	328.43166	0.00304	0.20304	4.92502
22	73.82269	0.01359	402.25434	0.00249	0.20249	4.93861
23	90.16723	0.01113	492.42158	0.00203	0.20203	4.94974
24	110.13051	0.00911	602.55209	0.00166	0.20166	4.95885
25	134.51371	0.00746	737.06580	0.00136	0.20136	4.96631
26	164.29541	0.00611	901.36121	0.00111	0.20111	4.97242
27	200.67087	0.00500	1102.03208	0.00091	0.20091	4.97742
28	245.09996	0.00409	1347.13204	0.00074	0.20074	4.98151
29	299.36576	0.00335	1646.49780	0.00061	0.20061	4.98486
30	365.64617	0.00274	2012.14397	0.00050	0.20050	4.98761
35	993.92933	0.00101	5478.16579	0.00018	0.20018	4.99544
40	2701.78005	0.00037	14899.78994	0.00007	0.20007	4.99832
45	7344.19961	0.00014	40510.41964	0.00002	0.20002	4.99938
50	19963.60433	0.00005	110127.32897	0.00001	0.20001	4.99977

***r = 25.00%**

n	F/P*r,n	P/F*r,n	F/A*r,n	A/F*r,n	A/P*r,n	P/A*r,n
1	1.13610	0.88480	1.13610	0.88020	1.13020	0.88480
2	1.45878	0.68908	2.59489	0.38537	0.63537	1.57388
3	1.87311	0.53666	4.46800	0.22381	0.47381	2.11053
4	2.40513	0.41795	6.87313	0.14549	0.39549	2.52848
5	3.08824	0.32550	9.96137	0.10039	0.35039	2.85398
6	3.96538	0.25350	13.92676	0.07180	0.32180	3.10748
7	5.09165	0.19742	19.01841	0.05258	0.30258	3.30490
8	6.53781	0.15375	25.55622	0.03913	0.28913	3.45866
9	8.39472	0.11974	33.95094	0.02945	0.27945	3.57840
10	10.77903	0.09326	44.72998	0.02236	0.27236	3.67166
11	13.84055	0.07263	58.57053	0.01707	0.26707	3.74429
12	17.77162	0.05656	76.34215	0.01310	0.26310	3.80085
13	22.81921	0.04405	99.16136	0.01008	0.26008	3.84490
14	29.30045	0.03431	128.46181	0.00778	0.25778	3.87921
15	37.62252	0.02672	166.08433	0.00602	0.25602	3.90593
16	48.30827	0.02081	214.39260	0.00466	0.25466	3.92674
17	62.02905	0.01621	276.42165	0.00362	0.25362	3.94294
18	79.64688	0.01262	356.06853	0.00281	0.25281	3.95556
19	102.26861	0.00983	458.33714	0.00218	0.25218	3.96539
20	131.31550	0.00765	589.65264	0.00170	0.25170	3.97305
21	168.61244	0.00596	758.26507	0.00132	0.25132	3.97901
22	216.50266	0.00464	974.76773	0.00103	0.25103	3.98365
23	277.99491	0.00362	1252.76264	0.00080	0.25080	3.98727
24	356.95253	0.00282	1609.71517	0.00062	0.25062	3.99008
25	458.33612	0.00219	2068.05130	0.00048	0.25048	3.99228
26	588.51523	0.00171	2656.56653	0.00038	0.25038	3.99399
27	755.66852	0.00133	3412.23505	0.00029	0.25029	3.99532
28	970.29758	0.00104	4382.53263	0.00023	0.25023	3.99635
29	1245.88676	0.00081	5628.41939	0.00018	0.25018	3.99716
30	1599.75027	0.00063	7228.16966	0.00014	0.25014	3.99779
35	5583.67707	0.00018	25238.75243	0.00004	0.25004	3.99937
40	19488.94794	0.00005	88101.86318	0.00001	0.25001	3.99982
45	68023.11220	0.00001	307515.67906	0.00000	0.25000	3.99995
50	237423.99060	0.00000	1073345.14608	0.00000	0.25000	3.99999

***r = 30.00%**

n	F/P*r,n	P/F*r,n	F/A*r,n	A/F*r,n	A/P*r,n	P/A*r,n
1	1.16620	0.86394	1.16620	0.85749	1.15749	0.86394
2	1.57420	0.64002	2.74040	0.36491	0.66491	1.50396
3	2.12495	0.47414	4.86534	0.20554	0.50554	1.97810
4	2.86838	0.35125	7.73372	0.12930	0.42930	2.32935
5	3.87191	0.26021	11.60563	0.08617	0.38617	2.58957
6	5.22653	0.19277	16.83216	0.05941	0.35941	2.78234
7	7.05507	0.14281	23.88723	0.04186	0.34186	2.92515
8	9.52335	0.10579	33.41059	0.02993	0.32993	3.03094
9	12.85518	0.07837	46.26577	0.02161	0.32161	3.10931
10	17.35268	0.05806	63.61846	0.01572	0.31572	3.16738
11	23.42367	0.04301	87.04213	0.01149	0.31149	3.21039
12	31.61865	0.03186	118.66078	0.00843	0.30843	3.24225
13	42.68072	0.02361	161.34150	0.00620	0.30620	3.26586
14	57.61294	0.01749	218.95444	0.00457	0.30457	3.28335
15	77.76933	0.01296	296.72377	0.00337	0.30337	3.29630
16	104.97762	0.00960	401.70139	0.00249	0.30249	3.30590
17	141.70497	0.00711	543.40636	0.00184	0.30184	3.31301
18	191.28170	0.00527	734.68805	0.00136	0.30136	3.31828
19	258.20328	0.00390	992.89134	0.00101	0.30101	3.32218
20	348.53798	0.00289	1341.42931	0.00075	0.30075	3.32507
21	470.47706	0.00214	1811.90637	0.00055	0.30055	3.32721
22	635.07760	0.00159	2446.98396	0.00041	0.30041	3.32880
23	857.26509	0.00118	3304.24905	0.00030	0.30030	3.32997
24	1157.18683	0.00087	4461.43588	0.00022	0.30022	3.33084
25	1562.03883	0.00065	6023.47471	0.00017	0.30017	3.33149
26	2108.53188	0.00048	8132.00659	0.00012	0.30012	3.33197
27	2846.22033	0.00035	10978.22692	0.00009	0.30009	3.33232
28	3841.99557	0.00026	14820.22249	0.00007	0.30007	3.33258
29	5186.15157	0.00019	20006.37406	0.00005	0.30005	3.33278
30	7000.57237	0.00014	27006.94643	0.00004	0.30004	3.33292

*r = 40.00%

n	F/P*r,n	P/F*r,n	F/A*r,n	A/F*r,n	A/P*r,n	P/A*r,n
1	1.22956	0.82420	1.22956	0.81330	1.21330	0.82420
2	1.83429	0.55248	3.06385	0.32639	0.72639	1.37668
3	2.73644	0.37034	5.80029	0.17241	0.57241	1.74701
4	4.08229	0.24824	9.88258	0.10119	0.50119	1.99526
5	6.09006	0.16640	15.97264	0.06261	0.46261	2.16166
6	9.08530	0.11154	25.05794	0.03991	0.43991	2.27321
7	13.55368	0.07477	38.61162	0.02590	0.42590	2.34797
8	20.21971	0.05012	58.83133	0.01700	0.41700	2.39809
9	30.16426	0.03360	88.99559	0.01124	0.41124	2.43169
10	44.99979	0.02252	133.99538	0.00746	0.40746	2.45421
11	67.13180	0.01510	201.12717	0.00497	0.40497	2.46931
12	100.14887	0.01012	301.27604	0.00332	0.40332	2.47943
13	149.40456	0.00678	450.68060	0.00222	0.40222	2.48621
14	222.88541	0.00455	673.56602	0.00148	0.40148	2.49076
15	332.50597	0.00305	1006.07198	0.00099	0.40099	2.49380
16	496.04061	0.00204	1502.11259	0.00067	0.40067	2.49585
17	740.00563	0.00137	2242.11823	0.00045	0.40045	2.49722
18	1103.95868	0.00092	3346.07691	0.00030	0.40030	2.49813
19	1646.91283	0.00062	4992.98974	0.00020	0.40020	2.49875
20	2456.90523	0.00041	7449.89497	0.00013	0.40013	2.49916
21	3665.27190	0.00028	11115.16687	0.00009	0.40009	2.49944
22	5467.94315	0.00019	16583.11002	0.00006	0.40006	2.49962
23	8157.21263	0.00012	24740.32265	0.00004	0.40004	2.49975
24	12169.13127	0.00008	36909.45391	0.00003	0.40003	2.49983
25	18154.21057	0.00006	55063.66449	0.00002	0.40002	2.49989
26	27082.89970	0.00004	82146.56419	0.00001	0.40001	2.49992
27	40402.93865	0.00003	122549.50284	0.00001	0.40001	2.49995
28	60274.10174	0.00002	182823.60458	0.00001	0.40001	2.49997
29	89918.39361	0.00001	272741.99819	0.00000	0.40000	2.49998
30	134142.48036	0.00001	406884.47855	0.00000	0.40000	2.49998

***r = 50.00%**

n	F/P*r,n	P/F*r,n	F/A*r,n	A/F*r,n	A/P*r,n	P/A*r,n
1	1.29744	0.78694	1.29744	0.77075	1.27075	0.78694
2	2.13912	0.47730	3.43656	0.29099	0.79099	1.26424
3	3.52681	0.28950	6.96338	0.14361	0.64361	1.55374
4	5.81473	0.17559	12.77811	0.07826	0.57826	1.72933
5	9.58688	0.10650	22.36499	0.04471	0.54471	1.83583
6	15.80609	0.06460	38.17107	0.02620	0.52620	1.90043
7	26.05983	0.03918	64.23090	0.01557	0.51557	1.93961
8	42.96540	0.02376	107.19630	0.00933	0.50933	1.96337
9	70.83796	0.01441	178.03426	0.00562	0.50562	1.97778
10	116.79206	0.00874	294.82632	0.00339	0.50339	1.98652
11	192.55755	0.00530	487.38386	0.00205	0.50205	1.99183
12	317.47372	0.00322	804.85759	0.00124	0.50124	1.99504
13	523.42568	0.00195	1328.28327	0.00075	0.50075	1.99699
14	862.98305	0.00118	2191.26632	0.00046	0.50046	1.99818
15	1422.81851	0.00072	3614.08483	0.00028	0.50028	1.99889
16	2345.83115	0.00044	5959.91597	0.00017	0.50017	1.99933
17	3867.62171	0.00026	9827.53768	0.00010	0.50010	1.99959
18	6376.63017	0.00016	16204.16786	0.00006	0.50006	1.99975
19	10513.28580	0.00010	26717.45366	0.00004	0.50004	1.99985
20	17333.47793	0.00006	44050.93159	0.00002	0.50002	1.99991
21	28578.07376	0.00004	72629.00535	0.00001	0.50001	1.99994
22	47117.27808	0.00002	119746.28343	0.00001	0.50001	1.99997
23	77683.25859	0.00001	197429.54202	0.00001	0.50001	1.99998
24	128078.04082	0.00001	325507.58284	0.00000	0.50000	1.99999
25	211164.99020	0.00000	536672.57304	0.00000	0.50000	1.99999
26	348152.21098	0.00000	884824.78402	0.00000	0.50000	2.00000
27	574005.95568	0.00000	1458830.73970	0.00000	0.50000	2.00000
28	946375.82863	0.00000	2405206.56833	0.00000	0.50000	2.00000
29	1560309.95875	0.00000	3965516.52708	0.00000	0.50000	2.00000
30	2572516.21787	0.00000	6538032.74494	0.00000	0.50000	2.00000

APPENDIX D

PRODUCTION COST VARIATIONS AND BREAK-EVEN ANALYSIS

D.1 Fixed and Variable Costs

Project costs for production activities generally vary with the level of production activity of the project. The costs of labor and material are typical operating costs that tend to vary directly with the number of units produced and hence are called *variable costs.* Some costs tend to remain relatively constant regardless of the level of production activity and are called *fixed costs.* Fixed costs tend to be constant for a given period of time and independent of the number of units produced. Fixed costs frequently are referred to as "overhead costs" and include such costs as supervisory and management salaries, other administrative expenses, insurance, property taxes, license fees, heat, light, rent, supplies, repayment of investment principal, research and development, and certain maintenance and repair charges. This list of fixed costs is not intended to be all-inclusive, but it gives an indication of the type of expenses that can fall into this category. However, it must be noted that it is not uncommon for many of the expenses listed as fixed costs to become variable costs under widely varying business conditions. For example, administrative expenses and research and development costs may be increased or decreased by hiring or firing personnel if business warrants the changes, so these costs become variable under these conditions. Analysis of fixed and variable costs must be made relative to conditions that exist at the time of the analysis and for the projected period of future time for which the analysis is expected to be valid.

Unit costs are input costs divided by the number of units produced in the period of time being evaluated. Unit costs may be based on the total cost or on individual fixed and variable costs. Illustration of the use of variable, fixed, and unit costs is provided in the following example, which assumes that variable costs, and therefore total costs, vary linearly with production rate instead of non-linearly as illustrated in the general schematic shown in Figure D-1. The linear approximation case often is found to be a useful simplification of the general nonlinear cost situation.

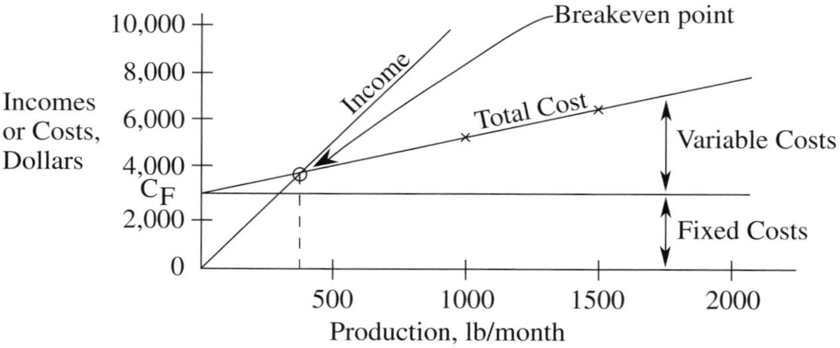

Figure D-1 General Graph of Income and Costs vs. Production Rate

EXAMPLE D-1 Illustration of Linear Variation in Costs

The total cost of producing 1000 lb of a chemical product per month is \$5000. The total cost of producing 1500 lb of the chemical per month is \$6000. Assuming that variable costs vary directly with production rate (that is, assuming they vary linearly with production rate), determine the following:

a) What is the variable cost per unit?
b) What is the total fixed cost?
c) What is the fixed cost per unit for the first 1000 units/month?
d) What is the total cost per unit for the first 1000 units/month?
e) If the chemical product is sold for \$10 per lb, what production rate is required for costs to break-even with income? What is the profit or loss to produce and sell 200 lb/month of the chemical? 1000 lb/month?

Solution:

Figure D-1a graphically illustrates this problem. However, the graph is not developed with sufficient accuracy to give good numerical results for the questions asked so the mathematical solutions are presented.

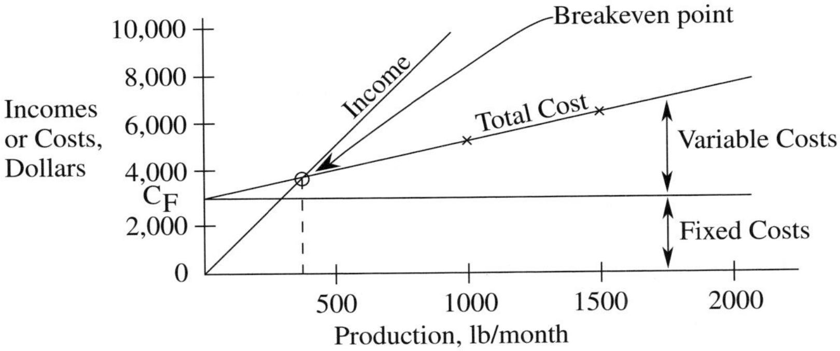

Figure D-1a Linear Approximation of Figure D-1

a) Variable Cost per lb, C_V is the slope of the total cost curve. Therefore,

$$C_V = \frac{6000 - 5000}{1500 - 1000} = \$2.00 \text{ per lb.}$$

C_V also is the variable, marginal, or incremental cost/unit.

b) The total fixed cost can be calculated either graphically or mathematically. Graphically we see in Figure D-1a the total cost curve intersects the zero production rate axis where fixed cost, C_F = \$3000. Mathematically, C_F can be calculated by writing the equation for the straight line that represents the total cost curve.

$$\text{Cost} = C_V\,(\text{Production Rate}) + C_F \qquad \text{D-1}$$

Substituting the numbers into Equation D-1 for the two points given yields:

$$\$5000 = C_V\,(1000) + C_F \qquad \text{D-2}$$

and

$$\$6000 = C_V\,(1500) + C_F \qquad \text{D-3}$$

If we had not already calculated C_V from the slope of the total cost curve, we could subtract Equation D-2 from D-3 and obtain C_V = \$2.00/lb. Knowing C_V, we can substitute C_V = 2.00 into either Equation D-2 or D-3 and calculate C_F = \$3000.

c) Knowing C_F = \$3000 gives a \$3.00 fixed cost per lb for the first 1000 units.

d) The total cost per unit for the first 1000 lb/month is \$5000/1000 or = \$5.00/lb. It could also be found from $C_V + C_F/1000$ = \$2.00 + \$3.00 = \$5.00/lb.

e) The break-even point can be found graphically to equal 375 lb/month. Mathematically, it is the intersection of the total cost equation and the income equation. Let X represent production rate per month.

Total Cost = (\$2.00/lb)(X lb/month) + 3000 D-4
Income = (\$10/lb)(X lb/month) + 0 D-5

Solving Equations D-4 and D-5 for the production rate, X, that will make Total Cost equal Income gives the break-even production rate.

2X + 3000 = 10 X or X = 375 lb/month to break-even.

Production rates below 375 lb/month yield a loss and production rates greater than 375 lb/month yield a profit.

The loss at a production rate of 200 lb/month is

Income – Total Cost = (\$10/lb)(200 lb/month) – (\$2/1b)(200 lb/mo – 3000 = –\$1400/month or a \$1400/month loss.

At a production rate of 1000 lb/month

Income – Total Cost = 10(1000) – 2(1000) – 3000 = +\$5000/month profit.

It is worth mentioning at this point that in numerous places in journal literature and textbooks you will find the following equation given to calculate the break-even production rate:

$$\text{Break-even Production Units} = \frac{\text{Fixed Cost}}{\text{Selling Price/Unit-Variable Cost/Unit}}$$

Note that this equation is based on assuming linear variation in costs and income and that it can be obtained directly from setting Income = Total Cost in generalized Equations D-4 and D-5 as follows:

Total Cost = (Variable Cost/Unit) (X Units) + Fixed Cost
Income = (Selling Price/Unit) (X Units) + 0
Setting Income = Total Cost gives the break-even production units, X.

D.2 Specify Break-even Assumptions

The term "break-even" has been used in Example D-1 to describe the production level of operation at which income exactly equals total cost. There are many other possible break-even criteria. The investor must be careful to understand break-even analysis assumptions. The following example illustrates break-even price analysis to break-even with an existing loss and with no loss.

EXAMPLE D-2 Break-even with Existing Loss Illustration

60 tons of rice hulls per day must be disposed of by a rice company. Pollution problems concerning incinerating or burying the hulls have forced the company to accelerate efforts to convert the waste rice hulls into a usable product. The cost of disposing of the rice hulls is \$4 per ton for the 60 tons per day, 300 days per year operation. A proposed process estimated to have a fixed capital cost of \$200,000 can be installed to convert the waste rice hulls into 60 tons per day of usable product. Operating costs are expected to be \$200 per day of operation. If the \$200,000 first cost of the process is recovered in 3 years, what selling price per ton must be recovered for the product to break-even with the present loss of \$240 per day? Assume the minimum ROR is 15% before taxes. What selling price will completely eliminate the present loss of \$240 per day? Use before-tax analysis.

Solution:

Disposal Annual Cost = (60 tons/day)(\$4/ton)(300 days/year)

= \$72,000

$$\text{Process Annual Cost} = 200{,}000\overset{.4380}{(A/P_{15,3})} + 60{,}000 = 147{,}600$$

Annual Sales = (60 tons/day)(300 days/yr)(\$X/ton) = \$18,000 X.

To break-even with present loss and realize a 15% ROR on new investment:

$$\$18{,}000\,X = 147{,}600 - 72{,}000 = \$75{,}600$$
$$X = \$4.20/\text{ton}$$

To break even with no loss and realize a 15% ROR on new investments:

$$\$18{,}000\,X = 147{,}600$$
$$X = \$8.20/\text{ton}$$

When people talk about a break-even parameter, be very careful to pin down the meaning of “break-even”.

D.3 Incremental Analysis Applied to Production Situations With Non-Linear Cost Variations

The incremental cost concept is very important to evaluate optimum levels of production activities and to determine pricing to yield satisfactory profit margins. Marginal cost per unit and differential cost per unit are other common names used interchangably for incremental cost in the literature. Different production levels are mutually exclusive, so the incremental cost concept is applicable to this type of problem.

Incremental operating costs can be calculated either from total cost versus production rate data or variable cost versus production rate data. Since the total cost curve is found by adding the constant fixed cost to the variable cost, change in total cost for a given change in production level is identical to the change in variable cost. That is, incremental total cost equals incremental variable cost. The following example illustrates the use of incremental operating costs for the economic evaluation of a manufacturing process.

EXAMPLE D-3 Optimization of Manufacturing Profit

The costs per period at different levels of output for a manufacturing process to make small pumps are given in the following table. The sales price of the pumps is $20 each. The manufacturing plant is operating at 100% of rated capacity when a purchase order from a company is received for an extra 1000 pumps at a reduced sales price of $14.00/pump.

Rated Capacity, %	Pumps Manufactured	Fixed Cost	Variable Cost	Total Cost	Total Cost/Pump	Incremental Cost/Pump
0	0	$10,000	0	$10,000	$	
25%	1000	10,000	15,000	25,000	25.00	$15.00
50%	2000	10,000	20,000	30,000	15.00	5.00
75%	3000	10,000	23,000	33,000	11.00	3.00
100%	4000	10,000	28,000	38,000	9.50	5.00
125%	5000	10,000	43,000	53,000	10.60	15.00
150%	6000	10,000	62,000	72,000	12.00	19.00
175%	7000	10,000	85,000	95,000	13.57	23.00

The pumps would be retailed in a foreign market and should not affect other domestic sales. Should the sales manager accept the order if the decision is based on whether accepting the order will increase the period profit? Where is the break-even point at the regular $20 per pump price? Graph the break-even chart. At what rated capacity should the plant be operated to maximize total profit if sales at $20 per pump are unlimited? Solution:

Evaluation of the Total Cost/Pump data shows that the cost of making 5000 pumps is $10.60 per pump, which is less than the proposed selling price of $14.00 per pump. However, it was shown in Chapter 4 that evaluation of total cost data does not answer the question of what an investor receives or pays for each extra incremental investment between mutually exclusive choices. The incremental unit costs given in the last column of the table show that it would actually cost $15.00 per pump for the 1000 pumps needed to increase production from the 100% capacity to 125% capacity level. Selling the units for $14.00 per pump would leave the company with a $1 per pump loss for each of the 1000 increment of pumps. Obviously, total profitability for the company will be greater at the end of the period if the sales manager rejects the order.

Note that the minimum incremental cost/pump equals $3.00 at 75% of rated capacity while the minimum total cost/pump of $9.50 occurs at 100% of rated capacity. As incremental costs decrease, total cost/pump must decrease, because total cost per pump at each level of operation is made up of a weighted average of the total cost per pump at the next lower level plus the incremental cost per pump between the levels. As long as the incremental cost per pump is lower than the total cost per pump at the last level, the new total cost per pump must be lower than the previous one. Thus, minimum incremental cost per unit and minimum total cost per unit usually do not occur at the same production level. It is only coincidence if they do.

The break-even point for cost to equal income at the regular $20 per pump price may be seen to be about 1300 pumps on the break-even chart shown in Figure D-2. Mathematically, the break-even point may be found more exactly as follows:

Evaluate the data given in the problem statement and find that the break-even point occurs between 25% and 50% of rated capacity. Assume the total cost curve is a straight line in this range with slope = (30,000 – 25,000)/(1000) = 5.0. The equation for the cost curve in the break-even range is

$$\text{Total Cost} = 5.0(X) + K \qquad \text{D-6}$$

where X equals production rate for $1000 \leq X \leq 2000$ and K is the pseudo fixed cost where the total cost line intercepts the cost axis at zero production rate. Since Total Cost = 25,000 when X = 1000, we see that K = 20,000. Obviously this K value is a pseudo fixed cost because we know the actual fixed cost is $10,000.

$$\text{Total Cost} = 5.0\,X + 20{,}000 \qquad \text{D-7}$$

The equation for the income line is

$$\text{Income} = 20\,X \qquad \text{D-8}$$

The point where Total Cost equals Income is

$$5.0\,X + 20{,}000 = 20\,X \text{ or } X = 1333 \text{ pumps.}$$

At this break-even production rate, Total Cost = Income = $26,666.

Note on the break-even chart that the slope of the total cost curve between operating levels equals the increment cost between those levels. For $20 per pump sold, maximum profit occurs at 6000 units sold. To maximize total profit, increase sales until the slope of the total cost curve equals the slope of the income curve. At that point, selling price per unit equals incremental cost per unit. Further increase in sales would erode profits.

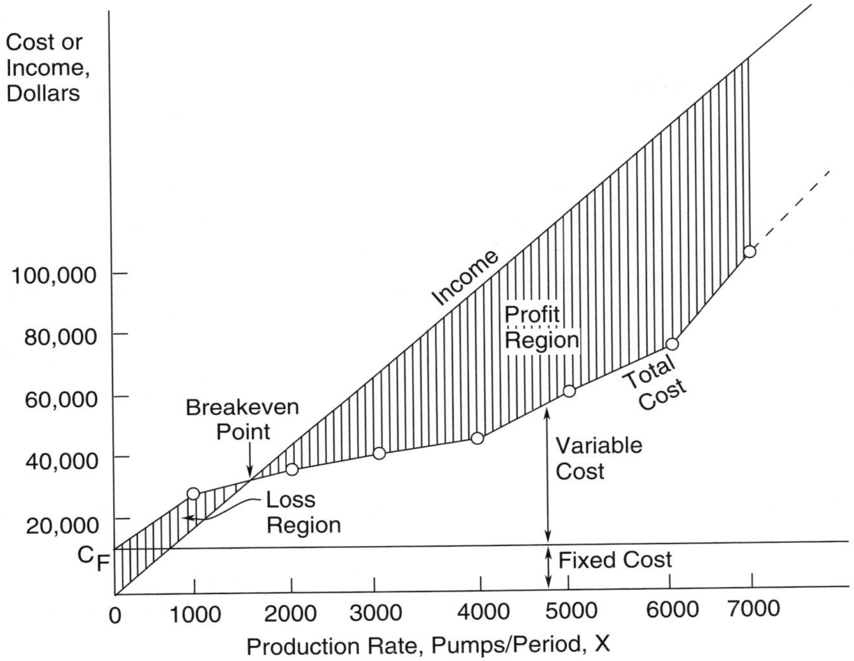

Figure D-2 Graphical Analysis of Example D-3

D.4 Incremental Analysis Applied to Product Make or Buy Decisions

Management and managerial accounting literature is full of the so-called "classic textbook cases" illustrating how numerous companies over the years have made incorrect management decisions because of improper or non-use of incremental economic analysis. This covers decisions such as those illustrated in the last example concerning whether to accept or reject new orders at a given selling price per unit or where to operate an existing facility to maximize the profit that it can generate. Another very important decision-making area that requires incremental analysis as well as total cost analysis concerns whether it is economically best to produce a product internally or to purchase it from an outside supplier. These are mutually exclusive alternative choices, you must select one or the other, not both, and mutually exclusive alternative decisions always require incremental analysis no matter what method of analysis you are using. For example, whether you are using rate of return analysis or cost per unit analysis, with mutually exclusive alternatives you must look at incremental rate of return or incremental cost per unit results to be sure that they are satisfactory. One of the most common causes of incorrect management decision making concerning mutually exclusive alternative decisions is to base a decision on total investment analysis or total cost per unit analysis instead of properly evaluating incremental analysis results.

In many make or buy decision situations, it is desirable to keep an existing manufacturing/production facility in operable condition even if part or all of present production is eliminated to buy product from an outside source. In this common make or buy situation the fixed costs of the facility or operation are going to be incurred whether the product is purchased externally or produced internally. Proper incremental analysis will show clearly that only the variable costs are relevant to make or buy decisions for the situation described. The following example illustrates analysis of this type of make or buy decision.

EXAMPLE D-4 Make or Buy Decision Illustration

A manufacturing operation has the capacity to produce 1,000,000 product units per year. The present production rate is 75% of capacity, where the firms annual income is $750,000. Annual fixed costs are $200,000 and variable production costs are constant at $0.50 per unit of product .

a) What is the profit or loss at present capacity?
b) At what volume of sales does the operation break-even?
c) At what purchase price would it be better to buy the product from a competitor for resale rather than to produce internally if it is assumed the plant will be maintained in operating condition?

Solution: Costs and Income in Thousands of Dollars, Price in Dollars

a)

Income	= 750	Variable O.C.	= 375
–Total OC	= 575	+Fixed O.C.	= 200
Profit	= 175	Total O.C.	= 575

b) Income = ($1/unit) (X units) + O
Cost = (0.50) (X units) + 200,000
For break-even, X = 0.5 X + 200,000 so 0.5 X = 200,000
∴ X = 400,000 units to break-even
At break-even, Income = $400,000 = Cost

c) Variable cost/unit		= \$0.50
+Fixed cost/unit	= \$200/750	= \$0.27
Total cost/unit		= \$0.77 at 750,000 units of production

At first glance these calculations often lead people to the incorrect conclusion that it is economically desirable to purchase externally for any purchase price less than \$0.77/unit. Actually, *if it costs more than the \$0.50 variable cost/unit to purchase externally, the economics favor producing internally* because the difference between the external cost/ unit and the \$0.50/unit out-of-pocket variable cost/unit can be applied to pay part of the fixed costs, which will be incurred whether we buy or produce. The incremental difference between the total costs at any two levels of operation leaves the incremental variable cost which in this problem is \$0.50 per unit at all levels of operation.

APPENDIX E

ARITHMETIC GRADIENT SERIES FACTOR DEVELOPMENT

Represent a gradient series of payments which has a first term of B and constant positive gradient g between terms as the sum of the two series of payments as shown in Figure E-1.

	B	B	B				B	B
0	1	2	3	–	–	–	– n–1	n

	0	g	2g				(n–2)g	(n–1)g
0	1	2	3	–	–	–	– n–1	n

Figure E-1 Arithmetic Gradient Series Factor Development

B is spread uniformly each period over the project life. Now if we can spread the arithmetic gradient payments uniformly over each period of the project life we will have converted the gradient series to an equivalent series of equal period payments. The future worth of the gradient terms at year n is:

$$F = g\left(F/P_{i,(n-2)}\right) + 2g\left(F/P_{i,(n-3)}\right) + \ldots + (n-2)g\left(F/P_{i,2}\right) + (n-1)g \qquad \text{E-1}$$

Multiplying this equation by $F/P_{i,1}$ gives

$$F\left(F/P_{i,1}\right) = g\left(F/P_{i,(n-1)}\right) + 2g\left(F/P_{i,(n-2)}\right) + \ldots + (n-2)g\left(F/P_{i,2}\right) + (n-1)g\left(F/P_{i,1}\right) \qquad \text{E-2}$$

Subtracting Equation E-1 from Equation E-2 yields

$$F - F\left(F/P_{i,1}\right) = -g\left(F/P_{i,(n-1)}\right) - g\left(F/P_{i,(n-2)}\right)$$

$$- \ldots - g\left(F/P_{i,2}\right) - g\left(F/P_{i,1}\right) + (n-1)g =$$

$$-g\underbrace{\left[1 + F/P_{i,1} + F/P_{i,2} + \ldots + F/P_{i,(n-2)} + F/P_{i,(n-1)}\right]}_{F/A_{i,n}} + ng$$

$$F - F(1+i) = -g\left[F/A_{i,n}\right] + ng \qquad \text{E-3}$$

or $Fi = +g\left[F/A_{i,n}\right] - ng$

Dividing by i gives

$$F = g\left[\frac{F/A_{i,n}}{i} - \frac{n}{i}\right] \qquad \text{E-4}$$

Our objective is to calculate the uniform series of end of period payments, A, that is equivalent to the arithmetic gradient series. Recall that $F(A/F_{i,n}) = A$ and multiply each side of Equation E-4 by $A/F_{i,n}$

$$A = F\left(A/F_{i,n}\right) = g\left[\frac{1}{i} - \frac{n}{i}\left(A/F_{i,n}\right)\right] = g\left(A/G_{i,n}\right) \qquad \text{E-5}$$

The arithmetic series factor (also called a gradient conversion factor in engineering economy literature) is bracketed. Adding the first term in a gradient series, B, to Equation E-5 gives the total arithmetic gradient series equation presented in chapter 2 as Equation 2-12

$$A = B \pm g\left(A/G_{i,n}\right) \qquad \text{2-12}$$

APPENDIX F

DISCRETE INTEREST, MID-PERIOD FACTOR VALUES

Appendix F: Discrete Interest, Mid-Period Factor Values

	10%		12%		15%	
n	**F/Pi,n**	**P/Fi,n**	**F/Pi,n**	**P/Fi,n**	**F/Pi,n**	**P/Fi,n**
0.5	1.0488	0.9535	1.0583	0.9449	1.0724	0.9325
1.5	1.1537	0.8668	1.1853	0.8437	1.2332	0.8109
2.5	1.2691	0.7880	1.3275	0.7533	1.4182	0.7051
3.5	1.3960	0.7164	1.4868	0.6726	1.6310	0.6131
4.5	1.5356	0.6512	1.6653	0.6005	1.8756	0.5332
5.5	1.6891	0.5920	1.8651	0.5362	2.1569	0.4636
6.5	1.8580	0.5382	2.0889	0.4787	2.4805	0.4031
7.5	2.0438	0.4893	2.3396	0.4274	2.8526	0.3506
8.5	2.2482	0.4448	2.6203	0.3816	3.2804	0.3048
9.5	2.4730	0.4044	2.9348	0.3407	3.7725	0.2651
10.5	2.7203	0.3676	3.2869	0.3042	4.3384	0.2305
11.5	2.9924	0.3342	3.6814	0.2716	4.9891	0.2004
12.5	3.2916	0.3038	4.1231	0.2425	5.7375	0.1743
13.5	3.6208	0.2762	4.6179	0.2165	6.5981	0.1516
14.5	3.9828	0.2511	5.1720	0.1933	7.5878	0.1318
15.5	4.3811	0.2283	5.7927	0.1726	8.7260	0.1146
16.5	4.8192	0.2075	6.4878	0.1541	10.0349	0.0997
17.5	5.3012	0.1886	7.2663	0.1376	11.5402	0.0867
18.5	5.8313	0.1715	8.1383	0.1229	13.2712	0.0754
19.5	6.4144	0.1559	9.1149	0.1097	15.2619	0.0655
20.5	7.0559	0.1417	10.2087	0.0980	17.5512	0.0570
21.5	7.7614	0.1288	11.4337	0.0875	20.1838	0.0495
22.5	8.5376	0.1171	12.8058	0.0781	23.2114	0.0431
23.5	9.3914	0.1065	14.3425	0.0697	26.6931	0.0375
24.5	10.3305	0.0968	16.0636	0.0623	30.6971	0.0326

Appendix F: Discrete Interest, Mid-Period Factor Values Continued

	20%		30%		40%	
n	**F/Pi,n**	**P/Fi,n**	**F/Pi,n**	**P/Fi,n**	**F/Pi,n**	**P/Fi,n**
0.5	1.0954	0.9129	1.1402	0.8771	1.1832	0.8452
1.5	1.3145	0.7607	1.4822	0.6747	1.6565	0.6037
2.5	1.5774	0.6339	1.9269	0.5190	2.3191	0.4312
3.5	1.8929	0.5283	2.5050	0.3992	3.2467	0.3080
4.5	2.2715	0.4402	3.2565	0.3071	4.5454	0.2200
5.5	2.7258	0.3669	4.2334	0.2362	6.3636	0.1571
6.5	3.2710	0.3057	5.5034	0.1817	8.9091	0.1122
7.5	3.9252	0.2548	7.1544	0.1398	12.4727	0.0802
8.5	4.7102	0.2123	9.3008	0.1075	17.4618	0.0573
9.5	5.6523	0.1769	12.0910	0.0827	24.4465	0.0409
10.5	6.7827	0.1474	15.7183	0.0636	34.2251	0.0292
11.5	8.1392	0.1229	20.4338	0.0489	47.9151	0.0209
12.5	9.7671	0.1024	26.5639	0.0376	67.0811	0.0149
13.5	11.7205	0.0853	34.5331	0.0290	93.9136	0.0106
14.5	14.0646	0.0711	44.8930	0.0223	131.4790	0.0076
15.5	16.8775	0.0593	58.3609	0.0171	184.0707	0.0054
16.5	20.2531	0.0494	75.8692	0.0132	257.6989	0.0039
17.5	24.3037	0.0411	98.6299	0.0101	360.7785	0.0028
18.5	29.1644	0.0343	128.2189	0.0078	505.0899	0.0020
19.5	34.9973	0.0286	166.6846	0.0060	707.1258	0.0014
20.5	41.9967	0.0238	216.6899	0.0046	989.9761	0.0010
21.5	50.3961	0.0198	281.6969	0.0035	1385.9666	0.0007
22.5	60.4753	0.0165	366.2060	0.0027	1940.3533	0.0005
23.5	72.5704	0.0138	476.0678	0.0021	2716.4946	0.0004
24.5	87.0844	0.0115	618.8881	0.0016	3803.0924	0.0003

Equivalence and Conversion Information

Weight and Volume:

1 short ton (st)	=	2,000	pounds
1 long ton (lt)	=	2,240	pounds
1 metric ton (mt)	≈	2,205	pounds*
1 gram (g)	≈	0.035	ounce*
1 kilogram (kg)	≈	2.205	pounds*
1 metric ton (mt)	=	1,000	kilograms

M = 1,000
MM = 1,000,000

1 Mcf	=	1,000	cubic feet
1 MMcf	=	1,000,000	cubic feet
1 barrel (bbl)	=	42	U.S. gallons

Area and Distance:

1 acre	=	43,560	square feet
1 square mile	=	640	acres
1 section	=	1	square mile
1 township	=	36	square miles
1 meter (m)	≈	3.279	feet*
1 kilometer (km)	≈	0.622	mile*

Energy:

1 kilowatt (kw)	≈	3,412.969	Btu (British thermal unit)*
1 kilowatt (kw)	≈	1.341	horsepower*
1 Mcf of natural gas	≈	1,027,400	Btu (British thermal unit)**
1 kilowatt-hour (kwh)	=	1,000 watts of power applied or received continuously for one hour	
1 megawatt	=	1,000,000 watts	
1 mill	=	0.001 U.S. dollar (1/10 of one cent)	

* Metric to English conversions are rounded for convenience. Exact conversions can be found in an International System of Units (SI) table.

** Based on a national (U.S.) average of energy contained in a cubic foot of natural gas.

SELECTED REFERENCES

Barish, Norman N. *Economic Analysis for Engineering and Managerial Decision Making*. Second Edition. McGraw Hill Book Company: New York, NY. 1978.

Bennett, H.J., Thompson, J.G., Quiring, H.J., and Toland, J.E. *Financial Evaluation of Mineral Deposits Using Sensitivity and Probabilitic Analysis Methods.* (I.C. 8495). US Bureau of Mines: Washington DC. 1970.

Bierman, H.J., and Smidt, S. *The Capital Budgeting Decision.* Eighth Edition. MacMillian Company: New York, NY. 1992.

Brealy, Richard A., and Meyers, Stewart C. *Principles of Corporate Finance*. McGraw-Hill Book Company: New York, NY. 2002.

Campbell, John M., and Campbell, Robert A. *Analysis and Management of Petroleum Investments: Risk, Taxes and Time.* Second Edition. CPS: Norman, Oklahoma. 1991.

Chilton, Cecil. *Cost Engineering in the Process Industries.* McGraw Hill Book Company: New York, NY. 1960.

Chriss, Neil A. *Black-Scholes and Beyond: Option Pricing Models.* McGraw Hill Book Company: New York, NY. 1996.

Commerce Clearing House. *Energy Tax Incentives Act of 2005: Safe, Accountable, Flexible, Efficient Transportation Equity Act of 2005.* CCH Inc.: Chicago, IL. 2005.

Commerce Clearing House. *2005 US Master Tax Guide*. CCH Inc.: Chicago, IL. 2005.

DeGarmo, E.P., et al. *Engineering Economy*. Ninth Edition. MacMillian Company: New York, NY. 1992.

Burman, Len; Rohaly, Jeffery. *Alternative Minimum Tax: What is the AMT?* Tax Policy Center Urban Institute and Brookings Institution. www.taxpolicycenter.org. 2011.

Drucker, Peter F. *The Practice of Management*. Harper & Row: New York, NY. 1964.

Fortune Magazine. "The Real Key to Creating Wealth." Sept. 20, 1993.

Fortune Magazine, "EVA Works—But Not If You Make These Mistakes." May 1, 1995.

Gentry, D.W. and O'Neil, T.J. *Mine Investment Analysis*. American Institute of Mining, metallurgical, and Petroleum Engineers, Inc.: New York, NY. 1984.

Grant, E.L., Ireson, W.G. and Leavenworth, R.S. *Principles of Engineering Economy*. Eighth Edition. Ronald Press Co.: New York, NY, 1990.

Henderson, W. Matthew. *Impacts of the Alternative Minimum Tax on Crude Oil Production Economics*. Thesis, Department of Mineral Economics, Colorado School of Mines: Golden, CO. 1992.

Hennessee, Patrick A. *Oil and Gas: Federal Income Taxation*. CCH Inc.: Chicago, IL. 2005.

Hillier, F.S., Lieberman, G.J., Hillier, F. and Lieberman, G. *Introduction to Operations Research*. Eighth Edition. McGraw Hill Book Company: New York, NY. 2004.

Hull, John C. *Options, Futures, and Other Derivatives*. Sixth Edition. Prentice Hall: Upper Saddle River, NJ. 2005

McCray, Arthur W. *Petroleum Evaluations and Economic Decisions*. Prentice Hall: Englewood Cliffs, NJ, 1975.

Newendorp, Paul D. *Decision analysis for Petroleum Exploration*. Second Edition. Planning Press. OGCI: Tulsa, OK. 2000.

Newman, Donald G. *Engineering Economic Analysis*. Ninth Edition. Oxford Press: New York, NY.

Ostwald, Phillip F. *Engineering Cost Estimating*. Third Edition. Prentice Hall: Englewood Cliffs, NJ. 1991.

Peters, Max S. and Timmerhaus, Klaus D. *Plant Design and Economics for Chemical Engineers*. Fifth Edition. McGraw Hill Book Company: New York, NY. 2002.

Ostwald, Phillip F. *Engineering Cost Estimating*. Third Edition. Prentice Hall: Englewood Cliffs, NJ. 1991.

Ostwald, Phillip F., McLaren, Timothy S. *Cost Analysis and Estimating for Engineering and Management*. Prentice Hall: Englewood Cliffs, NJ. 2003.

Palepu, Krishna; Healy, Paul; Bernard, Victor. *Business Analysis & Valuation*. South-Western College Publishing: Cincinnati, OH. 2000.

Palepu, Krishna; Healy, Paul; Bernard, Victor. *Introduction to business Analysis and Valuation*. South-Western College Publishing: Cincinnati, OH. 1997.

Prentice Hall. *Federal Tax Course*. Prentice Hall: Englewood Cliffs, NJ. 1993.

Popper, Herbert. *Modern Cost Engineering Tecniques*. McGraw Hill Book Company: New York, NY. 1970.

Richardson Engineering Services, Inc. *General Construction Estimating Standards*. Richardson Engineering Services: Mesa, AZ. 1994.

Riggs, James L. *Economic Decision Models*. Third Edition. McGraw Hill Book Company: New York, NY. 1983.

Samuelson, Paul A. and Nordhaus, William D. *Economics*. Eighteenth Edition. McGraw Hill Book Company: New York, NY. 2004.

Sandretto, Peter C. *The Economic Management of Research and Engineering*. Krieger: New York, NY. 1980.

Securities Research Company. *SRC Green, Blue and Red Books of 5 Trend Security Charts*. Securities Research Company: Boston, MA. 2005.

Smith, Gerald W. *Engineering Economy: Analysis of Capital Expenditures*. Fourth Edition. The Iowa State University Press: Ames, IA. 1987.

Stewart, G. Bennett III. *The Quest for Value—The EVATM Management Guide*. Harper Collins Publishers Inc.:

The Options Institute. *Options: Essential Concepts & Trading Strategies*. Third Edition. The Educational Division of the Chicago Board Operations Exchange. McGraw Hill Book Company: New York, NY. 1991.

Thompson, Robert S. and Wright, John D. *Oil Property Evaluation*. Thompson-Wright Associates: Golden, CO. 1984.

Thuesen, H.G., Fabrycky, W.J. and Thuesen, G.J. *Engineering Economy*. Ninth Edition. Prentice Hall: Englewood Cliffs, NJ. 2000.

Weston, J. Fred and Copeland, Thomas. *Essentials of Managerial Finance*. Tenth Edition. The Dryden Press: London, England. 1992.

Woolsey, R.E.D. and Swanson H.S. *Operations Research for Immediate Application*. Harper and Row: New York, NY. 1975.

INDEX